Everyday Mathematics®

The University of Chicago School Mathematics Project

Meeting All Expectations

Everyday Mathematics *Meeting* all expectations

An inspired mission

Everyday Mathematics was developed through the University of Chicago School Mathematics Project (UCSMP) in order to enable children in elementary grades to learn more mathematical content and become life-long mathematical thinkers.

- ✦ The National Science Foundation, Amoco, GTE and other leading corporations supported the project through substantial, long-term funding.

- ✦ A strong partnership was developed among researchers, mathematics educators, classroom teachers, students and administrators.

- ✦ A core author team at the University of Chicago collaborates on all grade levels to provide a cohesive and well-articulated K-6 curriculum.

Research that matters

Everyday Mathematics begins with the premise that young children can, and must, learn more mathematics than has been expected from them in the past. This premise is based on the research the UCSMP author team undertook prior to writing the curriculum. Here are some of the major findings of this research:

- ✦ The typical U.S. mathematics curriculum is arithmetic-driven, slow-paced with isolated instruction, and broad without depth of content.

- ✦ International studies show that U.S. students learn much less mathematics than students in other countries.

- ✦ Children are capable of learning more mathematics in a richer curriculum.

- ✦ All children can be successful mathematical thinkers.

- ✦ Mathematics is meaningful to children when it is varied, rich, and rooted in real world problems and applications.

Instruction with impact

The *Everyday Mathematics* instructional design was carefully crafted to capitalize on student interest and maximize student learning.

+ High expectations for all students
+ Concepts and skills developed over time and in a wide variety of contexts
+ Balance among mathematical strands
+ Dynamic applications
+ Multiple methods and strategies for problem solving
+ Concrete modeling as a pathway to abstract understanding
+ Collaborative learning in partner and small group activities
+ Cross-curricular applications

Field test validation

Everyday Mathematics was originally field tested for one full year per grade level in hundreds of classrooms across the U.S. Prior to second edition development, additional classroom observation and research was conducted. One research component included evaluation of all first edition lessons by numerous teachers using the curriculum. Second edition content was then developed and field tested in a variety of educational settings.

Based on teacher and student feedback, and classroom observation by authors, revisions were made prior to publication.

Everyday Mathematics *Doing* more with mathematics

Everyday Mathematics is organized into six mathematical content strands that cover a number of skills and concepts. This provides a rich yet balanced curriculum—attention to numeration and computation without neglecting geometry, data, and algebraic thinking.

Every strand is addressed throughout all grade levels of the program. Each grade level builds on and extends concept understanding so that children approach each new challenge from a firmly established foundation.

Within the content of *Everyday Mathematics*, emphasis is placed on

✦ Establishing links from past experience

✦ Discussing and sharing ideas

✦ Using and comparing equivalent expressions

✦ Expressing numbers in context by including units

✦ Learning about the reversibility of most things

By becoming a part of everyday work and play, these ideas gradually shape children's ways of thinking about mathematics and foster the development of mathematical intuition and understanding.

skills & concepts K–6

content strands

OPERATIONS & COMPUTATION	NUMERATION	PATTERNS, FUNCTIONS & ALGEBRA	DATA & CHANCE	MEASUREMENT & REFERENCE FRAMES	GEOMETRY
Facts	Counting	Number and Visual Patterns	Mean	Linear Measures	Two Dimensional
Mental Math	Order	Properties	Median	Weight	Three Dimensional
Algorithms	Relations	Sequences	Range	Capacity	
Estimation	Estimation	Functions	Mode	Money	Symmetry
Number Stories	Odd/Even	Number Sentences	Tally Charts	Time	Congruence
Money	Fractions	Equations and Inequalities	Line Plots	Temperature	Angles
Powers of Ten	Decimals	Variables	Graphs	Perimeter	
Exponents	Percents	Formulas	Probability	Area	
				Volume	
				Diameter and Circumference	
				Angle	

Everyday Mathematics *Providing* classroom support

Everyday Mathematics was written in collaboration with teachers, for teachers as well as for students. *Everyday Mathematics* provides all the tools needed for instruction.

student materials

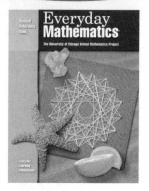

Student Reference Book (Grades 3-6)

Students use this hardbound reference book to access mathematical information and procedures that support the program. Game rules, ongoing routines, reference tables, a glossary of terms and calculator usage information are all included.

Student Math Journal, Volumes 1 & 2 (Grades 1-6)

These consumable books provide lesson support material for students to solve and complete. They provide a long-term record of each student's mathematical development.

teacher materials

Teacher's Lesson Guide, Volumes 1 & 2 (Grades 1–6)

Easy-to-follow three-part daily lesson plans. A unit organizer provides learning goals, planning tips, content highlights, and suggestions on problem solving, cross-curricular links, and support for special student populations.

Math Masters (Grades 1–6)

Blackline masters that support daily lesson activities. Includes Home/Study Link and Assessment Masters.

Minute Math+ (Grades1–3)

Brief activities for transition time and for spare moments throughout the day.

teacher resources

Teacher's Reference Manual

Contains comprehensive background information about mathematical content and program management for Grades K–3 and 4–6.

Home Connection Handbook

Provides suggestions for enhancing home-school communication and involvement in the program for Grades K–6.

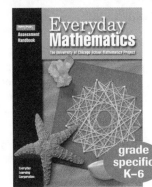

Assessment Handbook

Grade level specific handbook that provides ideas for portfolio, ongoing, and product assessment.

grade specific K–6

kindergarten materials

Teacher's Guide to Activities

Classroom activities and ongoing daily routines. Includes detailed notes, illustrations, and progress guideposts.

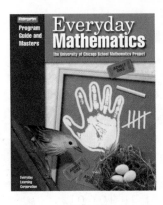

Program Guide and Activity Masters

Teacher support material including program overview and philosophy, activity listings by mathematical content strand, curriculum and classroom management strategies and a comprehensive glossary. Ready-to-use masters provide printed material for student activities and Home Links.

Minute Math

Contains brief activities for transition time and for spare moments through-out the day.

Everyday Mathematics Unit Organizer

Each Unit begins with comprehensive support information to assist in successful implementation and instruction. In addition to the sections detailed on the following pages, the Unit Organizer also includes:

✦ Unit Overview
✦ Table of Contents
✦ Problem Solving Opportunities
✦ Cross-Curricular Links
✦ Materials Chart
✦ Detailed Content Highlights

Program Content Links
Connections to prior and future content both within and across grade levels.

Unit 9
Multiplication & Division

learning goals in perspective

learning goals	links to the past	links to the future
9a **Beginning Goal** Solve number stories involving positive and negative numbers. **(Lesson 9.13)**	In second grade, children experienced negative numbers by working with temperatures, number lines, and number grids. *(Related Grade 3 lessons: 4.1–4.4, 7.4, 7.5, 7.9, 8.7)*	In fourth grade, children will use positive and negative numbers in "credits and debits" number stories. *(Related Grade 3 lesson: 11.9)*
9b **Beginning/Developing Goal** Multiply multidigit numbers by 1- or 2-digit numbers. **(Lessons 9.4, 9.5, 9.9, 9.11, and 9.12)**	In second grade, children developed their own strategies for solving multidigit multiplication problems. In Grade 3 Unit 2, children worked with addition and subtraction algorithms. *(Related Grade 3 lessons: 2.7, 2.8, 4.8, 7.1–7.3, 7.6, 7.8)*	In fourth grade, children will review the basic principles of multiplication with multidigit numbers, and practice using the partial-products algorithm. The partial-products algorithm is used in later grades, in algebra, to find the products of binomials, such as $(x + 2)(x + 5)$. *(Related Grade 3 lessons: 10.2, 10.6)*
9c **Beginning/Developing Goal** Find factors of a number. **(Lesson 9.6)**	Skip counting by 2s, 5s, and 10s in previous grades prepared children to learn multiplication by these factors. Children were also introduced to multiplication/division fact families in second grade. *(Related Grade 3 lessons: 1.8, 4.2, 4.4–4.8, 7.1–7.3, 7.6, 7.8)*	In later grades, children will further explore factors and products in a branch of mathematics called number theory. Children will develop factoring skills by using arrays to identify all the possible factor pairs for a given number.
9d **Beginning/Developing Goal** Interpret remainders in division problems. **(Lesson 9.8)**	Second graders used counters to solve real-life division problems, and were introduced to the idea of remainders. *(Related Grade 3 lessons: 3.1, 4.3, 4.4, 4.6, 7.6)*	Children will continue to interpret remainders in division problems throughout the grades.
Developing Goal Solve	In second grade, children worked with	Children will continue to work with fact ...ns in *Fourth Grade Everyday* ...matics.

...out the grades, children will continue ...e and solve division number stories.

Unit Learning Goals
Indicates developmental level expected and lesson reference.

assessment
ongoing • product • periodic

☑ Informal Assessment

Math Boxes These *Math Journal* pages provide opportunities for cumulative review or assessment of concepts and skills.

Ongoing Assessment: Kid Watching Use the Ongoing Assessment suggestions in the following lessons to make quick, on-the-spot observations about children's understanding of:
• Operations and Computation **(Lessons 9.4–9.13)**
• Measurement and Reference Frames **(Lessons 9.7 and 9.13)**

Portfolio Ideas Samples of children's work may be obtained from the following assignments:
• Solving an Allowance Problem **(Lesson 9.2)**
• Using Count-By Patterns **(Lesson 9.4)**
• Sharing Money **(Lesson 9.7)**
• Multiplying and Dividing Multiples of 10 in the Context of Time **(Lesson 9.9)**
• Finding Number Patterns by Filing Equilateral Triangles **(Lesson 9.10)**

☑ Unit 9 Review and Assessment

Math Message Use the question in Lesson 9.14 to assess children's progress toward the following learning goal: Goal 9b

Slate Assessments Use oral or slate assessments during Lesson 9.14 to assess children's progress toward the following learning goals: Goals 9e and 9f

Written Assessment Use a written review during Lesson 9.14 to assess children's progress toward the following learning goals: Goals 9a, 9b, 9c, 9d, 9e, and 9f

Performance/Group Assessment Use a small-group activity in Lesson 9.14 to assess children's progress toward the following learning goals: Goals 9c, 9e, and 9f

assessment handbook

For more information on how to use different types of assessment in Unit 9, see the Assessment Overview on pages 69–71 in the *Assessment Handbook*. The following Assessment Masters can be found in the *Math Masters* book:
• Unit 9 Checking Progress, pp. 386 and 387
• Unit 9 Class Checklist, p. 420
• Unit 9 Individual Profile of Progress, p. 421
• Class Progress Indicator, p. 441
• Math Logs, pp. 446–448

Assessment Support
Suggestions for informal assessments and use of the Assessment Handbook are also included.

Ongoing Assessment
Built-in evaluation techniques and opportunities teachers may use to assess student attainment of unit learning goals.

Examples from Third Grade, Unit 9

Adjusting the Activity
Found at point of use within the lesson, it allows the teacher to immediately reteach, enrich, or address language diversity when needed.

meeting
INDIVIDUAL needs

✦ RETEACHING

The following features provide additional instructional support:

Adjusting the Activity
- **Lesson 9.1, Part 1**
- **Lesson 9.2, Part 1**
- **Lesson 9.4, Part 1**
- **Lesson 9.5, Parts 1, 2**
- **Lesson 9.6, Part 2**
- **Lesson 9.7, Part 1**
- **Lesson 9.8, Part 2**
- **Lesson 9.9, Part 1**
- **Lesson 9.10, Part 1**
- **Lesson 9.11, Part 1**
- **Lesson 9.12, Part 1**
- **Lesson 9.13, Part 1**

✦ ENRICHMENT

The following features suggest enrichment and extension activities:

Adjusting the Activity	Options for Individualizing
• **Lesson 9.5, Part 1**	• **Lesson 9.1** Finding Out More about Animals
• **Lesson 9.6, Part 1**	• **Lesson 9.2** Solving an Allowance Problem
• **Lesson 9.7, Part 1**	• **Lesson 9.4** Using Count-By Patterns
• **Lesson 9.8, Part 1**	• **Lesson 9.8** Solving Division Number Stories
• **Lesson 9.13, Part 1**	• **Lesson 9.9** Multiplying and Dividing Multiples of 10 in the Context of Time
	• **Lesson 9.12** Using the Lattice Method to Multiply 3-Digit Numbers by 2-Digit Numbers
	• **Lesson 9.13** Using Data Expressed with Positive and Negative Numbers from a Table

Options for Individualizing
Lesson-related support material and activities for students to complete. Includes additional practice and extension.

✦ MULTIAGE CLASSROOM

The following chart lists related lessons from Grades 2 and 4 that can help you meet your instructional needs:

Grade 2	7.3 10.8 11.5	7.4 12.4	8.1 8.2 9.8	5.3 6.10 11.5	4.6 7.4 11.3	6.7 11.7 12.5	6.8 6.11 7.6	1.10 6.11 11.4	5.3 6.10 11.5	5.2 6.9 6.10	5.3 6.10 11.5	5.3 6.10 11.5	1.9 4.3 4.4
Grade 3	9.1	9.2	9.3	9.4	9.5	9.6	9.7	9.8	9.9	9.10	9.11	9.12	9.13
Grade 4	3.4 5.9	3.1	5.1	5.5	5.5		5.1	3.4	5.7	1.3 5.1	5.6	5.6	

Multiage Companion Lessons
A chart of companion lessons from previous and future grades helps to meet the needs of multiage classrooms.

planning tips

Planning
Ideas for pacing, project use, home communication, and connections to NCTM Standards 2000.

Pacing
Pacing depends on a number of factors, such as children's individual needs and how long your school has been using *Everyday Mathematics*. At the beginning of Unit 9, review your Content by Strand Poster to help you set a monthly pace.

	← MOST CLASSROOMS →	
FEBRUARY	MARCH	APRIL

Using the Projects
Use Project 2, Watermelon Feast and Seed-Spitting Contest, during Units 3, 4, 7, or 9 to measure the distances children spit watermelon seeds, and to find landmarks of the data. The Projects can be found at the back of this book.

Home Communication
Share Home Links 9.1–9.13 with families to help them understand the content and procedures in this unit. At the end of the unit, use Home Link 9.14 to introduce Unit 10. Supplemental information can be found in the *Home Connection Handbook*.

NCTM Standards

Standard	1	2	3	4	5	6	7	8	9	10
Unit 9 Lessons	1–13	1–13	3, 4, 10–12	3, 5, 7, 10, 12	2	1–13	1–13	1–13	1–13	1–13

Content Standards	Process Standards
1 Number and Operations	**6** Problem Solving
2 Algebra	**7** Reasoning and Proof
3 Geometry	**8** Communication
4 Measurement	**9** Connections
5 Data Analysis and Probability	**10** Representation

PRACTICE through Games

Everyday Mathematics uses games to help children develop good fact power and other math skills.
- Comparing fractions with *Fraction Top-It* **(Lesson 9.3)**
- Identifying the factors of whole numbers in *Factor Bingo* **(Lessons 9.6, 9.7, and 9.10)**
- Practicing multiplication facts pictured on dot arrays in *Array Bingo* **(Lesson 9.6)**
- ...ngle measurements with *Angle Race* **(Lesson 9.11)**

Everyday Mathematics Lesson Highlights

Each lesson has been designed to follow an easy-to-use three-part plan. This assists teachers in focusing on lesson objectives, provides ongoing practice for all students, and addresses individual student needs for a variety of populations.

Lesson Summaries
A concise chart which provides a summary of lesson activities and materials, content strand coverage, background information and references, advance preparation needed, and lesson vocabulary.

Getting Started
Contains quick mental math activities, Math Message (an independent warm-up for the lesson), and Home/Study Link follow-up suggestions.

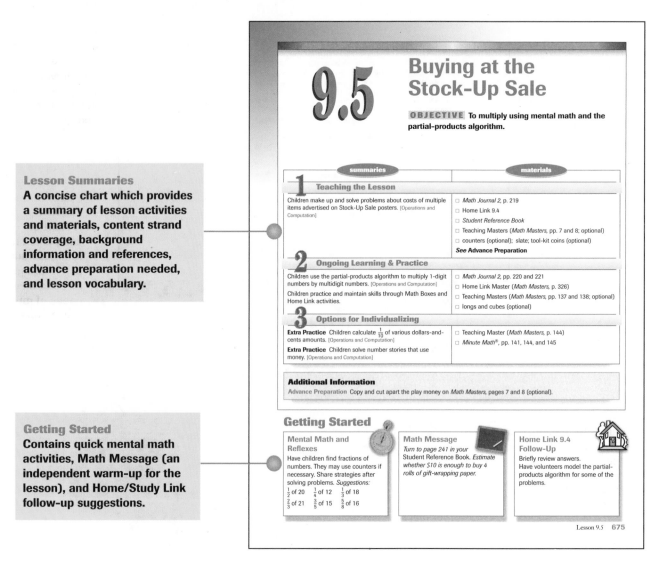

9.5 Buying at the Stock-Up Sale

OBJECTIVE To multiply using mental math and the partial-products algorithm.

summaries	materials
1 Teaching the Lesson	
Children make up and solve problems about costs of multiple items advertised on Stock-Up Sale posters. [Operations and Computation]	□ Math Journal 2, p. 219 □ Home Link 9.4 □ Student Reference Book □ Teaching Masters (Math Masters, pp. 7 and 8; optional) □ counters (optional); slate; tool-kit coins (optional) **See Advance Preparation**
2 Ongoing Learning & Practice	
Children use the partial-products algorithm to multiply 1-digit numbers by multidigit numbers. [Operations and Computation] Children practice and maintain skills through Math Boxes and Home Link activities.	□ Math Journal 2, pp. 220 and 221 □ Home Link Master (Math Masters, p. 326) □ Teaching Masters (Math Masters, pp. 137 and 138; optional) □ longs and cubes (optional)
3 Options for Individualizing	
Extra Practice Children calculate $\frac{1}{10}$ of various dollars-and-cents amounts. [Operations and Computation] **Extra Practice** Children solve number stories that use money. [Operations and Computation]	□ Teaching Master (Math Masters, p. 144) □ Minute Math®, pp. 141, 144, and 145

Additional Information
Advance Preparation Copy and cut apart the play money on Math Masters, pages 7 and 8 (optional).

Getting Started

Mental Math and Reflexes
Have children find fractions of numbers. They may use counters if necessary. Share strategies after solving problems. *Suggestions:*
$\frac{1}{2}$ of 20 $\frac{1}{4}$ of 12 $\frac{1}{3}$ of 18
$\frac{2}{3}$ of 21 $\frac{3}{5}$ of 15 $\frac{5}{8}$ of 16

Math Message
Turn to page 241 in your Student Reference Book. *Estimate whether $10 is enough to buy 4 rolls of gift-wrapping paper.*

Home Link 9.4 Follow-Up
Briefly review answers. Have volunteers model the partial-products algorithm for some of the problems.

Lesson 9.5 **675**

Examples from Third Grade, Unit 9, Lesson 5

ten 100/10 ⊪⊪

Data Bank
Stock-Up Sale Poster #2

Greeting Cards Set of 12 $3.29	Bath Soap $0.88	Gift Wrapping Paper $2.35
Toothbrush $1.83	Video Stories $3.75	Nightlight Bulbs $0.96
Audio Tape 40 Minutes $2.47	Construction Paper $0.67	Pair of shoelaces $1.27

◆ *Student Reference Book*, p. 241

▼ Backs of bills are provided on *Math Masters*, page 8.

$1 Bills

1 Teaching the Lesson

◆ **Math Message Follow-Up**
(*Student Reference Book*, p. 241;
Math Masters, pp. 7 and 8)

WHOLE-CLASS DISCUSSION

Discuss children's answers. Possible estimation strategies:

▷ $4 \times \$2.50 = \$10.00$ (double $2.50 twice). I could buy 4 rolls if they were $2.50 a roll. Since $2.50 is more than $2.35, the cost of 4 rolls at $2.35 is less than $10.

▷ Change $2.35 to a close but easier amount, such as $2.40. $4 \times \$2.00 = \$8.00$, and $4 \times \$0.40 = \$1.60$. Therefore, $4 \times \$2.40 = \$9.60$. Since $2.40 is more than $2.35, the cost is less than $10.

Remind children that many problems can be solved with estimation instead of exact calculation. An efficient estimation strategy requires simple mental math and gives an answer reasonably close to the exact answer. For most people, the most efficient estimation strategy for the problem above would probably be the first one listed.

Now ask children to work in small groups to find the exact cost, using mental math or an algorithm. $9.40 Take time to have children share strategies. *For example:*

$4 \times \$2.00 = \$8.00$
$4 \times \$0.30 = \$1.20$
$4 \times \$0.05 = \$0.20$
$\$8.00 + \$1.20 + \$0.20 = \$9.40$

Adjusting the Activity Some children may want to act out the situation with play money. Provide dollar bills (*Math Masters*, pages 7 and 8) and tool-kit coins. Extend the problem by asking if $10 will still be enough if $\frac{1}{10}$ or 10% of the $9.40 cost is added for sales tax. Children try to solve this problem and then share their strategies. If only a few are successful, work with the class first on the dollars and then on the cents:

What is $\frac{1}{10}$ of $9.00? 9 dimes: $0.90

676 Unit

◆ **Home Link 9.5** (*Math Masters*, p. 326)

Home Connection Children use mental math or the partial-products algorithm to solve multiplication number stories.

3 Options for Individualizing

◆ EXTRA PRACTICE Calculating $\frac{1}{10}$ of Amounts of Money (*Math Masters*, p. 144)

INDEPENDENT ACTIVITY   5–15 min

Children find $\frac{1}{10}$ of various dollars-and-cents amounts.

◆ EXTRA PRACTICE Minute Math

SMALL-GROUP ACTIVITY   5–15 min

To offer children more experience with calculating with money, see the following pages in *Minute Math*:
Number Stories: pp. 141, 144, and 145

1 Teaching the Lesson
Main instructional activities for the lesson, where most new content is introduced.

Stock-Up Sale

... #2 on page 241 in the *Student Reference* ... below. Show how you got the answers.

... of soap at the Stock-Up ... least 5. He has $4.00 ... buy 5 bars of soap? yes

... $\times \$0.65 = \$3.25$

... 00 bill to buy a toothbrush? ... an he buy 5 toothbrushes? no

... Exactly how much ... order to be able to ... sale price? $5.65

... $\times \$1.13 = \$5.65$

... apes. How much more ... apes at the sale price ... regular price? $4.91 more

... ercent sales tax, ... 5 audio tapes be? $10.84
... 5 + \$0.99 = \$10.84

... e story of your own.

... How much will Shakida save if ... ks of nightlights at the sale price?

... $.80 - \$3.80 = \$1.00$

◆ *Math Journal 2*, p. 219

◆ **Solving Stock-Up Sale Stories**
(*Math Journal 2*, p. 219;
Student Reference Book, p. 240)

PARTNER ACTIVITY

Children work together in partnerships to solve the problems on journal page 219 using the information on page 240 in their *Student Reference Books*. Some problems call for an exact answer, while others require only an estimate. Children should show the number models that they are using to make their estimates.

2 Ongoing Learning & Practice

◆ **Using the Partial-Products Algorithm to Multiply** (*Math Journal 2*, p. 220;
Math Masters, pp. 137 and 138)

INDEPENDENT ACTIVITY

Circulate and assist as necessary.

Adjusting the Activity Children who are still confused by the partial-products algorithm should write the number model next to each partial product.

$$68$$
$$\times \ 2$$
$$2 \, [60s] \rightarrow \ 120$$
$$2 \, [8s] \rightarrow \ \underline{+ \ 16}$$
$$120 + 16 \rightarrow \ 136$$

Children may also use the array grid (*Math Masters*, pages 137 and 138) with base-10 blocks to model the problems.

◆ **Math Boxes 9.5** (*Math Journal 2*, p. 221)

INDEPENDENT ACTIVITY

Mixed Review This journal page provides opportunities for cumulative review or assessment of concepts and skills.

Math Boxes 9.5

1. Estimate the cost of these items:
   4 giant stickers at $0.88 each
   about $ 3.60
   2 packs of file cards at $1.69 each
   about $ 3.40

2. Fill in the unit box.
   Unit
   $49 - 7 = 7$
   $36 - 9 = 4$
   $54 - 6 = 9$
   $5 = 40 - 8$
   $64 = 8 \times 8$

3. What 3-D shape is this a picture of?
   ○ sphere
   ● cylinder
   ○ pyramid

   What is the shape of the base?
   A circle

4. Solve.
   $678 + 492 = 1,170$
   $704 - 358 = 346$

5. Use the partial-products algorithm to solve.
   $49 \times 7 = 280 + 63 = 343$
   $652 \times 3 = 1800 + 150 + 6 = 1,956$
   $408 \times 8 = 3200 + 64 = 3,264$

6. Fill in the empty frames and the rule box.
   $+ 40$ $- 25$
   43   83   123   98
   113   73

◆ *Math Journal 2*, p. 221

96 × 5	→ 450 → +30 → 480
85 × 9	→ 720 → +45 → 765
508 × 5	→ 2500 → + 40 → 2,540

2 Ongoing Learning & Practice
Essential for developing and maintaining skills, these activities provide review and practice in the form of Math Journal assignments, Math Boxes, Home/Study Links and games.

3 Options for Individualizing
Optional activities for reteaching, extra skill practice, enrichment, and meeting the needs of particular populations (ESL, etc.). Usually extensions of "Teaching the Lesson" section.

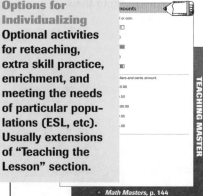

...mounts
... or coin.

...dollars-and-cents amount.

...50
...00.00
...00

◆ *Math Masters*, p. 144

Saving at the Stock-Up Sale   Home Link 9.5

Family Note Today the class used mental math and the partial-products algorithm to solve shopping problems. Note that for some of the problems below, an estimate will answer the question. For others, an exact answer is needed. If your child is able to make the calculations mentally, encourage him or her to explain the solution strategy to you.

Please return this Home Link to school tomorrow.

Decide whether you will need to estimate or calculate an exact answer to solve each problem below. Then solve the problem. Record the answer and write a number model (or models) to show how you found the answer.

1. Phil has $6.00. He wants to buy Creepy Creature erasers. They cost $1.05 each. If he buys more than 5, they are $0.79 each. Does he have enough money to buy 7 Creepy Creature erasers? yes
   Number model: $0.79 \times 7 = \$5.53$

2. Mrs. Katz is buying cookies for a school party. The cookies cost $2.48 per dozen. If she buys more than 4 dozen, they cost $2.12 per dozen. How much are 6 dozen? $12.72
   Number model: $2.12 \times 6 = \$12.72$

3. Baseball cards are on sale for $1.29 per card, or 5 cards for $6. Marly bought 10 cards. How much did he save with the special price? $0.90
   On the back of this page, explain how you found your answer.

4. Ursula buys 8 pencils. They are $0.55 each, or $3.85 for a package of 10. Which is cheaper—8 pencils at $0.55 each or the package of 10 pencils? pack of 10
   How much would she save? $0.55
   On the back of this page, explain how you found your answer.

◆ *Math Masters*, p. 326

Everyday Mathematics
Student Reference Book
Grades 3–6

The grade-specific Student Reference Book contains

✦ **Mathematical Essays** Sections organized around mathematical topics which provide explanations and examples. Students may use these pages during lesson instruction and when they need information to complete independent work.

✦ **Game Section** Provides directions for games introduced at each grade level. They are helpful for clarification of rules, adaptations for various abilities, and home use.

✦ **Data Section** Contains charts, tables, and other information provided for use with student lesson activities and projects.

In addition, a comprehensive glossary, an answer key for every **Check Your Understanding,** and an index are found at the back of the book.

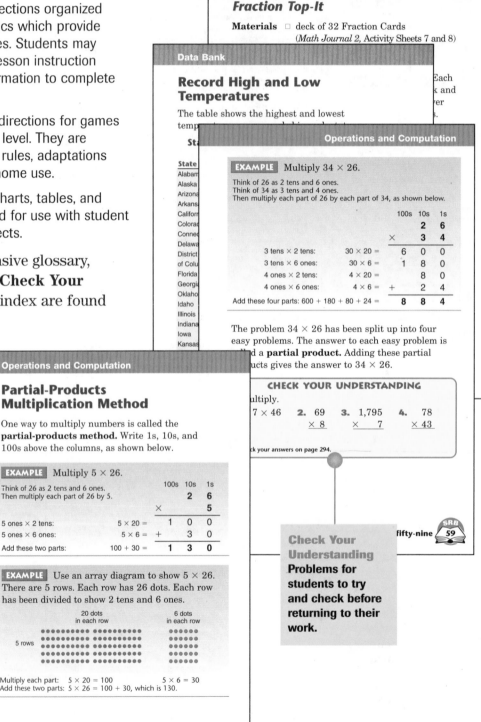

Games

Fraction Top-It

Materials ☐ deck of 32 Fraction Cards
(*Math Journal 2,* Activity Sheets 7 and 8)

Data Bank

Record High and Low Temperatures

The table shows the highest and lowest temp...

Operations and Computation

EXAMPLE Multiply 34 × 26.

Think of 26 as 2 tens and 6 ones.
Think of 34 as 3 tens and 4 ones.
Then multiply each part of 26 by each part of 34, as shown below.

		100s	10s	1s
			2	**6**
	×		**3**	**4**
3 tens × 2 tens:	30 × 20 =	6	0	0
3 tens × 6 ones:	30 × 6 =	1	8	0
4 ones × 2 tens:	4 × 20 =		8	0
4 ones × 6 ones:	4 × 6 = +		2	4
Add these four parts: 600 + 180 + 80 + 24 =		**8**	**8**	**4**

The problem 34 × 26 has been split up into four easy problems. The answer to each easy problem is ...ed a **partial product.** Adding these partial ...ucts gives the answer to 34 × 26.

CHECK YOUR UNDERSTANDING
...ultiply.

7 × 46   **2.** 69   **3.** 1,795   **4.** 78
         × 8   × 7   × 43

...ck your answers on page 294.

State

State
Alabam
Alaska
Arizona
Arkans
Californ
Colorac
Connec
Delawa
District of Colu
Florida
Georgia
Oklaho
Idaho
Illinois
Indiana
Iowa
Kansas

fifty-nine 59

Title Bar
Highlights page contents

Vocabulary
Notes words that may also be found in the glossary

Examples
Provides examples of mathematical processes

Operations and Computation

Partial-Products Multiplication Method

One way to multiply numbers is called the **partial-products method.** Write 1s, 10s, and 100s above the columns, as shown below.

EXAMPLE Multiply 5 × 26.

Think of 26 as 2 tens and 6 ones.
Then multiply each part of 26 by 5.

		100s	10s	1s
			2	**6**
	×			**5**
5 ones × 2 tens:	5 × 20 =	1	0	0
5 ones × 6 ones:	5 × 6 = +		3	0
Add these two parts:	100 + 30 =	**1**	**3**	**0**

EXAMPLE Use an array diagram to show 5 × 26. There are 5 rows. Each row has 26 dots. Each row has been divided to show 2 tens and 6 ones.

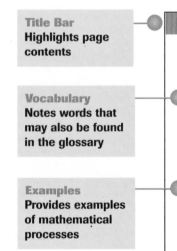

20 dots in each row   6 dots in each row

5 rows

Multiply each part: 5 × 20 = 100   5 × 6 = 30
Add these two parts: 5 × 26 = 100 + 30, which is 130.

SRB 58 fifty-eight

Check Your Understanding
Problems for students to try and check before returning to their work.

Examples from Third Grade Student Reference Book

Assessment Handbook

The grade-specific Assessment Handbook provides ideas to make assessment and instruction more manageable, productive, and exciting, as well as offer a more complete picture of each child's progress and instructional needs. It guides teachers as they develop a plan that balances techniques and tools from four different assessment areas.

✦ **Ongoing Assessment** Informal student observation and anecdotal record keeping during teacher-guided instruction, strategy sharing, game play, and slate routines.

✦ **Product Assessment** Samples of student work from Math Boxes, Math Journals, Explorations, and Projects.

✦ **Periodic Assessment** Unit, mid-year and end-of-year assessments and Math Boxes.

✦ **Outside Tests** School, district, or state assessments and standardized achievement tests.

Ongoing Assessment
Suggestions from lesson activities throughout the unit. Refers teachers back to unit learning goals and development levels.

Periodic Assessment
Suggestions for recording students' periodic progress from the unit assessment lesson. Refers teachers back to unit learning goals and development levels.

Product Assessment
Detailed sample rubric for a product assessment opportunity.

Unit 9
Assessment Overview

At this stage in *Everyday Mathematics*, children are expected to be at a Beginning/Developing level for multiplying multidigit numbers by 1- or 2-digit numbers. Because this is such a critical skill, five ongoing assessment opportunities are provided in Unit 9 (see Goal 9b in the chart below).

By this time, perhaps you have tried several different types of assessment strategies. Remember, as you use a balance of assessment approaches, the overall effectiveness of your assessment plan should improve. If there is still a major type of assessment, such as Ongoing, Product, or Periodic, that you haven't used, this unit might be a good time to try it.

Ongoing Assessment Opportunities

Ongoing assessment opportunities are opportunities to observe children during regular interactions, as they work independently and in groups. You can conduct ongoing assessment during teacher-guided instruction, Math Boxes sessions, mathematical mini-interviews, games, Mental Math and Reflexes sessions, strategy sharing, and slate work. The chart below provides a summary of ongoing assessment opportunities in Unit 9, as they relate to specific Unit 9 learning goals.

Beginning Goal Solve number stories involving positive and negative numbers. (Lesson 9.13)	Lesson 9.13, p. 722
Beginning/Developing Goal Multiply multidigit numbers by 1- or 2-digit numbers. (Lessons 9.2, 9.4, 9.5, 9.9, 9.11, and 9.12)	Lesson 9.2, p. 660 Lesson 9.4, p. 672 Lesson 9.9, p. 699 Lesson 9.11, p. 710 Lesson 9.12, p. 715
Beginning/Developing Goal Find factors of a number. (Lessons 9.6 and 9.10)	Lesson 9.6, p. 681 Lesson 9.10, p. 705
Beginning/Developing Goal Interpret remainders in division problems. (Lesson 9.8)	Lesson 9.8, p. 693

Product Assessment Opportunities

Math Journals, Math Boxes, activity sheets, masters, Math Logs, and the results of Explorations and Projects all provide product assessment opportunities. Here is an example of how you might use a rubric to assess children's abilities to solve equal-sharing problems.

Lesson 9.7, p. 689

EXTRA PRACTICE Sharing Money

Circulate around the room as children work in pairs to complete *Math Masters*, page 148. Children record the problem, a number model, and the answer. This activity can help you assess children's ability to solve equal-sharing problems with remainders. The sample rubric below will help you evaluate children's work.

Sample Rubric

Beginning (B)
The pair of children is able to set up the problem by rolling the die and drawing two cards. However, the number model may be written incorrectly or children may need teacher assistance. Problems b–f are difficult for partners to solve without teacher assistance. Children may get through only one of the equal-sharing problems.

Developing (D)
The pair of children sets up the problem without teacher assistance using the die and number cards. The number model is written correctly in both problems and the numbers of $10 bills and $1 bills are correct. It may be difficult for children to calculate how many cents each friend would receive if the leftover money were shared equally (Problem e). Therefore, their final answer may be incorrect.

Secure (S)
The pair of children sets up and solves the problems without teacher assistance. The number sentences are written correctly, and the numbers of $10 bills and $1 bills are correct. Children are able to calculate how the leftover money can be shared equally; thus they have a correct total for the amount that each friend would receive. Children may also be able to solve more than two problems.

Periodic Assessment Opportunities

Here is a summary of the periodic assessment opportunities that are provided in Unit 9. Refer to Lesson 9.14 for details.

Oral and Slate Assessment

In Lesson 9.14, you will find oral and slate assessment problems on pages 725–727.

Written Assessment

In Lesson 9.14, you will find written assessment problems on pages 727–728 (*Math Masters*, pages 386 and 387).

See the chart on the next page to find slate and written assessment problems that address specific learning goals.

Examples from Third Grade
Assessment Handbook

Everyday Mathematics *Making a mark in education*

Everyday Mathematics is used in a variety of settings throughout the United States as shown here on the map.

Over 2 million students in 100,000 classrooms are engaged in this exciting curriculum.

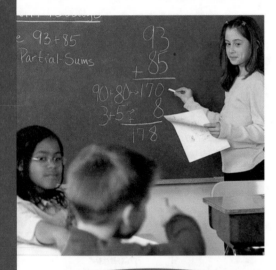

Look for users in your area.

WASHINGTON
Northshore SD 417
Longview SD 122
Franklin Pierce SD 402
South Kitsap SD 402
Silverdale Elementary

MONTANA
Livingston SD 1 & 4
Bigfork SD 38

OREGON
Beavertown SD 48J
Portland Jewish Academy

IDAHO
Coeur D'Alene SD 271
Lewiston ISD 1

SOUTH DAKOTA
Beresford SD 61-2
Pierre Indian School

WYOMING
Sheridan County SD 2

CALIFORNIA
Rocklin SD
Glendale SD
Poway SD
Hacienda-La Puente Unified SD
Center for Early Education

UTAH
Rolling Meadows School
Park City SD

COLORADO
Douglas County SD R-1
Cherry Creek SD 5
Julesburg SD R-1
Eagleton Elementary
Lewis-Palmer SD 38

ARIZONA
Kyrene Elementary SD 28

NEW MEXICO
Rio Rancho Public SD
Bloomfield SD
Taos Day School-Bureau of Indian Affairs
Bernalillo Public SD
Pojoaque Valley SD

ALASKA
Anchorage SD

HAWAII
Waipahu Elementary
Nanakuli Elementary
Ewa Beach Elementary

NEBRASKA
Millard Public
  Schools 17
Westside Community
  SD 66
Hebron City SD 7
Seward Public SD 9
Tri-County SD 300

WISCONSIN
Kenosha USD
Sheboygan Area SD
Oak Creek-Franklin SD
Wauwatosa SD
Menasha Joint SD

ILLINOIS
Rockford SD 205
Sunset Ridge SD 29
Community
  Consolidated SD 93
Aptakisic-Tripp SD 102
Mt. Prospect SD 57

MICHIGAN
Ann Arbor Public SD
Troy SD
Rochester Community SD
Kalamazoo Public SD
Walled Lake
  Consolidated SD

VERMONT
Addison Rutland
  Supervisory Union 4
Barre Town SD
Colchester SD
East Montpelier SD
Montpelier SD 45

NEW YORK
Bronx SD 11
Staten Island SD 31
Valley Stream SD 30
Monroe Woodbury
  Central SD
Williamsville Central SD

NEW HAMPSHIRE
District 8 Concord
District 24 Weare
District 41 Hollis
District 46 Merrimack
  Valley

OHIO
Worthington SD
Upper Arlington City SD
Northwest Local SD
Clyde-Green Springs
  Exempt Village SD
Lakewood City SD

INDIANA
Penn Harris
  Madison SD
Lafayette Christian
  School

MINNESOTA
Minneapolis Public SD 1
Edina Public SD 273
Wayzata SD 284
Brainerd ISD 181
Moorhead ISD 152

MAINE
Cape Elizabeth SD
Sanford SD
School Administration
  District 60 North
  Berwick
York School District

PENNSYLVANIA
Abington SD
Haverford Township SD
Butler Area SD
Pittsburgh Public SD
Quaker Valley SD

MASSACHUSETTS
Lexington SD
Lynnfield SD
Newton Public SD
Reading Public SD
Westborough SD

IOWA
College Community SD
Bettendorf Community SD
Sheldon Community SD
Pleasant Valley
  Community SD
Cedar Rapids Catholic
  Schools

RHODE ISLAND
Barrington Town SD
East Providence City SD
Middletown Public SD
Tivertown SD
West Warwick Town SD

KANSAS
Winfield USD 465
Geary County USD 475
Cheney USD 268
Bonner Springs
  USD 204

MISSOURI
Melhville SD R9
Webster Groves SD
Affton SD 101
Blue Spring SD R4

MARYLAND
Cecil County SD

CONNECTICUT
New Milford SD
Norwich SD
Old Saybrook SD
South Windsor Public SD
Wilton Public SD
Colchester Public SD

NEW JERSEY
Hackensack Public
  Schools
South Orange
  Maplewood SD
Tenafly SD
East Brunswick Public SD
Spotswood SD

OKLAHOMA
Holland Hall School

KENTUCKY
Brandeis Elementary
Sayre School
The Lexington School
Grapevine Elementary
East View Elementary

ARKANSAS
Corning SD 8

VIRGINIA
Virginia Beach City SD

MISSISSIPPI
St. Andrew's Episcopal
  School

GEORGIA
Lovett School
Westminster Lower
  School
Trinity School
Greater Atlanta
  Christian School

NORTH CAROLINA
Charlotte Country Day
  School
McDougle Elementary
Mangum Primary
The Summit School

TEXAS
Leander ISD
Temple ISD
Houston ISD
Lockhart ISD
River Oaks Baptist
  School

ALABAMA
Birmingham City
  Public SD
Vestavia Hills City SD
Randolph School

SOUTH CAROLINA
Fort Mill Primary
Heathwood Hall
  Episcopal
Hilton Head Primary &
  Elementary
Memminger Elementary
Richland County SD 2

FLORIDA
Dunbar Magnet School
Gene Witt Elementary
  School
Osceola Magnet School
Putnam County SD

TENNESSEE
Memphis City SD
Hamilton County Schools
Oak Ridge SD
Bright School
St. Mary's Episcopal
  School

fifteen ░░░░░ 5*3 **XV**

Everyday Mathematics Acknowledgments

The first edition of the K–6 *Everyday Mathematics* program was made possible by sustained support over several years from the GTE Corporation and the National Science Foundation. Additional help came from the Amoco Foundation through its support of the University of Chicago School Mathematics Project (UCSMP).

Earlier projects supported by the National Science Foundation, the National Institute of Education, and the Benton Foundation provided us with insights into the often surprising capabilities of young children.

This second edition of the K–6 *Everyday Mathematics* program is funded by Everyday Learning Corporation and by the authors.

For both editions, feedback and advice from teachers willing to take risks in trying development versions have been essential and enormously helpful. There are too many such teachers to list, but their contributions are gratefully acknowledged.

For both editions, many University of Chicago and UCSMP colleagues have been helpful. Finally, we acknowledge dedicated and resourceful help on production and technical tasks by many people on our various development staffs and also at Everyday Learning Corporation.

James McBride
Director, Second Edition

Max Bell
Director, First Edition

First Grade

Everyday Mathematics®

Teacher's Lesson Guide
Volume 1

**The University of Chicago
School Mathematics Project**

A Division of The McGraw-Hill Companies

Columbus, Ohio
Chicago, Illinois

UCSMP Elementary Materials Component

Max Bell, Director

Authors

Max Bell
Jean Bell
John Bretzlauf*
Amy Dillard*
Robert Hartfield
Andy Isaacs*
James McBride, Director
Kathleen Pitvorec*
Peter Saecker

Technical Art

Diana Barrie*

Second Edition only

Photo Credits

Phil Martin/Photography
Jack Demuth/Photography
Cover: Bill Burlingham/Photography
Photo Collage: Herman Adler Design Group

www.sra4kids.com

SRA/McGraw-Hill

*A Division of The **McGraw·Hill** Companies*

Send all inquiries to:
SRA/McGraw-Hill
P.O. Box 812960
Chicago, IL 60681

Printed in the United States of America.

ISBN 1-57039-819-4

4 5 6 7 8 9 QW 07 06 05 04 03 02

Contents

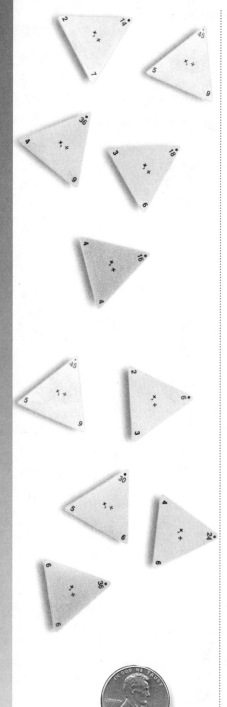

Volume 2

Welcome to *Everyday Mathematics*, the elementary school mathematics curriculum developed by the University of Chicago School Mathematics Project (UCSMP). *Everyday Mathematics* offers you and your children a broad background and rich experiences in mathematics.

First Grade *Everyday Mathematics* content emphasizes the following content strands, skills and concepts:

- ❖ **Numeration** Counting; reading and writing numbers; investigating place-value of whole numbers; exploring fractions and money.
- ❖ **Operations and Computation** Learning addition and subtraction facts, fact families, and extended facts; beginning informal work with properties of numbers and problem solving.
- ❖ **Data and Chance** Collecting, organizing, and displaying data using tables, charts, and graphs; exploring concepts of chance.
- ❖ **Geometry** Exploring 2- and 3-dimensional shapes.
- ❖ **Measurement and Reference Frames** Using tools to measure length, capacity, and weight; using clocks, calendars, timelines, thermometers, and ordinal numbers.
- ❖ **Patterns, Functions, and Algebra** Exploring attributes, patterns, sequences, relations, and functions; finding missing numbers and rules in Frames-and-Arrows and "What's My Rule?" problems; studying properties of operations.

Within the content of *Everyday Mathematics*, emphasis is placed on:

- ❖ A problem-solving approach based on everyday situations that develops critical thinking.
- ❖ Frequent practice of basic skills through ongoing program routines and mathematical games.
- ❖ An instructional approach that revisits topics regularly to ensure full concept development.
- ❖ Activities that explore a wide variety of mathematical content and offer opportunities for students to apply their basic fact skills to geometry, measurement, and algebra.

Everyday Mathematics will provide you with ample opportunities to monitor implementation. At the beginning of the school year, focus on Parts 1 and 2 of the three-part lesson plan and try at least one assessment technique from each of the four sources: ongoing, product, and periodic assessment and outside tests. As the school year progresses, incorporate activities from Part 3 of your lesson plan as appropriate for your children and try some of the other assessment suggestions to gain a clearer picture of student development. During your first year, you will become increasingly comfortable with the content, components, and strategies of *First Grade Everyday Mathematics*.

You and your children will incorporate mathematical processes as a part of everyday work and play. These processes will gradually shape children's ways of thinking about mathematics and foster the development of mathematical intuition and understanding.

Have an exciting year!

Professional Preparation

Components for
First Grade Everyday Mathematics

Go to...	When you need...
Teacher's Lesson Guide	Daily lessons; unit support information; key vocabulary; scope and sequence Grades K–2
Math Masters	Blackline masters for Math Boxes, Home Links, projects, and assessments
Assessment Handbook	Suggestions for portfolio, ongoing, and product assessment
Teacher's Reference Manual	Background on mathematical content; ideas for curriculum and classroom management for K–3
Home Connection Handbook	Suggestions for home-school communication for K–6
Minute Math®	Quick activities for transition time
Content by Strand Poster	Skills organized by content strand and paced by month (side one); learning goals organized by unit for the year (side two)
Student Math Journal	Lesson support material for students to analyze and complete; a year-long record of each student's mathematical development

Suggested Reading & Lesson Preparation

In order to prepare for effective classroom and curriculum management, we suggest that the following activities take place before you teach *Everyday Mathematics* for the first time.

Reading and Planning

❑ Review each of the components in your Teacher's Resource Package (TRP). Take time to analyze where information and materials are located so that you may access them as needed throughout the school year. See the chart above.

❑ Read Unit 1 Organizer and the first three to four lessons in your *Teacher's Lesson Guide*.

❑ Prepare a general daily math schedule. This schedule should include time for morning routines (calendar, weather, attendance, etc.), Teaching the Lesson, and Ongoing Learning and Practice activities such as games and Math Boxes.

Materials Preparation

Prepare materials as indicated in the first three to four lessons. Special items for consideration include:

❑ Review the *Penny-Dice Game*. See *Teacher's Lesson Guide* Unit 1, Lesson 3, page 24. Make note of the game skills (i.e., rolling the dice) you will need to teach before play begins. Try the game with a colleague. Consider any adaptations you may need to make for various abilities.

❑ Create Tool Kits. See *Teacher's Lesson Guide*, Unit 1, Lesson 3, page 22.

❑ Prepare slates for student use. See *Teacher's Lesson Guide*, Unit 1, Lesson 4, page 26.

❑ Write and copy a list of coins for each student to bring from home (10 pennies, 5 nickels). Suggest that students bring the coins in either a small plastic bag or a 35 mm plastic film container. An additional class collection of pennies is also useful.

❑ Prepare a supply of paper:

Blank $8\frac{1}{2} \times 11$ (full, half, and quarter size sheets)
Primary grade handwriting paper
Colored construction paper
Graph paper (1-inch)

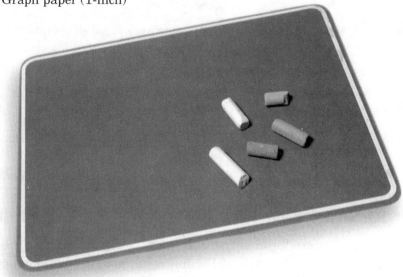

Organizing Your Classroom

Items for Display

Before the school year begins, we suggest that you prepare the following items for classroom display. By taking time to prepare these items your first year and laminating them if possible, you will be able to re-use them year after year. See the Management Guide of your *Teacher's Reference Manual* for more information and suggestions.

❑ Number cards with words

❑ Number Line (−35–180)

❑ Number Grid Poster (In your TRP)

❑ Monthly Calendar

❑ Weather/Temperature Recording Chart

❑ Attendance Chart

❑ Daily Class Schedule

❑ Job Chart

❑ N, S, E, W directional indicators

❑ Class Data Pad

Classroom Set-Up

The following items should be considered as you set-up your *Everyday Mathematics* classroom. Try several configurations until you find one that is comfortable and effective for both you and your students. Visit other classrooms in your building to observe and discuss what works for your colleagues.

❑ Prepare and label a location in the classroom where students may deposit their written work: Math Messages and Home Links.

❑ Arrange classroom desks/tables to allow for easy access to manipulatives and to facilitate efficient transitions for individual, partner, and small group activities.

❑ Organize class and individual manipulatives for easy access and efficient use of storage space.

❑ Allow (table) space for math center(s). Particular games and activities may then be left in this space for ongoing practice or free exploration.

Manipulatives for *First Grade Everyday Mathematics* Activities

The following list has been organized to highlight the items that are used on a regular basis throughout *First Grade Everyday Mathematics*. Some lessons call for minor additional materials, which you or your students may bring in at the appropriate time.

Additional Valuable Classroom Resources

Number Cards, 0–100, with numerals and words

Demonstration Clock

Overhead Projector Materials

Class Data Pad (12 x15 spiral flip chart)

Quantity	Item
1 set	Attribute Blocks
1 set	Base-10 Blocks
10 sets	Play Money Bills
1 per student	Calculator* (TI-108 recommended)
1 per student	Clock Face
1 set	Clock Face Stamps
1 set	Coin Stamps, heads
1 pkg. (2000)	Connectors (twist ties)
1 pkg. (1000)	Counting (Craft) Sticks
1 pkg. (16 total)	Dice, blanks
1 per student	Die, dot
3 pkg. (18 total)	Dice, polyhedra
5 sets	Dominoes, Double-9
15 decks	Everything Math Decks
8	Geoboards
10	Meter Sticks, dual scale
1	Number Line (−35–180)
2 sets	Pattern Blocks
1 per student	Pattern Block Template
1 pkg.	Rubber Bands (for geoboards)
1 per student	Ruler, 6-inch
1 per student	Slate (chalk or marker board)
2	Stamp Pads
1 pkg. (500)	Straws
15	Tape Measures, retractable
1	Thermometer (°F and °C)
1 per student	Tool-Kit Bag*

All of the above items are available from Everyday Learning Corporation. They may be purchased either as a comprehensive classroom manipulative kit or by individual components. The Everyday Learning classroom kit provides appropriate quantities for a class of 25 and comes packaged in durable plastic tubs with labels.

*Calculators and tool-kit bags available from Everyday Learning Corporation for individual purchase only.

Instruction

The following sections introduce instructional methods and suggestions for successful *Everyday Mathematics* implementation. Teachers are encouraged to read these pages and refer to them as needed throughout the school year.

Daily Routines

Children learn a great deal of mathematics through daily routines that they perform independently and with the class. These daily activities may include tracking attendance, calendar, weather, temperature, and choral counting. Numerous mathematical concepts are reinforced on a daily basis and help children become aware of how mathematics pervades our everyday lives.

Most of the daily routines in *First Grade Everyday Mathematics* are introduced within the lessons of Unit 1 and should be maintained throughout the school year. Refer to Unit 1 lessons and the Management Guide of the *Teacher's Reference Manual* for more information.

Program Routines

Everyday Mathematics uses a number of program routines that are incorporated throughout all grade levels. These allow for ongoing developmental practice in a number of skill and content areas. Below is a list of the routines you will encounter in *First Grade Everyday Mathematics*. The unit and lesson in which each routine is first used have been noted. Refer to the Management Guide in the *Teacher's Reference Manual* for more information.

    Mental Math and Reflexes (Unit 1, Lesson 1)
    Games (Unit 1, Lesson 3)
    *Home Links (Unit 1, Lesson 8)
    Math Boxes (Unit 2, Lesson 3)
    Frames and Arrows (Unit 3, Lesson 8)
    Math Message (Unit 4, Lesson 1)
    * "What's My Rule?"/Function Machines (Unit 5, Lesson 12)
    Name Collection Boxes (Unit 6, Lesson 2)
    Fact Triangles/Fact Families (Unit 6, Lesson 4)

*Routine used in *Kindergarten Everyday Mathematics*

Explorations

You will find an Explorations lesson in virtually every unit in *First Grade Everyday Mathematics*. The term "Exploration" is used to indicate independent, small-group activities that are informal and open-ended. The Explorations have been designed so that you can position the various activities at different stations around the room and have small groups rotate among them.

Each Explorations lesson suggests three exploratory activities, with the option of adding other familiar activities as desired. In each set of activities, Exploration A contains the main content of the lesson and requires the most teacher facilitation, especially at the outset.

Explorations are not intended as optional activities for students to do when they have finished their other work. Be sure to set aside enough class time so that all students can experience the Explorations. They provide critical initial exposure to content that is developed later in *Everyday Mathematics*.

Refer to the Management Guide in the *Teacher's Lesson Manual* for more information.

Projects

The projects outlined in this program cover an array of mathematics activities and concepts, and are built around various themes that interest children. Projects also incorporate science, social studies, art and language arts skills. Projects are suggested in Unit Organizers in the *Teacher's Lesson Guide* at appropriate times throughout the year. They typically take one to two days to complete, depending upon how many of the suggested activities you incorporate. This time is well spent as it allows the teacher to assess the students' abilities in mathematics applications and in cross-curricular skills. They also are memorable events for children.

Refer to the Management Guide in the *Teacher's Reference Manual* and Unit Organizers in the *Teacher's Lesson Guide* for more information.

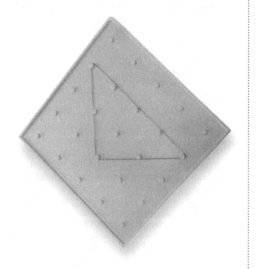

Assessment

Everyday Mathematics encourages a balanced approach to student assessment, one that reveals the development of a child's mathematical understanding while giving the teacher useful feedback about instructional needs. They also provide information and documentation to help assign grades.

Refer to the *Assessment Handbook* and the Unit Organizers in the *Teacher's Lesson Guide* for detailed information regarding ongoing, product, and periodic assessment.

Providing for Home-School Connections

Comprehensive and consistent home-school communication regarding program content, routines, and student assessment is essential for successful implementation. *Everyday Mathematics* provides a number of support materials to facilitate this communication. The *Home Connection Handbook* is a tool that can help you introduce parents and primary caregivers to the *Everyday Mathematics* curriculum. Grade specific Family Letters and Home Links serve as a basis for ongoing communication as well as a vehicle to engage parents as partners in the learning process. Individual assessment checklists enable teachers to describe in detail the developmental progress of each child. They are a valuable communication tool during conferences.

Refer to the *Home Connection Handbook* for more information.

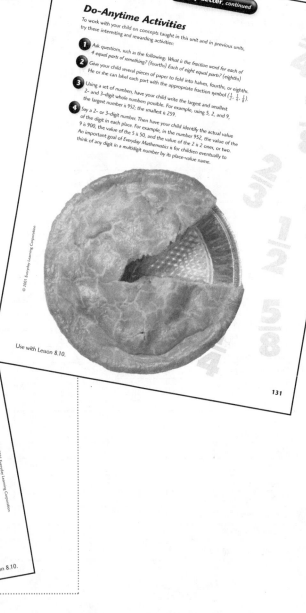

K–3 Games Correlation Chart

Skill and Concept Areas

Game	K Title Page #	Grade 1 Lesson	Grade 2 Lesson	Grade 3 Lesson	Numeration	Mental Math	Basic Facts	Operations	Patterns	Geometry	Money	Time	Probability	Calculator
Addition Card Draw			12.5			■	■	■						
Addition Spin			4.2			■	■	■						
Addition Top-It		6.1	1.4	1.4	■	■	■	■						
Addition Top-It with Dominoes			2.5			■	■	■						
Angle Race				6.9						■				
Animal Weight Top-It		5.5			■	■	■	■						
Array Bingo			6.10	9.6			■	■						
Attribute Train Game		7.2	7.2						■	■				
Base-10 Exchange		8.4			■		■							
Baseball Multiplication				4.7		■	■	■						
Basketball Addition			7.4			■	■	■						
Beat the Calculator		5.11	2.2	1.8		■	■	■						■
Before and After		3.1			■									
The Block-Drawing Game				11.6						■			■	
Broken Calculator			1.10	*	■									■
Buyer and Vendor Game		10.3		1.9							■			
Class Clock Game			1.3									■		
Clock Concentration			5.1									■		
Coin-Dice		3.12									■			
Coin Exchange	194	6.10									■			
Coin Top-It		2.10	1.4		■						■			
Concentration with Number Cards & Dominoes	89				■									
Dice-Roll and Tally Game		1.8	1.5		■								■	
Difference Game		5.7			■			■						
Digit Discovery			1.12		■									
Digit Game	267		3.2		■									
Dime–Nickel–Penny Grab		3.12									■			
Disappearing Train	217					■		■						
Division Arrays				4.3			■	■						
Division Coin-Drop								■						
Dollar Rummy			3.4		■						■			
Domino Top-It		3.14			■									
Double-Digit Dice Game	268				■									
Equivalent Fractions Game			8.5	8.4	■									
Fact Power Game		6.4					■							
Fact Triangle Flip				4.6			■							
Factor Bingo				9.6			■	■						
Fraction Top-It			8.6	8.5	■									
Guess the Rule		7.2							■					
High Roller	297	2.12			■									
Hit the Target			7.3											■
Less Than You!				1.3	■		■							
Magic Bag Game		5.10							■					
Making Change			3.8								■			
Matching Coin Game	40										■			
Memory Addition/Subtraction				10.9		■		■						■
Missing Terms				*										■
Money Exchange Game ($)			1.6		■						■			
Monster Squeeze Game	84				■									

Number indicates first exposure at grade level. *Additional games available in *Student Reference Book*

Game	K Title Page #	Grade 1 Lesson	Grade 2 Lesson	Grade 3 Lesson	Numeration	Mental Math	Basic Facts	Operations	Patterns	Geometry	Money	Time	Probability	Calculator
Multiplication Bingo				7.3		█	█	█						
Multiplication Coin-Drop						█	█	█			█			
Multiplication Draw			11.5	✳		█	█	█						
Multiplication Top-It				10.5	█		█	█						
Name That Number			2.9	1.6	█	█	█	█						
Nickel/Penny Grab		2.11			█						█			
Number-Grid Game	216	9.2	1.11		█									
Number-Line Squeeze*		1.2			█									
Number Top-It				5.2	█									
One-Dollar Exchange		8.2									█			
One-Dollar Game	266										█			
$1, $10, $100 Exchange		10.3									█			
Ones, Tens, Hundreds Game	295				█			█			█			
Paper Money Exchange	292				█						█			
Penny-Cup		2.8	1.7		█		█				█			
Penny-Dice Game		1.3			█						█			
Penny-Dime Exchange				5.8							█			
Penny-Drop Addition		2.11			█			█			█			
Penny Grab		2.8	6.2	2.6	█						█			
Penny Guessing		2.9									█			
Penny-Nickel Exchange		2.10									█			
Penny-Nickel-Dime Exchange		5.13									█			
Pick-a-Coin			10.3	✳							█			
Pin the Number (Number Grid)	216	1.11			█									
Plus or Minus Game	227					█		█						
Pocket Game	201							█						
Prize Time			3.3									█		
Raft Game	221				█									
Robot Game				6.3						█				
Rolling for 50		2.1			█			█						
Scissors, Paper, Stone		1.8											█	
Secret Number		5.3			█									
Shaker Addition Top-It		4.12			█		█	█						
Shopping			4.6					█			█			
Spin a Number (1–10)	80				█									
Spinning for Money			3.2								█			
Spinning to Win				11.5									█	
Stand Up If.....		7.7							█	█				
Subtraction Top-It				3.6	█		█	█						
Tens-and-Ones Trading Game		5.3			█									
3, 2, 1 Game		8.5							█					
Three Addends Game			6.1	2.9	█	█	█	█						
Tic-Tac-Toe Addition		10.4					█	█						
Time Match		4.4										█		
Top-It	170	1.6			█									
Touch-and-Match Quadrangles				6.5						█				
Turn-Around Facts Game		5.10			█		█	█						
Two-Fisted Penny Addition		2.3	1.7	2.4	█		█	█			█			
"Who Am I Thinking Of?"		7.1							█	█				
"What's My Rule?" Fishing	99		2.11	2.3					█	█				
"What's My Attribute Rule?"			5.1						█	█				

Number indicates first exposure at grade level. *Additional games available in *Student Reference Book*

Unit 1
Establishing
Routines

SEPTEMBER
S M T W T F S

SEPTEMBER

S	M	T	W	T	F	S
					1	2
3	4	5	6	7	8	9
10	11	12	13	14	15	16
17	18	19	20	21	22	23
24	25	26	27	28	29	30

overview

In this unit, an active learning environment is established in which children will build mathematical knowledge in cooperation with you and their classmates.

Routines are introduced that will be followed both throughout the school year and in later grades. These routines provide a structure within which you and the children will begin work on a number of rich mathematical activities.

contents

learning goals in perspective

learning goals	links to the past	links to the future
1a **Developing Goal** Count by 5s to 40. **(Lessons 1.4, 1.7, and 1.11)**	In Kindergarten, children were introduced to skip counting by 2s, 5s, and 10s.	Proficiency with skip counting by 5s will help children to count money, tell time using analog clocks, and learn multiplication facts in subsequent grades. *(Related Grade 1 lessons: 2.9–2.10, 3.3, 3.5, 3.11, 3.12, 6.9–6.10, 8.1, 8.2, 8.5)*
1b **Developing Goal** Count by 2s to 40. **(Lessons 1.9–1.13)**	Children skip counted by 2s and counted pairs of things in Kindergarten.	Skip counting by 2s is related to finding even and odd numbers, and will also help children with counting on and counting back. *(Related Grade 1 lessons: 3.2–3.6, 4.11)*
1c **Developing Goal** Write numbers from 1 to 20. **(Lessons 1.1-1.6) (Lessons 1.4, 1.5, and 1.7–1.11)**	In Kindergarten, children began to develop the skill of writing numbers.	Children practice writing the numbers 7, 8, 9, and 0 in Unit 2. *(Related Grade 1 lessons: 2.2–2.5)*
1d **Developing Goal** Compare pairs of numbers less than 16. **(Lessons 1.2–1.4, 1.6, 1.7, and 1.10)**	Children played the game "Monster Squeeze" in Kindergarten, in which they found a number using "too big" and "too little" clues. Children also began ordering numbers in Kindergarten, and played the comparison game, "Top It."	Comparisons are fundamental for understanding many mathematical relationships, number stories, and analyzing data. Children will make comparisons of many types throughout the grades. *(Related Grade 1 lessons: 2.11, 2.12, 5.3, 5.6–5.9, 9.7)*
1e **Developing Goal** Write and count tallies. **(Lessons 1.2, 1.7, 1.8, and 1.12)**	Children were introduced to the use of tally marks to count and record numbers of things in Kindergarten.	Children will continue to use tallies to record data throughout the grades. *(Related Grade 1 lessons: 3.13, 6.12)*
1f **Secure Goal** Count up and back by 1s, starting with any number up to and including 20. **(Lessons 1.1–1.5, 1.7 and 1.9–1.11)**	Children practiced counting up and back in a number of situations in Kindergarten, including doing countdowns, counting on from any start number up to 50, and using calculators to count on.	Counting on and counting back will be practiced throughout first grade in a variety of situations and will continue to be useful skills throughout the grades. *(Related Grade 1 lessons: 2.1, 2.10, 3.6, 3.9, 3.10, 8.5)*
1g **Secure Goal** Count up to 20 objects. **(Lessons 1.1–1.5, 1.8, 1.10, and 1.13)**	Children practiced counting objects in various situations throughout Kindergarten.	Children will continue to practice counting objects, and will find efficient ways to count large numbers of objects in later grades.

assessment
ongoing • product • periodic

☑ Informal Assessment

Ongoing Assessment: Kid Watching Use the Ongoing Assessment suggestions in the following lessons to make quick, on-the-spot observations about children's understanding of:
• Numeration **(Lessons 1.6, 1.8, and 1.10)**
• Operations and Computation **(Lessons 1.5 and 1.13)**
• Measurement and Reference Frames **(Lessons 1.9 and 1.12)**

Portfolio Ideas Samples of children's work may be obtained from the following assignments:
• Drawing Portraits **(Lesson 1.1)**
• Draw What Mathematics Means **(Lesson 1.2)**
• Reviewing the Meaning of Mathematics **(Lesson 1.3)**
• Writing the Numbers 1 and 2 **(Lesson 1.5)**
• Writing the Numbers 3 and 4 **(Lesson 1.8)**
• Writing the Numbers 5 and 6 **(Lesson 1.10)**
• Writing the Numbers 1 through 6 **(Lesson 1.11 and 1.13)**
• Making a Weather Activity Booklet **(Lesson 1.12)**
• Play *Top-It* **(Lesson 1.14)**

☑ Unit 1 Review and Assessment

Oral and Slate Assessments Use oral or slate assessments during Lesson 1.14 to assess children's progress toward the following learning goals: **Goals 1a, 1b, 1c, 1d, 1f, and 1g**

Written Assessment Use a written review during Lesson 1.14 to assess children's progress toward the following learning goals: **Goals 1c, 1d, 1e, 1f, and 1g**

Performance/Group Assessment Use a small-group activity in Lesson 1.14 to assess children's progress toward the following learning goals: **Goals 1d and 1g**

assessment handbook

For more information on how to use different types of assessment in Unit 1, see the Assessment Overview on pages 42–44 in the *Assessment Handbook*. The following Assessment Masters can be found in the *Math Masters* book:

• Unit 1 Checking Progress, p. 303
• Unit 1 Class Checklist, p. 328
• Unit 1 Individual Profile of Progress, p. 329
• Class Progress Indicator, p. 358
• Math Logs, pp. 362–364
• Self-Assessment Forms, pp. 365–366
• Interest Inventory, p. 361

problem►◄solving

A process of modeling everyday situations using tools from mathematics

Encourage children to use a variety of strategies when attacking a given problem—and to explain those strategies. *Strategies children might use in this unit:*

- Identifying and using patterns
- Using a number line
- Modeling with manipulatives
- Using a table
- Using logical reasoning
- Drawing a picture

Four Problem-Solving REPRESENTATIONS

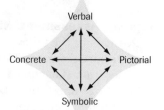

Lessons that teach *through* problem solving, not just *about* problem solving.

Lesson	Activity	Lesson	Activity
1.2	Finding the number of children who are absent	1.9	Introducing the class calendar
1.5	Telling "One More" & "One Less" number stories	1.9	Filling in the calendar for the month
1.6	Comparing and ordering numbers using number cards	1.12	Introducing the thermometer
1.7	Making a tally chart to count pets	1.13	Telling simple number stories
1.8	Playing the *Dice-Roll and Tally* game		

For more information about problem solving in *Everyday Mathematics,* see the *Teacher's Reference Manual,* pp. 197–208.

cross-curricularlinks

science

- Discuss the term *full moon* with children. Draw a picture of a full moon on the calendar to mark the next occurrence. **(Lesson 1.9)**
- Explain to children how mercury behaves in a thermometer and helps people gauge temperatures. **(Lesson 1.12)**

social studies

- Discuss various road signs and make a list of the signs children see during a walk. **(Lesson 1.3)**

literature and reading

- Read and act out action rhymes and finger plays to practice rote-counting skills. **(Lessons 1.1–1.3)**
- Practice counting skills with a counting book. **(Lesson 1.2)**

meeting INDIVIDUAL needs

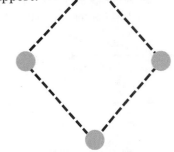

✦ RETEACHING

The following features provide some additional instructional support:

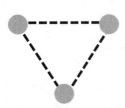

Adjusting the Activity
- **Lesson 1.2, Part 1**
- **Lesson 1.3, Part 3**
- **Lesson 1.5, Part 1**
- **Lesson 1.7, Part 1**
- **Lesson 1.8, Part 1**
- **Lesson 1.12, Part 1**

Options for Individualizing
- **Lesson 1.5** Connect the Dots

✦ ENRICHMENT

The following features suggest some enrichment and extension activities:

Adjusting the Activity
- **Lesson 1.1, Part 1**
- **Lesson 1.3, Part 1**
- **Lesson 1.4, Part 3**
- **Lesson 1.5, Part 1**
- **Lesson 1.6, Part 1**
- **Lesson 1.9, Part 1**
- **Lesson 1.12, Part 1**

Options for Individualizing
- **Lesson 1.1** Drawing Portraits
- **Lesson 1.3** Making Geometric Designs
- **Lesson 1.7** A Listening Tally
- **Lesson 1.8** *Scissors, Paper, Stone*
- **Lesson 1.10** Pattern-Block Designs
- **Lesson 1.11** Drawing Pattern-Block Designs
- **Lesson 1.12** Making a Weather Activity Booklet

✦ LANGUAGE DIVERSITY

The following features suggest ways to support children who are acquiring proficiency in English:

Adjusting the Activity
- **Lesson 1.2, Part 1**
- **Lesson 1.11, Part 3**

Options for Individualizing
- **Lesson 1.2** Reviewing the Meaning of Mathematics
- **Lesson 1.4** Other Names for Numbers

✦ MULTIAGE CLASSROOM

The following chart lists related activities from the *Kindergarten Teachers Guide to Activities* and lessons from Grade 2 that can help you meet your instructional needs:

Grade K Pages	Grade 1 Lessons	Grade 2 Lessons

Grade K Pages	10 18 52	10 176 198		112 114	33 34 94 291	262	176	296 297	30 54	170	16	24	90 228
Grade 1 Lessons	1.1	1.2	1.3	1.4	1.5	1.6	1.7	1.8	1.9	1.10	1.11	1.12	1.13
Grade 2 Lessons		1.1	1.2		1.12	1.12	1.5		1.3	1.4	1.13	4.3 4.4	2.1 4.1 4.2

materials

lesson	math masters pages	manipulative kit items	other items
1.1	Home Link Masters, pp. 149–152		Job Chart; Attendance Chart half-sheet of drawing paper *See* **Advance Preparation, p. 14**
1.2		Class Number Line	"fences" to bracket number-line intervals *See* **Advance Preparation, p. 18**
1.3		Pattern-Block Template pattern blocks (optional)	tool kit half-sheet of drawing paper *See* **Advance Preparation, p. 22**
1.4		slate 1 die per partnership	number cards 10–50 20 pennies per partnership plastic bag; craft sticks; rubber band *See* **Advance Preparation, p. 26**
1.5	Teaching Masters, p. 1 and 2 *See* **Advance Preparation, p. 30**		pennies
1.6	Teaching Master, p. 3 *See* **Advance Preparation, p. 34**	Everything Math Deck *See* **Advance Preparation, p. 34**	envelope, paper clip, or rubber band 2 pennies per partnership *See* **Advance Preparation, p. 34**
1.7		slate craft sticks (optional) Class Number Line (optional) number cards	Class Data Pad (optional) tally chart pennies and can or other container *See* **Advance Preparation, p. 39**
1.8	Teaching Masters, p. 2 and 4 Home Link Master, p. 153 *See* **Advance Preparation, p. 43**	die craft sticks (optional)	
1.9	transparency of Teaching Master, p. 5 (optional) Home Link Master, p. 154 Teaching Master, p. 5; 12 copies per child		construction paper, 2 sheets per child
1.10	Teaching Master, p. 2 Home Link Master, p. 155 *See* **Advance Preparation, p. 51**	slate; pattern blocks Everything Math Deck Pattern-Block Template *See* **Advance Preparation, p. 51**	Rules for Small Groups Poster (optional) pennies
1.11	Teaching Masters, pp. 2 and 3 Home Link Master, p. 156 *See* **Advance Preparation, p. 56**	pattern blocks base-10 blocks geoboards and rubber bands attribute blocks	number cards from tool kit
1.12	Teaching Master, p. 6 Home Link Master, p. 157 *See* **Advance Preparation, p. 60**	classroom thermometer Class Thermometer Poster *See* **Advance Preparation, p. 60**	Class Weather Chart Class Data Pad blank paper, 7 sheets per child construction paper, 2 sheets per child glass of cold water
1.13	Teaching Master, p. 2 Home Link Master, p. 158	slate number cards 1–10	tool-kit pennies
1.14	Assessment Master p. 303 Teaching Master, p. 3 Home Link Masters, pp. 159–162 *See* **Advance Preparation, p. 72**	slate craft sticks rubber bands number cards	pennies, 2 per child plastic bags, 11 per group *See* **Advance Preparation, p. 72**

planningtips

Pacing

Pacing depends on a number of factors, such as children's individual needs and how long your school has been using *Everyday Mathematics*. At the beginning of Unit 1, review your Content by Strand Poster to help you set a monthly pace.

AUGUST	SEPTEMBER	OCTOBER

← MOST CLASSROOMS →

Home Communication

Share Home Links 1.8–1.13 with families to help them understand the content and procedures in this unit. At the end of the unit, use Home Link 1.14 to introduce Unit 2. Supplemental information can be found in the *Home Connection Handbook*.

NCTM Standards

Standard	1	2	3	4	5	6	7	8	9	10
Unit 1 Lessons	1-6, 10, 13	11	3, 11	2, 9, 12	7, 8, 12	1-13	1-13	1-13	1-13	1-13

Content Standards
1 Number and Operation
2 Patterns, Functions, and Algebra
3 Geometry and Spatial Sense
4 Measurement
5 Data Analysis, Statistics, and Probability

Process Standards
6 Problem Solving
7 Reasoning and Proof
8 Communication
9 Connections
10 Representations

PRACTICE *through* Games

Everyday Mathematics uses games to help children develop good fact power and other math skills.

- Practice numeration with *Number-Line Squeeze* **(Lessons 1.2, 1.6, 1.11, and 1.14)**
- Practice counting and comparing numbers with *Penny-Dice Game* **(Lessons 1.3 and 1.4)**
- Compare numbers in *Top-It* **(Lessons 1.6, 1.7, 1.10, 1.11, and 1.14)**
- Practice tallying in *Scissors, Paper, Stone* **(Lesson 1.8)**

The notes below highlight the major content ideas presented in Unit 1. These notes may help you establish instructional priorities.

Daily Routines (Lesson 1.1 and following)

If the children used *Kindergarten Everyday Mathematics,* many of the routines in Grade 1, Unit 1 and later units may already be familiar to them. If this is the first time you are using *Everyday Mathematics,* most of the routines will be new to you.

To help you become acquainted with these routines, background information is provided in the Management Guide section of the *Teacher's Reference Manual* and in the Content Highlights section of each Unit Organizer. Occasionally, the Content Highlights section will have additional references to the Mathematical Topics essays in the *Teacher's Reference Manual.* The authors can't emphasize enough the importance of reading about these referenced topics in advance, of talking to other teachers, and then making tentative decisions about how you want to set up and begin these daily routines. If certain routines don't work exactly as planned, feel free to adapt them as necessary.

A good deal of time and energy may be required to initiate a routine. However, once the routine has been established, it will make teaching easier, since it will be supported by both your children's energy and your involvement.

The time needed to incorporate the routines will vary from group to group, especially if your children come from a half-day *Kindergarten Everyday Mathematics* experience or if they have not been in the program before. If you or the children begin to feel overwhelmed by the number of routines, delay introducing some of them until later, or omit some, especially if this is your first year using the program. Children will still have rich experiences upon which to build their future mathematical development.

On the other hand, if you have a strong, experienced group, don't hesitate to move through these first lessons fairly quickly. Renew familiar routines, begin new routines (especially partner and small-group interactions), get some notion of the range of numbers the children are comfortable with—and then move on. The routines will become habitual as they are put into practice over and over in this and subsequent units.

The table on the next page lists the routines that are introduced in Unit 1 and the lessons in which they first occur.

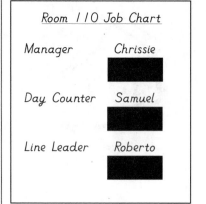

Room 110 Job Chart

Manager	Chrissie
Day Counter	Samuel
Line Leader	Roberto

Children's jobs are displayed on the Job Chart.

Routines	Lesson
*Choral counting	1.1
*Class Number Line	1.1
*Managing classroom jobs	1.1
Mental Math and Reflexes	1.1
*Keeping track of attendance	1.1
Tool kits and identification numbers	1.3
Working with a partner	1.3
*Using slates	1.4
Home Links	1.8
*Calendars	1.9
Working in small groups	1.10
Explorations	1.11
Keeping a weather record	1.12
*Keeping a temperature record	1.12

* Denotes a routine introduced in *Kindergarten Everyday Mathematics*

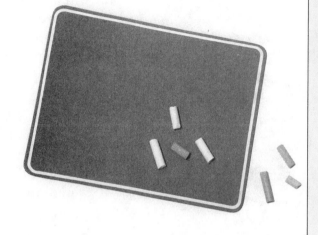

Investigating the Number Line (Lesson 1.2)

Young children need to develop the ability to count by rote as a prerequisite to rational counting (the counting of objects). The number line provides a visual display for such rote-counting activities. It may also be used for tracking the number of school days in the year and for other numeration activities, such as comparing pairs of numbers and finding numbers between two numbers. Children practice the latter activity by playing *Number-Line Squeeze*. In subsequent units, children will use the number line in their work with number patterns, addition, and subtraction.

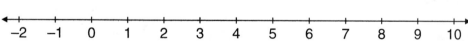

Tools for Doing Mathematics (Lesson 1.3)

As they progress through the grades, children will learn to use many of the tools of mathematics. In this lesson, they begin to use three mathematical tools: pennies, which are used for counting practice and for modeling problem situations; dice, which are usually used in games and probability experiments; and Pattern-Block Templates, which are used for drawing shapes. More mathematical tools will be added later on.

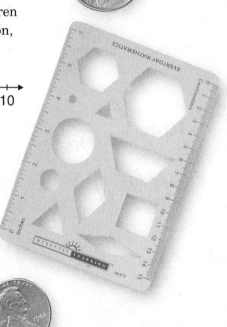

In this lesson, children work in partnerships for the first time this year. They play the *Penny-Dice Game,* the first of many partnership and small-group games they will play throughout *Everyday Mathematics.*

Games are an integral part of *Everyday Mathematics.* They build skills with number facts, operations, numeration, and place value. Games also reinforce calculator skills, money-exchange skills, and shopping skills. In addition, game playing provides children with opportunities to build intuition about probability, chance, patterns, and logic.

Number-Writing Practice (Lesson 1.4)

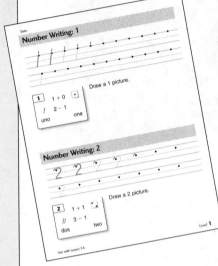

Since *Everyday Mathematics* encourages the recording and writing of numbers in Unit 1, it is important that children practice correct number-writing forms. At this stage, children's small-motor skills vary greatly, so you will need to use your best judgment to determine how rapidly to work through the initial number-writing activities.

In this lesson, children begin to use two recording devices: slates, which, when used in whole-class activities, make it possible for everyone to display answers quietly and at the same time; and journals, which will comprise a record of children's work in mathematics for the entire year.

One More, One Less (Lesson 1.5)

Children solve "one-more" and "one-less" number stories, which provide concrete experiences in preparation for later work with addition and subtraction.

Comparing Numbers (Lesson 1.6)

Having had a certain amount of rote-counting practice, children should be ready to begin comparing small numbers. They practice this skill by playing *Top-It,* a popular game that was introduced in *Kindergarten Everyday Mathematics.*

Recording Tally Counts (Lessons 1.7 and 1.8)

Tally counts are a good way to keep track of counts and data collected over time. Tally counts are important because they enhance counts by 5s and show each number between 5 and 10 as five *plus* one or more ones. Tallies may serve as a way for children to represent numbers they can count to and say but cannot yet write.

Home Links are sent home for the first time in Lesson 1.8. A Home Link is provided for each lesson. The purpose of Home Links is to involve parents or other members of the household in the children's mathematical activities and to encourage children to take responsibility for returning the completed Home Links to school.

The Calendar (Lesson 1.9)

By using the calendar on a daily basis, children gradually acquire calendar skills. Throughout the year, there will be many opportunities to use the calendar to record such data as special days and events.

Working in Small Groups (Lesson 1.10)

Children will spend much of their time working cooperatively in small groups. For cooperative work to be effective, children need to observe small-group etiquette and rules. Be prepared to spend extra time reinforcing these principles. In this lesson, children practice small-group interactions by cooperatively counting pennies and playing *Top-It* with several players.

Explorations (Lesson 1.11)

Explorations give children opportunities to share manipulatives in small groups. Explorations are usually informal and open-ended. Children are encouraged to verbalize their discoveries and to follow the rules for cooperative behavior.

Weather and Temperature Routines (Lesson 1.12)

These routines involve collecting, recording, and analyzing data. Working with various sets of data is an important part of *Everyday Mathematics* at every grade level. Through these activities, children experience real-world applications of mathematics.

Number Stories (Lesson 1.13)

Throughout *Everyday Mathematics,* number stories emphasize the use of a variety of solution strategies, including concrete, pictorial, and verbal strategies, as well as solution strategies with number models. An important part of the work with number stories is the children's sharing of their thinking with their classmates.

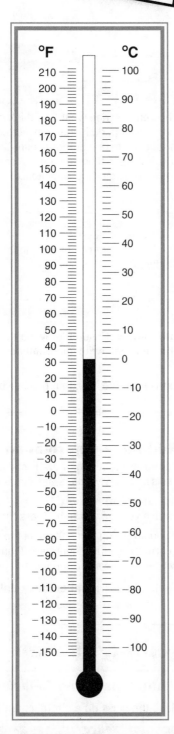

For **additional information** on the following topics, see the *Teacher's Reference Manual:*

- calendars
- cooperative grouping
- Explorations
- number lines
- number stories
- organizing routines and displays
- rote and rational counting
- temperature

1.1

Daily Routines

OBJECTIVE To introduce the count-the-days-of-school, job-management, and attendance-recording routines.

---

summaries   ## materials

1 Teaching the Lesson

Children describe what they think mathematics is and what they expect to do in mathematics class in first grade. They are introduced to one or more count-the-days-of-school routines and, if there is time, to routines for managing classroom jobs and recording school attendance. [Numeration]

□ Job Chart
□ Attendance Chart
□ Other materials for ongoing classroom routines
***See* Advance Preparation**

2 Ongoing Learning & Practice

Children revisit favorite counting rhymes and songs from Kindergarten. [Numeration]

□ Home Link Masters (*Math Masters,* pp. 149–152)

3 Options for Individualizing

Enrichment Children draw portraits of their family members or friends and write important numbers about their drawings. [Numeration]

Extra Practice Children practice basic counting skills. [Numeration]

□ half-sheet of drawing paper
□ *Minute Math*®, pp. 5 and 29

Additional Information

Background Information For additional information on Program Highlights, Daily Routines, the Class Number Line, and Home Links and Family Letters, see the *Teacher's Reference Manual.*

Advance Preparation For Part 1, if you are using the Growing Number Line routine, write the number 1 on a 3" by 5" index card. If you are using the Class Number Line routine, prepare a large cutout arrow or frame that you can clip onto the line.

If you are using coins to count the days of school, you will need a penny today and additional pennies, nickels, dimes, and quarters on subsequent days. (You will also need a clear plastic cup.) If you are using straws to count the days of school, you will need straws and three cups—one cup labeled ONES, another labeled TENS, and a third labeled HUNDREDS.

Vocabulary • **number line** • **Job Chart** • **attendance**

Getting Started

Mental Math and Reflexes

Have the class do a choral count by 1s, starting at 1. Go as high as the children are able.

1 Teaching the Lesson

✦ Introducing *First Grade Everyday Mathematics*

WHOLE-CLASS DISCUSSION 👥👥👥

Ask children to describe what they think mathematics is and what they think they might be doing in mathematics class in first grade.

Mention that mathematics is used in counting and measuring things, in exploring shapes and patterns, and in solving all kinds of problems.

Have children find numbers, shapes, and patterns in the classroom (for example, the numbers on the number line, on the classroom clock, and on the calendar; the shapes of the door and the clock; and the patterns made by the tiles on the floor or ceiling).

✦ Counting the Days of School

WHOLE-CLASS ACTIVITY 👥👥👥

Use one of the following **number-line** routines for designating this first day of the school year:

▷ The *Growing Number Line:* Post the "1" card.

▷ The *Class Number Line:* Place an arrow on or a frame around the number 1 on the Class Number Line.

🔽 **Adjusting the Activity** You may want to use the Class Number Line as a timeline for recording special events. Each event can be recorded on an index card and then attached to the number of the day on which it occurs. For example, "Susie lost a tooth!" or "Halloween!"

Explain that at the end of this first day, children will have been in first grade one day.

• Which number represents the *next* day of first grade? 2

• Which number represents the day *before* school started? 0

Showing the first day of first grade on the Growing Number Line

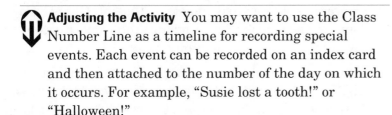

Showing the first day of first grade on the Class Number Line

NOTE: For the first routine, some teachers use "coins" with magnets (or tape): 5 pennies, 2 nickels, 2 dimes, and 7 quarters.

If you use the second routine, set up your ONES, TENS, and HUNDREDS cups from the beginning. This is one way to develop a sense of magnitude.

Consider also using one (or both) of the following routines:

Count the Days Using Coins

Display a penny to designate Day 1. Then add a penny each day. **On Day 5,** add a penny, but then replace the 5 pennies with a nickel. **On Day 10,** replace the nickel and 5 pennies with a dime. **On Day 20,** replace the dime, nickel, and 5 pennies with 2 dimes. **On Day 25,** replace the 2 dimes and 5 pennies with a quarter, and so on.

Count the Days Using Straws

Put a straw in the ONES cup to designate Day 1. Then add a straw each day. **On Day 10,** take the 10 straws out of the ONES cup, bundle them, and put them in the TENS cup. **On Day 20,** put another bundle of 10 straws into the TENS cup, and so on. **On Day 100,** take the 10 bundles out of the TENS cup, bundle them, and put them in the HUNDREDS cup.

◆ Assigning Classroom Jobs

WHOLE-CLASS DISCUSSION

Ask children to describe jobs they do at home (for example, setting the table). Then invite them to suggest jobs they could do at school that would help make the classroom and the school day run more smoothly.

Choose two or three jobs, such as Manager (the person who rotates the job assignments on the **Job Chart**), Day Counter (the person who designates the number of the day in the school year), and Line Leader.

Explain what your expectations are for each job. You might ask children to role-play how they would do each of these jobs. Discuss how the Job Chart will be used to keep track of job assignments. Then assign jobs for the first time period. (You may want to rotate jobs every week.)

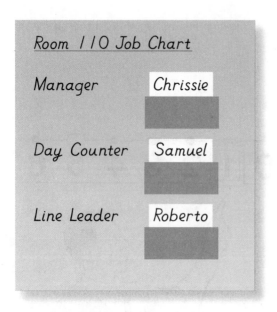

Children's classroom jobs are displayed on the Job Chart.

◆ Taking the Attendance

WHOLE-CLASS ACTIVITY

Explain your attendance-recording procedure, and have children role-play how to gather and display the **attendance** information. Then, with the children, count how many children are present.

2 Ongoing Learning & Practice

✦ Revisiting Rhymes and Songs

Since the school year is just beginning, you may want to practice counting by revisiting some of the children's favorite rhymes and songs from Kindergarten. (You may even wish to create and display role-play/choral reading posters like the one shown in the margin.)

✦ Home Link (*Math Masters,* pp. 149–152)

 Home Connection Distribute copies of the beginning-of-the-year Family Letter for children to take home. This letter introduces parents and guardians to *First Grade Everyday Mathematics* in general and to Unit 1 in particular. Home Links are provided for every lesson, beginning with Lesson 1.8.

One, Two, Buckle My Shoe

1
2   Buckle my shoe.
3
4   Shut the door.
5
6   Pick up sticks.
7
8   Lay them straight.
9
10   A big fat hen.

Children practice their rote-counting skills as they recite classic counting rhymes in unison.

◐ Literature and Reading Link

Children love to recite and act out favorite action rhymes and finger plays. Doing so while referring to posters like the one above helps them bridge the gap between spoken language and written language, while they practice their rote-counting skills.

3 Options for Individualizing

✦ ENRICHMENT Drawing Portraits

INDEPENDENT ACTIVITY   15–30 min

Briefly introduce the idea of a portrait.

Have children use half-sheets of drawing paper and crayons to draw portraits of their family members or friends. Ask children if they can name (and if they are able, write) numbers that go with their pictures. For example: the number of people in the drawing, the ages of the people, and the people's favorite numbers.

Portfolio Ideas

✦ EXTRA PRACTICE Minute Math

SMALL-GROUP ACTIVITY   5–15 min

To offer children more experience with counting, see the following pages in *Minute Math:*

Basic Routines: p. 5; **Counting:** p. 29

PLANNING AHEAD

In Lesson 1.3, enough pennies will be needed so that each child can put 10 pennies in her or his tool kit.

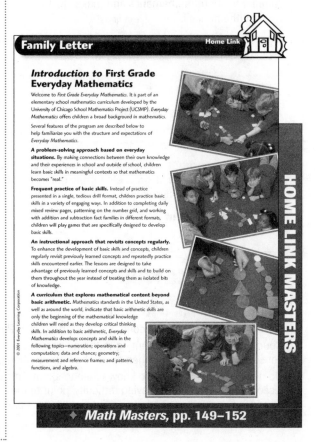

Family Letter   Home Link

Introduction to First Grade Everyday Mathematics

Welcome to *First Grade Everyday Mathematics.* It is part of an elementary school mathematics curriculum developed by the University of Chicago School Mathematics Project (UCSMP). *Everyday Mathematics* offers children a broad background in mathematics.

Several features of the program are described below to help familiarize you with the structure and expectations of *Everyday Mathematics.*

A problem-solving approach based on everyday situations. By making connections between their own knowledge and their experiences in school and outside of school, children learn basic skills in meaningful contexts so that mathematics becomes "real."

Frequent practice of basic skills. Instead of practice presented in a single, tedious drill format, children practice basic skills in a variety of engaging ways. In addition to completing daily mixed review pages, patterning on the number grid, and working with addition and subtraction fact families in different formats, children will play games that are specifically designed to develop basic skills.

An instructional approach that revisits concepts regularly. To enhance the development of basic skills and concepts, children regularly revisit previously learned concepts and repeatedly practice skills encountered earlier. The lessons are designed to take advantage of previously learned concepts and skills and to build on them throughout the year instead of treating them as isolated bits of knowledge.

A curriculum that explores mathematical content beyond basic arithmetic. Mathematics standards in the United States, as well as around the world, indicate that basic arithmetic skills are only the beginning of the mathematical knowledge children will need as they develop critical thinking skills. In addition to basic arithmetic, *Everyday Mathematics* develops concepts and skills in the following topics—numeration; operations and computation; data and chance; geometry; measurement and reference frames; and patterns, functions, and algebra.

© 2001 Everyday Learning Corporation

✦ *Math Masters,* pp. 149–152

HOME LINK MASTERS

1.2 Investigating the Number Line

OBJECTIVES To introduce number-line routines; to practice counting up on the number line; and to introduce tallying.

summaries	materials
1 Teaching the Lesson	
Children play the *Number-Line Squeeze* game. They also use the Class Number Line to find the number of children who are absent. [Numeration]	□ Class Number Line □ "fences" to bracket number-line intervals *See* **Advance Preparation**
2 Ongoing Learning & Practice	
Children revisit favorite counting rhymes and songs from Kindergarten. [Numeration]	
3 Options for Individualizing	
Language Diversity Children review their previous comments about mathematics and make illustrations to show what mathematics is. [multiple strands] **Extra Practice** Children practice finding numbers between a given pair of numbers. [Numeration]	□ *Minute Math*®, pp. 3, 4, 27, and 38 □ *1, 2, 3* by Tana Hoban (optional) □ *Fish Eyes: A Book You Can Count On* by Lois Ehlert (optional) □ *Can You Count Ten Toes?: Count to 10 in 10 Different Languages* by Leslie Evans (optional)

Additional Information

Background Information For information about the importance of games in the *Everyday Mathematics* program, see Games in the *Teacher's Reference Manual*.

Advance Preparation For Part 1, prepare two brackets or frames for the *Number-Line Squeeze* game. Some teachers make two "creatures" to use as brackets for the game. Some use two yardsticks, with a bracket attached to one end of each stick. Others use two large flyswatters (with their centers cut out) as frames.

Vocabulary • **absent**

Getting Started

Mental Math and Reflexes

Have the class do a choral count by 1s, starting at 1. Point to the numbers on the Class Number Line as you count.

Count again by 1s while pointing to the numbers on the number line. This time, however, have children *whisper* four consecutive numbers and then *shout* the fifth number, as follows: Whisper 1, 2, 3, 4, shout **5;** whisper 6, 7, 8, 9, shout **10.**

Do not expect all children to know when to shout. This choral-counting routine will be repeated many times in subsequent lessons. To help children having difficulty, point to the numbers on the number line with one hand and show the count with fingers on your other hand. When five fingers are up, shout the number.

Teaching the Lesson

✦ Playing *Number-Line Squeeze*

WHOLE-CLASS ACTIVITY

The leader thinks of a mystery number and then calls out two numbers such that the mystery number is somewhere between the two numbers. The other children then try to guess the mystery number.

Sample Game

1. The leader chooses 5 as the mystery number and says, "I am thinking of a number between 1 and 9. What's my number?"

2. Two children act as bracket holders. (You might also call the brackets *fences* or *boundary markers*.) One child covers the 1 on the number line with a bracket; the other child covers the 9.

3. The leader calls on someone to make a guess. The guesser guesses 7. The leader says, "No, my number is smaller than (or less than) 7," or "7 is more than (or bigger than or greater than) my number." The right bracket is then moved to cover the 7.

4. Another child guesses 4. The leader says that the mystery number is greater than 4. The left bracket is then moved to cover the 4.

5. Children continue to guess. Eventually, the mystery number will be "squeezed" between the two brackets. The child who guesses the mystery number becomes the next leader.

Number-Line Squeeze is similar to Monster Squeeze, a favorite game in Kindergarten Everyday Mathematics.

Take the part of the leader and play a demonstration round with the class.

Adjusting the Activity If necessary, the game leader may write down the mystery number so as not to forget it when answering children's questions. It may also be helpful if you label the left and right sides of the number line with words like *smaller* or *less* and *larger* or *more*.

At first, you might limit the range to numbers up to 15. With more able children, extend the range to test the limits of their ability.

Attendance Chart

25
children are in our class.

23
children are here today.

2
children are absent today.

NOTE: Tallying is addressed more extensively in Lessons 1.7 and 1.8.

◆ Finding the Number of Children Who Are Absent

WHOLE-CLASS ACTIVITY

On the board, write the total number of children who are enrolled in your class. With the class, count the number of children who are present and write that number on the board. Then ask:

• How would you find the number of children who are **absent** today?

After children have discussed strategies for finding the number of absentees, model the following strategy on the Class Number Line: Find the two numbers (the number of children present and the number of children enrolled) on the number line and count up from the smaller number to the larger number. For example, if there are 25 children in your class and 23 children are present, start at 23 and count up 2 to 25. This, of course, means that two children are absent today.

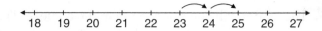

Repeat this procedure, using the attendance data from the previous day(s).

Consider including the following procedure as part of your attendance-taking routine. Make a table like the one shown below. Each day, make a tally mark in the appropriate column of the table. About once a week, find the total number of tallies in each column and the total number of tallies in all four columns. Compare this total number of tallies to the total number of school days so far. (The two numbers should be the same. Do not expect children to do this activity on their own at this time.)

The Number of Children Who Are Absent Today

1 is absent.	2 are absent.	3 or more are absent.	Everyone is here.
////	//	//	∕∕∕∕ //

2 Ongoing Learning & Practice

✦ Revisiting Rhymes and Songs

WHOLE-CLASS ACTIVITY

Practice counting by revisiting more of the children's favorite rhymes and songs from Kindergarten.

See the *Kindergarten Everyday Mathematics* materials or one of your school's Kindergarten teachers for suggestions. You may even wish to create and display role-play/choral reading posters like the one shown in the margin.

If you use the rhyme suggested in the margin, encourage children to offer appropriate substitutions for the word *hare* (*fish, duck, pig,* and so on).

3 Options for Individualizing

✦ LANGUAGE DIVERSITY Reviewing the Meaning of Mathematics

WHOLE-CLASS ACTIVITY 15–30 min

Briefly review the suggestions from the discussion in Lesson 1.1 about what mathematics is and what children expect to learn in first grade mathematics.

Portfolio Ideas

Have children draw a picture of one or more of their suggestions, such as a ruler, a clock, or geometric shapes.

✦ EXTRA PRACTICE Minute Math

SMALL-GROUP ACTIVITY 5–15 min

To offer children more experience with counting, see the following pages in *Minute Math:*

Basic Routines: pp. 3 and 4

Counting: pp. 27 and 38

PLANNING AHEAD

Send a note home asking each child to bring one clean sock to school. Children will use these socks as erasers for their slates, starting in Lesson 1.4.

1, 2, 3, 4, 5
1, 2, 3, 4, 5, I caught a hare alive.
6, 7, 8, 9, 10, I let him go again.

Children practice their rote-counting skills as they recite classic counting rhymes in unison.

⬤ Literature and Reading Link

Practice counting skills with a counting book. Consider using one or more of the following books:

1,2,3 by Tana Hoban (William Morrow & Company, 1985) is a simple counting book illustrated with beautiful photographs that capture children's attention. There is no text on a page, only the numeral and word name.

Fish Eyes: A Book You Can Count On by Lois Ehlert (Harcourt Brace, 1992) shows colorful sets of fish, illustrating the numbers 1 through 10. An added twist is that readers are encouraged to add one lone black fish to the total on each page.

Can You Count Ten Toes?: Count to 10 in 10 Different Languages by Leslie Evans (Houghton Mifflin Co., 1999) provides phonetic pronunciations for counting to ten in ten languages. At the end of the book, there is a map of the world with labels showing where the ten languages are spoken.

1.3

Tools for Doing Mathematics

OBJECTIVE To introduce and use mathematical tools for drawing and counting.

summaries	materials
1 **Teaching the Lesson**	
The teacher distributes the tool kits and discusses children's identification numbers. Children then use their Pattern-Block Templates to practice drawing shapes. After a discussion of the guiding principles for working with partners (Guide, Check, Praise), children play the *Penny-Dice Game* to practice counting. [Geometry; Numeration]	☐ tool kit (Pattern-Block Template, 10 pennies, 1 die) ☐ half-sheet of paper ***See* Advance Preparation**
2 **Ongoing Learning & Practice**	
Children revisit favorite counting rhymes and songs from Kindergarten. [Numeration]	☐ *City by Numbers* by Stephen T. Johnson (optional)
3 **Options for Individualizing**	
Enrichment Children create colored shape patterns using their Pattern-Block Templates. [Geometry; Patterns, Functions, and Algebra] **Extra Practice** Children practice counting. [Numeration]	☐ Pattern-Block Template ☐ half-sheet of drawing paper ☐ pattern blocks (optional) ☐ *Minute Math*®, pp. 5 and 29

Additional Information

Background Information For additional information on Tool Kits and Cooperative Groupings, see the *Teacher's Reference Manual*.

Advance Preparation For Part 1, choose the set of numbers you will use to identify the tool kits and the Pattern-Block Templates. For example, instead of using 1, 2, 3, …, you might want to use 101, 102, 103, …. The advantage of doing this is that it gives children early experiences with numbers in the hundreds. (If there is more than one section of first grade at your school, each classroom might use a different set of hundreds. For example, another classroom might use 201, 202, 203, ….)

Assign a number to each child. Then number the tool kits and the Pattern-Block Templates, using a permanent, fine-point marker. Place a Pattern-Block Template, 10 pennies, and a die in each of the tool kits. The tool-kit and Pattern-Block Template numbers should match.

Put a Lost-and-Found Box in a prominent place in the room.

Post the rules for working with partners. (See page 24.)

Vocabulary • tool kit • Pattern-Block Template

Getting Started

Mental Math and Reflexes

As was done in Lesson 1.2, do a choral count by 1s, in which children shout every fifth number and whisper the numbers in between.

1 Teaching the Lesson

◆ Exploring the Tool Kits

WHOLE-CLASS ACTIVITY

Ask children to give examples of tools and to describe what they are used for. Tell them that they will use tools with which to do mathematics and that they will each keep their tools in a little bag, called a **tool kit.** (Hold up a tool kit.)

Distribute the tool kits. After children have had a chance to examine the kit contents, tell them that they will keep their own tool kits for the entire school year. Other children will use the tool kits next year, so children should take good care of them. Tell children they will be adding tools to their tool kits throughout the year. They should keep their mathematical tools in their tool kits whenever they are not using the tools.

Ask children to count the pennies to check that there are 10 pennies in each kit.

Point out that each child has been assigned a number and that the number appears both on the tool kit and on the **Pattern-Block Template.**

Show children the Lost-and-Found Box and tell them that if they find someone else's tool kit or template, they should put it in the box. The number on the tool kit can then be used to identify its owner!

Adjusting the Activity If you use numbers in the hundreds, you may want to have children count off by their tool-kit numbers. Provide frequent opportunities for them to read and say their tool-kit numbers. For example, you might have children put their kits away one at a time, calling out their numbers as they do so. Or, when they are working in small groups, you might have children say one another's numbers and put the tool kits in numerical order.

NOTE: Continue following all previously introduced daily routines yourself until children are able to take responsibility for following them on their own.

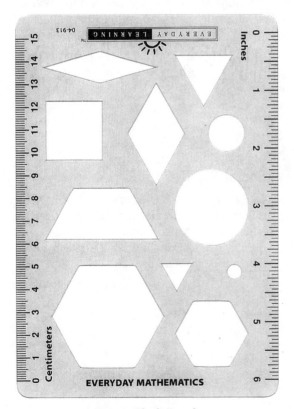

A Pattern-Block Template

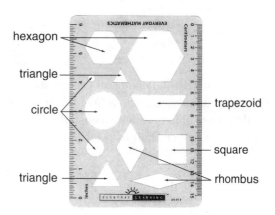

hexagon
triangle
circle
triangle
trapezoid
square
rhombus

Social Studies Link

Take a neighborhood walk with the class. Encourage children to note any road signs they see. When you return to the classroom, make a list of signs seen by the children. Include the number of sides for each sign or tally the signs by type.

◆ Using the Pattern-Block Template

WHOLE-CLASS ACTIVITY

Hold up a template (or display it on the overhead projector). Ask children to identify the shapes whose names they know, but do not dwell on the shapes with which they are unfamiliar. Then ask:

• Have you seen these shapes anywhere else? Children may have seen them on pattern blocks. They may name things in the room that have some of these shapes.

To practice using the Pattern-Block Template, ask children to draw a row of shapes on a half-sheet of paper. Remind them to put their templates back in their tool kits when they have finished.

◆ Playing the *Penny-Dice Game*

PARTNER ACTIVITY

Since this game involves rolling a die, demonstrate how to do it in a way that keeps the noise level down while also preventing the die from rolling away: Shake the die in both hands, open your hands within 4 or 5 inches of the tabletop, and then let the die drop.

Before the start of the game, discuss the principles of being a good partner: Guide, Check, Praise. Demonstrate these principles, perhaps through role playing.

> *Partnership Principles*
>
> *1. Guide*
> *2. Check*
> *3. Praise*

At this point, limit the number of players in a game to two. Later on, three or four players may play the game.

Demonstrate how to play the game. Partners pool their tool-kit pennies so that they have 20 pennies to play with. They take turns rolling the die and picking up as many pennies as indicated on the die, until all the pennies have been picked up. Either the player with more pennies wins the game, or partners may flip a penny to determine whether the player with more or fewer pennies wins.

HEADS: The player with more pennies wins.

TAILS: The player with fewer pennies wins.

To pick up the last pennies, the number on the die must match the number of pennies remaining.

2 Ongoing Learning & Practice

✦Revisiting Rhymes and Songs

WHOLE-CLASS ACTIVITY

Continue counting practice by creating and displaying role-play/choral reading posters like the one shown in the margin.

You may also want to revisit the counting rhymes from Lessons 1.1 and 1.2.

✦Reading a Counting Book

WHOLE-CLASS ACTIVITY

Use the book *City by Numbers* by Stephen T. Johnson (Viking, 1999) to practice identifying each of the numbers 1–20. Each number is hidden in a richly textured painting of a city scene. For example, you will discover the outline of a 3 defined in a wrought-iron gate.

3 Options for Individualizing

✦ENRICHMENT Making Geometric Designs

INDEPENDENT ACTIVITY   15–30 min

Using their Pattern-Block Templates, children draw shapes in patterns on half-sheets of paper and color their shapes according to a color pattern. You might want to collect the children's work for a bulletin-board display.

Portfolio Ideas

⬇ **Adjusting the Activity** If necessary, children can build their patterns with pattern blocks first and then copy them, using their templates.

✦EXTRA PRACTICE Minute Math

SMALL-GROUP ACTIVITY   5–15 min

To offer children more experience with counting, see the following pages in *Minute Math:*

Basic Routines: p. 5

Counting: p. 29

One, Two

1
2   Chocolate goo.

3
4   Want some more?

5
6   Pudding mix.

7
8   Bring your plate.

9
10 Hungry again!

Children practice their rote-counting skills as they recite classic counting rhymes in unison.

○Literature and Reading Link

As children recite and act out action rhymes and finger plays, they practice their rote-counting skills. When they combine recitation with role-play reading by referring to posters like the one shown above, the gap between spoken language and written language is narrowed.

1.4 Number-Writing Practice

OBJECTIVES To introduce and practice a slate routine; and to practice writing the numbers 1 and 2.

summaries	materials
1 Teaching the Lesson	
Children practice a slate routine by writing on their slates numerical answers to questions posed by the teacher. Children also practice writing the numbers 1 and 2 on their slates and in their journals. [Numeration]	□ *Math Journal 1*, p. 1 □ slate or marker board □ chalk or dry-erase marker □ eraser (sock or facial tissue)
2 Ongoing Learning & Practice	
Partners play the *Penny-Dice Game*. [Numeration]	□ 20 pennies per partnership □ 1 die per partnership
3 Options for Individualizing	
Extra Practice Children practice counting objects by bundling given numbers of craft sticks. [Numeration] **Language Diversity** Children learn other names for numbers. [Numeration] **Extra Practice** Children practice basic counting skills. [Numeration]	□ *Math Journal 1*, p. 1 □ number cards 10–50 □ craft sticks □ plastic bag □ rubber band □ *Minute Math*®, pp. 5, 29, and 31 ***See* Advance Preparation**

Additional Information

Background Information For additional information on Slates and Number-Writing Practice, see the *Teacher's Reference Manual.*

Advance Preparation For Part 1, decide how you will manage the slates. Some teachers label the slates with student numbers; children then keep the slates in their tool kits. Other teachers keep the slates stacked somewhere in the room, and children take them when they need them. Or, passing out slates can be a classroom job.

For Part 3, write a number from 10 to 50 on ten quarter-pieces of paper or on 3" by 5" index cards, cut in half.

Vocabulary • slate

Getting Started

Mental Math and Reflexes

Repeat the whisper-and-shout count for multiples of 5. Count up to at least 20. Then do a choral chant of only the "shout" numbers (*5, 10, 15, 20, ...*) while pointing to the numbers on the Class Number Line.

Note: You may want to highlight the count-by-5s pattern on the number line for as high as the children have counted. (For example, circle multiples of 5, or, as the number line grows, designate multiples of 5 with different colors or with different frame shapes.)

Reminder: If you are doing counts for the days of school using coins, you will soon need to exchange the pennies for a nickel. Emphasize that the exchange makes it easier to count the days. Instead of counting 5 pennies, you know that a nickel represents 5 days—and there is no need to count individual pennies. Then, for days 6, 7, 8, and 9, begin your counts at 5 and count up by 1s.

1 Teaching the Lesson

✦ Introducing Slates as a Classroom Tool

WHOLE-CLASS ACTIVITY

Distribute the slates and chalk (or dry-erase markers). Children will use the socks they brought to school both as erasers and as storage "containers" for their chalk. Give children a chance to draw and erase freely.

Explain that during whole-class activities, the **slates** give everyone a chance to answer quietly and at the same time.

Suggest that children follow the steps shown in the margin when using slates to answer questions.

Ask children to erase their slates completely between problems.

Use some of the following suggestions, or make up your own, to help children practice the slate routine. Children write their answers to the questions on their slates.

- How old are you?
- How old were you last year?
- How old will you be next year?
- How many girls are in our room?
- How many boys are in our room?
- How many teachers are in our room?
- How many swimming pools are in our room?
- What number comes after 4?
- What number comes before 7?

Finally, have children practice writing the numbers 1 and 2 on their slates.

NOTE: Distribute facial tissue to any child who has not brought a sock.

How to Use Slates to Answer Questions

- LISTEN
- THINK
- WRITE
- SHOW
- ERASE

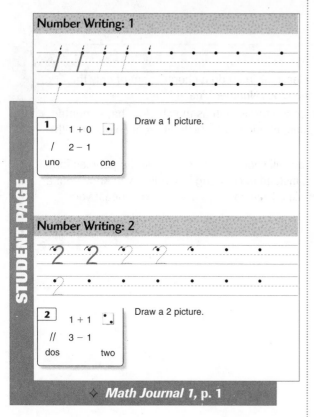

Number Writing: 1

Draw a 1 picture.

1	1 + 0	·
	/ 2 − 1	
uno		one

Number Writing: 2

Draw a 2 picture.

2	1 + 1	··
	// 3 − 1	
dos		two

✦ *Math Journal 1*, p. 1

Adjusting the Activity If necessary, suggest things that children can draw for the numbers 1 or 2. You might even draw a few examples on the board.

Children draw pictures to represent the numbers 1 and 2.

✦ Introducing *Math Journal 1*

WHOLE-CLASS ACTIVITY

Pass out copies of *Math Journal 1* and have children write their names on the back cover. Give them time to look through their journals. Remind them that they are to write in their journals only when directed to do so.

Discuss the reason for the number 1 in the title: This is the first of two math journals that children will use this year. Explain that all the pages, except a few in the back, will stay in the journal, so that when children finish their journals, they (and their parents) will be able to see how much they have learned in first grade.

✦ Writing the Numbers 1 and 2
(*Math Journal 1*, p. 1)

INDEPENDENT ACTIVITY

Children practice writing the numbers 1 and 2 in their journals. Remind them that speed is not important. Keep in mind that many children may not be good at writing numbers at this time. Encourage them; help them feel good about beginning best efforts.

Explain that the arrows on the numbers are there to remind them of the strokes needed for efficient number writing, strokes that will help them become better writers. Encourage children to use these strokes.

Have children circle what they think are their best numbers. As children finish their writing practice, have them draw a picture to represent each number (for example, a sun for the number 1, eyes for the number 2). When most children have finished, they can display and describe their drawings to one another.

2 Ongoing Learning & Practice

✦ Playing the *Penny-Dice Game*

PARTNER ACTIVITY

Children practice numeration skills by playing the *Penny-Dice Game*. For detailed instructions, see Lesson 1.3.

Remind children of the partnership principles.

3 Options for Individualizing

✦ EXTRA PRACTICE Counting Craft Sticks

PARTNER ACTIVITY   5–15 min

To practice counting objects, pass out a number to each child or partnership. Children then count that number of craft sticks, bundle them together with a rubber band, and place them in a small plastic bag with the number inside so that you can see it.

If children work in partnerships, they should check each other's counts.

 Adjusting the Activity For larger numbers, children can make bundles of 10 and keep the remaining sticks unbundled.

✦ LANGUAGE DIVERSITY Discussing Other Names for Numbers (*Math Journal 1*, p. 1)

WHOLE-CLASS ACTIVITY   5–15 min

Direct children's attention to the Spanish words for 1 and 2 on this journal page. Invite children who know other languages to share the names for numbers in their native languages.

✦ EXTRA PRACTICE Minute Math

SMALL-GROUP ACTIVITY   5–15 min

To offer children more experience with counting, see the following pages in *Minute Math:*

Basic Routines: p. 5; **Counting:** pp. 29 and 31

PLANNING AHEAD

Starting in Lesson 1.6, children will use the number cards found on Activity Sheets 1 and 2 in their journals. These sheets will have to be cut apart, a task that many children may not be able to perform at this stage. You might ask upper-grade volunteers or a teacher's aide to cut them apart, perhaps using a paper cutter.

Since children will sometimes combine their card decks for an activity, they should identify all the cards in their decks with a distinctive shape, mark, letter, or color. That way, combined decks can be separated easily.

To store their number cards in their tool kits, children may want to put them in an envelope, or put a rubber band around them. If they use envelopes, label the envelopes with the children's tool-kit numbers.

1.5 One More, One Less

OBJECTIVE To practice finding the number that is 1 more or 1 less than a given number.

summaries	materials

1 Teaching the Lesson

Children solve "one more" and "one less" number stories. They practice finding the numbers that are 1 more and 1 less than a given number, using pennies as counters. [Numeration; Operations and Computation]

☐ *Math Journal 1*, inside back cover
☐ pennies

2 Ongoing Learning & Practice

Children practice writing the numbers 1 and 2. [Numeration]

☐ Teaching Master (*Math Masters*, p. 2)
***See* Advance Preparation**

3 Options for Individualizing

Extra Practice Children complete a picture by connecting dots numbered from 1 to 20. [Numeration]

Extra Practice Children practice basic counting skills. [Numeration]

☐ Teaching Master (*Math Masters*, p. 1)
☐ *Minute Math®*, pp. 3, 27, and 29

Additional Information

Advance Preparation For Part 2, make a copy of *Math Masters*, page 2. On this copy, write the first "1" on the first line of each half of the page and the first "2" on the third line of each half. Then make enough copies of this page so that each child will have a half-sheet. Cut the pages in half. Save the original *Math Masters*, page 2 for later use.

Getting Started

Mental Math and Reflexes

Ask questions like the following:

What number comes after 7? After 3? After 5? After 9?

What number comes before 5? Before 2? Before 9? Before 1?

Have children write their answers on their slates. If necessary, use the Class Number Line to help children find the answers.

Teaching the Lesson

✦ Telling "One More" and "One Less" Stories
(*Math Journal 1,* inside back cover)

WHOLE-CLASS ACTIVITY 🏃🏃🏃🏃

Ask children to turn to their number lines on the inside back cover of their journals. Tell several "one more" and "one less" stories. Use the Class Number Line to demonstrate how to use the number line to figure out the answers to the questions posed by the following stories:

• Reginald walks 8 steps to get from his bathroom to the door of his bedroom. If he takes one more step, he will be inside his bedroom. How many steps does Reginald have to take in all to get from the bathroom to the inside of his bedroom? (Begin with your finger on 0 on the number line. Then move your finger 8 hops forward to model getting to the door of the bedroom. Then move your finger 1 hop to 9 to model getting inside the bedroom. The answer is 9 steps. The number 9 is 1 more than 8.)

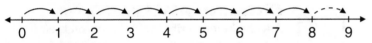

• Lisa went to the cookie shop to buy fresh, hot cookies. She bought 5 cookies. On the way home, she ate 1; so she had 1 less. How many cookies did Lisa have when she got home? (Children move their fingers from 0 to 5 to show the number of cookies Lisa bought. Then they move their fingers 1 hop back to 4 to show how many cookies were left after she ate one. The answer is 4 cookies. The number 4 is 1 less than 5.)

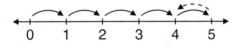

Tell more number stories as time allows.

⬇ **Adjusting the Activity** Children may use a shortcut, wherein they start by putting their fingers on the first number, without first counting from 0. For example, when solving the second problem above, children using the shortcut would start by putting their fingers on 5, without first counting from 0 to 5.

Some children may be ready to make up "one more" or "one less" stories for the class to solve.

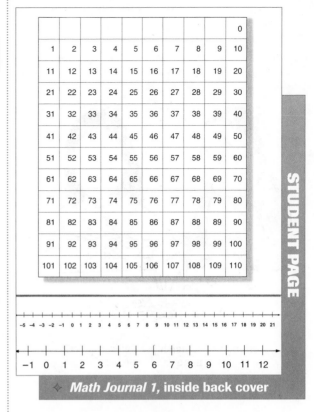

STUDENT PAGE

✦ *Math Journal 1,* **inside back cover**

Children will use the number line on the inside back cover of their journals throughout the year. In subsequent units, children will use this number line in their work with number patterns, addition, and subtraction.

NOTE: Children should be reminded to include the applicable unit in each of their answers. For example, the answer to the first problem is "9 steps," not simply "9."

Do not penalize or criticize children who do not use a unit; rather, simply continue to model the preferred answer format.

Working in partnerships, children practice
"one more" and "one less."

✦ Finding "One More" and "One Less" Using Pennies

PARTNER ACTIVITY

Have children count 5 pennies. Then tell them to take 1 more penny. Ask: *How many pennies do you have now?* 6 pennies Tell children to take 1 penny away. Ask: *How many pennies do you have now?* 5 pennies

Children work in partnerships and pool their pennies. They do the following:

Directions

1. Partner A takes a handful of pennies.

2. Partner B counts the pennies and says how many there are. Then he or she takes 1 more penny (or takes 1 penny away).

3. Partner A tells how many pennies there are then.

4. Partner B checks the answer by counting the pennies.

Repeat. After each turn, partners trade roles.

 ONGOING ASSESSMENT
Ask children to write their answers on their slates. As you circulate, verify that children know how to find 1 more and 1 less for numbers up to and including 20.

 Adjusting the Activity Encourage children who are having difficulty to use the number line as was done in the lesson.

② Ongoing Learning & Practice

◆ Writing the Numbers 1 and 2
(*Math Masters*, p. 2)

INDEPENDENT ACTIVITY

Pass out the half-sheets from *Math Masters*, page 2, and have children practice writing the numbers 1 and 2. Have them circle their best effort for each number when they complete the page.

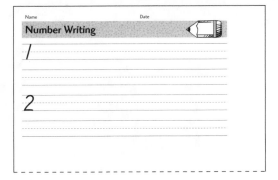

▲ Children practice writing the numbers 1 and 2, using models provided by their teacher.

③ Options for Individualizing

◆ EXTRA PRACTICE Connecting the Dots
(*Math Masters*, p. 1)

INDEPENDENT ACTIVITY   **5–15 min**

To practice counting by 1s, children draw a picture by connecting dots numbered from 1 to 20.

◆ EXTRA PRACTICE Minute Math

SMALL-GROUP ACTIVITY   **5–15 min**

To offer children more experience with counting, see the following pages in *Minute Math:*

Basic Routines: p. 3

Counting: pp. 27 and 29

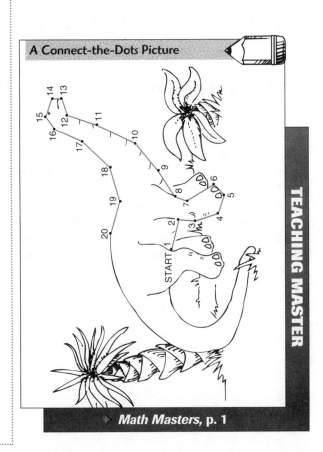

A Connect-the-Dots Picture

Math Masters, p. 1

TEACHING MASTER

1.6 Comparing Numbers

OBJECTIVE To practice comparing pairs of numbers.

summaries	materials
1 Teaching the Lesson	
Children use number cards to compare pairs of numbers and to order sets of numbers. They also play *Top-It*. [Numeration]	☐ number cards from *Math Journal 1,* Activity Sheet 1 or the Everything Math Deck ☐ envelope, paper clip, or rubber band ☐ counters and/or pennies ***See* Advance Preparation**
2 Ongoing Learning & Practice	
Children play *Number-Line Squeeze*. [Numeration]	☐ Teaching Master (*Math Masters,* p. 3) ☐ 2 pennies per partnership ***See* Advance Preparation**
3 Options for Individualizing	
Extra Practice Children estimate and compare distances. [Measurement and Reference Frames]	

Additional Information

Advance Preparation For Part 1, prepare a demonstration set of number cards, consisting of one each of the numbers 0 through 15. Write the numbers as large as you can on 4" by 6" index cards.

Each child will need a set of cards, numbered from 0 through 15. Children may each use the 0–15 cards from an Everything Math Deck or the 0–15 cards from *Math Journal 1,* Activity Sheet 1. If you use the cards on the journal page, they will have to be cut apart. Since card decks will sometimes be combined for an activity, all the cards in individual decks should be identifiable by distinctive shapes, marks, letters, or colors. That way, combined decks can be easily separated.

Decide how children will store their number cards in their tool kits. You may want to provide small envelopes, paper clips, or rubber bands. If you use envelopes, the envelopes can be labeled with the children's tool-kit numbers.

For Part 2, run off several copies of *Math Masters,* page 3 for use in making number-line sections. Cut out the number-line sections and write appropriate sets of numbers under the dots. If you want to make longer number-line sections, you can tape two sections together.

8 9 10 11 12 13 14 15 16 17 18 19 20 21

Getting Started

Mental Math and Reflexes

Children record their answers on their slates. Remind them of the slate routine: "Listen … think … write … show … erase." Ask questions like the following:

What number comes after 5? What number comes before 10? What number is 1 more than 11? What number is 1 less than 8? What number is 1 larger than 6? What number is 1 smaller than 14?

Continue as time permits.

1 Teaching the Lesson

◆ Comparing and Ordering Numbers
(*Math Journal 1,* Activity Sheet 1)

WHOLE-CLASS ACTIVITY

Give each child a deck of number cards, and give the class a little time to examine the cards. Then do several whole-class activities. *Suggestions:*

- Put the cards in a stack. Take the top two cards. Which card shows the larger number? Check your answer on the number line.

Adjusting the Activity Children can use counters to represent each number. If they do, they should line up the two sets of counters next to each other and match them one-to-one to see which number is larger.

ⓟ – – – – – ⓟ
ⓟ – – – – – ⓟ
ⓟ – – – – – ⓟ
ⓟ
ⓟ

5 is larger than 3.

- Order the 0–15 cards from the smallest to the largest number.

Adjusting the Activity To make this activity more challenging, have children randomly select 10 cards and then put those cards in order from smallest to largest.

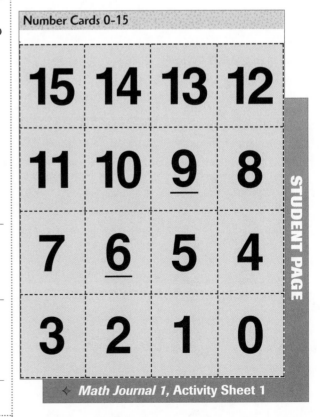

Number Cards 0–15

15	14	13	12
11	10	9	8
7	6	5	4
3	2	1	0

STUDENT PAGE

◆ *Math Journal 1,* Activity Sheet 1

- (Display a card from your teacher set.) Hold up the card that shows the number that is 1 more (or 1 less) than this number.

 Adjusting the Activity If necessary, draw a number line on the board and label the ends with the terms *less, more, before, after, smaller,* and *larger.*

 ONGOING ASSESSMENT
Children should be able to tell the number that is 1 more and 1 less than any number up to 10. Most children should be able to do this for numbers as high as 20.

✦ Introducing *Top-It*

PARTNER ACTIVITY

Review the rules for working with a partner.

This game is for two players. If you are using an Everything Math Deck, remove the numbers 16 through 22 from the deck. If you are using the cards from the journal page, have players combine their sets of number cards, mix them together, and put them in a stack with the number side facing down.

Each player takes a card from the top of the deck, turns it over, and says the number on the card. The player who has the larger number takes both cards. If the two cards show the same number, each player takes another card from the top of the deck. The player with the larger number then takes all the cards facing up.

The game is over when all cards have been taken. The player with more cards wins.

To determine who wins at the end of the game, flip a penny.

HEADS: The player with more cards wins.

TAILS: The player with fewer cards wins.

When finished with the activity, children sort the number cards into decks and store their decks in their tool kits.

 Adjusting the Activity If necessary, limit the range of numbers children use. For example, begin play with the 0–10 cards.

2 Ongoing Learning & Practice

◆ Playing *Number-Line Squeeze*
(*Math Masters*, p. 3)

PARTNER ACTIVITY

In Lesson 1.2, children played *Number-Line Squeeze* as a whole-class activity. In this lesson, the game is adapted for two players.

Give each partnership a number-line section.

Children use pennies as brackets and take turns choosing and guessing the mystery number. After a few games, partnerships trade number-line sections with other partnerships.

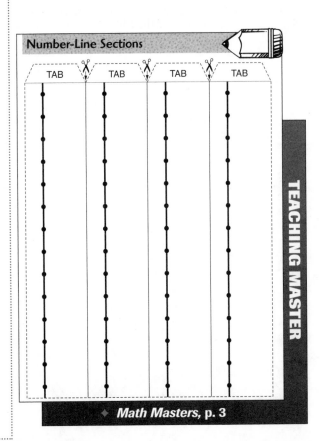

Number-Line Sections

TAB   TAB   TAB   TAB

◆ *Math Masters*, p. 3

TEACHING MASTER

◆ EXTRA PRACTICE Taking a "Counting Walk"

WHOLE-CLASS ACTIVITY 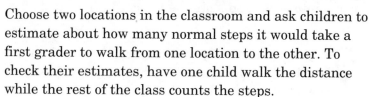 5–15 min

Choose two locations in the classroom and ask children to estimate about how many normal steps it would take a first grader to walk from one location to the other. To check their estimates, have one child walk the distance while the rest of the class counts the steps.

Pick two locations that are farther apart. For example: the classroom door and the girls' bathroom door. Ask children whether they think it will take more or fewer steps to walk between these two locations than it took to walk between the first two locations. Have children estimate the number of steps.

Then, if possible, have the entire class walk the distance, counting together the number of steps it takes. Compare the number of steps between these two locations to the number of steps between the first set of locations. Choose other locations and repeat the procedure.

Children count the steps between their classroom and the end of the hall.

1.7 Recording Tally Counts

OBJECTIVE To introduce the representation of data with tally marks.

summaries	materials

1 Teaching the Lesson

Children read numbers represented by tally marks and make tally marks to represent numbers. Then they collect data about pets owned by their classmates and keep track of the data by using tally marks. [Numeration; Data and Chance]

- ☐ Class Data Pad (optional)
- ☐ craft sticks (optional)
- ☐ Class Number Line (optional)
- ☐ tally chart
- ☐ slate

See Advance Preparation

2 Ongoing Learning & Practice

Children practice writing the numbers 3 and 4. They also play *Top-It*. [Numeration]

- ☐ *Math Journal 1*, p. 2
- ☐ number cards 0–15

3 Options for Individualizing

Enrichment Children use tally marks to keep track of the number of pennies dropped into a can one at a time. [Numeration; Data and Chance]

Extra Practice Children practice counting by 1s. [Numeration]

- ☐ pennies
- ☐ can or other container
- ☐ slate
- ☐ *Minute Math*®, pp. 3, 29, and 31

See Advance Preparation

Additional Information

Advance Preparation For Part 1, on the Class Data Pad or board, prepare a tally chart like the one shown in the margin on page 41.

If you are doing counts of the days of school with coins, be prepared to replace the nickel and five pennies with a dime on the 10th day of school. If you are doing counts of the days of school with straws, you will need to bundle 10 straws and move them to the TENS cup on the 10th day of school. Emphasize that the exchange makes it easier to count the days. Instead of counting each coin or straw individually, you know that the dime or the bundle represents 10. When counting each day between the 10th and 20th days, begin with the number 10 and count up.

For the first optional activity in Part 3, you will need a can (or container) and at least 10 pennies. If you do not use a can, be sure that your container is made of something that will make a loud sound when pennies are dropped into it.

Vocabulary • **tally mark**

Getting Started

Mental Math and Reflexes

Do a choral count by 1s from 1 to 10. Then count back from 10 to 1. Point to the Class Number Line as children count back.

Does anyone know what the number that comes before 0 is called? Negative one; do not expect children to know or to remember this fact at this time.

Do a whisper-and-shout count by 5s to 40. Then say only the "shout" numbers up to 40: 5, 10, 15, 20, 25, 30, 35, 40. Point to the Class Number Line as you count.

1 Teaching the Lesson

✦ Introducing Tally Marks

WHOLE-CLASS ACTIVITY

Counting Tally Marks

Write /////// on the board (see margin) and ask children to count the **tally marks** with you. 7

Now count aloud, 1, 2, 3, 4, 5, 6, 7, as you write ⊬⊦⊦ // (see margin).

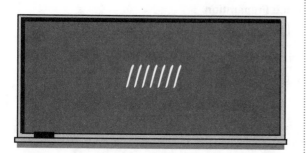

- How are these tally marks different from the tally marks we made before? The fifth tally mark is crossing the first four.

- What is the advantage of having the fifth mark cross the first four? It makes it easier to count the tally marks.

When we record numbers this way, the groups always have 5 tallies, and each group is counted as 5 (more).

Write other single-digit numbers greater than 5 with tally marks on the board. Model the counting process starting with 5 and counting on by 1s.

Writing Numbers with Tallies

Call out single-digit numbers and have children practice writing them with tally marks on their slates. Each time, they should write the 5s first and then the 1s.

 Adjusting the Activity If children are having difficulty, as you call out a number, point to it on the Class Number Line or hold up the appropriate number card.

- Can you guess how to show the number 10 with tally marks? ⊬⊦⊦ ⊬⊦⊦ The number 11? ⊬⊦⊦ ⊬⊦⊦ / The number 18? ⊬⊦⊦ ⊬⊦⊦ ⊬⊦⊦ ///

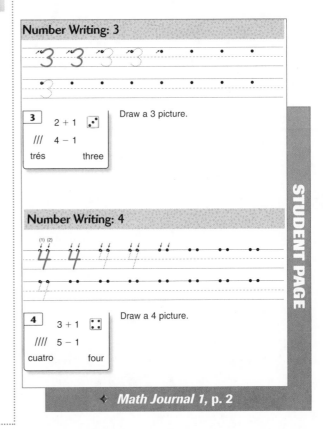

Adjusting the Activity If necessary, model the process of making tallies by using craft sticks. Have children line up 9 craft sticks, "standing tall." Count by 1s. Then make a "tally" bundle of 5 sticks and leave the other 4 standing tall and unbundled. Now count 5, 6, 7, 8, 9.

The Pets We Own		
Pet	Tallies	Total
Cat		
Dog		
Other		
No Pet		

◆ Making a Tally Chart to Count Children's Pets

WHOLE-CLASS ACTIVITY

Have children come up to the Class Data Pad or board, a few at a time, to make tally marks in the appropriate cell(s) in the second column of the table. They should make one tally mark for each pet they own. Make sure that every fifth tally mark is made across a group of four vertical marks.

When all children have had a turn, have them count the tally marks in each row, in unison. Then write the number in the appropriate cell in the third column of the table. Always count the 5s first and then the 1s.

NOTE: If having children come up to the board creates too much commotion, ask children to raise their hands for each category, one row or one group of desks at a time.

For example: All children in this group who own one cat raise your hands. *Then:* All children who own two cats raise your hands.

Continue until all categories have been covered.

2 Ongoing Learning & Practice

◆ Writing the Numbers 3 and 4
(*Math Journal 1*, p. 2)

INDEPENDENT ACTIVITY

Children practice writing the numbers 3 and 4.

Remind them that they should take their time and that the arrows show them the most efficient and easiest ways to form the numbers. When children have finished their number-writing practice, have them circle the numbers that they think are their best.

Then children draw pictures to represent the numbers.

◆ Playing *Top-It*

PARTNER ACTIVITY

Children practice addition skills by playing *Top-It*. For detailed instructions, see Lesson 1.6.

✦ *Math Journal 1*, p. 2

Children listen carefully as the teacher drops a small number of pennies into a container removed from view.

3 Options for Individualizing

◆ ENRICHMENT Making a Listening Tally

WHOLE-CLASS ACTIVITY   5–15 min

To give children practice making and counting tally marks, drop a selected number of pennies into a container, one at a time. Make sure you do this out of the children's view. Tell them to make a tally mark on their slates each time they hear a penny drop. Then have them count the tally marks and write the total number of pennies on their slates. Check that children have grouped their tally marks by 5s. Repeat as time allows.

Adjusting the Activity Extend this activity by dropping pennies and an object that makes a different sound—such as a plastic cube. Children tally only the pennies.

◆ EXTRA PRACTICE Minute Math

SMALL-GROUP ACTIVITY   5–15 min

To offer children more experience with counting by 1s, see the following pages in *Minute Math:*

Basic Routines: p. 3

Counting: pp. 29 and 31

1.8 Investigating Equally Likely Outcomes

OBJECTIVE To investigate equal-chance events.

summaries	materials
1 Teaching the Lesson	
Children roll a die and record the results with tally marks in the *Dice Roll and Tally Game*. Then they speculate about whether one number is more likely to come up than any of the others. [Data and Chance]	☐ *Math Journal 1*, p. 3 ☐ die ☐ craft sticks (optional)
2 Ongoing Learning & Practice	
Children practice writing the numbers 3 and 4. [Numeration] Children practice and maintain skills through Home Link activities.	☐ Teaching Master (*Math Masters*, p. 2) ☐ Home Link Master (*Math Masters*, p. 153) ***See* Advance Preparation**
3 Options for Individualizing	
Enrichment Children play the *Scissors, Paper, Stone* game and record the results with tally marks. They speculate about whether one gesture is more likely to win than either of the others. [Data and Chance]	☐ Teaching Master (*Math Masters*, p. 4) ***See* Advance Preparation**

Additional Information

Background Information For additional information on Home Links, see **Providing for Home-and-School Communication** in the *Teacher's Reference Manual*.

Advance Preparation For Part 2, make a copy of *Math Masters*, page 2. On this copy, write the first "3" on the first line of each half of the page and the first "4" on the third line of each half. Then make enough copies of this page so that each child will have a half-sheet. Cut the pages in half. Save the original *Math Masters*, page 2 for later use.

For Part 3, make enough copies of *Math Masters*, page 4 so that each child will have 1 half-sheet. Cut the copies in half.

Getting Started

Mental Math and Reflexes

Call out single-digit numbers. Children write tallies for the numbers on their slates. After they display their answers, they count the tally marks in unison, always beginning with 5 if the number is 5 or more.

If children are ready, try tally counts for numbers from 10 through 15.

Dice-Roll and Tally Game

1. Roll a die. Use tally marks to record the results on this chart.

	Tallies
1	
2	
3	
4	
5	
6	

2. Record the number of times each number came up.

STUDENT PAGE

◆ *Math Journal 1, p. 3*

NOTE: Theoretically, each number has the same chance of coming up. However, in practice, it is unlikely that all numbers will come up the same number of times.

This is a sophisticated idea that will be discussed in later grades. At this time, children should simply observe that the results were not the same for all partnerships.

Teaching the Lesson

◆ **Playing the *Dice-Roll and Tally Game***
(*Math Journal 1,* p. 3)

PARTNER ACTIVITY

Divide the class into partnerships and review the partner principles: Guide, Check, Praise.

On the board, make a tally chart for the numbers 1 through 6 (see margin). Then describe how the game is played:

Directions

1. Partners take turns rolling a die.

2. Both children then make tally marks next to the appropriate number in the chart in their journals.

3. Each partner has 6 turns for a total of 12 rolls of the die.

4. When all partnerships have completed their tally charts, tell them that they will continue to roll a die and record the results for 3 more minutes.

5. Before they begin, ask them whether they can predict which number or numbers will come up most often. Record their predictions but do not take sides.

6. After 3 minutes, have children record the number of times each number came up.

Adjusting the Activity If necessary, have students bundle craft sticks by 5s for each ＋＋＋＋ tally count.

You might want to end the activity with a cumulative tally of the results for all partnerships. You can expect the numbers to come up *about* the same number of times, even though in some partnerships one number may have come up much more often than the other numbers.

ONGOING ASSESSMENT
Check to make sure that children are showing each set of 5 as ＋＋＋＋.

➋ Ongoing Learning & Practice

✦ Writing the Numbers 3 and 4
(*Math Masters*, p. 2)

INDEPENDENT ACTIVITY

Pass out the half-sheets from *Math Masters*, page 2. Children practice writing the numbers 3 and 4. They circle their best effort for each number after they have completed the page.

✦ Home Link 1.8 (*Math Masters*, p. 153)

Home Connection Have children write their names and today's date at the top of the page.

Discuss the purpose of Home Links and what children should do with them. *For example:*

- Always put your name on your Home Link.

- Be sure to take home the Home Link.

- Discuss and complete the assignment with someone at home—a parent, a guardian, a caregiver, or an older brother or sister.

- Bring the completed assignment page back to school the next school day. (Occasionally, an assignment may take a couple of days or more to complete. Assure children that, when this is the case, the Family Note on the Home Link will notify their families that they have more than one day to complete the assignment.)

For Home Link 1.8, children collect examples of numbers and bring them to school. They continue to look for more examples during the next few days.

Invite children to continue bringing in examples of various numbers and their uses throughout the school year.

Name	Date
Number Writing	

3 _____

4 _____

Name	Date
Number Writing	

3 _____

4 _____

Children practice writing the numbers 3 and 4, using models provided by their teacher.

Numbers Are Everywhere   Home Link 1.8

Family Note

In *First Grade Everyday Mathematics*, children "do mathematics." We expect that children will want to share their enthusiasm for mathematics activities with members of their families. Therefore, your child will bring home assignments and activities throughout the year. These assignments, called "Home Links," will be identified by the symbol in the upper right-hand corner of this page. The assignments will not take very much time to complete, but most of them involve interaction with an adult or an older child.

There are good reasons for including Home Links in the first grade program:
- The assignments encourage children to take initiative and responsibility for completing them. As you respond with encouragement and assistance, you help your child build independence and self-confidence.
- Home Links reinforce newly learned skills and concepts. They provide thinking and practice time at each child's own pace.
- These assignments are often designed to relate what is done in school to children's lives outside school. This helps tie mathematics to the real world, which is very important in the *Everyday Mathematics* program.
- Home Links will give you a better idea of what mathematics your child is learning.

Generally, you can help by listening and responding to your child's requests and comments about mathematics. You can also help by linking numbers to real life, pointing out ways in which you use numbers (time, TV channels, page numbers, telephone numbers, bus routes, shopping lists, and so on). Extending the notion that "children who have someone read to them learn to read," *Everyday Mathematics* supports the belief that children who have someone do math with them, learn math. Playful counting and thinking games that are fun for both you and your child are very helpful for such learning.

For this first Home Link, your child might look for a newspaper ad for grocery items, a calendar page, or a picture of a clock. The purpose of this activity is to expand your child's awareness of numbers in the everyday world.

Please return this Home Link to school tomorrow.

Collect examples of numbers.
Paste some examples on the back of this page.

Bring examples that will not fit on this page to school.
Do not bring anything valuable or breakable!

HOME LINK MASTER

✦ *Math Masters*, p. 153

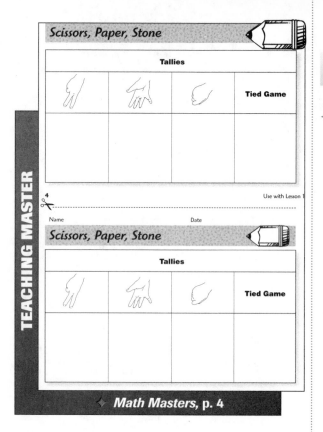

TEACHING MASTER

Scissors, Paper, Stone

	Tallies		
			Tied Game

Use with Lesson 1

Name _____ Date _____

Scissors, Paper, Stone

	Tallies		
			Tied Game

♦ Math Masters, p. 4

PLANNING AHEAD

Starting in Lesson 1.10, children will use full decks of number cards. If you are using the cards from the pages at the back of the children's journals, you will need to prepare decks of cards from journal Activity Sheet 2.

When combined with the cards from Activity Sheet 1, which you may have distributed in Lesson 1.6, each new deck of number cards will consist of 32 cards.

As before, the journal pages will have to be cut apart, and each new set of number cards will need the same distinctive marks, letters, shapes, or colors as the first set.

3 Options for Individualizing

♦ **ENRICHMENT** Playing *Scissors, Paper, Stone*
(*Math Masters*, p. 4)

PARTNER ACTIVITY   5–15 min

Some children may be familiar with this ancient game. It is known by many other names and is played all over the world. The game is for two players.

Three objects — scissors, a piece of paper, and a stone — are represented by the following hand gestures:

scissors   **paper**   **stone**

Players hide one hand behind their backs and make one of the three gestures. One player counts to 3. On the count of 3, both players show their hands. If the players' gestures are not the same, one of the players wins the round according to the following rules:

▷ *Scissors and paper:* Scissors wins because scissors can cut paper.

▷ *Paper and stone:* Paper wins because paper can be wrapped around a stone.

▷ *Stone and scissors:* Stone wins because it can blunt scissors (make them less sharp).

▷ If both players choose the same gesture, the round ends in a tie.

Players play 20 rounds. After each round, they make a tally mark in the chart on their half-sheet of paper to indicate either the winning gesture or that the round ended in a tie.

Encourage children to speculate about whether one gesture will probably win more often than the others, but do not take sides.

NOTE: Some children may think that the gesture that won most often is the one that is always likely to win more often than the others. Point out that if one of the gestures *were* more likely to win than the others, then players would choose that gesture every time—and games would always end in a tie!

1.9 The Calendar

OBJECTIVE To introduce the calendar as a device for keeping track of the days of the month.

summaries	materials
1 **Teaching the Lesson**	
The elements that make up a calendar are discussed. The class fills in the Class Calendar for the month up to and including the current day. Children then make their own calendars for the month. [Numeration; Measurement and Reference Frames]	☐ *Math Journal 1*, p. 4 ☐ Home Link 1.8 ☐ Teaching Master transparency (*Math Masters*, p. 5; optional)
2 **Ongoing Learning & Practice**	
Children practice writing the numbers 5 and 6. [Numeration] Children practice and maintain skills through Home Link activities.	☐ *Math Journal 1*, p. 5 ☐ Home Link Master (*Math Masters*, p. 154)
3 **Options for Individualizing**	
Extra Practice Children begin working on a calendar book for the year. [Numeration; Measurement and Reference Frames] **Extra Practice** Children work on their calendar skills. [Numeration; Measurement and Reference Frames]	☐ Teaching Master (*Math Masters*, p. 5; 12 copies per child) ☐ construction paper, 2 sheets per child ☐ *Minute Math*®, p. 63

Additional Information

Background Information For additional information on the Class Calendar routine, see **Organizing Routines and Displays** in the *Teacher's Reference Manual*.

Advance Preparation Display your Class Calendar in a place where children can reach it.

Vocabulary • **calendar** • **date**

Getting Started

Mental Math and Reflexes

Teach children the special first grade chant— "2, 4, 6, 8, first graders are really great!"—in preparation for counting by 2s.

Do a choral count by 1s, counting up or back from a number you specify. For example: *Start at 5 and count up.* 5, 6, 7, 8, ... *Start at 18 and count back.* 18, 17, 16, 15, ...

Home Link 1.8 Follow-Up

Children share examples of numbers they brought from home. Save these numbers for the Numbers All Around Museum, which will be assembled in Unit 2.

Encourage children to bring more examples of uses of numbers to school.

Teaching the Lesson

✦ Introducing the Class Calendar

Post the Class Calendar for the month. Examine the **calendar** with the children as you point to its parts, or elements:

• What is the name of the month?

• What are the names of the days of the week?

• What is the number for the year?

• What day of the week is today? What is today's **date**? (Write it in the appropriate cell of the Class Calendar.)

Ask children to repeat after you the complete date for today (the weekday, the month, the number of the day, and the number of the year). For example: Today is Monday, September 10, 2001.

• What was yesterday's date? (Write it in the calendar. Then fill in the missing dates from the beginning of the month up to today.)

If the following questions can be answered using this month's calendar, ask:

• What will the date be one week from today?

• What was the date one week ago?

Discuss some uses of calendars. For example, calendars help us keep track of the passage of time, of appointments, and of special days like birthdays and holidays.

Add the calendar job to the Job Chart. The child in charge of keeping up the Class Calendar will fill in the date for each day and also weekend dates and dates for school holidays.

 Adjusting the Activity You may want to ask children to read yesterday's, today's, and tomorrow's dates from the calendar, as you or a volunteer points to the appropriate information on the calendar. For example: *Today is Wednesday, September 12th, 2001. Yesterday was Tuesday, September 11th, and tomorrow will be Thursday, September 13th.*

NOTE: Write the current date on the board every day. Use forms like **September 10, 2001,** or **9/10/01,** or both. Later in the year, some children may be able to help with this job. Encourage children to write the date on their work each time they start a new assignment.

If appropriate, ask non-native English speakers if they have ever seen the date for September 10, 2001 written as 10/09/01. Explain to the class that in this country the form **month/day/year** is used, but in some other countries of the world the form **day/month/year** is used.

Today is Monday, September 10, 2001.
Today's date is 9/10/01.

✦ Filling in the Calendar for the Month
(*Math Journal 1*, p. 4; *Math Masters*, p. 5)

WHOLE-CLASS ACTIVITY

Children start their own calendars for this month. If you plan to have children make a calendar page for every month, see the first Options for Individualizing activity on the next page.

You may want to use an overhead transparency of *Math Masters*, page 5 to demonstrate where to write the various words and numbers. Help children get started with this page by asking questions like the following:

• Which month goes at the top of the page?

• Where does the 1 go? Why?

Keep this activity brief. Children can work on it independently or with a partner at a later time.

✓ ONGOING ASSESSMENT

Do not expect children to know much about the calendar at this time; with repeated exposure, they will become skillful at using it to keep track of time.

In this lesson, children should begin to find their way from the end of one week to the beginning of the next week by moving to the first cell in the next row of the calendar.

---

2 Ongoing Learning & Practice

✦ Writing the Numbers 5 and 6
(*Math Journal 1*, p. 5)

INDEPENDENT ACTIVITY

Children practice writing the numbers 5 and 6. Remind them that they should take their time and that the arrows show them the most efficient and easiest ways to form the numbers.

When children have finished their number-writing practice, have them circle their best effort for each number.

Then children draw pictures to represent the numbers 5 and 6.

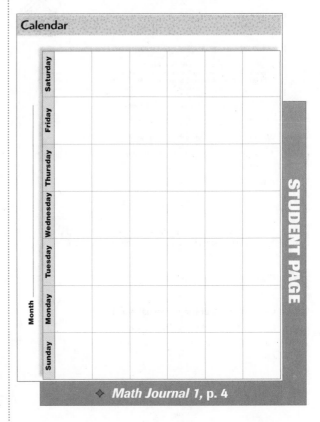

✦ *Math Journal 1*, p. 4

▲ This journal page is also available as a Teaching Master on *Math Masters*, page 5.

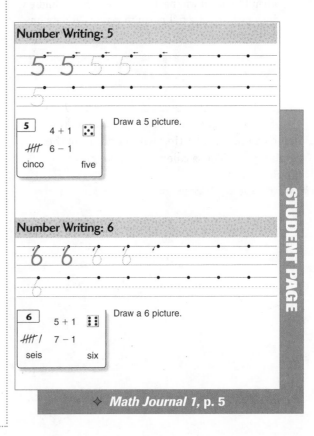

✦ *Math Journal 1*, p. 5

Family Note

Children might find dates on items like the following: watches, VCRs, newspapers, magazines, and mail with canceled stamps.

Every few days, ask your child to look at a calendar and tell you that day's date. We are just beginning to record counts with tallies. Remind your child how to show 5: Make four tallies "standing tall" and then make the fifth mark across the 4 tallies, as follows: ////

Please return this Home Link to school tomorrow.

What do you think of when you hear the word *date*?

Ask someone in your home to write what she or he thinks *date* means.

Date means <u>Answers vary.</u>

_____

_____

Look for calendars in your home. Have someone help you. Make a tally count of the number of calendars you find.

Count your total tally marks.

I found _____ calendars.

Can you find other things with dates on them?

Draw pictures of them on the back of this page.

◆ *Math Masters*, p. 154

Science Link

Discuss the term *full moon* with children. Find out when the moon will next be full, and have children draw pictures of a full moon to mark that date on their calendars.

NOTE: You might have children make take-home calendars, starting with January of the coming year. These calendars make great holiday gifts!

◆ Home Link 1.9 (*Math Masters*, p. 154)

Home Connection Have children write their names and today's date at the top of the page.

Children ask someone at home to write what they think the word *date* means. They find the number of calendars in their homes and make a tally mark each time they find a calendar.

Remind children to keep looking for more examples of numbers to bring to school.

3 Options for Individualizing

◆ EXTRA PRACTICE Making Calendar Books
(*Math Masters*, p. 5)

WHOLE-CLASS ACTIVITY 15–30 min

This is an ongoing project. Children make a calendar for each month, starting with the current month. They will assemble individual calendar pages into a book. Note that their journal page 4 is the same as *Math Masters*, page 5.

Children begin by making covers for their books and by completing the calendar for the current month. They write the name of the month at the top of the page and fill in the dates. Suggest that they make drawings on certain dates to illustrate important events at school.

Later in the year, you may have children fill in dates for a month out of order. For example, after children have filled in the first five days of the month, you might ask them to figure out which date to enter for the day one week from today, or 9 days from today, and then 3 days ago. Have children share how they found the answers.

◆ EXTRA PRACTICE Minute Math

SMALL-GROUP ACTIVITY 5–15 min

To offer children more experience with the calendar, see the following page in *Minute Math*:

Measurement: p. 63

1.10 Working in Small Groups

OBJECTIVE To discuss and put into practice rules for working in small groups.

summaries	materials
1 **Teaching the Lesson**	
Children discuss rules for working in small groups. Groups of children sort and count pennies and play *Top-It*. [Numeration]	□ Home Link 1.9 □ Rules for Small Groups Poster (optional) □ pennies □ slate □ counters (optional) □ number cards from *Math Journal 1,* Activity Sheets 1 and 2 or the Everything Math Deck ***See* Advance Preparation**
2 **Ongoing Learning & Practice**	
Children practice writing the numbers 5 and 6. [Numeration] Children practice and maintain skills through Home Link activities.	□ Teaching Master (*Math Masters,* p. 2) □ Home Link Master (*Math Masters,* p. 155) ***See* Advance Preparation**
3 **Options for Individualizing**	
Enrichment Working in small groups, children make pattern-block designs and copy them using their Pattern-Block Templates. [Geometry] **Extra Practice** Children read, write, and compare the numbers in a number pair. [Numeration] **Extra Practice** Children compare and order numbers. [Numeration]	□ Pattern-Block Template □ pattern blocks □ slate □ *Minute Math*®, pp. 3, 27, 28, and 38 ***See* Advance Preparation**

Additional Information

Advance Preparation For Part 1, each child will need a set of cards numbered from 0 through 22. Children may use an Everything Math Deck or a deck created from *Math Journal 1,* Activity Sheets 1 and 2.

Optional: Make a poster listing rules for working in small groups. (See margin on page 52.)

For Part 2, make a copy of *Math Masters,* page 2. On this copy, write the first "5" on the first line of each half of the page and the first "6" on the third line of each half. Then make enough copies of this page so that each child will have a half-sheet. Cut the pages in half. Save the original *Math Masters,* page 2 for later use.

For the first optional activity in Part 3, set up one or two stations with sets of pattern blocks.

Getting Started

<table>
<tr><td>

Mental Math and Reflexes

Say the special first grade chant: *2, 4, 6, 8, first graders are really great!*

Put your finger on the number 5 on your number line. Count up 3 hops. Where do you end up? On the 8

Pose similar problems and have children write answers on their slates. Watch for children who include the starting number in their counts. If children are having difficulty, have them count up to the starting number first and *then* count the number of hops.

</td><td>

Home Link 1.9 Follow-Up

Children share what people at home said about the word *date*.

If time permits, find the largest number of dates someone found at home. Collect examples of where (besides calendars) children found dates.

</td></tr>
</table>

1   Teaching the Lesson

◆ Extending Partner Expectations to Small Groups

WHOLE-CLASS ACTIVITY

It pays to take the time to discuss orderly small-group interaction. Doing so will encourage a cooperative attitude and reduce children's reliance on you for answers to their problems and their questions.

First, review the partner expectations: Guide, Check, and Praise. Then ask the class to suggest additional rules that might help groups of children work together. These rules might include the ones listed on the poster in the margin.

Post these rules where children can refer to them often!

◆ Counting Pennies in Small Groups

SMALL-GROUP ACTIVITY

Divide the class into groups of 3 or 4 children each. Children in each group pool their tool-kit pennies. One child takes a fistful of pennies and spreads them out on the desk. Children work together to sort the pennies into groups of 5. Then each child makes tally marks on his or her slate to represent the total number of pennies. Finally, children count their tally marks and compare one another's totals.

Children take turns taking fistfuls of pennies and checking answers.

After a few turns, each child takes 10 pennies to put back in his or her tool kit.

Rules for Small Groups

1. *Use quiet voices.*
2. *Be polite.*
3. *Share materials.*
4. *Take turns.*

NOTE: If children do not agree on the total number of pennies, one child counts the pennies one by one to find the actual count.

✦ Playing *Top-It* in Small Groups
(*Math Journal 1,* Activity Sheets 1 and 2)

SMALL-GROUP ACTIVITY ᴀ̂ᴀ̂ᴀ̂ᴀ̂

If a group is using an Everything Math Deck, group members use the entire deck. (Children will be using cards numbered 0–20.)

If a group is using the Activity Sheet cards, ask two children in each group to combine the 0–22 cards in their respective card decks into one large deck. Write the following symbols on the board:

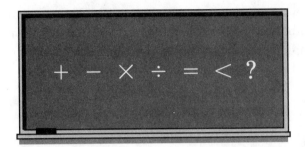

Tell children to set aside all the cards that show the above symbols, as well as the two "wild cards"; this leaves the 0–22 cards.

Then mix the cards and put the mixed deck facedown on the playing surface.

To play *Top-It,* each player in the group draws a card, reads the number aloud, and shows it to the other players. The player with the largest number wins all the cards.

If two players tie with the largest number, they draw another card. The player with the larger number then takes all the cards. Play ends when no more cards remain to be drawn. The player who has the most cards wins.

Variation 1

The last child to win a hand wins the game.

Variation 2

Add the wild cards to the deck. A player who draws a wild card may choose any number. The player must write the number on scratch paper or a slate so that the other players can see it.

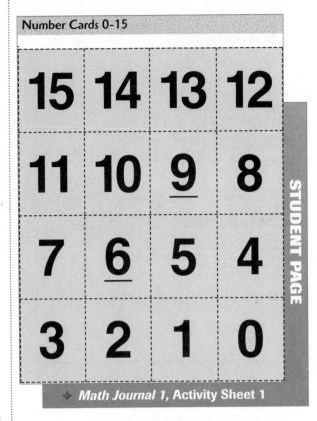

✦ *Math Journal 1,* **Activity Sheet 1**

STUDENT PAGE

Number Cards 16-22

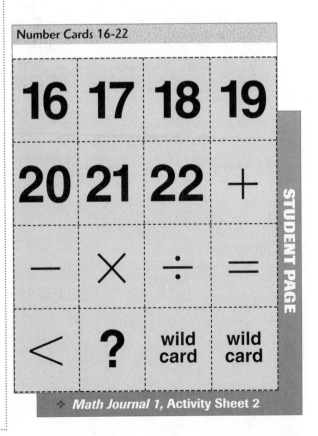

✦ *Math Journal 1,* **Activity Sheet 2**

STUDENT PAGE

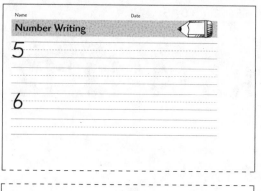

5

6

5

6

▲ Children practice writing the numbers 5 and 6, using models provided by their teacher.

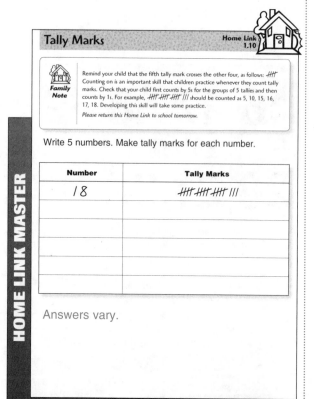

Tally Marks

Home Link 1.10

Family Note

Remind your child that the fifth tally mark crosses the other four, as follows: ⨐⨐⨐⨐⨐. Counting on is an important skill that children practice whenever they count tally marks. Check that your child first counts by 5s for the groups of 5 tallies and then counts by 1s. For example, ⨐⨐⨐ ⨐⨐⨐ ⨐⨐⨐ ||| should be counted as 5, 10, 15, 16, 17, 18. Developing this skill will take some practice.

Please return this Home Link to school tomorrow.

Write 5 numbers. Make tally marks for each number.

Number	Tally Marks
18	⨐⨐⨐ ⨐⨐⨐ ⨐⨐⨐ ///

Answers vary.

HOME LINK MASTER

✦ *Math Masters, p. 155*

ONGOING ASSESSMENT
Expect that many children will be able to decide which number is the larger of the two.

Adjusting the Activity If necessary, children can use the number line to figure out which number is larger. If they are still having trouble, they can use counters to display each number and then compare the two piles by matching counters one to one.

When they have finished playing, children separate their number cards into two decks. Each child then stores a complete deck of 32 cards in his or her tool kit.

2 Ongoing Learning & Practice

✦ Writing the Numbers 5 and 6
(*Math Masters*, p. 2)

INDEPENDENT ACTIVITY

Pass out the half-sheets of paper from *Math Masters*, page 2. Children practice writing the numbers 5 and 6. Have them circle their best effort for each number when they complete the page.

Portfolio Ideas

✦ Home Link 1.10 (*Math Masters*, p. 155)

Home Connection Have children write their names and today's date at the top of the page.

Children choose five numbers and make tally marks for each of the numbers.

Remind children to keep looking for more examples of numbers to bring to school.

3 Options for Individualizing

◆ **ENRICHMENT** Making Pattern-Block Designs

SMALL-GROUP ACTIVITY 15–30 min

Small groups share sets of pattern blocks. Each child makes a pattern-block design, copies the design using the Pattern-Block Template, and then colors the design.

> NOTE: Making pattern-block designs is one of the Exploration activities in the next lesson. You may want to have one or two groups work on this activity today and have the rest of the children work on it in Lesson 1.11.

◆ **EXTRA PRACTICE** Reading, Writing, and Comparing Numbers

WHOLE-CLASS ACTIVITY 5–15 min

Dictate a pair of numbers (each less than 10) for children to write on their slates. Have them circle the larger number and then read back the two numbers, saying the larger number first.

Then consider giving pairs that highlight place-value concepts, such as:

    23, 43   32, 34   34, 43

Ask children how they know which number is larger.

◆ **EXTRA PRACTICE** Minute Math

SMALL-GROUP ACTIVITY 5–15 min

To offer children more experience with comparing and ordering numbers, see the following pages in *Minute Math*:

Basic Routines: p. 3

Counting: pp. 27, 28, and 38

1.11
EXPLORATIONS

Exploring Math Materials

OBJECTIVE To introduce Explorations with manipulative materials.

summaries

materials

1 Teaching the Lesson

The meaning and purpose of Explorations in *Everyday Mathematics* are discussed. Children "play" with pattern blocks, base-10 blocks, and geoboards to familiarize themselves with these materials. [Geometry; Patterns, Functions, and Algebra]

☐ Home Link 1.10

☐ pattern blocks; base-10 blocks

☐ geoboard and rubber bands (preferably colored ones)

See **Advance Preparation**

2 Ongoing Learning & Practice

Children practice previously introduced skills by playing *Number-Line Squeeze,* by playing *Top-It,* or by practicing number writing. [Numeration]

Children practice and maintain skills through Home Link activities.

☐ Teaching Masters (*Math Masters,* pp. 2 and 3)

☐ Home Link Master (*Math Masters,* p. 156)

☐ number cards from tool kit

See **Advance Preparation**

3 Options for Individualizing

Enrichment Children sort attribute blocks by color or shape.
[Geometry; Patterns, Functions, and Algebra]

Enrichment Children draw colorful pattern-block designs.
[Geometry; Patterns, Functions, and Algebra]

Extra Practice Children practice basic counting skills.
[Numeration]

☐ attribute blocks

☐ pattern blocks

☐ *Minute Math*®, pp. 3, 27, and 29

Additional Information

Background Information For additional information on Explorations, see **Managing the Curriculum** in the *Teacher's Reference Manual.*

Advance Preparation Decide how you will organize the Explorations. If there are enough materials for everyone to work on the same Exploration at the same time, you may choose to go that route. But if more than one Exploration is being worked on at one time, you will need to plan how to manage several different activities at the same time. Decide how many stations you will need to accommodate groups of 3 to 5 children each. Each station should have one kind of material (pattern blocks, base-10 blocks, or geoboards) for children to share. You may want to do the following:

▷ Set up two stations for each Exploration.

▷ Set up additional familiar activities or games for children to work on or play while other groups are working on Explorations.

▷ Make and display a Rules for Explorations Poster like the one shown in the margin on page 57.

For Part 2, prepare number-line sections. (See Advance Preparation in Lesson 1.6.) Also, prepare *Math Masters,* page 2.

For Part 3, set up stations with attribute blocks and pattern blocks.

Vocabulary • **explorer** • **Exploration** • **pattern blocks** • **base-10 blocks** • **geoboard**

Getting Started

Mental Math and Reflexes

Say the special first grade chant: "2, 4, 6, 8, first graders are really great!"

Put your finger on the number 12 on your number line. Count back 5 hops. Where do you end up? On the 7

Pose similar problems and have children write answers on their slates. Watch for children who include the starting number in their counts. If children are having difficulty, have them count up to the starting number before they count back.

Do some "stop and start" counting by 1s or 5s. "Stop and start" counting can be done with individuals or small groups. Point to one child or group of children, who begin the count. Say "Stop," and then point to another child or group of children and say "Start." Children resume the count where the last group left off.

Home Link 1.10 Follow-Up

Ask someone to name the largest number he or she tallied. Ask whether someone tallied an even larger number. Continue in this way until you identify the largest number in the class. Make the tally marks for that number on the board. Then count the tally marks together.

1 Teaching the Lesson

◆ Introducing Explorations

WHOLE-CLASS ACTIVITY

Ask the class what Christopher Columbus is famous for. Tell children that Columbus is called an **explorer.** An explorer is someone who tries to discover something that he or she did not know before. When Columbus set out on his voyage, he was trying to find a route to the East Indies, but he could not predict where he was going to end up.

Tell children that sometimes they will become explorers in mathematics. When doing a mathematical **Exploration,** they will try to find the answer to something they did not know before, without being told how to do it.

Usually, they will work on an Exploration in small groups so that they can share ideas and help one another. They will also share materials (mathematical tools), such as pattern blocks, geoboards, dominoes, base-10 blocks, weighing scales, calculators, rulers, and attribute blocks.

Ask the class to suggest a few rules for keeping a relatively quiet and orderly atmosphere in the room and for sharing and caring for the materials. Refer to your Rules for Explorations Poster, and add any other rules the children suggest that seem appropriate.

Post the rules along with the partnership principles: Guide, Check, Praise.

Rules for Explorations

1. Cooperate with others.
2. Move about quietly.
3. Keep voices low.
4. Treat materials as tools, not as toys.
5. Give everyone in the group a chance to use the materials.
6. Straighten up when finished. Put materials back where they belong.
7. Try to settle disputes quietly within the group. If necessary, one person can go to the teacher for help.

✦ Exploring with Pattern Blocks, Base-10 Blocks, and Geoboards

SMALL-GROUP ACTIVITIES

The purpose of the Explorations in this lesson is to familiarize children with some of the materials they will use for more directed activities in later lessons. It is essential that children have time to "play" with materials before they are expected to use them in lesson activities.

Divide the class into groups of 4 or 5 children. Each group works at its own station. After 10 to 15 minutes, groups rotate to new stations so that children can work with materials they have not used before.

Tell children to use the materials any way they want. Children who are using **pattern blocks** will probably create wonderful designs. Encourage children who are working with **base-10 blocks** to build different structures with them. Those who are using **geoboards** can make various shapes and pictures using the rubber bands.

▼ Children practice writing the numbers 1 through 6. Some children may wish to circle their best efforts.

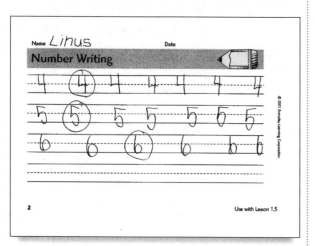

2 Ongoing Learning & Practice

✦ Playing *Number-Line Squeeze* or *Top-It* (*Math Masters*, p. 3)

PARTNER ACTIVITY

Children review greater-than and less-than number relations by playing *Number-Line Squeeze*. They practice comparing numbers by playing *Top-It*. For detailed instructions, see Lesson 1.6.

✦ Writing the Numbers 1 through 6 (*Math Masters*, p. 2)

INDEPENDENT ACTIVITY

Children write the numbers 1 through 6. They circle their best numbers or draw pictures on the back to represent the numbers 1 though 6.

Portfolio Ideas

◆ Home Link 1.11 (*Math Masters*, p. 156)

Home Connection Have children write their names and today's date at the top of the page.

Children tell someone at home about the favorite Exploration they did today.

Remind children to keep looking for more examples of numbers to bring to school.

3 Options for Individualizing

◆ ENRICHMENT Exploring with Attribute Blocks

INDEPENDENT ACTIVITY   **5–15 min**

Encourage children to sort the blocks by color or by shape. Sorting by size will be introduced in Lesson 7.1.

◆ ENRICHMENT Drawing Pattern-Block Designs

INDEPENDENT ACTIVITY   **15–30 min**

Encourage children to make pattern-block designs, copy their designs using their Pattern-Block Templates, and then color their designs.

 Adjusting the Activity If necessary, help non-native English speakers with the color words "yellow," "red," and "blue" and with the shape words "circle," "triangle," "square," and "rectangle." Prepare a poster showing each pattern block labeled with its "color" written in that color and its "shape" written in black.

◆ EXTRA PRACTICE Minute Math

SMALL-GROUP ACTIVITY   **5–15 min**

To offer children more experience with counting, see the following pages in *Minute Math*:

Basic Routines: p. 3

Counting: pp. 27 and 29

 Family Note Time is set aside regularly in *First Grade Everyday Mathematics* for Exploration activities that involve children in data collecting, problem solving, familiarization with math manipulatives, and games in independent and small-group settings. Children will have the opportunity to participate in several activities during each Exploration session. Please ask your child about our class's mathematics Explorations.

Please return this Home Link to school tomorrow.

Tell someone at home about your favorite mathematics Exploration. Draw something you did in your Explorations today. Answers vary.

◆ *Math Masters*, p. 156

HOME LINK MASTER

NOTE: Before making copies of Home Link 1.11: Explorations, you might want to list on it the various Explorations children did today. This will help the person at home initiate a discussion. For example, the person at home might say, "Tell me about the pattern blocks you used today."

1.12 Weather and Temperature Routines

OBJECTIVES To introduce the routines for recording the day's weather and approximate temperature; and to learn how a thermometer works.

summaries	materials

1 Teaching the Lesson

Plan to spend 2 days on this lesson. Because the activities for Day 1 take less time than those for Day 2, consider completing the Ongoing Learning & Practice activities on Day 1.

On Day 1, children are introduced to the routine for recording the day's weather.

On Day 2, children examine the Fahrenheit temperature scale and learn the routine for recording the temperature by using colors to identify temperature zones. [Measurement and Reference Frames]

- ☐ *Math Journal 1*, pp. 6 and 7
- ☐ Home Link 1.11
- ☐ Class Weather Chart (*Math Masters,* p. 6 provides symbols you might want to use.)
- ☐ classroom thermometer
- ☐ Class Thermometer Poster

***See* Advance Preparation**

2 Ongoing Learning & Practice

Children collect data about a question they want to investigate and record the results with tally marks. [Data and Chance]

Children practice and maintain skills through Home Link activities.

- ☐ Class Data Pad
- ☐ Home Link Master (*Math Masters,* p. 157)

3 Options for Individualizing

Enrichment Children make booklets consisting of pictures of appropriate activities for each of the color zones on the thermometer. [Measurement and Reference Frames]

Enrichment Children perform experiments using the outdoor thermometer. [Measurement and Reference Frames]

- ☐ blank paper, 7 sheets per child
- ☐ construction paper, 2 sheets per child
- ☐ glass of cold water

Additional Information

Background Information For additional information on the *Everyday Mathematics* weather and temperature routines, see **Organizing Routines and Displays** in the *Teacher's Reference Manual.*

Advance Preparation Prepare the Class Weather Chart. (*Math Masters,* page 6 provides symbols you might want to use.) You will need an outdoor thermometer large enough so that children can easily see the level of the mercury. Cover the Celsius scale of the thermometer with masking tape. Also, cover the marks between tens on the Fahrenheit scale with tape so that only the numbers and marks for tens of degrees are visible. (Match the thermometer on journal page 6.) You may find it helpful to color the temperature zones of the outdoor thermometer so that it matches the Class Thermometer Poster. (See assembly instructions for the poster on page 63.) Display the side of the Class Thermometer Poster that shows tens of degrees Fahrenheit.

Vocabulary • **thermometer** • **mercury** • **degree** • **temperature** • **Fahrenheit**

Getting Started

Mental Math and Reflexes

Children use the number line on the inside back cover of their journals as they count by 2s in unison. They move their fingers along the number line, using the whisper-and-shout routine: Whisper 1, shout **2,** whisper 3, shout **4,** …. Count up to 20.

Home Link 1.11 Follow-Up

Ask a few children to talk about their favorite Explorations and explain why they liked them.

1 Teaching the Lesson

DAY 1

◆ Introducing the Weather Routine
(*Math Masters,* p. 6)

WHOLE-CLASS ACTIVITY

Ask children which words they know that describe the weather. Sample answers: rainy, snowing, sunny, hot, cold, freezing, cloudy, foggy Write these words on the board.

• Which word or words describe the weather today?

Display the Class Weather Chart and ask children to suggest weather words to describe the various symbols on the chart.

• Which symbol describes the weather today?

Tell the class that one of the class jobs will be to record on the Class Weather Chart what the weather is like each day. Model how to do this by making a tally mark under the appropriate symbol.

Expect to supervise this routine in the beginning, but with experience, children will be able to record the weather without your help. The job of Weather Person can be rotated among the children in the class.

◆ Introducing the Thermometer

WHOLE-CLASS ACTIVITY

Display the outdoor **thermometer.**

• What is this device called? A thermometer

• What are some kinds of thermometers? What are they used for? An indoor/outdoor thermometer is used to tell

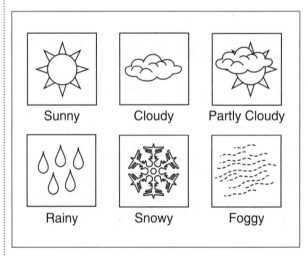

Symbols that can be used on the Class Weather Chart are found on *Math Masters,* page 6.

Science Link

You might want to tell the class that when mercury is heated, it expands (gets larger). When the air gets warmer, the expanding mercury in a thermometer has nowhere to go but up.

NOTE: You can do these experiments with small groups. (See the second Options for Individualizing activity later in this lesson.)

A Thermometer

°F

140	
130	red
120	
110	
Body Temperature → 100 →	
90	orange
80	
Room Temperature → 70	yellow
60	
50	green
40	
Water Freezes → 30 →	blue
20	
10	purple
0	
−10	
−20	white
−30	
−40	

STUDENT PAGE

↑ Math Journal 1, p. 6

how warm or cold the air is; a fever thermometer is used to check whether a person is sick; a meat thermometer is used to check whether a turkey has been in the oven long enough; an oven thermometer tells the temperature of the oven.

A thermometer has a little glass tube with a bulb at the bottom that contains a red liquid. This liquid is called **mercury.**

• What happens to the mercury in the thermometer when the air around us gets warmer? It goes up. When the air gets colder? It goes down.

• What do you think will happen if we put one of our hands over the bulb at the bottom of the glass tube? The mercury will rise because the hand is warmer than the air around it.

• What do you think will happen if we place the bulb of the thermometer in cold water? The mercury will go down because the water is colder than the air around it.

Point to the numbers on the outdoor thermometer. These numbers measure how warm or cold it is, in **degrees.** For example, if the top of the mercury reaches the number 60, we say that the **temperature** is 60 degrees. The temperature is the number of degrees recorded by the thermometer.

DAY 2

◆ Discussing the Fahrenheit Thermometer Scale (*Math Journal 1,* p. 6)

WHOLE-CLASS ACTIVITY

Have children turn to the picture of the thermometer in their journals. Ask them to describe what they see. Numbers of degrees, words for colors, the letter *F* at the top of the thermometer with the symbol " ° " in front of it

The letter *F* stands for the word **Fahrenheit.** A Fahrenheit thermometer measures temperature in *degrees Fahrenheit.* Point out that the symbol " ° " appears before the letter *F.* This " ° " symbol is the symbol for *degrees.* " °F " is read *degrees Fahrenheit.* Write "60°F" on the board. This is read "60 degrees Fahrenheit."

Look at the numbers on the thermometer. Ask children to put their fingers on 0 and to move up the scale as they chant the numbers of degrees in unison: *0 degrees, 10 degrees, 20 degrees, …*

Explain that a scale is like a number line. Temperature scales are made by choosing a cold point and a hot point and then marking a number of equal spaces between them.

Point out the numbers under the number 0. Each is written with a little dash in front of it. (−10°, −20°, …) These numbers are read "10 degrees below zero," "20 degrees below zero," and so on.

⬇ **Adjusting the Activity** You may want to point out that these numbers can also be read "negative 10 degrees," "negative 20 degrees," and so on. On the number line, negative numbers are displayed to the left of 0.

NOTE: Do not expect children to remember the "°F" symbol at this time. This topic will be revisited in greater detail in Lesson 4.1.

You may want to take a minute to explain that there is a second scale on many thermometers. It is called the *Celsius temperature scale*. The Celsius temperature scale will be introduced in second grade.

◆ Introducing the Daily Temperature Routine

WHOLE-CLASS ACTIVITY 👥👥👥

Have someone place the thermometer outside for a few minutes while you discuss the color codes on the Class Thermometer Poster. Point out that the temperature at which water freezes is shown in the blue section, the normal room temperature in the yellow section, and the normal body temperature near the top of the orange section. As children will soon discover, the outdoor temperature will vary over time.

The Weather Person may be put in charge of the daily temperature routine, or the job may be assigned to someone else. The routine has two parts:

1. Set the temperature on the Class Thermometer Poster to show the outside temperature.

2. Record the color of the temperature zone.

On the Class Thermometer Poster, the red ribbon represents the mercury in a regular thermometer. At about the same time each day during the school year, a child moves the red ribbon on the Class Thermometer Poster to approximately match the temperature on the outdoor thermometer. Model how to do this for the current day's temperature reading and ask children to describe the temperature reading. Encourage them to use phrases like *between ___ and ___ degrees Fahrenheit, almost ___ degrees Fahrenheit,* and *about halfway between ___ and ___ degrees Fahrenheit.*

NOTE: Color the various zones of the Class Thermometer Poster. To assemble the poster, cut along the slot in the bulb at the bottom. Feed a 4-foot length of red ribbon or red crepe paper through the slot, from back to front, and pull it up to the required temperature mark. Attach it to the poster with a piece of removable tape.

Finally, describe and model the routine you plan to use for recording the color of the zone of the current day's temperature.

Expect to supervise this routine in the beginning, but with experience, children will be able to complete the job independently.

◆ Coloring the Zones on a Fahrenheit Thermometer (*Math Journal 1*, p. 6)

WHOLE-CLASS ACTIVITY

Children color the zones on the thermometer in their journals to match the colors on the Class Thermometer Poster. To get them started, ask them to put their fingers on the word *red* and to make a red "X" on the word. Repeat this procedure with each of the other colors.

Once children have marked all the colors, they color the entire rectangle for each zone.

◆ Drawing a Picture to Illustrate a Temperature (*Math Journal 1*, pp. 6 and 7)

WHOLE-CLASS ACTIVITY

Have children look at the colored zones on the thermometer in their journals. Choose a zone and ask children how they would feel if the temperature were in that zone. Encourage them to use words like *hot, cold, warm, cool, freezing,* and *boiling.* For example, ask someone to pick a temperature in the orange zone (such as 90°). How would people feel? hot Repeat, using several other zones.

Do the first problem on journal page 7 with the class. Children are to find the temperature zone for the temperature reading shown on the small thermometer. Then they color the thermometer with the appropriate zone color. orange

Next, ask children to draw a picture that shows people wearing the type of clothing they would wear if the temperature were in the orange temperature zone. The picture might be of a person wearing a swimming suit.

Children complete the other problems on the page on their own or with partners. Circulate and assist as they try to find the color zone for each thermometer.

Date

Temperatures

Color each thermometer.

Draw a picture of a person wearing the right kind of clothing for that temperature.

1. 90° orange

2. 70° yellow

3. 30° blue

4. 50° green

Use with Lesson 1.12.

(seven) **7**

On page 7 of their Math Journals, children draw pictures showing what people might wear in different temperature zones.

Adjusting the Activity Review the type of clothing a person might wear for each zone on the thermometer.

ONGOING ASSESSMENT

The activities in this lesson mark the beginning of children's work with thermometers. Children should begin to recognize the relationship between the height of the mercury and the degree of warmth or cold it represents.

2 Ongoing Learning & Practice

◆ Making a Class Tally Count

WHOLE-CLASS ACTIVITY

Remind children of the tally count of their pets in Lesson 1.7. Ask them to suggest other questions they might want to investigate, and record these suggestions on the Class Data Pad. Examples of questions for investigation might include the following:

• What is our favorite cereal?

• How do we get to school?

• What kind of pizza do we like best?

• Which season do we like best?

• What is our favorite sport?

For the question the class decides to investigate, make a tally chart on the board like the one used in Lesson 1.7.

Save the rest of the questions for investigations at other times during the year.

◆ Home Link 1.12 (*Math Masters*, p. 157)

 Home Connection Have children write their names and today's date at the top of the page.

Children look for thermometers in their homes. They look for other things in their homes that tell or set a temperature.

Remind children to keep looking for more examples of numbers to bring to school.

Our Favorite Cereal		
Cereal	Tallies	Total
Sweet Wheat	⳾⳾⳾1 1	6
Fruit Flakes	⳾⳾⳾1	5
Oat O's	⳾⳾⳾1 ⳾⳾⳾1 11	12

Thermometers

 Home Link 1.12

Family Note Objects that show temperatures might be kitchen items (such as a meat thermometer) or health care items (such as a heating pad). These items do not need to show degrees Fahrenheit—they may have their own temperature gauges showing levels of heat or cold.

Please return this Home Link to school tomorrow.

1. Look for thermometers in your home.

   I found _____ thermometers in my home.

2. Do a temperature hunt. Ask someone at home to help you find other things that show temperatures.

   a. Draw some of the things you find.

   b. Write the name for each of your drawings.

   Have someone at home help you.

   Answers vary.

 ◆ *Math Masters, p. 157*

HOME LINK MASTER

My Weather Book

Children illustrate the covers
of their weather activity booklets.

3 Options for Individualizing

◆ ENRICHMENT Making a Weather Activity Booklet

WHOLE-CLASS ACTIVITY 👥👥👥👥   30+ min

Have children make booklets consisting of one page for each temperature zone. Have them use sheets of construction paper to make covers for their booklets.

Children choose a temperature in a zone and record it on a page, along with the name of the season of the year when that temperature might occur. Then they draw a picture of things they might do in that season.

◆ ENRICHMENT Doing Experiments with the Thermometer

SMALL-GROUP ACTIVITY   5–15 min

Bring the outdoor thermometer inside and wait a few minutes until it shows the approximate room temperature.

Have children work in small groups so that everyone can see the results of the experiments.

1. Display the room temperature on the Class Thermometer Poster. *Which color zone is the temperature in?*

2. Ask a child to put his or her hand over the bulb at the bottom of the glass tube on the outdoor thermometer and hold it for about 20 seconds. Then display the new temperature on the Class Thermometer Poster. *Which color zone is the temperature in now?*

3. Ask another child to place the bulb of the outdoor thermometer in a glass of cold water and to keep it in the water for about 20 seconds. Then display the new temperature on the Class Thermometer Poster. *Which color zone is the temperature in now?*

A child places a thermometer in a glass of cold water to see how the water affects the temperature reading.

1.13 Number Stories

OBJECTIVE To practice telling and solving number stories.

summaries	materials

1 Teaching the Lesson

The teacher tells several number stories, which children act out and solve. Children share their strategies for solving the problems posed in the stories. Children make up and solve their own number stories. [Operations and Computation]

- ☐ Home Link 1.12
- ☐ tool-kit pennies

2 Ongoing Learning & Practice

Children continue to work on number writing. [Numeration]

Children practice and maintain skills through Home Link activities.

- ☐ Teaching Master (*Math Masters*, p. 2)
- ☐ Home Link Master (*Math Masters*, p. 158)

3 Options for Individualizing

Extra Practice Partners use randomly generated numbers to make up and solve number stories. [Operations and Computation]

- ☐ number cards 1–10
- ☐ tool-kit pennies
- ☐ slate

Additional Information

Background Information For additional information on number stories and problem solving, see **The Importance of Problem Solving** in the *Teacher's Reference Manual*.

Vocabulary • **number story**

Getting Started

Mental Math and Reflexes

Children use the number line on the inside back cover of their journals as they count by 2s from 1 to 20 in unison. They continue counting by 2s to 30.

What patterns do you notice when counting by 2s past 20?

Continue counting by 2s into the 30s and 40s.

If necessary, write the digits 2, 4, 6, 8, and 0 on the board and point to them as children count by 2s.

Home Link 1.12 Follow-Up

Briefly survey children to find out how many thermometers they found in their homes. Share ideas about other objects that tell temperature.

1 Teaching the Lesson

◆ Telling Simple Number Stories

WHOLE-CLASS ACTIVITY

Tell a simple **number story** about animals, and draw a picture on the board or overhead to illustrate it. The picture might consist of little circles or Xs to represent the animals in the story.

Example: The zoo has 5 new storks and 3 new herons. How many new birds does the zoo have?

(You may have to tell children that storks and herons are birds.) Ask children to solve the problem in the story. Encourage them to use any strategy they like. Strategies might include some of the following:

▷ Use pennies to represent birds.

▷ Draw pictures like the one on the board.

▷ Use fingers to represent birds.

▷ Start with the number of storks (or herons) and count on the number of herons (or storks). For example, start with 5 storks and count on the 3 herons:

5 birds, 6 birds, 7 birds, 8 birds

3 herons

▷ Count on a number line.

After a few minutes, ask children to share their answers and their solution strategies. Write both correct and incorrect answers on the board. Each time, add the unit label "birds." As children discuss their strategies, try to guide the class to an understanding of why certain strategies will not result in the correct answer.

Be sensitive to children with incorrect answers. Assure them that we learn as much or more by trying to understand why certain strategies do not work as we learn by finding and using strategies that do work.

Pose several other problems like the following and have children share their solution strategies:

• Portia belongs to a children's club. Whenever she goes to the club, she pays $1 to get in. Last week, she went on Monday, Tuesday, and Friday. How much money did Portia spend last week to get into the club? $3

XXXXX storks
XXX herons

- Frank goes fishing every Saturday. He caught 7 fish last Saturday. But he had to throw 6 fish back because they were too small. How many fish did Frank bring home last Saturday? 1 fish

- Gina found 3 pennies on her walk Monday morning. Unfortunately, she lost one penny on the way home. How many pennies did Gina still have when she got home? 2 pennies

- Michael read 8 books last summer. His best friend, Brendan, read 5 books. How many more books did Michael read? 3 more books

- Mona's dog had 3 puppies. How many dogs does Mona have now? (You may need to remind children that puppies are dogs!) 4 dogs

◆ Sharing Simple Number Stories

WHOLE-CLASS ACTIVITY

Have children think of number stories for 10 pennies. Ask volunteers to share their stories. Expect stories like the following:

▷ I had 6 pennies, and my mom gave me 4 more. How many do I have now?

▷ I saved 9 pennies in my bank, and then I found 1 more at school and added it to my bank when I got home. How many pennies do I have in my bank now?

▷ I had 10 pennies, but I lost 1 of them. How many do I have now?

ⓅⓅⓅⓅⓅⓅ
(6 pennies)
ⓅⓅⓅⓅ
(4 more) How many now?

ⓅⓅⓅⓅⓅⓅⓅⓅⓅⓅ
(10 pennies, lost 1) How many now?

Children use pennies to act out original number stories.

ONGOING ASSESSMENT
Some children may run into difficulty because they will try to add to the 10 pennies. Ask them to start with 10 pennies on their desks, and tell them that they may use only these pennies to act out their stories. If necessary, have them think of a story about a smaller number of pennies.

Illustrate some of the stories with pennies on the overhead or draw pictures on the board.

If some children suggest number models for their stories (for example: 6 + 4 = 10), record the number models on the board. However, number models should not be emphasized at this time.

Have partners pool their pennies and act out and tell penny stories to each other.

2 Ongoing Learning & Practice

◆ Number Writing (*Math Masters,* p. 2)

INDEPENDENT ACTIVITY 👤

Children practice writing the numbers 1 through 6. Have them circle their best numbers when they complete the page.

Portfolio Ideas

◆ Home Link 1.13 (*Math Masters,* p. 158)

Home Connection Have children write their names and today's date at the top of the page.

Children each find a picture of a group of things and tell a number story about it. They bring the pictures to school.

Remind children to keep looking for more examples of numbers to bring to school.

3 Options for Individualizing

◆ EXTRA PRACTICE Telling and Solving Number Stories

PARTNER ACTIVITY 👥 **5–15 min**

Partners combine and mix 2 sets of 0–10 number cards. They put the cards facedown in a stack. Then they take turns doing the following:

▷ One partner draws 2 cards from the top of the deck and tells a number story using those two numbers.

▷ Both partners solve the problem in the story, write their answers on their slates, and compare answers and solution strategies.

Adjusting the Activity If children are having difficulty telling number stories, have them select a subject for the stories—for example, pennies—before they start.

You may want to extend the activity by having children record their stories with illustrations and then combine the illustrated stories to make a Class Number Story Book.

Number Stories

Home Link 1.13

Family Note
"Number story" is another name for what is traditionally called a "story problem" or a "word problem." *Everyday Mathematics* uses the term "number story" to emphasize the fact that the story must involve numbers.
Please return this Home Link to school tomorrow.

1. Find a picture of a group of things, such as animals, people, flowers, or toys.

   Have someone at home help you.

2. Tell a number story about your picture to someone at home.

3. Then glue or tape your picture to this page.

   Answers vary.

HOME LINK MASTER

◆ *Math Masters,* p. 158

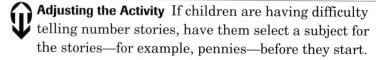

1.14 Unit 1 Review and Assessment

OBJECTIVE To review and assess children's progress on the material covered in Unit 1.

1 Assess Progress

learning goals	activities
1a **Developing Goal** Count by 5s to 40. (**Lessons 1.4, 1.7, and 1.11**)	☐ Oral Assessment, Problem 3
1b **Developing Goal** Count by 2s to 40. (**Lessons 1.9–1.13**)	☐ Oral Assessment, Problem 4
1c **Developing Goal** Write numbers from 1 to 20. (**Lessons 1.4, 1.5, and 1.7–1.11**)	☐ Slate Assessment, Problems 1–7 ☐ Written Assessment, Problems 1, 3, and 6
1d **Developing Goal** Compare pairs of numbers less than 16. (**Lessons 1.2–1.4, 1.6, 1.7, and 1.10**)	☐ Slate Assessment, Problems 1–5 ☐ Written Assessment, Problems 3–5
1e **Developing Goal** Write and count tallies. (**Lessons 1.2, 1.7, 1.8, and 1.12**)	☐ Written Assessment, Problems 1 and 2
1f **Secure Goal** Count up and back by 1s, starting with any number up to and including 20. (**Lessons 1.1–1.5, 1.7, and 1.9–1.11**)	☐ Oral Assessment, Problems 1 and 2 ☐ Written Assessment, Problem 3
1g **Secure Goal** Count up to 20 objects. (**Lessons 1.1–1.5, 1.8, 1.10, and 1.13**)	☐ Slate Assessment, Problems 6 and 7 ☐ Written Assessment, Problem 3

materials

☐ Assessment Master (*Math Masters,* p. 303)

☐ Home Link 1.13

☐ slate

☐ pennies, 2 per child (optional)

☐ Teaching Master (*Math Masters,* p. 3; optional)

☐ number cards (optional)

☐ craft sticks; plastic bags, 11 per group; rubber bands (optional)

☐ half-sheet of paper (optional)

***See* Advance Preparation**

2 Build Background for Unit 2

summaries	materials
Children practice and maintain skills through Home Link activities.	☐ Home Link Masters (*Math Masters,* pp. 159–162)

Each **learning goal** listed above indicates a level of performance that might be expected at this point in the *Everyday Mathematics* K–6 curriculum. For a variety of reasons, the levels indicated may not accurately portray your class's performance.

Additional Information

Background Information For additional information on **Assessment,** see the *Teacher's Reference Manual.*

Advance Preparation For additional information on assessment for Unit 1, see the *Assessment Handbook,* pages 36–38. For assessment checklists, see *Math Masters,* pages 328, 329, and 355–358. *Optional:* Display pictures children brought from home for Home Link 1.13 to use when children share their stories with the class.

For Alternative Assessment Options, prepare number-line sections from *Math Masters,* page 3. (See Advance Preparation in Lesson 1.6.) Write the numbers 10 through 20 on quarter-sheets of paper or on 3" by 5" index cards, cut in half. You will need one set of cards for each small group of children.

Getting Started

Home Link 1.13 Follow-Up

Have children share some of the pictures they brought from home and the number stories they made up to go with their pictures.

Assess Progress

◆ Oral and Slate Assessments

WHOLE-CLASS ACTIVITIES

Instead of doing the oral and slate activities with the whole class, you might want to work with small groups of children, one group at a time, over several days. While you do this, the rest of the class can work on the written review page. It is not necessary to record every child's performance on every problem. Instead, you need to keep a record only of children who are struggling. You can go back later and note children's progress.

If the suggested problems that follow are not appropriate for your class's level of performance, adjust the numbers or the problems themselves to better assess your children's abilities.

Oral Assessment Suggestions

1. Count up by 1s, starting with 8; with 14; with 27; with 45. **Goal 1f**

2. Count back by 1s, starting with 10; with 17; with 23; with 32. **Goal 1f**

3. Count up by 5s to 20; to 40. **Goal 1a**

4. Count up by 2s to 20; to 40. **Goal 1b**

Slate Assessment Suggestions

1. Write the number that is 1 more than 5; than 9; than 12; than 24. **Goals 1c and 1d**

2. Write the number that is 1 less than 4; than 8; than 10; than 21. **Goals 1c and 1d**

3. Write the numbers 7 and 9. Circle the larger one. **Goals 1c and 1d**

4. Write the numbers 3 and 13. Circle the smaller one. **Goals 1c and 1d**

5. Write the numbers 18 and 12. Circle the larger one. **Goals 1c and 1d**

6. The teacher claps hands a given number of times. Children record on their slates how many times the teacher clapped. Clap 6 times; 9 times; 12 times; 20 times. **Goals 1c and 1g**

7. The teacher tells the following number stories. Children record their answers on their slates. If time permits, children share their strategies for how they figured out the answers. (Encourage children to use manipulatives, drawings, doodles, or other strategies to solve the problems.) **Goals 1c and 1g**

    a. Max counted the number of birds he saw on his way to school one morning. He saw 3 in his yard and another 2 along the way. How many birds did Max see on his way to school that morning? 5 birds

    b. Sue began the school year with 7 coloring pencils in her box. Now she has only 6 coloring pencils left. How many coloring pencils has Sue lost? 1 coloring pencil

    c. Brenda got $1 from her father for bringing in the mail all last week. Her mom gave her 3 more dollars for feeding the cat all last week. And Brenda found another dollar in the couch. How much money did Brenda earn and find altogether last week? $5

    d. Jim loved to flip pennies. He decided that he won if the penny came up HEADS. He flipped a penny 10 times. It came up HEADS (and he won) only 4 times. Out of the 10 flips, did he win more times or lose more times? Lost more times How many times did the penny come up TAILS? 6 times

Unit 1 Checking Progress

1. Write the number for each set of tally marks.

___8___ = 卌 ||| ___11___ = 卌 卌 |

2. Make tally marks for each number below.

7 = __卌 ||__   16 = __卌 卌 卌 |__

3. Write the number that is 1 more than 15. ___16___

4. Circle the number that could be the mystery number in this game of Number-Line Squeeze.

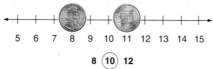

8 (10) 12

5. Circle the winner in this round of *Top-It*.

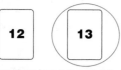

6. Write the three numbers from 1 through 6 that you do the best.

_____

_____

◆ *Math Masters*, p. 303

ASSESSMENT MASTER

◆ Written Assessment (*Math Masters,* p. 303)

INDEPENDENT ACTIVITY

Read the problems on the Unit 1 "Checking Progress" Assessment Master (*Math Masters,* page 303) with the class. If appropriate, complete the page together—that is, wait for children to complete a problem before reading the next one to them. You may want to do an example with the class for each of the problems.

- Write the number for each set of tally marks. (Problem 1) **Goals 1c and 1e**
- Make tally marks for each number. (Problem 2) **Goal 1e**
- Write the number that is more than 15. (Problem 3) **Goals 1c, 1d, 1f, and 1g**
- Circle the number that could be the mystery number in *Number-Line Squeeze*. (Problem 4) **Goal 1d**
- Circle the winner in this round of *Top-It*. (Problem 5) **Goal 1d**
- Write three numbers between 1 and 6 that you do the best. (Problem 6) **Goal 1c**

Circulate and assist as children work.

◆ ALTERNATIVE ASSESSMENT OPTION
Bundle Craft Sticks

SMALL-GROUP ACTIVITY

Use this activity from Lesson 1.4 to assess children's skill in counting objects (rational counting).

Children count, bundle, and label (with numbers) collections of craft sticks. For example, small groups of children might make bags of craft sticks for the numbers 10 through 20. Group members then check one another's work by putting the bags in numerical order and by counting to check that the correct number of sticks is inside each of the bags.

◆ ALTERNATIVE ASSESSMENT OPTION
Play *Top-It*

PARTNER ACTIVITY

Use this game to assess children's skill in comparing numbers. For detailed instructions, see Lesson 1.6.

For each round, children record the two numbers on their papers and circle the larger number. Collect the papers and save them for a portfolio collection. This activity can be repeated later in the year to assess growth in writing and comparing numbers.

✦ ALTERNATIVE ASSESSMENT OPTION
Play *Number-Line Squeeze* (*Math Masters*, p. 3)

WHOLE-CLASS ACTIVITY

Use this game to assess children's skill in comparing and ordering numbers. For detailed instructions, see Lesson 1.6.

Distribute number-line sections (from *Math Masters*, page 3) within an appropriate range.

Variation 1

The entire class (or a small group) plays against the teacher. All children have the same number-line section. The teacher gives a beginning range. Children use pennies as brackets to cover the beginning and ending numbers of that range. The teacher invites a guess from the class and then says, "My number is less than (more than) that." Check to see if children are able to move their brackets correctly. Continue until the number is guessed.

Variation 2

Children play in partnerships while the teacher circulates and makes assessment notes.

2 Build Background for Unit 2

✦ Home Link 1.14: Unit 2 Family Letter
(*Math Masters*, pp. 159–162)

Home Connection This Home Link is a four-page newsletter that introduces parents and guardians to Unit 2's topics and terms. The letter also offers ideas for home-based mathematics activities that are supportive of the classroom work.

Have children write their names and today's date at the top of the first page.

✦ *Math Masters*, pp. 159–162

Unit 2
Everyday Uses of Numbers

overview

In our world, billions of numbers are used in some way every day. Young children use numbers mostly to count objects; to measure the sizes, weights, or capacities of objects; and to identify locations, such as the height of the mercury in a thermometer. Children also use numbers as codes, such as those found in their telephone numbers and addresses.

Teaching the uses of numbers is an important part of the school mathematics experience. It is also important that children be aware from the very beginning that numbers make sense only if they are known in context, usually through the use of labels or units.

Unit 2 introduces children to several uses of numbers—in particular, telling time and counting money. Understanding of these important uses will be developed throughout *First Grade Everyday Mathematics.* Children will also take part in many activities designed to prepare them for addition and subtraction, both as computational skills and as tools for problem solving.

contents

UNIT

2

learning goals in perspective

learning goals	links to the past	links to the future
2a **Developing Goal** Calculate the values of various combinations of pennies and nickels. **(Lessons 2.10–2.13)**	Children were introduced to pennies and nickels in Kindergarten and in Unit 1. Further practice in Unit 1 with skip counting by 5s helped prepare children to count nickels.	Children will use quarters and dollars as they continue their practice with money in grade 1. *(Related Grade 1 lessons: 3.10–3.12, 6.8–6.10, 6.12, 8.1, 8.2, 8.5, 8.7)*
2b **Developing Goal** Find complements of 10. **(Lessons 2.3, 2.4)**	In Kindergarten, children worked with single-digit addition.	Becoming familiar with complements of ten will help children learn basic facts, understand place value, and become skilled with mental computation. *(Related Grade 1 lessons: 3.3, 3.5, 3.6, 3.9, 4.1, 4.2, 4.5–4.9, 4.11, 4.12, 5.8, 5.9, 5.12, 6.1–6.5, 6.7, 6.12, 7.2, 8.8, 8.9)*
2c **Developing Goal** Solve simple addition and subtraction number stories. **(Lesson 2.6–2.8, 2.10, 2.12, and 2.13)**	Children began telling and solving number stories in Kindergarten.	Throughout the grades, children will continue to create and solve number stories. *(Related Grade 1 lessons: 3.6, 5.6–5.8, 8.4)*
2d **Developing/Secure Goal** Count up and back by 1s on the number grid. **(Lessons 2.1–2.4)**	Children practiced counting up and counting back and were introduced to the number grid in Kindergarten. *(Related Grade 1 lesson: 1.5)*	Children will continue to find patterns on the number grid throughout first grade. *(Related Grade 1 lessons: 3.3, 3.4, 4.10, 9.1–9.4)*
2e **Developing/Secure Goal** Tell time to the nearest hour. **(Lessons 2.5, 2.6, and 2.13)**	In Kindergarten, children began telling time to the nearest hour, and were introduced to the minute hand.	Children will tell time to the nearest half-hour in Units 3 and 4, and work with the minute and second hands in Unit 6. *(Related Grade 1 lessons: 3.7, 4.8, 6.10, 6.11)*
2f **Developing/Secure Goal** Exchange pennies for nickels. **(Lesson 2.9–2.11 and 2.13)**	Children were introduced to pennies and nickels in Kindergarten. In Unit 1, practice with skip counting by 5s helped prepare children to count nickels. *(Related Grade 1 lessons: 1.4, 1.7, 1.11)*	Children will continue to practice counting and using money throughout the grades. *(Related Grade 1 lessons: 3.11, 3.12, 6.9, 8.1, 8.2, 8.5, 8.8)*
2g **Secure Goal** Count by 2s to 20. Count by 5s to 50. **(Lesson 2.2, 2.4, 2.7, 2.9, 2.10, and 2.13)**	In Kindergarten, children were introduced to skip counting by 2s, 5s, and 10s. Skip counting was reviewed in Unit 1. *(Related Grade 1 lessons: 1.4, 1.7, 1.9–1.13)*	Proficiency with skip counting by 5s will help children to count money, tell time using analog clocks, and learn multiplication facts in subsequent grades. Skip counting by 2s is related to finding even and odd numbers, and will also help children with counting on and counting back. *(Related Grade 1 lessons: 3.2–3.7, 3.11, 3.12, 4.9, 4.11, 6.10, 8.1, 8.5)*

assessment
ongoing • product • periodic

✓ Informal Assessment

Math Boxes These *Math Journal* pages provide opportunities for cumulative review or assessment of concepts and skills.

Ongoing Assessment: Kid Watching Use the Ongoing Assessment suggestions in the following lessons to make quick, on-the-spot observations about children's understanding of:
• Numeration **(Lessons 2.1, 2.3, 2.4, 2.8, and 2.13)**
• Operations and Computation **(Lessons 2.9 and 2.11)**
• Measurement and Reference Frames **(Lessons 2.5, 2.6, and 2.10)**

Portfolio Ideas Samples of children's work may be obtained from the following assignments:
• Practicing 7s and 8s **(Lesson 2.3)**
• Practicing 9s and 0s **(Lesson 2.5)**
• Telling Time **(Lesson 2.13)**
• Play *Two-Fisted Penny Addition* **(Lesson 2.14)**
• Find 2-Addend Combinations for Sums of 10 **(Lesson 2.14)**

✓ Unit 2 Review and Assessment

Oral and Slate Assessments Use oral or slate assessments during Lesson 2.14 to assess children's progress toward the following learning goals: **Goals 2b, 2c, 2d, 2e, and 2g**

Written Assessment Use a written review during Lesson 2.14 to assess children's progress toward the following learning goals: **Goals 2a, 2e, and 2f**

Performance/Group Assessment Use a small-group activity in Lesson 2.14 to assess children's progress toward the following learning goals: **Goals 2a and 2b**

assessment handbook

For more information on how to use different types of assessment in Unit 2, see the Assessment Overview on pages 45–47 in the *Assessment Handbook*. The following Assessment Masters can be found in the *Math Masters* book:

• Unit 2 Checking Progress, p. 304
• Unit 2 Class Checklist, p. 330
• Unit 2 Individual Profile of Progress, p. 331
• Class Checklist: 1st Quarter, p. 346
• Individual Profile of Progress: 1st Quarter, p. 347
• Class Progress Indicator, p. 358
• Math Logs, pp. 362–364
• Self-Assessment Forms, pp. 365–366
• Interest Inventory, p. 361

problemsolving

A process of modeling everyday situations using tools from mathematics

Encourage children to use a variety of strategies when attacking a given problem—and to explain those strategies. *Strategies children might use in this unit:*

- Using a number grid
- Acting it out
- Modeling with manipulatives
- Using estimation
- Using a diagram
- Using number models

Four Problem-Solving REPRESENTATIONS

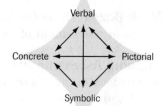

Verbal
Concrete — Pictorial
Symbolic

Lessons that teach *through* problem solving, not just *about* problem solving

Lesson	Activity	Lesson	Activity
2.1	Finding differences between two numbers	2.7	Estimating relative lengths of objects
2.3	Finding complements of 10	2.8	Solving change-to-less number stories
2.5	Estimating time on an hour-hand clock only	2.9	Exchanging pennies for nickels
2.6, 2.13	Solving simple number stories	2.10	Finding the total value of combinations of nickels and dimes
2.7	Solving change-to-more number stories	2.11, 2.12	Recording change-to-more and change-to-less situations

For more information about problem solving in *Everyday Mathematics,* see the *Teacher's Reference Manual*, pp. 197–208.

cross-curricularlinks

science

- Encourage children to discuss other ways of keeping track of time, such as the movement of the sun and moon. **(Lesson 2.5)**

social studies

- Discuss museums with children. **(Lesson 2.2)**
- Discuss community helpers like firefighters, police officers, and nurses, and list their phone numbers. **(Lesson 2.2)**

music

- Sing the song "Paper Clocks" by Hap Palmer while setting clocks to match the times in the song. **(Lesson 2.6)**

language arts

- Discuss the abbreviations A.M. and P.M. **(Lesson 2.5)**
- Discuss the meaning of the word *shorthand* and show how we use shorthand symbols for money notation. **(Lesson 2.11)**
- Discuss using initial consonants to represent coins. **(Lesson 2.9)**

meeting INDIVIDUAL needs

◆ RETEACHING

The following features provide additional instructional support:

Adjusting the Activity
- **Lesson 2.1, Part 1**
- **Lesson 2.3, Part 1**
- **Lesson 2.6, Part 1**
- **Lesson 2.8, Parts 1 & 3**
- **Lesson 2.9, Part 3**
- **Lesson 2.10, Parts 1 & 2**
- **Lesson 2.11, Part 2**

Options for Individualizing
- **Lesson 2.4** Stop-and-Start Counting
- **Lesson 2.11** Acting Out Number Models

◆ ENRICHMENT

The following features suggest enrichment and extension activities:

Adjusting the Activity
- **Lesson 2.1, Part 1**
- **Lesson 2.3, Part 1**
- **Lesson 2.4, Part 2**
- **Lesson 2.5, Part 3**
- **Lesson 2.8, Part 1**
- **Lesson 2.9, Parts 1 & 3**
- **Lesson 2.10, Parts 2 & 3**
- **Lesson 2.11, Part 2**
- **Lesson 2.13, Part 3**

Options for Individualizing
- **Lesson 2.1** Making a Number Line from a Number Grid
- **Lesson 2.2** Classroom Telephone Book
- **Lesson 2.3** Playing *Two-Fisted Penny Addition* with Larger Numbers
- **Lesson 2.4** Combinations of Two Numbers Whose Sum Is 10
- **Lesson 2.5** Illustrating Daily Activities
- **Lesson 2.6** Setting Clocks to Match the Times in a Song
- **Lesson 2.9** Ordering Nickels and Playing *Penny Guessing*
- **Lesson 2.10** Playing *Coin Top-It*
- **Lesson 2.12** Shopping at Playing *Who Am I Thinking Of?*
- **Lesson 2.13** Shopping at the Classroom Store

◆ LANGUAGE DIVERSITY

The following features suggest ways to support children who are acquiring proficiency in English:

Adjusting the Activity
- **Lesson 2.8, Part 1**
- **Lesson 2.9, Part 3**

Options for Individualizing
- **Lesson 2.13** Acting Out Number Models

◆ MULTIAGE CLASSROOM

The following chart lists related activities from the *Kindergarten Teacher's Guide to Activities* and lessons from Grade 2 that can help you meet your instructional needs:

Grade K Pages	34 222 285	68 287 288	87		51	134 191 192	12 137 150	41 88	144 172	41 88 144 172	90 228	90 196 228	90 177 228
Grade 1 Lessons	2.1	2.2	2.3	2.4	2.5	2.6	2.7	2.8	2.9	2.10	2.11	2.12	2.13
Grade 2 Lessons	1.9 7.2		73		1.3 3.3 12.2	1.3 3.3 12.2	4.7 9.2	3.2 3.7 10.1	3.2 3.8 10.1	3.7 3.8 10.1	2.1 4.1 11.1	2.6 11.2	2.1 4.2 11.1

materials

lesson	📖 math masters pages	🧊 manipulative kit items	✂️ other items
2.1	Home Link Masters, p. 163 Teaching Master, p. 8 **See Advance Preparation, p. 88.**	1 die per partnership Class Number Grid Poster number cards	marker glue or tape
2.2	Teaching Master, p. 7 Home Link Master, p. 164		construction paper
2.3	Teaching Masters, pp. 2 and 9 Home Link Master, p. 165 **See Advance Preparation, p. 97.**	slate Class Number Line	pennies
2.4	Home Link Master, p. 166 Teaching Master, p. 10 **See Advance Preparation, p. 101.**	slate	can or container; pennies calculator **See Advance Preparation, p. 101.**
2.5	Teaching Masters, pp. 11–12 Home Link Master, p. 167	slate (optional)	demonstration clock paper door-clock **See Advance Preparation, p. 106.**
2.6	Teaching Masters, pp. 13 and 14 Home Link Master, p. 168		paper plate, glue, brad demonstration clock timer or stopwatch **See Advance Preparation, p. 111.**
2.7	Teaching Masters, pp. 15–17 Home Link Master, p. 169 **See Advance Preparation, p. 116.**	dominoes ruler 1 die per partnership **See Advance Preparation, p. 116.**	objects pennies **See Advance Preparation, p. 116.**
2.8	Home Link Master, p. 170	slate (optional)	pennies Class Data Pad 1 magnifying lens per group large cup or can per partnership **See Advance Preparation, p. 120.**
2.9	Home Link Master, p. 171	slate or scratch paper	1 magnifying lense per group overhead coins (optional) pennies and nickels **See Advance Preparation, p. 125.**
2.10	Home Link Master, p. 172	slate 1 die per partnership Pattern-Block Template	pennies and nickels overhead coins (optional) index cards per partnership
2.11	Home Link Master, p. 173	slate 20 craft sticks number cards	container and cup pennies and nickels number-model cards **See Advance Preparation, p. 135.**
2.12	Home Link Master, p. 174	slate (optional) 2 dice per partnership number cards	20 paper cups demonstration clock (optional)
2.13	Teaching Master, p. 14 Home Link Master, p. 175 **See Advance Preparation, p. 144.**		tool-kit coins 2 large boxes large cards; objects from home **See Advance Preparation, p. 144.**
2.14	Teaching Master, p. 18 Assessment Masters, p. 304, 348, and 349 Home Link Masters, pp. 176–179		demonstration clock pennies and nickels

planningtips

Pacing

Pacing depends on a number of factors, such as children's individual needs and how long your school has been using *Everyday Mathematics*. At the beginning of Unit 2, review your Content by Strand Poster to help you set a monthly pace.

	←——— MOST CLASSROOMS ———→	
SEPTEMBER	OCTOBER	NOVEMBER

Using the Projects

Your class can celebrate fall using several Projects. Project 1 involves classifying, counting and comparing numbers of apples and measuring their girth and weight. For Project 2, children collect, observe, compare, and sort fall leaves. And for Project 3, children estimate the weight and girth of pumpkins, compare pumpkins in several ways, and count pumpkin seeds. The Projects can be found at the back of this book.

Home Communication

Share Home Links 2.1–2.13 with families to help them understand the content and procedures in this unit. At the end of the unit, use Home Link 2.14 to introduce Unit 3. Supplemental information can be found in the *Home Connection Handbook*.

NCTM Standards

Standard	1	2	3	4	5	6	7	8	9	10
Unit 2 Lessons	1-4, 8-13	1, 3, 7, 11, 12	7	2, 4-6, 8-10	7, 8, 11, 12	1-13	1-13	1-13	1-13	1-13

Content Standards
1. Number and Operation
2. Patterns, Functions, and Algebra
3. Geometry and Spatial Sense
4. Measurement
5. Data Analysis, Statistics, and Probability

Process Standards
6. Problem Solving
7. Reasoning and Proof
8. Communication
9. Connections
10. Representations

PRACTICE through Games

Everyday Mathematics uses games to help children develop good fact power and other math skills.

- Practice counting by 1s in *Rolling for 50* **(Lessons 2.1 and 2.7)**
- Compare numbers in *Top-It* **(Lesson 2.1)**
- Find complements of 10 with *Two-Fisted Penny Addition* **(Lessons 2.3, 2.4, and 2.7)**
- Find the total value of coins in *Penny Grab* and *Nickel/Penny Grab* **(Lessons 2.8 and 2.11)**
- Give exposure to addends in *Penny-Cup* **(Lessons 2.8 and 2.11)**
- Estimate exchanging of coins in *Penny Guessing* **(Lesson 2.9)**
- Find the total values and compare with *Coin Top-It* **(Lesson 2.10)**
- Exchange nickels for pennies in *Penny-Nickel Exchange* **(Lesson 2.10)**
- Introduce change-to-more situations in *Penny-Drop Addition* **(Lesson 2.11)**

The notes below highlight the major content ideas presented in Unit 2. These notes may help you establish instructional priorities.

Number Lines and Number Grids (Lesson 2.1 and following)

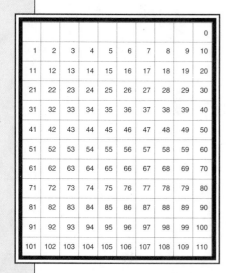

The number line was introduced in Unit 1 as a device for developing counting skills. Number-line activities are extended in Unit 2. As children begin to deal with larger numbers, personal number lines become impractical and are therefore replaced by number grids. These grids will be used throughout first grade to develop counting, addition, subtraction, and place-value skills. Number-grid activities are important in the primary grades.

Numbers All Around Museum (Lesson 2.2)

Everyday Mathematics encourages teachers to assemble classroom "museums"—bulletin-board or table displays where items linked to a topic under discussion can be collected, categorized, and labeled. Such classroom "museums" help to bridge the gap that exists between the classroom and the outside world. The first instance of an *Everyday Mathematics* museum is the Numbers All Around Museum, which includes examples of number uses from this year's first Home Link (Home Link 1.8). Discussed informally as children start bringing them from home, these examples of number uses are dealt with more formally beginning in Lesson 2.2. For more information about museums, see the Management Guide in the *Teacher's Reference Manual.*

Note: Draw attention to the uses of numbers as counts, measures, money, reference frames (for example, dates and addresses), and codes, but don't expect children to be able to classify numbers at this time.

Personal and Class Information (Lesson 2.2)

In Lesson 2.2, children make a classroom telephone book.

Children (as well as adults) are particularly interested in matters that affect them personally. *Everyday Mathematics* tries to take advantage of this fundamental human trait by encouraging children to collect and use numerical information about themselves and to combine this information with information collected by their classmates in order to draw conclusions about the entire class. The process began in Lesson 1.7 when children collected information about their pets. In Lesson 2.2, children analyze their own telephone numbers and use them to make a class telephone book. There will be other such personal activities throughout the year. For example, children will measure their heights in Unit 4 and again at the end of the school year. In addition to using the suggested mathematics activities that occur throughout the program, be on the lookout for opportunities to record counts, measures, dates, or other numbers that are of particular interest to children or that arise in other subject areas, such as language arts, science, and social studies.

Developing Readiness for Addition and Subtraction
(Lesson 2.3 and following)

One of the major first grade goals is for children to begin attaining automaticity with the addition and subtraction facts. This goal will be reached primarily in two ways: through the use of real-life situations to develop an understanding of the meanings of addition and subtraction and through the use of a variety of games to develop facility with the basic facts. In Lesson 2.3, children learn to play *Two-Fisted Penny Addition*. The authors have chosen this activity as a good starting point because of its focus on complements of 10, which are important in developing mental-computation skills. Mathematics games are anything but frivolous. They are excellent avenues for practicing basic skills— avenues that avoid the drudgery of drill sheets and that provide an infinite number of problem combinations. For more information about the game, see page 98 in this book.

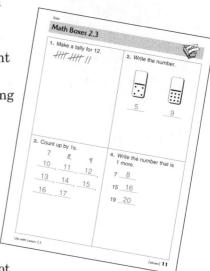

Children's first Math Boxes
practice page

Math Boxes (Lesson 2.3 and following)

Every teacher knows that children seldom "learn" facts or concepts upon first exposure to them, that frequent practice and review are needed, and that children often forget and need reminders of things not explicitly used for some time. The Math Boxes routine is one way to promote ongoing practice and review of concepts and skills over an extended period of time after the first introduction to them. At this stage, most children will need help in reading the Math Boxes directions and understanding what to do, but, as children mature, they will learn to "do Math Boxes" on their own. For more information, see page 99 in this book.

Units and Unit Boxes (Lesson 2.4)

Counts are always counts *of something* (people, buttons, elephants, purple cows, and so on), and measures are meaningless unless they include one or more measure units (inches, meters, pounds, miles per hour, and so on). While some people, including some children, love numbers and number relationships in and of themselves, for most people, numbers make the most sense when they are thought of in real-world contexts. Since it is often tedious to attach a label to every number separately (especially in counting or arithmetic practice), *Everyday Mathematics* encourages the use of unit boxes. For more information about unit boxes, see page 102 in this book.

Unit box

Clocks and Telling Time (Lessons 2.5 and 2.6)

Demonstration clock

The development of time-telling concepts and skills in most young children takes many experiences over an extended period of time. The objective of these two lessons is to continue Kindergarten experiences with clocks. In this unit, the focus is on telling time to the hour on an analog clock (a clock with a minute hand and an hour hand). In units to follow, children will learn to tell time to the half-hour, to the quarter-hour, and then to the nearest 5 minutes and the nearest minute.

A common error children make is to give correct minute readings but incorrect hour readings (usually an hour off). The *Everyday Mathematics* researchers and developers have found that estimating the time with an analog clock that has just an hour hand and no minute hand helps children avoid such errors. When the hour hand is pointing exactly to 3, for example, the time is 3 o'clock. When the hour hand is just before or just after a number, or between two numbers, the time is recorded as "before *x* o'clock," "just after *x* o'clock," or "between *x* and *y* o'clock."

Lesson 2.6 also gives children their first exposure to the division of the day into 24 hours and into A.M. and P.M. times. Formal lessons on digital clocks and digital time notation are postponed to a time when children are able to understand the division of the hour into 60 minutes and the parts of an hour as fractions of 60 minutes.

Money Notation, Coin Values, and Coin Exchanges (Lessons 2.8–2.10)

Children's mastery of money begins with pennies and nickels.

These lessons review and extend interactions begun in Kindergarten. If most children are comfortable with the content of these lessons, move through them at a brisk review pace; then perhaps spend more time on some of the interesting history of and information about specific coins.

If children lack experience with money, do not feel the need to develop mastery of the material in these lessons; there will be frequent practice over an extended period of time. Dimes will be added to the set of coins in Unit 3; quarters, in Unit 5.

If possible, children should use real coins. There is no good substitute for the look and feel of real coins; however, play money is provided in the manipulatives kit. Many teachers ask parents to provide the coins, but you will need extras for the inevitable losses and for children whose families cannot easily supply the coins.

Problem Solving (Lessons 2.7, 2.8, and 2.13)

Problem solving is a creative activity. It involves combining common sense with past experience, trial-and-error with systematic approaches. The ability to solve problems can be developed only with a great deal of experience and through the sharing of ideas and strategies.

Everyday Mathematics encourages children to solve problems in any way they can: by using counters, by drawing pictures or doodles, by using whichever means can help them to model a situation. Along with this intuitive approach, Lessons 2.7 and 2.8 begin to lay the foundation for a systematic approach to solving number-problem stories that involve addition and subtraction. The Mental Math and Reflexes problems in these lessons consist of "change-to-more" and "change-to-less" number stories. As part of the discussion of the solutions to these problems, you are encouraged to display the appropriate situation diagrams. With repeated exposure to these and other kinds of situation diagrams, children will gradually build a framework they may draw upon when solving number stories. Allow time for sharing solution strategies.

Start	Change	End
	↷	

For more information about problem solving, see the Management Guide and Essay 10, which are both found in the *Teacher's Reference Manual.*

Number Models (Lessons 2.11 and 2.12)

Mathematical symbols convey information more compactly than words, but it is important that children have the symbols clearly linked to the words and phrases they replace. In *Kindergarten Everyday Mathematics*, children learned to read the equal symbol (=) as *the same as* and to expect that whatever is on one side of the symbol balances whatever is on the other side. In these two lessons, children use number models to represent change-to-more and change-to-less situations. Again, keep in mind that mastery is not expected at this time; mastery will be achieved via repeated experiences throughout the year.

Quarterly Assessment

If you are planning a quarterly assessment for Units 1–2, you may want to refer to the *Assessment Handbook.* For first quarter assessment checklists, see *Math Masters,* pages 346 and 347.

For **additional information** on the following topics, see the *Teacher's Reference Manual:*	
• calculators	• money
• number uses	• time
• operations and use classes	• number models and number
• problem solving	sentences

2.1

Number Grids

OBJECTIVE To practice counting up and back on the number grid.

summaries	materials

1 Teaching the Lesson

Children play *Rolling for 50* to practice navigating from row to row on the number grid. Using the grid, they practice counting up and back by 1s and finding the difference between two numbers. [Numeration; Operations and Computation]

- ☐ *Math Journal 1* inside back cover and p. 8
- ☐ 1 die per partnership
- ☐ marker
- ☐ Class Number Grid Poster (or transparency of *Math Masters*, p. 7)

***See* Advance Preparation**

2 Ongoing Learning & Practice

Children play *Top-It.* [Numeration]

Children practice and maintain skills through Home Link activities.

- ☐ number cards
- ☐ Home Link Master (*Math Masters*, p. 163)

3 Options for Individualizing

Enrichment Children construct a number line by cutting apart a number grid. [Numeration; Patterns, Functions, and Algebra]

- ☐ Teaching Master (*Math Masters*, p. 8)
- ☐ scissors
- ☐ glue or tape

Additional Information

Advance Preparation For Part 1, display the Class Number Grid Poster where everyone can see it.

Vocabulary • **number grid**

Getting Started

Mental Math and Reflexes

Ask children to turn to the number line on the inside back cover of their journals.

Pose problems like the following (and model the first problem on the Class Number Line):

- Put your finger on 5. Count up 6 hops. Where do you end up? 11

- Put your finger on 12. Count back 3 hops. Where do you end up? 9
Pose more problems like these, as needed.

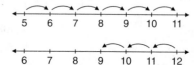

Teaching the Lesson

◆ Playing *Rolling for 50*
(*Math Journal 1,* inside back cover and p. 8)

PARTNER ACTIVITY

As children develop the ability to deal with larger numbers, the number line becomes too limited as an aid to problem solving. For this reason, the **number grid** is introduced at this time.

The purpose of playing *Rolling for 50* is to provide practice navigating on the number grid. At first, children will play the game on the gameboard on journal page 8. On this gameboard, the rows of the number grid are separated from one another—but connected with arrows. This arrangement facilitates moving from row to row. After children have played a couple of games on this gameboard, they should play the game on the standard number grid found on the inside back cover of their journals.

The rules of the game are simple. Players place their markers on START. They take turns rolling a die and moving their markers a specified number of spaces, forward or back. The first player to cross FINISH wins the game. ("FINISH" can be any agreed-upon number, up to and including 50.)

> **Adjusting the Activity** If children are having a difficult time navigating back and forth on the number grid, have them ignore the table on the journal page, start at 1, and move their markers *only forward* the number of spaces shown on the die. When they are proficient at navigating forward, have them start at 50 and move their markers *only backward* the number of spaces shown on the die.

When playing the game on the number grid in their journals, players should begin by placing their markers on START. Players should agree before starting which number on the grid is "the FINISH line."

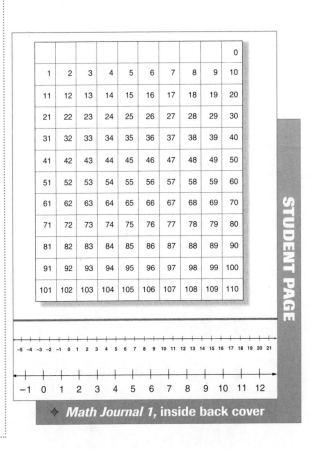

◆ *Math Journal 1,* p. 8

◆ *Math Journal 1,* inside back cover

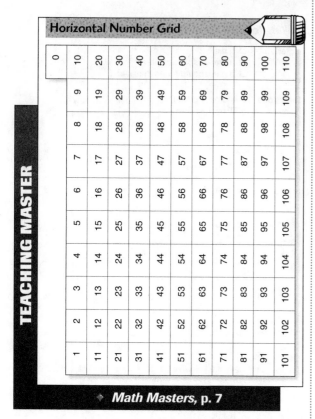

Horizontal Number Grid

0	10	20	30	40	50	60	70	80	90	100	110
	9	19	29	39	49	59	69	79	89	99	109
	8	18	28	38	48	58	68	78	88	98	108
	7	17	27	37	47	57	67	77	87	97	107
	6	16	26	36	46	56	66	76	86	96	106
	5	15	25	35	45	55	65	75	85	95	105
	4	14	24	34	44	54	64	74	84	94	104
	3	13	23	33	43	53	63	73	83	93	103
	2	12	22	32	42	52	62	72	82	92	102
	1	11	21	31	41	51	61	71	81	91	101

TEACHING MASTER

◆ *Math Masters*, p. 7

NOTE: Counting up and back on the number grid and finding the number of spaces between two numbers on the grid help prepare children to use the grid for addition and subtraction.

◆ Introducing Number-Grid Counting
(*Math Masters*, p. 7)

WHOLE-CLASS ACTIVITY

Use the Class Number Grid Poster (or an overhead transparency of *Math Masters*, page 7) as children follow along on the number grid on the inside back cover of their journals.

Begin by counting up by 1s. *For example:*

- Start at 12 and count up 5 spaces. Where do you end up? 17
- Start at 38 and count up 9 spaces. Where do you end up? 47

Next, count back by 1s. *For example:*

- Start at 26 and count back 4 spaces. Where do you end up? 22
- Start at 13 and count back 6 spaces. Where do you end up? 7

Finally, count up by 1s to find the number of spaces between two numbers. *For example:*

- Start at 21 and count up to 27. How many steps did you take? 6 steps
- Start at 28 and count up to 35. How many steps did you take? 7 steps

ONGOING ASSESSMENT
This is the first time that children count up and back on the number grid beginning with numbers other than 1. Assess your class's proficiency with this skill. Watch for children who count "1" as they put their fingers on the starting number. They should put their fingers on the starting number and then count "1" as they move to the next number. Many children may still struggle with navigating up and back on the number grid. Number-grid problems like these will be repeated in future lessons.

Adjusting the Activity If the children in your class are more skilled, you may want to discuss the numbers that would appear in the empty spaces to the left of 0 on the number grid. These are called *negative numbers*. Remind children that they have seen such numbers before—on thermometers to show temperatures below 0 degrees.

② Ongoing Learning & Practice

◆ Playing *Top-It*

PARTNER ACTIVITY

Children practice comparing numbers skills by playing *Top-It*. For detailed instructions, see Lesson 1.6.

◆ Home Link 2.1 (*Math Masters*, p. 163)

 Home Connection Children record their home telephone numbers and emergency daytime telephone numbers, including area codes. These numbers will be used in Lesson 2.2, so emphasize that children should bring their completed Home Links to school the next school day.

③ Options for Individualizing

◆ ENRICHMENT Making a Number Line from a Number Grid (*Math Masters*, p. 8)

SMALL-GROUP ACTIVITY 15–30 min

Have children cut along the outline of the grid and then cut out each row (–9 through 0, 1 through 10, 11 through 20, 21 through 30, 31 through 40, and 41 through 50). Then have them glue or tape the rows end to end to make a number line.

Discuss how the number grid has become a number line. The two arrows show that the number line can go further in both directions. The tick marks help to show a location for each number.

Some teachers report that children have fun rolling up their long number lines and keeping them for a few days.

Make a Number Line

Cut out each row. Glue or tape the rows together to make a number line.

41	31	21	11	1	–9
42	32	22	12	2	–8
43	33	23	13	3	–7
44	34	24	14	4	–6
45	35	25	15	5	–5
46	36	26	16	6	–4
47	37	27	17	7	–3
48	38	28	18	8	–2
49	39	29	19	9	–1
50	40	30	20	10	0
↓	Glue	Glue	Glue	Glue	Glue

Math Masters, p. 8

TEACHING MASTER

2.2 Numbers All Around

OBJECTIVES To explore various uses of numbers; and to introduce the parts of telephone numbers.

summaries	materials

1 Teaching the Lesson

Children discuss the examples of numbers they brought from home and some ways in which numbers are used. They record personal information and important telephone numbers in their journals and learn about the parts of telephone numbers. [Numeration; Data and Chance]

□ *Math Journal 1*, p. 9 and inside back cover
□ Home Link 2.1
□ Teaching Master (*Math Masters*, p. 7; optional)
See **Advance Preparation**

2 Ongoing Learning & Practice

Children practice writing the numbers 7 and 8. [Numeration]

Children practice and maintain skills through Home Link activities.

□ *Math Journal 1*, p. 10
□ Home Link Master (*Math Masters*, p. 164)

3 Options for Individualizing

Enrichment Children make class telephone books.
[Numeration]

□ quarter-sheets of writing paper
□ quarter-sheets of construction paper (optional)

Additional Information

Advance Preparation For Part 1, display the Class Number Grid Poster.

Note that, beginning in Lesson 1.8, children were asked to bring examples of numbers from home. These numbers can be displayed on a bulletin board or in an area designated as the Numbers All Around Museum. You might set up separate areas in the museum for various categories of numbers—for example, counts (such as numbers of children, apples, or books), measures (such as the lengths, weights, or volumes of various objects), reference frames (such as clocks, calendars, thermometers, or addresses), identification numbers (such as license plate numbers or telephone numbers), and money (cost, value, and so on).

Have a list of children's home phone numbers available for children who have not completed Home Link 2.1. You will also need the phone numbers of your local police and fire stations.

Vocabulary • **area code** • **prefix**

Getting Started

Mental Math and Reflexes

Say the special first grade chant: "2, 4, 6, 8, first graders are really great!" Then count by 2s. You might use the following variation of the whisper-and-shout routine: The leader (you or a child) forms the front of a "train" (like a bunny-hop line). The children follow behind the leader, each child holding on to the waist of the child in front. They think *1*, hop and say "2," pause and think *3*, hop and say "4," pause and think *5*, hop and say "6," and so on.

Have children turn to the number line on the inside back cover of their journals.

• Start at 8 on the number line. Count up 6 hops. Where do you end up? 14

Pose similar problems. Children should end up on a number that is no greater than 20.

Have children use the number grid to solve the following problem.

• Start at 27 on the number grid. Count up 9 spaces. Where do you end up? 36

Pose similar problems, starting at numbers greater than 20. Limit the number of spaces to count up.

Home Link 2.1 Follow-Up

Discuss examples of numbers children have brought from home.

Note which children do not have Home Link 2.1 and will therefore need to get their telephone numbers from your list.

1 Teaching the Lesson

◆ Discussing Uses of Numbers

WHOLE-CLASS DISCUSSION

Tell children that they will make a Numbers All Around Museum in which they will display the numbers they bring from home. Ask them to share some of the numbers they have brought so far and to talk about them. (These numbers can be displayed on a bulletin board or in an area designated as the Numbers All Around Museum.)

Discuss some of the ways we use numbers in everyday life. To get the discussion started, you might elicit some uses of numbers by asking questions like the following:

• How old are you? What does this number tell about you?
  Your age

Social Studies Link

Ask children what they know about museums.
A museum is a place where artistic, historic, or scientific objects are displayed and cared for.

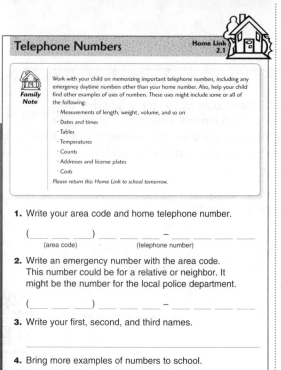

Family Note

Work with your child on memorizing important telephone numbers, including any emergency daytime numbers other than your home number. Also, help your child find other examples of uses of numbers. These uses might include some or all of the following:

· Measurements of length, weight, volume, and so on
· Dates and times
· Tables
· Temperatures
· Counts
· Addresses and license plates
· Costs

Please return this Home Link to school tomorrow.

1. Write your area code and home telephone number.

(___ ___ ___) ___ ___ ___ – ___ ___ ___ ___
(area code) · (telephone number)

2. Write an emergency number with the area code. This number could be for a relative or neighbor. It might be the number for the local police department.

(___ ___ ___) ___ ___ ___ – ___ ___ ___ ___

3. Write your first, second, and third names.

_____

4. Bring more examples of numbers to school.

Math Masters, p. 163

HOME LINK MASTER

Information about Me

My first name is _____

My second name is _____

My last name is _____

I am _____ years old.
Put candles on your cake.

My area code and home telephone number are

(___ ___ ___) ___ ___ ___ – ___ ___ ___ ___
(area code) (telephone number)

Important Phone Numbers

Emergency number: ___ ___ ___ Answers vary.

Police station number:

(___ ___ ___) ___ ___ ___ – ___ ___ ___ ___

Fire station number:

(___ ___ ___) ___ ___ ___ – ___ ___ ___ ___

STUDENT PAGE

◆ *Math Journal 1, p. 9*

- What do you do when you want to phone your grandmother? Dial, or key in, her telephone number. How do the numbers that make up her telephone number help you? The numbers tell you which buttons to dial, or press, on the telephone.

- How much does popcorn cost at the movies? How does this number help you? It tells you how much money you need to have.

- How do you find your favorite television show? Look up the channel in the TV listings. How does the number of the channel help you? It tells you which buttons to press on the remote control.

- How do you know when to watch your favorite television show? Look up the time in the TV listings. What does this number tell you? It tells you what time the show starts.

- How do you know which tool kit is yours? How does the identification number help you? It tells you to whom each tool kit belongs.

- How can you find out where someone lives? Look up the person's address in the telephone book. How does the number in the address help you? It tells you in which house or building a person lives.

Continue as long as children seem interested.

Remind children to keep looking for different uses of numbers to add to the Numbers All Around Museum.

◆ Recording Personal Information
(*Math Masters*, p. 163; *Math Journal 1*, p. 9)

WHOLE-CLASS ACTIVITY

Ask children to open their journals to page 9. Point out that on the top half of the page, children are asked to fill in personal information—their names, ages, and telephone numbers. Have them copy this information from their Home Links. They should also draw the appropriate number of candles on the cake.

Ask the following questions:

- Does anyone have more than three names? Some children may have two middle names or double last names. Some children may suggest that a nickname is another name.

- What else can we call a second name? A middle name

✦ Parts of Telephone Numbers
(*Math Journal 1*, p. 9)

WHOLE-CLASS ACTIVITY 👥👥👥👥

Write the school telephone number on the board. Discuss the different parts of the telephone number: the **area code**, the **prefix** (the first three digits after the area code), and the rest of the number. Explain how each of these three parts is used. The area code identifies the section of the country in which the school is located—it may be the state, a part of the state, the city, or a part of the city. The prefix identifies a smaller part of the area-code section—it may be the town or neighborhood in which the school is located. The last four digits identify the specific location of the telephone—in the school itself.

Have children record their telephone numbers in their journals. Ask someone to name his or her area code and record it on the board.

Ask the following questions:

• Does anyone have a different area code?

• Why do a number of children in our class have the same area code? They all live in the same neighborhood.

Next, find out whether there are children whose phone numbers do not have the same prefix. If so, record the number of children for each prefix in a tally chart.

Finally, have children record the phone numbers for emergencies (911) and for your local police and fire stations. Briefly discuss why these numbers are so important. Point out that the 911 number is a special phone number.

• What are some advantages of having a 3-digit emergency number? It is easy to memorize. It works in every part of the country—so there is no need to know the area code.

🔵 **Social Studies Link** Discuss the functions of community helpers, such as doctors, nurses, and librarians. You might have children write and illustrate simple sentences about helpers in your community, listing the advertised phone number for each category of helper.

NOTE: Children whose parents did not want to supply their home phone numbers can record the school phone number instead.

Class Telephone Prefixes	
Prefix	Number of Students
753	~~HH~~ III
789	IIII

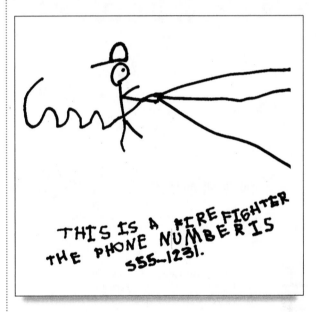

It is important for children to learn emergency numbers.

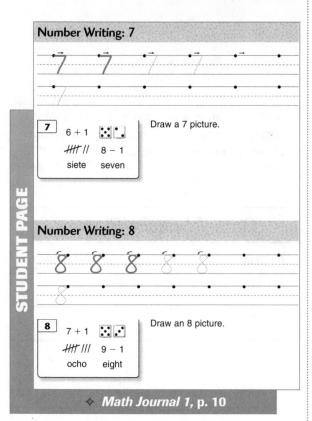

Number Writing: 7

7 7

7   6 + 1   Draw a 7 picture.
   ‖‖ //   8 - 1
   siete   seven

Number Writing: 8

8 8 8 8 8
8

8   7 + 1   Draw an 8 picture.
   ‖‖ ///   9 - 1
   ocho   eight

◆ *Math Journal 1,* p. 10

STUDENT PAGE

 Ongoing Learning & Practice

◆ Writing the Numbers 7 and 8
(*Math Journal 1*, p. 10)

INDEPENDENT ACTIVITY

Have children practice writing the numbers 7 and 8. Remind them to take their time. Tell them that the arrows show the most efficient and easiest way to form the numbers.

When children finish their work, have them circle their best effort for each number.

Have children draw pictures to represent the numbers 7 and 8.

◆ Home Link 2.2 (*Math Masters*, p. 164)

Home Connection Children practice counting for someone at home. They explain to someone at home how to use the number grid to help with counts.

Options for Individualizing

◆ ENRICHMENT Making Classroom Telephone Books

SMALL-GROUP ACTIVITY   **30+ min**

Each child makes a book containing enough quarter-sheets of paper so that each child in the class can write on one side of a page. For example, if there are 24 children in the class, each book will have 12 quarter-sheets. Children might also make covers for their telephone books.

Children write their names and phone numbers in one another's books. They can exchange books as they like, or you may want to structure the activity by having children pass the books around the room in a particular order.

Continue this activity for several days until everyone has a book with information about each child in the class.

Counting Up and Back

Home Link 2.2

Family Note To reinforce various types of counting, listen as your child counts by 1s and 10s. Children love to count for someone, and doing so provides wonderful practice in this essential first grade skill.
Please return this Home Link to school tomorrow.

1. Count for someone at home.
   Count up by 1s, starting with 1. I counted to _____.

2. Count back by 1s. Start with 20 or the highest number you can. I started with _____.

3. Count up by 10s. Start with 10. I counted to _____.

4. Count back by 10s. Start with 50 or the highest number you can. I started with _____.

5. Explain to someone at home how to use the number grid to help with counts. Answers vary.

									0
1	2	3	4	5	6	7	8	9	10
11	12	13	14	15	16	17	18	19	20
21	22	23	24	25	26	27	28	29	30
31	32	33	34	35	36	37	38	39	40
41	42	43	44	45	46	47	48	49	50
51	52	53	54	55	56	57	58	59	60
61	62	63	64	65	66	67	68	69	70
71	72	73	74	75	76	77	78	79	80
81	82	83	84	85	86	87	88	89	90
91	92	93	94	95	96	97	98	99	100
101	102	103	104	105	106	107	108	109	110

◆ *Math Masters,* p. 164

HOME LINK MASTER

2.3 Complements of 10

OBJECTIVES To explore complements of 10; and to introduce the Math Boxes routine.

summaries	materials
1 Teaching the Lesson	
Children play *Two-Fisted Penny Addition* with 10 pennies. They discuss the need for practice and complete their first Math Boxes page. [Numeration; Operations and Computation]	☐ *Math Journal 1,* p. 11 and inside back cover ☐ Class Number Line ☐ Home Link 2.2 ☐ Teaching Master (*Math Masters,* p. 9; optional) ☐ 10 pennies ☐ slate
2 Ongoing Learning & Practice	
Children practice writing the numbers 7 and 8. [Numeration] Children practice and maintain skills through Home Link activities.	☐ Teaching Master (*Math Masters,* p. 2) ☐ Home Link Master (*Math Masters,* p. 165) ***See* Advance Preparation**
3 Options for Individualizing	
Enrichment Children play *Two-Fisted Penny Addition* with more than 10 pennies. [Numeration; Operations and Computation] **Extra Practice** Children explore complements of 10. [Numeration]	☐ pennies (more than 10) ☐ slate ☐ *Minute Math®,* pp. 8 and 9

Additional Information

Background Information For additional information on Math Boxes, see **Managing the Curriculum** in the *Teacher's Reference Manual.*

Advance Preparation For Part 2, make a copy of *Math Masters,* page 2. On this copy, write the first "7" on the first line of each half of the page and the first "8" on the third line of each half. Then make enough copies of the page so that each child will have a half-sheet. Cut the pages in half. Save the original *Math Masters,* page 2 for later use.

Vocabulary • Math Boxes

Getting Started

Mental Math and Reflexes

Have children count up and back by 5s and 10s through 50. Then have them turn to the number line on the inside back cover of their journals and use it to solve problems like the following: *Start at 15. Count back 8 hops. Where do you end up?* 7 Pose similar problems, using starting numbers no greater than 20. Then have children use the number grid to solve problems like the following: *Start at 38. Count back 6 spaces. Where do you end up?* 32 Pose similar problems, using starting numbers greater than 20 and limiting the number of spaces to count back.

Home Link 2.2 Follow-Up

Children share how high they counted by 1s and by 10s. Invite them to explain how they used the number grid to help with their counts.

NOTE: Some teachers like to take this opportunity to review right and left by asking children to say, "I have (so many) pennies in my right hand and (so many) pennies in my left hand." If you choose to do this, note that some children may still be struggling to identify right and left. One suggestion is to put miniature handprints on children's desks labeled *left* and *right*.

1 Teaching the Lesson

✦ Playing *Two-Fisted Penny Addition*

WHOLE-CLASS ACTIVITY

Have children each take out 10 pennies. Then ask them to grab a handful of pennies with one hand and to pick up the rest with the other hand. Ask volunteers to tell the numbers of pennies they have in each hand. Record each pair of numbers in two columns on the board. As you record the numbers, be sure to say what they represent. *For example:* "You have 3 pennies in one hand and 7 pennies in the other hand." Using such language helps to reinforce the idea that each number is a count of real objects.

ONGOING ASSESSMENT

Watch for children whose number pairs do not add up to 10. Ask them to count aloud the number of pennies in each hand. Some children may observe that the numbers in a person's two hands always add up to 10 pennies, particularly since each person started out with 10 pennies—but do not expect all children to understand this fact at this time.

Adjusting the Activity If children are having difficulty with this activity, draw two large hands on the board and record the numbers of pennies inside the outlines of the hands, both as numbers and as circles. Encourage children to draw such circles on their slates. Then they can count the circles before recording their answers. You might also give each child a copy of *Math Masters,* page 9. Children can then put the pennies on the two hands and count them. Notice that the hands are pictured palm up.

Have children continue to perform this activity in partnerships, recording the number of pennies in each of their hands on their slates.

 Adjusting the Activity Challenge children to *predict* the number of pennies in the second hand before counting them. They can write down their predictions and then count the pennies to check them. Ask children how many pennies there are in all in both hands. 10

✦ Introducing the Math Boxes Routine

WHOLE-CLASS DISCUSSION

Ask children whether anyone is learning to play a musical instrument, to dance, to ride a two-wheeler, to do tricks with a yo-yo, or to play a sport, such as soccer, baseball, or basketball.

• What would happen if you never practiced?

• Can someone explain the meaning of the expression "Practice makes perfect"?

Explain that to become good at mathematics, it is necessary to practice one's mathematics skills. In *Everyday Mathematics,* one of the ways we practice these skills is by solving sets of problems called **Math Boxes.**

✦ Math Boxes 2.3 (*Math Journal 1,* p. 11)

INDEPENDENT ACTIVITY

 Mixed Review Go over the problems so that children understand what they are to do for each one. Then have children complete the journal page independently or with a partner. When they have solved the problems, briefly go over the answers.

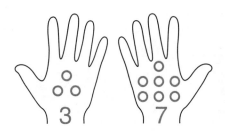

To help children with this activity, draw two large hands on the board and record the numbers of pennies inside the outlines of the hands.

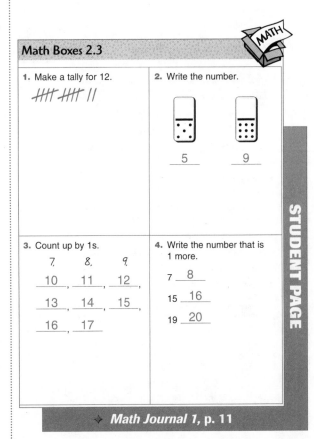

Math Boxes 2.3

1. Make a tally for 12.

   ~~HHT~~ ~~HHT~~ //

2. Write the number.

   5   9

3. Count up by 1s.

   7, 8, 9
   10, 11, 12,
   13, 14, 15,
   16, 17

4. Write the number that is 1 more.

   7 _8_
   15 _16_
   19 _20_

STUDENT PAGE

✦ *Math Journal 1,* p. 11

Children are given the opportunity
to analyze their work.

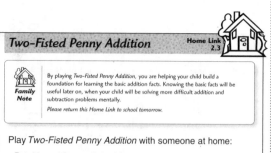

Two-Fisted Penny Addition

Home Link
2.3

Family Note By playing *Two-Fisted Penny Addition*, you are helping your child build a foundation for learning the basic addition facts. Knowing the basic facts will be useful later on, when your child will be solving more difficult addition and subtraction problems mentally.

Please return this Home Link to school tomorrow.

Play *Two-Fisted Penny Addition* with someone at home:

• Put 10 pennies on the table.

• Grab some pennies with one hand.
  Pick up the rest with the other hand.

• On a piece of paper, draw 2 large circles to show hands.
  Place 1 pile of pennies in each circle.

• Count the pennies on each circle.

• Write how many pennies are on each circle.

• Take turns with your partner.

1. Start with 10 pennies.   **2.** Start with 15 pennies.

Number of Pennies in One Hand	Number of Pennies in the Other Hand	Number of Pennies in One Hand	Number of Pennies in the Other Hand

Answers vary.

✦ Math Masters, p. 165

HOME LINK MASTER

Ongoing Learning & Practice

✦ **Practicing the Numbers 7 and 8**
(*Math Masters,* p. 2)

INDEPENDENT ACTIVITY

Pass out the half-sheets from *Math Masters,* page 2. Have children practice writing the numbers 7 and 8. Have them circle their best effort for each number after they complete the page.

Portfolio Ideas

✦ **Home Link 2.3** (*Math Masters,* p. 165)

Home Connection Children show someone at home how to play *Two-Fisted Penny Addition.* They play one game with 10 pennies and a second game with 15 pennies.

Options for Individualizing

✦ **ENRICHMENT** Playing *Two-Fisted Penny Addition* with Larger Numbers

PARTNER ACTIVITY   15–30 min

Partners pool their pennies and play *Two-Fisted Penny Addition* using more than 10 pennies.

✦ **EXTRA PRACTICE** Minute Math

SMALL-GROUP ACTIVITY   5–15 min

To offer children more experience with complements of 10, see the following pages in *Minute Math:*

Basic Routines: pp. 8 and 9

2.4 Unit Labels for Numbers

OBJECTIVE To introduce the need for unit labels for numbers.

summaries	materials
1 Teaching the Lesson	
The need for unit labels for numbers used in counting and measuring is discussed, and the unit box is introduced as a device for recording such unit labels. Children then practice counting and using unit boxes to reinforce the idea that counting numbers always refer to a unit. [Numeration]	☐ Home Link 2.3 ☐ can or container ☐ 20 pennies ***See* Advance Preparation**
2 Ongoing Learning & Practice	
Children practice entering numbers in their calculators. They also practice writing the numbers 9 and 0. [Numeration] Children practice and maintain skills through Math Boxes and Home Link activities.	☐ *Math Journal 1,* pp. 12 and 13 ☐ Home Link Master (*Math Masters,* p. 166) ☐ calculator ***See* Advance Preparation**
3 Options for Individualizing	
Enrichment Children find all possible combinations of pennies in *Two-Fisted Penny Addition* using 10 pennies. [Operations and Computation; Patterns, Functions, and Algebra] **Reteaching** Children practice stop and start counting. [Numeration] **Extra Practice** Children review skip counting. [Operations and Computation]	☐ *Math Journal 1,* inside back cover ☐ Teaching Master (*Math Masters,* p. 10; 2 per partnership) ☐ pennies ☐ slate ☐ *Minute Math®,* pp. 29 and 31 ***See* Advance Preparation**

Additional Information

Background Information For additional information on unit labels, unit boxes, and calculators, see **Managing the Curriculum** and **Tools** in the *Teacher's Reference Manual.*

Advance Preparation For Part 1, you will need a can or container that makes a loud sound when pennies are dropped into it. For Part 2, mark the calculators with children's tool-kit numbers.

For the first activity in Part 3, make 1 copy of *Math Masters,* page 10. Store the original for later use and write "10" on the copy in the blank next to the word "pennies." Make 2 copies for each partnership.

Vocabulary • **unit** • **unit box**

Getting Started

Mental Math and Reflexes

Have children say the special first grade chant: "2, 4, 6, 8, first graders are really great!"

Then have children turn to the number line on the inside back cover of their journals and use it to solve problems like the following:

- *Start at 7. Count up to 16. How many hops did you take?* 9
- *Start at 12. Count up to 19. How many hops did you take?* 7

Pose similar problems having ending numbers no greater than 20.

Then have children use the number grid on the inside back cover of their journals to solve problems like the following:

- *Start at 54. Count up to 60. How many spaces did you move?* 6
- *Start at 37. count up to 48. How many spaces did you move?* 11

Pose similar problems, using starting numbers greater than 20 and limiting the number of spaces between the two numbers.

Home Link 2.3 Follow-Up

Have volunteers share their results from playing *Two-Fisted Penny Addition*.

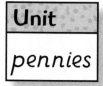

NOTE: Numbers do not necessarily stand for counts of objects; for example, the number 5 may refer to a measure of 5 feet; to a place in an ordered sequence, such as the 5th child in line; or to a code, such as Channel 5. Encourage children to give examples of number uses other than counts of objects.

Teaching the Lesson

◆ Labeling Numbers with Units

WHOLE-CLASS DISCUSSION

Write the number 5 on the board and tell the class that this number might stand for all sorts of things—for example, 5 fingers, 5 desks, or 5 pennies. Ask children to suggest other things the number 5 might stand for.

Ask children to point out 5 of something in the classroom such as 5 crayons or 5 windows. Repeat this activity using other numbers, including numbers in your Numbers All Around Museum. Emphasize that numbers that are used for counting or measuring always refer to units, such as nickels, eyes, miles, or pounds.

◆ Introducing the Unit Box

WHOLE-CLASS ACTIVITY

In *Everyday Mathematics,* a device called a **unit box** is often used as a reminder of the unit to which numbers refer.

Draw a unit box on the board. (See margin.) Tell children that they will be counting pennies and that you are writing the word "pennies" in the unit box as a reminder of what is being counted.

Start with an empty can or container. Show children that the can is empty. Then drop pennies into the can while children listen and count silently. After you stop, ask how many pennies are in the can. Then empty the contents of the can and have someone count the pennies to check the answer. Repeat this routine a few more times, using different numbers of pennies. As a variation, you might tell children that you want to drop a certain number of pennies into the can and that they are to say "Stop!" when you reach that number. ("I want to drop 15 pennies into the can. Tell me when to stop!")

◆ Using the Unit Box in a Counting Routine

WHOLE-CLASS ACTIVITY

Ask someone to suggest a new unit for the unit box. (It need not be something in the room.) Encourage children to come up with imaginative units, such as cats' feet, or units they especially like, such as brownies or apples.

Have a child start with 23 and count by 1s. The child should continue counting until you say "Stop!" Then point to another child, who then continues counting from the number where the last child left off.

Repeat the process as time allows. Each time, ask for a new suggestion to write in the unit box, and begin with the highest numbers you feel are appropriate for your class. Challenge more skilled children to do some "stop-and-start" counting by 2s, 5s, and 10s.

You might also vary the routine by having small groups of children count in unison.

2 Ongoing Learning & Practice

◆ Introducing Calculators

WHOLE-CLASS ACTIVITY

Give a calculator to each child. Tell children that the calculators are to be kept in their tool kits. Give children a few minutes to play with their calculators. Then ask them what they already know or may have discovered about calculators.

A basic calculator used in grades K–3

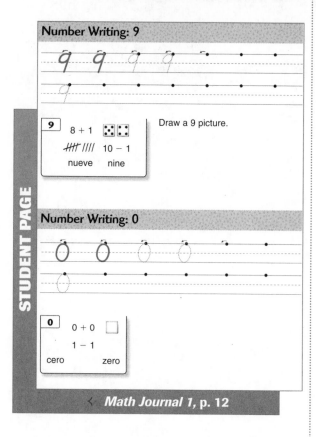

Number Writing: 9

9 9 9 9

9

9	8 + 1		Draw a 9 picture.
	⫫⫫ ////	10 − 1	
	nueve	nine	

Number Writing: 0

0 0 0 0

0

0	0 + 0	☐
	1 − 1	
	cero	zero

NOTE: The "Clear" key may be labeled differently on your calculators. *For example:* [CE/C] or [ON/C].

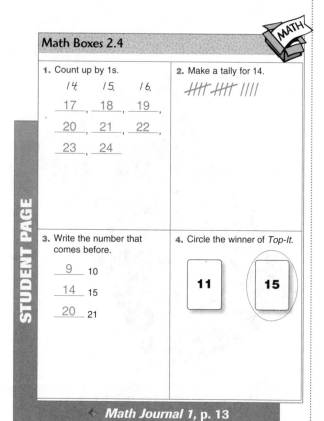

Math Boxes 2.4

1. Count up by 1s.

14, 15, 16,

17 , 18 , 19 ,

20 , 21 , 22

23 , 24

2. Make a tally for 14.

⫫⫫ ⫫⫫ ////

3. Write the number that comes before.

9 10

14 15

20 21

4. Circle the winner of *Top-It*.

| 11 | 15 |

To have children practice entering and clearing numbers, you might direct them as follows:

- Find the number for your age on the calculator. Press that key so that the calculator shows your age. Then find the **ON/C** key on your calculator. The letter "C" stands for the word "Clear," which means, "Erase the numbers in the calculator display." Clear your calculators by pressing the **ON/C** key.

- Enter the number of windows in the room. Then clear your calculator.

- Enter the number of teachers in the room. Clear.

- Enter the number of children who are absent. Clear.

- Enter the number of elephants in the classroom. Clear.

- Enter the number 19. Clear.

 Adjusting the Activity Challenge children to enter the number of hours in a day.

✦ Writing the Numbers 9 and 0
(*Math Journal 1*, p. 12)

INDEPENDENT ACTIVITY 👤

Have children practice writing the numbers 9 and 0. Remind them to take their time and that the arrows show them the most efficient and easiest way to form the numbers.

When children finish their number-writing practice, have them circle their best effort for each number.

Have children draw pictures to represent the number 9.

Finally, ask the following questions:

- Can anyone make up a zero number story? Example: How many children in the class have 3 ears?

- How would you draw a 0 picture? Just a blank space because "zero things" means that there is "no thing." For example, "zero apples" means that there are no apples.

✓ ONGOING ASSESSMENT
This activity provides an early opportunity to observe what the children know about the number zero. The number zero may pose special conceptual problems for some children and may need to be discussed with the group as a whole.

◆ **Math Boxes 2.4** (*Math Journal 1*, p. 13)

INDEPENDENT ACTIVITY

Mixed Review This journal page provides opportunities for cumulative review or assessment of concepts and skills.

◆ **Home Link 2.4** (*Math Masters*, p. 166)

Home Connection Children ask someone to write a number. Then they write the number that comes *before* and the number that comes *after* the number the person wrote.

---

3 Options for Individualizing

◆ ENRICHMENT **Combinations of Two Numbers Whose Sum Is 10** (*Math Masters*, p. 10)

PARTNER ACTIVITY   **15–30 min**

Partners work together to find all possible combinations for *Two-Fisted Penny Addition*, using 10 pennies. Children record their results on *Math Masters*, page 10. There are 11 possible combinations if combinations such as 9–1 and 1–9 are counted as two distinct combinations and if 10–0 and 0–10 are included.

◆ RETEACHING **Stop-and-Start Counting**

SMALL-GROUP ACTIVITY   **5–15 min**

Do stop-and-start counts by 1s, 2s, 5s, and 10s as appropriate while children follow along on their number grids (on the inside back covers of their journals). Have children use their index fingers to show where the count stopped and then move their fingers to the next number in the count before continuing.

◆ EXTRA PRACTICE **Minute Math**

SMALL-GROUP ACTIVITY   **5–15 min**

To offer children more experience with skip counting, see the following pages in *Minute Math:*

Counting: pp. 29 and 31

Family Note When working with "before" and "after" numbers in the table below, start with small numbers—up to 15. Then, if your child is doing well, increase the size of the numbers. Also, ask your child to suggest numbers to write in the middle column of the table.
Please return this Home Link to school tomorrow.

Ask someone to write a number in the middle column.

• Write the number that comes *after* that number.
• Write the number that comes *before* that number.

Try this with many different numbers. Answers vary.

	Before	Number	After
Example	8	9	10

◆ *Math Masters*, p. 166

HOME LINK MASTER

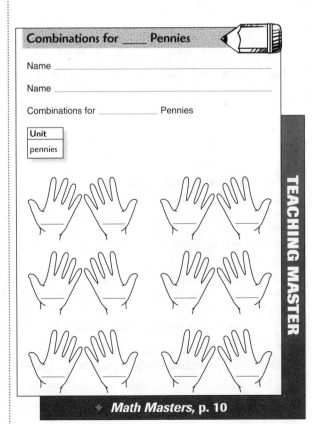

Combinations for _____ Pennies

Name _____

Name _____

Combinations for _____ Pennies

Unit
pennies

◆ *Math Masters*, p. 10

TEACHING MASTER

2.5 Analog Clocks

OBJECTIVE To introduce the analog clock.

summaries	materials

1 Teaching the Lesson

Children discuss some of the uses of clocks and watches. They observe the movement of the hour hand in relation to the movement of the minute hand. They estimate the time shown on a clock that has an hour hand only. [Numeration; Measurement and Reference Frames]

- ☐ Teaching Master (*Math Masters,* p. 11)
- ☐ Home Link 2.4
- ☐ demonstration clock
- ☐ demonstration clock with an hour hand only
- ☐ paper door-clock

***See* Advance Preparation**

2 Ongoing Learning & Practice

Children practice writing the numbers 9 and 0. [Numeration]

Children practice and maintain skills through Math Boxes and Home Link activities.

- ☐ *Math Journal 1,* p. 14
- ☐ Teaching Master (*Math Masters,* p. 2)
- ☐ slate (optional)
- ☐ Home Link Master (*Math Masters,* p. 167)

***See* Advance Preparation**

3 Options for Individualizing

Enrichment Children make drawings of some of their daily activities. For each drawing, they show the time when they usually do the activity by drawing the hands on a clock face. [Measurement and Reference Frames]

- ☐ Teaching Master (*Math Masters,* p. 12)
- ☐ scissors
- ☐ demonstration clock

***See* Advance Preparation**

Additional Information

Advance Preparation For Part 1, you need a demonstration clock with an hour hand only. You can make this demonstration clock by making a copy of *Math Masters,* page 11 on tagboard and attaching the hour hand to it with a brad. Also, if you do not currently have one, consider making a paper door-clock to inform others of your classroom schedule.

For Part 2, make a copy of *Math Masters,* page 2. On this copy, write the first "9" on the first line of each half of the page and the first "0" on the third line of each half. Then make enough copies of the page so that each child will have a half-sheet. Cut the pages in half. Save the original *Math Masters,* page 2 for later use.

For the Enrichment activity in Part 3, make copies of *Math Masters,* page 12 for children to cut into quarter-sheets.

Vocabulary • **analog clock** • **hour hand** • **minute hand** • **estimate**

We will be back at:

Getting Started

Mental Math and Reflexes

Ask children if they think they know how long a minute is. Tell them to sit quietly with their eyes closed.

When they think one minute is up, they should open their eyes and raise their hands. When the last child has done this, tell the class who came closest to estimating the length of a minute.

Repeat the activity. But this time inform the children when one minute is up so that they can all raise their hands at the correct time.

Have the children time approximately one minute by counting and clapping in unison: 1 (clap), 2 (clap), 3 (clap), and so on, up to 60 (clap).

Home Link 2.4 Follow-Up

Briefly go over the answers.

If children need more practice with numbers that come before or after, pose problems like the following and have children record their answers on their slates:

- My number is 25. Write the number that comes *before* 25. 24
- My number is 32. Write the number that comes *after* 32. 33
- My number is 18. Write the number that comes after 18. 19

You can lead the first round and then volunteers can pose problems using numbers from their Home Links.

Option: Have children record answers on slates.

1 Teaching the Lesson

◆ Discussing Tools for Telling Time

WHOLE-CLASS DISCUSSION

Talk about the different ways people use time and the tools for telling time. The discussion should include the following points:

▷ Clocks help us organize our day, get together with others, be on time for events, and know when it's time to go home.

▷ Stopwatches help us figure out who is faster in a race or how much time a player has to take a turn.

▷ Calendars help us keep track of the days and months. They also help us plan for important events, such as birthdays and holidays.

◆ Discussing the Position of the Hour Hand

WHOLE-CLASS ACTIVITY

Ask children to locate clocks in the classroom. It is likely that most clocks in your classroom are **analog clocks,** clocks that have hour hands and minute hands. If the subject of digital clocks comes up, point out that, unlike analog clocks, digital clocks have no hour or minute hand. (Digital time notation will be introduced in Lesson 6.10.)

Science Link

Encourage children to talk about other ways of keeping track of time, such as observing the movement of the sun and the moon and noticing the changes from season to season.

Use a demonstration clock for the following demonstrations:

▷ Identify the **hour hand** and the **minute hand**. Point out that the hour hand is shorter than the minute hand. Point the minute hand to the 12. Ask children to focus on the hour hand and to describe what they observe as you move the minute hand one full circle. The hour hand moves much more slowly than the minute hand. The hour hand moves from one number on the clock to the next, while the minute hand makes a full circle.

▷ Start with both the hour and minute hands on 12. Move the minute hand several times around the clock face and have children call out the hours as the hour hand passes from one number to the next.

▷ Move the minute hand several times around the clock face. Ask children to watch the hour hand only and to say "Stop" when they think it is exactly on a number. Do this several times and ask children near which number the minute hand is pointing when the hour hand points to a number. It's pointing to the 12, or near the 12.

Conclusion: When the minute hand points to the 12, the hour hand always points to a number. This number tells the time *on the hour.* For example, if the minute hand points to the 12 and the hour hand points to the 2, then we say that it is 2 o'clock. Show 2 o'clock on the demonstration clock and write "2 o'clock" on the board.

▷ Move the minute hand several times around the clock face. Ask children to watch the hour hand only and to say "Stop" when they think it is pointing about *halfway between two numbers.* Do this several times and ask children near which number the minute hand is pointing when the hour hand points to about halfway between two numbers. It's pointing to the 6, or near the 6.

◆ Estimating the Time Shown on an Hour-Hand-Only Clock (*Math Masters*, p. 11)

WHOLE-CLASS ACTIVITY

Discuss the fact that as soon as you say what time it is, it is already a little later! Therefore, telling the time is always an **estimate;** it is never exact.

Explain that we can tell about what time it is (make a rough estimate) by looking at the hour hand only.

1. Position the hands on the demonstration clock to show 4 o'clock. Move the minute hand so that it points to 2.

Paper Clock with Hour Hand

1. Cut out the clock face and the hour hand.

2. Punch a hole through the center of the clock face. Punch a hole through the X on the hour hand.

3. Fasten the hand to the clock face with a brad.

hour hand

a brad

◆ *Math Masters,* p. 11

- How would you describe the time shown? After 4 o'clock; between 4 o'clock and 5 o'clock; a little after 4 o'clock

2. Ask the class to watch the hour hand as you move the minute hand slowly around the clock face.

- Is the time getting closer to 4 o'clock or to 5 o'clock? Closer to 5 o'clock

3. Use your hour-hand-only demonstration clock, and move the hour hand so that it points to 2.

- Can you tell what time it is? 2 o'clock

4. Move the hour hand on the hour-hand-only clock so that it points about halfway between 8 and 9.

- How would you describe what time it is? Between 8 o'clock and 9 o'clock

5. Repeat this routine several times. Move the hour hand to various positions and ask the class to tell about what time it is. Emphasize the use of estimation language. For example, with the hour hand between two numbers, we can say the time using words and phrases like *about _____, almost _____, just before _____, a little after _____, and between _____ and _____*.

ONGOING ASSESSMENT
Telling time to the nearest hour should be a review for most children. Check to see whether children know the difference between the hour and minute hands. Most children should recognize that if the hour hand is on a number, the time is close to the exact hour.

2 Ongoing Learning & Practice

◆ Practicing the Numbers 9 and 0
(*Math Masters,* p. 2)

INDEPENDENT ACTIVITY

Pass out the half-sheets from *Math Masters,* page 2. Have children practice writing the numbers 9 and 0. Have them circle their best effort for each number.

Portfolio Ideas

◆ Math Boxes 2.5 (*Math Journal 1,* p. 14)

INDEPENDENT ACTIVITY

Mixed Review This journal page provides opportunities for cumulative review or assessment of concepts and skills.

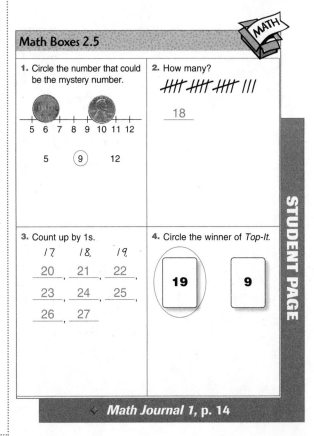

Math Boxes 2.5

1. Circle the number that could be the mystery number.

5 6 7 8 9 10 11 12

5   (9)   12

2. How many?

HHT HHT HHT III

18

3. Count up by 1s.

17, 18, 19,
20, 21, 22,
23, 24, 25,
26, 27

4. Circle the winner of *Top-It.*

(19)   9

STUDENT PAGE

↙ *Math Journal 1,* p. 14

Clocks and Watches

Family Note

Both analog clocks (clocks that have hour hands and minute hands) and digital clocks should be included in the tallies in the table below. In today's lesson, we observed what happens to the hour hand on an analog clock as the minute hand moves around the clock face. In the next lesson, we will practice telling the time when the minute hand is pointing to 12.

Please return this Home Link to school tomorrow.

Ask someone to help you find all of the clocks and watches in your home.

Record the numbers with tally marks.

	Tallies
Clocks	
Watches	

Total: _____ Answers vary.

Draw a picture of the most interesting clock or watch you found. It might be interesting because of the way it looks or where it is located.

HOME LINK MASTER

✦ *Math Masters,* p. 167

Clock Faces

TEACHING MASTER

✦ *Math Masters,* p. 12

✦ **Home Link 2.5** (*Math Masters,* p. 167)

Home Connection Children count the numbers of clocks and watches in their homes and record the results using tally marks.

Note: Suggest that children look at VCRs, microwave ovens, and other appliances that may have clocks.

3 Options for Individualizing

✦ **ENRICHMENT** **Illustrating Daily Activities**
(*Math Masters,* p. 12)

INDEPENDENT ACTIVITY   **15–30 min**

Children cut apart *Math Masters,* page 12 into quarter-sheets and then, on the blank sides of the quarter-sheets, draw pictures of things they do during the day. On the clock-face side of each sheet, they draw a minute hand pointing to 12 and an hour hand pointing to the approximate hour of the day when the activity occurs.

Adjusting the Activity To extend this activity, each child makes at least four quarter-sheets. Children then mix up the completed quarter-sheets clock-side up and try to put the clocks in order. They turn over the quarter-sheets and use the pictures to check their answers.

Partners trade cards and repeat the activity.

2.6 Telling Time to the Hour

OBJECTIVES To introduce the division of the day into A.M. and P.M. times; to practice telling time to the hour; and to develop a sense of the duration of a minute.

summaries	materials

1 Teaching the Lesson

Children make paper clocks. They use their clocks to practice showing and telling times to the hour. [Measurement and Reference Frames]

- ☐ *Math Journal 1,* p. 15
- ☐ Home Link 2.5
- ☐ Teaching Master (*Math Masters,* p. 13)
- ☐ demonstration clock with an hour hand only
- ☐ demonstration clock
- ☐ paper plate, scissors, glue, brad

See **Advance Preparation**

2 Ongoing Learning & Practice

Children estimate the duration of a minute. [Measurement and Reference Frames]

Children practice and maintain skills through Math Boxes and Home Link activities.

- ☐ *Math Journal 1,* p. 16
- ☐ stopwatch or a watch with a second hand
- ☐ Home Link Master (*Math Masters,* p. 168)

See **Advance Preparation**

3 Options for Individualizing

Enrichment Children show times on their paper clocks to match the words of the "Paper Clocks" song. [Measurement and Reference Frames]

Extra Practice Children get a sense of the duration of an hour. [Measurement and Reference Frames]

Extra Practice Children practice estimation and telling time to the nearest hour. [Measurement and Reference Frames]

- ☐ Teaching Master (*Math Masters,* p. 14; optional)
- ☐ *Learning Basic Skills Through Music,* Vol. II, by Hap Palmer
- ☐ timer or watch that beeps
- ☐ classroom clock
- ☐ *Minute Math*®, p. 71

See **Advance Preparation**

Additional Information

Advance Preparation For Part 1, you may need the demonstration clock with an hour hand only, which you made in Lesson 2.5. You will also need a demonstration clock with hour and minute hands. Children will be making paper clocks out of *Math Masters,* page 13, paper plates, and brads. You might want to pre-punch a hole in each paper plate, using a nail or a pencil.

For Part 2, you will need a stopwatch or a watch with a second hand.

For the Enrichment activity in Part 3, you will need the song "Paper Clocks" from the Hap Palmer cassette, *Learning Basic Skills Through Music,* Vol. II. (This cassette is available from Educational Activities, Inc., Box 392, Freeport, L.I., N.Y. 11520.) For the first Extra Practice activity in Part 3, you will need a timer or a watch that can be made to beep on the hour.

Vocabulary • **clockwise** • **midnight** • **noon** • A.M. • P.M.

Getting Started

Mental Math and Reflexes

Tell simple number stories. Children may use pennies to model them. Model the first story using counters on the overhead. *Suggestions:*

- Maria had 5 crayons. (Children lay out 5 pennies to show the 5 crayons.) She gave one crayon to David. (Children remove one penny.) She gave one crayon to her friend Kiri. (Children remove one more penny.) How many crayons does Maria have now? 3 crayons
- Bryant had 3 video games. For his birthday, he got 7 more. How many video games did Bryant have after his birthday? 10 video games
- Louise and Cherise went to the store together. They bought a box of chocolates with 12 candies inside. Louise ate 3 of the chocolates and Cherise ate 4 of them. How many chocolates did Louise and Cherise have left? 5 chocolates
- Marcus eats his peas with a spoon. In his first spoonful, he ate 5 peas. With his second spoonful, he ate 4 more peas. How many peas has Marcus eaten so far? 9 peas He ate one more spoonful with 6 peas in it. How many peas did Marcus eat altogether? 15 peas

Home Link 2.5 Follow-Up

Children tell about the clocks they found at home. To extend this activity, use tally marks to record the total number of clocks and watches children reported finding. Ask someone to count the tallies and to write the total.

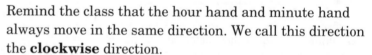

Teaching the Lesson

◆ Reviewing Clocks

WHOLE-CLASS DISCUSSION

Remind the class that the hour hand and minute hand always move in the same direction. We call this direction the **clockwise** direction.

Review the following facts:

▷ The numbers 1 through 12 are displayed on the faces of clocks and watches.

▷ The hour hand and the minute hand travel from one number to the next.

▷ It takes one hour for the minute hand to travel all the way around the clock face.

NOTE: You may want to have children stand up and turn slowly in a clockwise direction. While doing this, they can each hold out one arm as though it is a hand on a clock.

◆ Introducing the Division of the 24-Hour Day into A.M. and P.M. Hours

WHOLE-CLASS ACTIVITY

Ask children how many hours there are in 1 day. 24 hours Remind them that it takes 12 hours for the hour hand to go all the way around the clock face.

- How many times does the hour hand go all the way around the clock face in 1 day? Twice

 Adjusting the Activity If necessary, using the hour-hand-only clock, start with the hand pointing to the 12 and move the hand around the clock face as children count the hours. Continue moving the hour hand until it has gone around the clock face twice and the count has reached 24.

Tell the class that each day on the calendar starts at 12 o'clock at night.

- What is another name for 12 o'clock at night? **midnight**
- What do we call the time 12 hours later? 12 o'clock, or **noon**

Ask whether anyone has heard of **A.M.** and **P.M.** Point out that the first 12 hours of a day are the A.M. hours and that the second 12 hours of a day are the P.M. hours. Or, to put it another way, the hours from midnight to noon are the A.M. hours, and the hours from noon to midnight are the P.M. hours.

Ask children to share some things they do during the A.M. hours and some things they do during the P.M. hours.

Note: This is the first time children are seeing the vocabulary for A.M. and P.M. Do not expect children to remember or use these terms at this time.

◆ Making a Clock (*Math Masters*, p. 13)

INDEPENDENT ACTIVITY

Children write the numbers on the clock face, cut out the clock face, and glue it to a paper plate. Then they cut out the hour hand and the minute hand, and attach them to the center of the paper clock with a brad.

◆ Telling Time to the Nearest Hour
(*Math Journal 1*, p. 15)

WHOLE-CLASS ACTIVITY

Use the routine on the next page to practice telling time to the nearest hour.

Language Arts Link

You may want to tell the class that A.M. and P.M. are abbreviations for *ante meridian,* which means before the middle of the day, and *post meridian,* which means after the middle of the day.

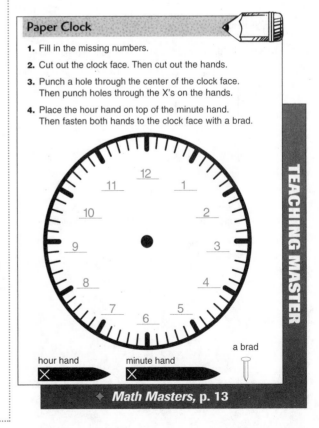

Paper Clock

1. Fill in the missing numbers.
2. Cut out the clock face. Then cut out the hands.
3. Punch a hole through the center of the clock face. Then punch holes through the X's on the hands.
4. Place the hour hand on top of the minute hand. Then fasten both hands to the clock face with a brad.

hour hand   minute hand   a brad

◆ *Math Masters*, p. 13

TEACHING MASTER

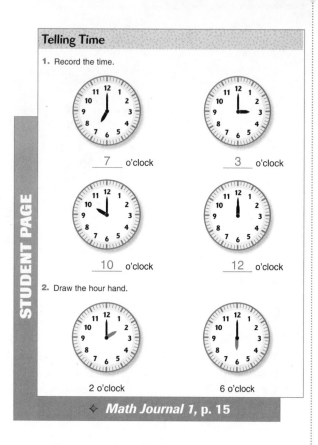

Telling Time

1. Record the time.

7 o'clock

3 o'clock

10 o'clock

12 o'clock

2. Draw the hour hand.

2 o'clock

6 o'clock

Math Boxes 2.6

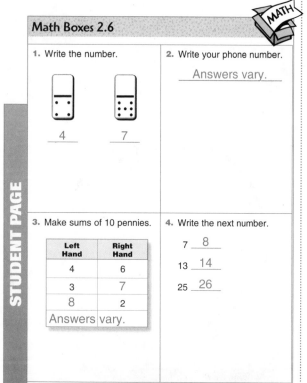

1. Write the number.

4

7

2. Write your phone number.

Answers vary.

3. Make sums of 10 pennies.

Left Hand	Right Hand
4	6
3	7
8	2
Answers	vary.

4. Write the next number.

7 _8_

13 _14_

25 _26_

1. Show a time on your demonstration clock with the minute hand pointing to the 12.

2. Have children show the same time on their clocks.

3. Have children tell what time is shown on the clock.

4. Record (or have a child record) the time on the board. (Since children have not yet learned to read or write digital time notation, record each time using the following notation: _____ o'clock.)

As a variation, give children a time, to the hour, to show on their clocks.

After a few minutes of practice, have children complete the journal page independently or with their partners.

ONGOING ASSESSMENT
Watch for children who are having trouble displaying the times. Ask them which numbers the hour hand and the minute hand are pointing to each time as they set their clocks.

When most children have finished, briefly review the answers.

2 Ongoing Learning & Practice

✦ Getting a Sense of the Duration of a Minute

WHOLE-CLASS ACTIVITY

Give a signal to start and tell children to stand up when they think that about 1 minute has passed from the time you gave the signal.

Repeat the activity several times. The goal is for children to get better at estimating the length of a minute.

✦ Math Boxes 2.6 (*Math Journal 1,* p. 16)

INDEPENDENT ACTIVITY

Mixed Review This journal page provides opportunities for cumulative review or assessment of concepts and skills.

✦ Home Link 2.6 (*Math Masters*, p. 168)

Home Connection Children take their paper clocks home and use them to practice telling time with someone at home. They record times on the hour and draw hour hands to show times to the hour.

3 Options for Individualizing

✦ ENRICHMENT Setting Clocks to Match the Times in a Song (*Math Masters*, p. 14)

SMALL-GROUP ACTIVITY 👥👥👥👥   15–30 min

Play the song "Paper Clocks" from the Hap Palmer cassette, and have children match the hands on their clocks to the words of the song. Children can sing along as they work.

If you wish to provide extra practice with telling time, make up a set of problems on a copy of *Math Masters*, page 14.

✦ EXTRA PRACTICE Getting a Sense of the Duration of an Hour

SMALL-GROUP ACTIVITY 👥👥👥👥   5–15 min

Set a timer (or a watch that can be set to beep on the hour) so that it will sound when it is a time to the hour (for example, 10 o'clock or 2 o'clock). Do this from time to time. Children will become accustomed to looking at the classroom clock and calling out the correct time. This activity is especially effective if done for 2 or 3 hours in a row.

✦ EXTRA PRACTICE Minute Math

SMALL-GROUP ACTIVITY 👥👥👥👥   5–15 min

To offer children more experience with estimating and telling time to the nearest hour, see the following page in *Minute Math*:

Measurement: p. 71

Telling Time to the Hour   Home Link 2.6

Family Note We have just begun our work with telling time. Your child is working on telling time to the hour. Ask your child to show times on the hour on the paper clock, as in Part 1 below.
Please return this Home Link to school tomorrow, but keep your child's paper clock for future use.

1. Show your paper clock to someone at home.
   • Show 3 o'clock.
   • Show 11 o'clock.
   • Ask someone to name an hour for you to show.

2. Record the time.

   5 o'clock   **9** o'clock

3. Draw the hour hand.

   7 o'clock   1 o'clock

✦ *Math Masters*, p. 168

🎵 Music Link

The song "Paper Clocks" from the Hap Palmer cassette is one of a number of math songs children enjoy singing. For other suggestions, check with your school's music teacher or librarian.

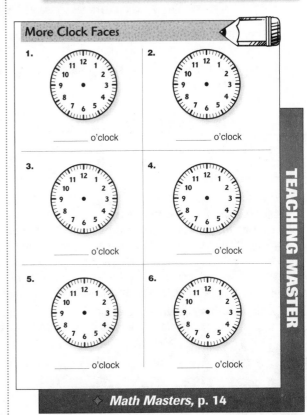

More Clock Faces

1. _____ o'clock
2. _____ o'clock
3. _____ o'clock
4. _____ o'clock
5. _____ o'clock
6. _____ o'clock

✦ *Math Masters*, p. 14

2.7
EXPLORATIONS

Exploring Lengths, Straightedges, and Dominoes

OBJECTIVES To compare lengths of objects; to practice drawing straight lines with a straightedge; and to develop familiarity with what constitutes a set of dominoes.

summaries

materials

1 Teaching the Lesson

Exploration A: Children estimate which objects in a set of objects are longer than their rulers and which are shorter. They check their estimates by physically comparing the objects to their rulers. Then they put the objects in order from shortest to longest. [Measurement and Reference Frames]

Exploration B: Children use their straightedges to draw stars. [Numeration; Geometry]

Exploration C: Children sort two mixed sets of dominoes into matching pairs. [Numeration; Patterns, Functions, and Algebra]

Exploration A: Per workstation:
- ☐ Teaching Master (*Math Masters*, p. 15; optional)
- ☐ ruler; quarter-sheet of paper
- ☐ objects

Exploration B: Per child:
- ☐ Teaching Master (*Math Masters*, p. 16)
- ☐ ruler; coloring pencils

Exploration C: Per workstation:
- ☐ Teaching Master (*Math Masters*, p. 17; optional)
- ☐ dominoes

See **Advance Preparation**

2 Ongoing Learning & Practice

Children play *Two-Fisted Penny Addition* or *Rolling for 50*. [Numeration; Operations and Computation]

Children practice and maintain skills through Math Boxes and Home Link activities.

- ☐ *Math Journal 1*, p. 17
- ☐ die per partnership
- ☐ pennies
- ☐ Home Link Master (*Math Masters*, p. 169)

3 Options for Individualizing

Extra Practice Children discuss measuring tools. [Measurement and Reference Frames]

- ☐ *Minute Math*®, pp. 61 and 62

Additional Information

Advance Preparation **Exploration A** and **Exploration C** are best done in small groups. **Exploration B** is an independent activity. Plan to spend most of your time with children working on Exploration A.

Math Masters, pages 15 and 17 give directions for the Explorations. You may want to place copies of these masters at the appropriate workstations if teacher's aides or volunteers are helping children. However, these masters are not required to do the Explorations. On the other hand, *Math Masters,* page 16 is required, since children use it to record their work.

For Exploration A, mark the tool-kit rulers with children's identification numbers. Each group will need about 8 objects that range in length from about 1 inch to 1 foot each. **For Exploration C,** each group will need 2 mixed sets of dominoes.

Vocabulary • **ruler**

Getting Started

Mental Math and Reflexes

Tell "change to more" number stories, and have children solve them any way they can. Have children share solution strategies after each problem. Then summarize by drawing a "change-to-more" diagram—*but only after children have had a chance to share how they solved the problem.*

- Maria had 5 cookies. David gave her 3 more cookies. How many cookies does Maria have now? 8 cookies
- Bryant had 7 games. He got 3 more games for his birthday. How many games does Bryant have now? 10 games
- Leliah had $15 in her savings account. Then her mom gave her $7 for keeping her room clean and neat for a month. If Leliah saved all her money, how much money did she have at the end of the month? $22
- When Larry woke up this morning, the temperature outside was only 5 degrees. By noon, the temperature had gone up to 12 degrees. By how many degrees had the temperature gone up? By 7 degrees

To summarize the solution to the first problem, draw a "change to more" diagram, and as you do, ask:

- How many cookies did Maria have before David gave her more cookies? 5
  That's how many she had to start with. (Write "5" in the first box.)
- How many cookies did David give her? 3 That's how many more she has now.
  (Write "3 more" under the curved arrow.)
- How many cookies does Maria have now? 8 (Write "8" in the second box.)

Start	Change	End
5	3 more	8

Home Link 2.6 Follow-Up

Briefly go over the times children wrote below the clock faces.

Children should keep rulers in their tool kits when not in use.

1 Teaching the Lesson

✦ Exploring the Uses of Rulers

WHOLE-CLASS ACTIVITY

Distribute the **rulers** and ask children to check that their rulers have the correct ID numbers. Mention that a ruler is a mathematical tool and that they will keep their rulers in their tool kits when they are not using them.

- What are rulers used for? To measure lengths; to draw straight lines

Tell children that they will learn to measure with a ruler another time. Today, they will practice using their rulers to draw straight lines.

Ask children to draw two dots on their quarter-sheets of paper. As you demonstrate, tell children to use their rulers to draw a straight line connecting the dots. Repeat until most children are fairly adept at drawing lines.

How Long Is It?

Materials ❑ ruler

❑ about 8 objects

1. Look at your ruler.

   Try to remember how long it is.

   Then put it away in your tool kit.

2. Put the objects you think are longer than your ruler into one pile.

   Put the objects you think are shorter than your ruler into another pile.

3. Take out your ruler and check your guesses.

4. Now, put the objects in order from shortest to longest.

   Show your objects to your teacher.

✦ *Math Masters*, p. 15

TEACHING MASTER

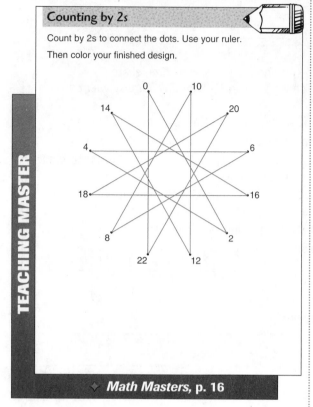

Counting by 2s

Count by 2s to connect the dots. Use your ruler.

Then color your finished design.

♦ *Math Masters*, p. 16

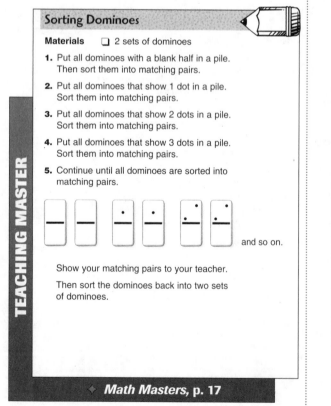

Sorting Dominoes

Materials ❑ 2 sets of dominoes

1. Put all dominoes with a blank half in a pile. Then sort them into matching pairs.

2. Put all dominoes that show 1 dot in a pile. Sort them into matching pairs.

3. Put all dominoes that show 2 dots in a pile. Sort them into matching pairs.

4. Put all dominoes that show 3 dots in a pile. Sort them into matching pairs.

5. Continue until all dominoes are sorted into matching pairs.

and so on.

Show your matching pairs to your teacher.

Then sort the dominoes back into two sets of dominoes.

♦ *Math Masters*, p. 17

TEACHING MASTER

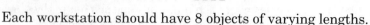

◆ Exploration A: Estimating the Relative Lengths of Objects (*Math Masters*, p. 15)

SMALL-GROUP ACTIVITY

Each workstation should have 8 objects of varying lengths.

Directions

1. Look at your ruler. Try to remember how long it is. Then put it into your tool kit.

2. Put the objects you think are longer than your ruler into one pile. Put the objects you think are shorter than your ruler into another pile.

3. Take out your ruler and check your guesses.

4. Now, put the objects in order from shortest to longest.

◆ Exploration B: Making a Star (*Math Masters*, p. 16)

INDEPENDENT ACTIVITY

Ask children to use their rulers to connect the dots, starting at 0 and counting by 2s. Then tell children to color their completed designs.

◆ Exploration C: Sorting Dominoes (*Math Masters*, p. 17)

SMALL-GROUP ACTIVITY

In this Exploration, children sort two sets of dominoes so that they end up with pairs of matching dominoes.

Let children try to figure out how best to go about the task. If, after a few minutes, they are unable to come up with a plan, give them the following directions to help them get started:

Directions

1. Put all dominoes with a blank half in a pile. Then sort them into matching pairs.

2. Put all remaining dominoes that show 1 dot in a pile. Sort them into matching pairs.

3. Put all remaining dominoes that show 2 dots in a pile. Sort them into matching pairs.

4. Put all remaining dominoes that show 3 dots in a pile. Sort them into matching pairs.

5. Continue until all dominoes are sorted into matching pairs.

2 Ongoing Learning & Practice

◆ Playing *Two-Fisted Penny Addition* or *Rolling for 50*

PARTNER ACTIVITY

Children practice finding complements of 10 by playing *Two-Fisted Penny Addition*. They practice navigating on the number grid by playing *Rolling for 50*. For detailed instructions, see Lessons 2.3 and 2.1.

◆ Math Boxes 2.7 (*Math Journal 1*, p. 17)

INDEPENDENT ACTIVITY

Mixed Review This journal page provides opportunities for cumulative review or assessment of concepts and skills.

◆ Home Link 2.7 (*Math Masters*, p. 169)

Home Connection Children examine the two sides of a penny. They also order a set of dominoes from least number of dots to greatest number of dots.

3 Options for Individualizing

◆ EXTRA PRACTICE Minute Math

SMALL-GROUP ACTIVITY **5–15 min**

To offer children more experience with measuring tools, see the following pages in *Minute Math:*

Measurement: pp. 61 and 62

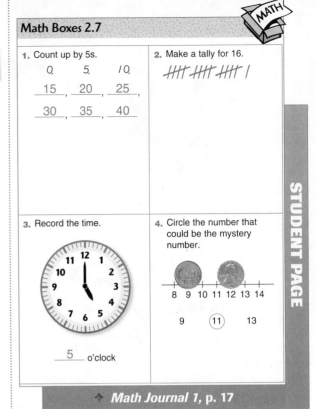

Math Boxes 2.7

1. Count up by 5s.

  0,   5,   10,
  15 , 20 , 25 ,
  30 , 35 , 40

2. Make a tally for 16.

  //// //// //// /

3. Record the time.

  _5_ o'clock

4. Circle the number that could be the mystery number.

  8 9 10 11 12 13 14

  9 (11) 13

◆ Math Journal 1, p. 17

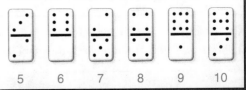

Ordering Numbers — Home Link 2.7

Family Note Over the next few weeks, we will be "getting to know coins" in our class. In the next lesson, we will learn about pennies. Here is some background information: Abraham Lincoln appears on the HEADS side. The Lincoln Memorial is shown on the TAILS side.

Your child is also learning how to order and compare numbers. Dominoes are a perfect tool for practicing this skill. If you have dominoes at home, you may want to play ordering games with your child. At first, use consecutive numbers like 1, 2, 3, and 4.

Please return this Home Link to school tomorrow.

1. Get a penny.
   • Who is on the HEADS side? __Abraham Lincoln__
   • What is on the TAILS side? __Lincoln Memorial__
2. Cut out the dominoes at the bottom of the page.
   • Count the total number of dots on each domino.
   • Put the dominoes in order from least to greatest number of dots.
   • Tape the dominoes in order on the back of this page.
   • Write the total number of dots under each domino.

  5   6   7   8   9   10

◆ Math Masters, p. 169

2.8

Pennies

OBJECTIVES To introduce pennies and cents notation; to record numbers of pennies; and to practice comparing numbers.

summaries	materials

1   Teaching the Lesson

Children examine a penny. They solve *Penny Grab* problems, using cent notation to record the results. [Numeration; Measurement and Reference Frames]

- ☐ *Math Journal 1*, p. 18
- ☐ Home Link 2.7
- ☐ 20 pennies
- ☐ Class Data Pad
- ☐ magnifying lenses (at least 1 per 4 or 5 children)
- ☐ slate (optional)

***See* Advance Preparation**

2   Ongoing Learning & Practice

Children practice and maintain skills through Math Boxes and Home Link activities.

- ☐ *Math Journal 1*, p. 19
- ☐ Home Link Master (*Math Masters*, p. 170)

3   Options for Individualizing

Extra Practice Children play *Penny Cup*. [Operations and Computation; Patterns, Functions, and Algebra]

- ☐ large cup or can per partnership
- ☐ pennies

***See* Advance Preparation**

Additional Information

Advance Preparation For Part 1, be prepared to distribute 10 more pennies to each child to add to his or her tool-kit penny collection. Using the Class Data Pad or posterboard, make a Story of Money Poster like the one shown on page 121. (If you use posterboard, you may want to laminate it so that you can clean it off and use it again next year.)

For the optional Extra Practice activity in Part 3, you will need a can or container for each partnership. Each can should be large enough so that, when turned upside down, up to 20 pennies can be hidden under it.

Vocabulary • penny • cent

Getting Started

Home Link 2.7 Follow-Up

Children share the order in which they taped their dominoes. (See page 121 for a discussion of the penny.)

Mental Math and Reflexes

Tell "change-to-less" number stories, and have children solve them any way they can. Have children share solution strategies after each problem. Then summarize by drawing a "change to less" diagram—*but only after children have had a chance to share how they solved the problem.*

Suggestions

• Rupert had 12 pennies when he left for school. He had a hole in his pocket and lost 7 pennies. How many pennies does he have left? 5 pennies

• Maurice's mom baked 20 cookies. After school, Maurice ate 15 of the cookies. How many cookies were left? 5 cookies

• Tanya bought an 18-inch pencil at the school fun fair. She used it all through the year. At the end of the year, she found she had used only 8 inches of the pencil. How long was Tanya's pencil at the end of the year? 10 inches

• Louise and Michael love to play dominoes. Yesterday, they started with 28 dominoes. While playing, they lost some of them. They had only 23 dominoes left when they were finished. How many dominoes did they lose? They lost 5 dominoes.

To summarize the solution to the first problem, draw a "change-to-less" diagram, and as you do, ask:

• How many pennies did Rupert have when he left for school? 12 That's how many he had to start with. (Write "12" in the first box.)

• How many pennies did he lose? 7 That's how many fewer pennies he has now. (Write "7 less" under the curved arrow.)

How many pennies does Rupert have left? 5 (Write "5" in the second box.)

Reminder: Diagrams are used only for the purpose of exposure at this early stage.

Start	Change	End
12	7 less	5

1 Teaching the Lesson

◆ Examining the Penny

WHOLE-CLASS ACTIVITY

Divide the class into small groups. Then ask:

• How many **pennies** do you have in your tool kit? 10 pennies

• How many more pennies will you need so that you will have 20 pennies in all? 10 more pennies

Quickly distribute pennies to each group. Have each child take 10 pennies for a total of 20 pennies.

Have children share magnifying lenses for a closer inspection of both sides of a penny. A picture of Abraham Lincoln is shown on the "heads" side of the penny, and the Lincoln Memorial appears on the "tails" side. Record this information in the "Penny" column on your Story of Money Poster. (See margin.)

Story of Money

	Penny 1¢ $.01	Nickel 5¢ $.05	Dime 10¢ $.10	Quarter 25¢ $.25	Dollar 100¢ $1.00
Heads	Head of Lincoln				
Tails	Lincoln Memorial				
Equivalencies	None	____ ℗	____ ℗ ____ Ⓝ	____ ℗ ____ Ⓝ	____ ℗ ____ Ⓝ ____ Ⓓ ____ Ⓠ

The Story of Money Poster

Spend a few minutes sharing other information about pennies. Two facts of interest:

▷ Pennies are made from copper and zinc.

▷ In the 1940s, no copper was used in pennies. They were silver-colored.

 Adjusting the Activity If appropriate, ask non-native English speakers to bring to school and describe foreign coins with which they are familiar.

If children are able to do so, have them name these coins in the order of their value, starting with the coin worth the least.

◆ Introducing Cents Notation

WHOLE-CLASS DISCUSSION

Remind the class that a penny is worth one **cent.** Write "one cent" and "1¢" on the board and tell children that the symbol "¢" is shorthand for the word "cent."

Explain that the word *cent* comes from the Latin word *centesimus,* which means "a hundredth part."

• How many pennies are there in 1 dollar? 100 pennies

• Does anyone know any words that start with the word *cent*? Centimeter, centipede, century, centigrade

• Can anyone think of something that can be bought for a penny? (Nowadays, it is difficult to think of anything that can be bought for a penny. However, listen to children's suggestions and encourage them to think about how little a penny is worth. You might tell them the cost in pennies of the items they suggest, if you have an idea of their approximate cost.)

• If each child in our class had a penny, how many cents would our class have in all? Can anyone think of something that could be bought for that amount?

NOTE: The term *penny* is believed to come from one of the following: the Old English *penig,* the German *pfennig,* or the Latin *pannus,* which was a unit of cloth used as a medium of exchange.

♦ Solving *Penny Grab* Problems
(*Math Journal 1*, p. 18)

PARTNER ACTIVITY

Partners combine their tool-kit pennies (40 pennies in all). Each partner grabs a handful and counts how many he or she has. Both partners record both numbers of pennies in their journals. Then they circle the greater number of pennies.

You may want to demonstrate how to record this information.

 Adjusting the Activity If 40 pennies are too many for some children to count accurately, partnerships can play with as few as 20 pennies.

If children have a difficult time telling who has more pennies, partners can line up their pennies in two rows, one below the other. The person who has some pennies that cannot be paired with the other person's pennies has the greater number of pennies.

Or, partners can put their pennies back into a common pile, one at a time. Whoever runs out of pennies first has the smaller number of pennies.

If children are able, they may also record how many more pennies one partner has than the other. Some children may even be able to write number models to show how many pennies the partners have in all—for example, $8 + 6 = 14$.

 ONGOING ASSESSMENT
Take note of children who are having a difficult time comparing numbers. Use one of the above "Adjusting the Activity" suggestions to help those children. Do not expect mastery at this time. Children will have more opportunities to further develop this skill.

Penny Grab Record Sheet

Round 1

I grabbed _____ pennies. | My partner grabbed _____ pennies.

I have _____ ¢. | My partner has _____ ¢.

Who has more? _____

Round 2

I grabbed _____ pennies. | My partner grabbed _____ pennies.

I have _____ ¢. | My partner has _____ ¢.

Who has more? _____

Round 3

I grabbed _____ pennies. | My partner grabbed _____ pennies.

I have _____ ¢. | My partner has _____ ¢.

Who has more? _____

Round 4

I grabbed _____ pennies. | My partner grabbed _____ pennies.

I have _____ ¢. | My partner has _____ ¢.

Who has more? _____

STUDENT PAGE

♦ *Math Journal 1*, p. 18

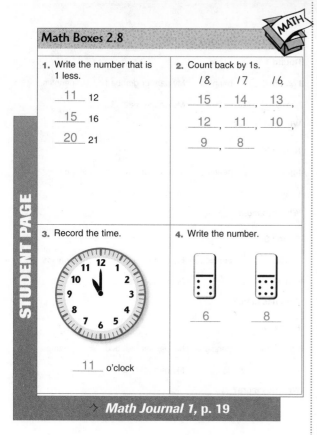

Math Boxes 2.8

STUDENT PAGE

1. Write the number that is 1 less.

   <u>11</u> 12

   <u>15</u> 16

   <u>20</u> 21

2. Count back by 1s.

   18, 17, 16,

   <u>15</u>, <u>14</u>, <u>13</u>,

   <u>12</u>, <u>11</u>, <u>10</u>,

   <u>9</u>, <u>8</u>

3. Record the time.

   <u>11</u> o'clock

4. Write the number.

   6   8

Math Journal 1, p. 19

Nickels

Family Note During the next few weeks, our class will learn about coins. For our next math lesson, your child will need 5 nickels. Please put these nickels in a sealed envelope with your child's name on it so that they will not get lost. (Your child will also need 10 dimes and 2 quarters in the coming days.)

Here is some background information about nickels: Thomas Jefferson appears on the HEADS side of the nickel. Monticello, Jefferson's home in Virginia, appears on the TAILS side.

Please return this Home Link to school tomorrow.

1. Ask someone at home for 5 nickels you can bring to school. Use one of them for this Home Link.

2. Look closely at a nickel. Ask someone to help you answer the following questions:

   • Who is on the HEADS side? <u>Thomas Jefferson</u>

   • What is on the TAILS side? <u>Monticello</u>

3. Ask someone to trade you the correct number of pennies for your nickel.

   • How many pennies did the person give you?

   <u>5</u> pennies

   • How many pennies would you get for 2 nickels?

   <u>10</u> pennies

   • Explain to someone at home how you found your answer.

Math Masters, p. 170

HOME LINK MASTER

---

2 Ongoing Learning & Practice

◆ Math Boxes 2.8 (*Math Journal 1,* p. 19)

INDEPENDENT ACTIVITY

 Mixed Review This journal page provides opportunities for cumulative review or assessment of concepts and skills.

◆ Home Link 2.8 (*Math Masters,* p. 170)

Home Connection Children begin their investigation of nickels. They trade a nickel for the correct number of pennies with someone at home.

3 Options for Individualizing

◆ EXTRA PRACTICE Playing *Penny Cup*

PARTNER ACTIVITY   **30+ min**

This game is played with a cup and a specified number of pennies, appropriate to the level of proficiency of the players. (Most partnerships begin with 10 pennies.)

Players take turns. Player A turns the cup upside down, hides some of the pennies under the cup, and places the rest of the pennies on top of the cup. Player B counts the pennies on top and guesses how many are hidden underneath. If the guess is correct, Player B gets a point. Players then trade roles.

Players keep a tally of their points. The player who has more points at the end of 5 rounds wins the game.

Variation: Players work together to guess how many pennies are under the cup. If their joint guess is correct, they get a team point. They do this 10 times. The goal is to improve the team score with every game.

 Adjusting the Activity If children are having difficulty, they can use circles to record the total number of pennies. They cross off one circle for each penny on top of the cup and then count the remaining number of circles to figure out how many pennies are under the cup.

2.9 Nickels

OBJECTIVES To introduce nickels; and to practice exchanging pennies for nickels.

summaries	materials
1 Teaching the Lesson	
Children examine a nickel. They replace up to 14 pennies with an equivalent combination of nickels and pennies. [Numeration; Measurement and Reference Frames]	☐ *Math Journal 1*, p. 20 ☐ Home Link 2.8 ☐ magnifying lens (at least 1 per small group) ☐ overhead coins (optional) ☐ pennies ☐ nickels (5 per child) ***See* Advance Preparation**
2 Ongoing Learning & Practice	
Children complete a connect-the-dots picture using multiples of 5. [Numeration] Children practice and maintain skills through Math Boxes and Home Link activities.	☐ *Math Journal 1*, pp. 21 and 22 ☐ Home Link Master (*Math Masters*, p. 171)
3 Options for Individualizing	
Enrichment Children put nickels in sequential order by the year they were minted. [Numeration] **Extra Practice** Children estimate how long it would take to count 100 pennies and 20 nickels. [Numeration] **Enrichment** Children play *Penny Guessing*. [Measurement and Reference Frames]	☐ pennies and nickels ☐ slate or scratch paper ☐ overhead coins (optional)

Additional Information

Advance Preparation For Part 1, display the Story of Money Poster (see Lesson 2.8). Each child will need 5 nickels. Have extra nickels (preferably real ones) on hand for children who did not bring any to school. Children should keep the nickels in their tool kits.

Vocabulary • **nickel**

Getting Started

Mental Math and Reflexes

Have children use the number grid on the inside back covers of their journals to count up and back by 5s. Start at various multiples of 5; for example, 5, 20, 45, or 60.

Home Link 2.8 Follow-Up

Children share magnifying lenses for a closer inspection of what's on a **nickel.**

You may wish to share some or all of the following information with the class:

▷ Until 1866, nickels were called *half-dimes.*
▷ Nickels are named for the metal that gives them their color.
▷ Nickels are made from copper and nickel.
▷ Thomas Jefferson is on the HEADS side, and Monticello (his Virginia home) is on the TAILS side.

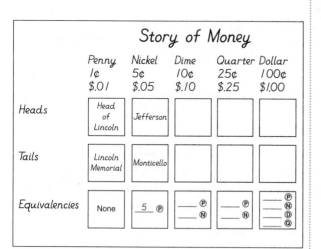

Filling in the Story of Money Poster

1 Teaching the Lesson

✦ Finding the Value of a Collection of Nickels

WHOLE-CLASS ACTIVITY

Remind children that a nickel is worth 5 cents. Ask them how many pennies they would get in exchange for 2 nickels. 10 pennies How did they figure out the answer? One way is to exchange each nickel for 5 pennies and then count the pennies.

Fill in the "Nickel" column on your Story of Money Poster.

Draw a unit box on the board and write *cents* in it. Then pose the following problem:

• If every child in our class had one nickel, how much money would our class have in all?

To solve the problem, have the class count by 5s, with each child saying one of the 5-counts, until all children have had a turn. Write the final amount on the board, using cent notation. Ask children whether they know of something they could buy for that amount.

 Adjusting the Activity Ask children: *Is this amount more or less than 1 dollar?*

✦ Exchanging Pennies for Nickels
(*Math Journal 1*, p. 20)

WHOLE-CLASS ACTIVITY 👥👥👥👥

1. Draw 8 pennies on the board using a Ⓟ to represent each penny.

   ▷ Have children take out 8 pennies. Ask them to arrange their pennies into two groups so that there are 5 pennies in one group and 3 pennies in the other group. If possible, model this procedure with overhead coins on the overhead projector.

   ▷ Next, have children exchange 5 pennies for 1 nickel. On the board, draw an Ⓝ under the 5 pennies to represent 1 nickel and draw 3 more Ⓟs. Write 8¢ under the coins. (See margin.)

   ▷ Explain that 1 nickel and 3 pennies are worth the same amount as 8 pennies but that we used fewer coins to represent 8 cents. If you went to the store to buy something that cost 8 cents, you could pay for it either with 8 pennies or with 1 nickel and 3 pennies.

   ▷ *Conclusion:* We can count nickels and pennies in the same way we count tally marks. To count 1 nickel and 3 pennies, start with "5" for the nickel and then count by 1s for the pennies—5, 6, 7, 8.

2. Ask children to take out 6 pennies and to show how they would pay for something that costs 6 cents, using fewer coins. 1 nickel and 1 penny

   Count together while pointing to each coin. 5, 6 Write 6¢ on the board.

3. Ask children to take out 10 pennies. Then ask them to show how they would pay for something that costs 10 cents, using fewer coins.

   ▷ As children share their solution strategies, model what they did on the overhead projector or on the board. Some children may have exchanged only 5 pennies for 1 nickel, ending up with 1 nickel and 5 pennies. This is perfectly acceptable, since children are just beginning to do coin exchanges. At this stage, you need not insist that children exchange pennies for the fewest number of coins.

   ▷ Whenever children do not end up with the fewest number of coins, ask them to try to exchange those coins for even fewer coins. For 10 pennies, they can arrange their pennies into two groups of 5 pennies each and then exchange the pennies in each group for 1 nickel, ending up with 2 nickels.

⬤ Language Arts Link

Ask children why we would represent pennies by drawing a circle with the letter *P* inside the circle. The word *penny* begins with the letter *P*. How could we represent a nickel? With the letter *N* in a circle

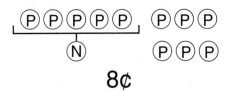

8¢

Two ways to show 8¢: 8 pennies; and 1 nickel and 3 pennies

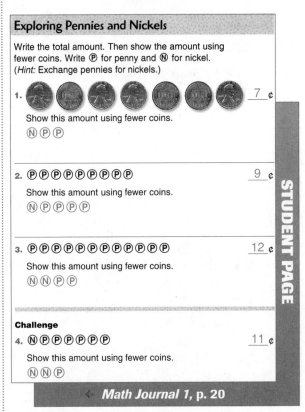

Exploring Pennies and Nickels

Write the total amount. Then show the amount using fewer coins. Write Ⓟ for penny and Ⓝ for nickel. (*Hint:* Exchange pennies for nickels.)

1. 🪙🪙🪙🪙🪙🪙🪙   __7__ ¢
   Show this amount using fewer coins.
   Ⓝ Ⓟ Ⓟ

2. Ⓟ Ⓟ Ⓟ Ⓟ Ⓟ Ⓟ Ⓟ Ⓟ Ⓟ   __9__ ¢
   Show this amount using fewer coins.
   Ⓝ Ⓟ Ⓟ Ⓟ Ⓟ

3. Ⓟ Ⓟ Ⓟ Ⓟ Ⓟ Ⓟ Ⓟ Ⓟ Ⓟ Ⓟ Ⓟ Ⓟ   __12__ ¢
   Show this amount using fewer coins.
   Ⓝ Ⓝ Ⓟ Ⓟ

Challenge

4. Ⓝ Ⓟ Ⓟ Ⓟ Ⓟ Ⓟ Ⓟ   __11__ ¢
   Show this amount using fewer coins.
   Ⓝ Ⓝ Ⓟ

⬅ *Math Journal 1*, p. 20

Counting by 5s

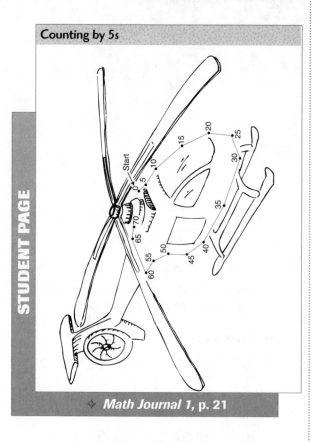

▷ Count together while pointing to each coin. 5, 10
Write 10¢ on the board.

4. Have children work independently or in partnerships to complete the journal page. They can use coins to help them solve the problems. Circulate and assist as needed.

ONGOING ASSESSMENT
Check to see that children are exchanging the correct number of pennies for nickels. If children are struggling with this concept, encourage them to model the problems with coins.

Briefly go over the answers.

2 Ongoing Learning & Practice

✦ Completing a Connect-the-Dots Picture
(*Math Journal 1*, p. 21)

INDEPENDENT ACTIVITY

Children count by 5s to connect the dots.

✦ Math Boxes 2.9 (*Math Journal 1*, p. 22)

INDEPENDENT ACTIVITY

 Mixed Review This journal page provides opportunities for cumulative review or assessment of concepts and skills.

✦ Home Link 2.9 (*Math Masters*, p. 171)

 Home Connection Children practice counting by 5s. They make and count tally marks.

Math Boxes 2.9

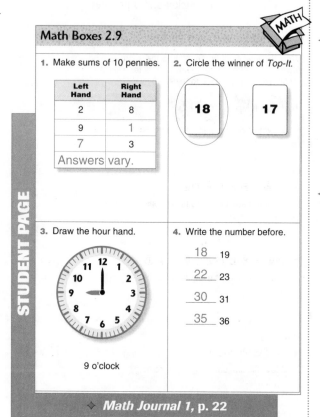

1. Make sums of 10 pennies.

Left Hand	Right Hand
2	8
9	1
7	3

Answers vary.

2. Circle the winner of *Top-It*.

18   17

3. Draw the hour hand.

9 o'clock

4. Write the number before.

_18_ 19

_22_ 23

_30_ 31

_35_ 36

3 Options for Individualizing

◆ **ENRICHMENT** Ordering Nickels

SMALL-GROUP ACTIVITY   5–15 min

Children, working in small groups, put their nickels in order according to their mint dates. They each try to find a nickel minted in the year in which they were born.

◆ **EXTRA PRACTICE** Counting Coins

SMALL-GROUP ACTIVITY   15–30 min

Children estimate how long it will take them to count to 1 dollar, first with pennies and then with nickels.

Chant together using the cent names as the counts are made: 1 cent, 2 cents, … to 100 cents and then 5 cents, 10 cents, … to 100 cents. Remember to note the amount of time each round takes.

 Adjusting the Activity To help children who are having difficulty, display coins on the overhead, one at a time, as children count 100 pennies and then 20 nickels. (*Note:* Children who are not proficient in English may find this activity beneficial.)

To challenge children, ask them which they think is the easier way to count 1 dollar in coins and to explain why.

◆ **ENRICHMENT** Playing *Penny Guessing*

PARTNER ACTIVITY   15–30 min

Partners pool their pennies. One partner grabs a handful of pennies and spreads them out on the desk. Each partner then guesses how many nickels the partners can trade for the pennies in the pile. Partners record their guesses on scratch paper or slates.

To check their guesses, partners work together to separate pennies in the pile into groups of 5. They replace each group of 5 pennies with 1 nickel and then count the nickels.

Partners play several times, taking turns grabbing a handful of pennies. The goal is to improve their guesses.

HOME LINK MASTER

Counting by 5s   Home Link 2.9

 Family Note   Counting by 5s is a useful skill for counting combinations of coins that include nickels. A good way to practice this skill is to count tally marks. *Please return this Home Link to school tomorrow.*

1. Count by 5s for someone at home.

   I counted up to _____. Answers vary.

2. Tell someone at home how many pennies you will get for 3 nickels. 15 pennies

3. Count the tally marks below.

   //// //// //// //// //// //// //

   I counted ___32___ tally marks.

4. Draw some tally marks below. Count them for someone at home.

   I drew _____ tally marks. Answers vary.

◆ *Math Masters*, p. 171

Lesson 2.9   **129**

2.10 Counting Nickels and Pennies

OBJECTIVE To practice finding the values of various combinations of nickels and pennies.

summaries	materials

1 Teaching the Lesson

Children explore an efficient way of finding the values of various collections of nickels and pennies. They practice this counting skill. [Numeration; Measurement and Reference Frames]

☐ *Math Journal 1*, p. 23
☐ Home Link 2.9
☐ 10 pennies and 5 nickels
☐ overhead coins (optional)
☐ slate

2 Ongoing Learning & Practice

Children play *Penny-Nickel Exchange.* [Numeration; Measurement and Reference Frames]

Children practice and maintain skills through Math Boxes and Home Link activities.

☐ *Math Journal 1*, p. 24
☐ Home Link Master (*Math Masters*, p. 172)
☐ 20 pennies and 10 nickels per partnership
☐ die per partnership (optional: 2 dice per partnership)

3 Options for Individualizing

Enrichment Children play *Coin Top-It.* [Numeration; Measurement and Reference Frames]

Extra Practice Children practice finding the values of various combinations of nickels and pennies. [Numeration; Measurement and Reference Frames]

☐ 3" by 5" index cards (7 per partnership)
☐ scissors
☐ Pattern-Block Template
☐ pennies and nickels (optional)
☐ *Minute Math*®, pp. 65–67

Getting Started

Mental Math and Reflexes

Do "stop and start" counting with individuals or groups. Count by 5s; stop; continue with a new child or group and count on from there by 1s. Stop. Pick a new starting number and repeat. *Suggestions:* Begin with 0, 25, 15, or 30.

Home Link 2.9 Follow-Up

Briefly review answers.

Find out who made the greatest number of tally marks. Ask that child to draw the tally marks on the board. Then count them in unison.

Teaching the Lesson

✦ Counting Nickels and Pennies

WHOLE-CLASS ACTIVITY

Ask children to take out 3 nickels and 2 pennies. Give them a few minutes to try to figure out the total value of the coins. Children then share how they found their answers.

To illustrate one way to count these coins, do the following:

1. Ask 3 children to come to the front of the room, each bringing a nickel, and 2 other children, each bringing a penny.

2. Move the children with nickels to the left end of the line (facing the class) and the children with pennies to the right end.

3. Have the children holding nickels hold up 5 fingers each. Have those holding pennies hold up 1 finger each.

4. Walk behind the children and tap each child lightly on the head as the class counts in unison: 5, 10, 15, 16, 17.

5. Draw Ⓝ Ⓝ Ⓝ Ⓟ Ⓟ on the board. Write 17¢ next to the drawing.

Point out that it really doesn't matter which coins we count first, but that it is easier to count the nickels first, because then we can count by 5s, beginning with the number 5.

✦ Practicing Coin Counts (Math Journal 1, p. 23)

WHOLE-CLASS ACTIVITY

Put combinations of nickels and pennies on the overhead projector or draw them on the board. Have children use their coins to model the suggested problems on page 132.

For the first couple of problems, have children count the coins in unison as they point to their own coins. Thereafter, they can count coins on their own and write their answers on their slates, using cent notation. Children share answers with the class after each problem and count the coins in unison.

Counting Pennies and Nickels

Write the total amount.

1. _9_ ¢

2. _13_ ¢

3. _15_ ¢

Challenge

Write the total amount.

4. Ⓟ Ⓝ Ⓟ Ⓟ Ⓟ Ⓟ Ⓟ Ⓝ Ⓟ Ⓟ Ⓟ Ⓟ Ⓟ _21_ ¢

Show this amount using fewer coins. Ⓝ Ⓝ Ⓝ Ⓝ Ⓟ

5. Ⓝ Ⓝ Ⓟ Ⓟ Ⓟ Ⓝ Ⓟ Ⓝ Ⓟ _25_ ¢

Show this amount using fewer coins. Ⓝ Ⓝ Ⓝ Ⓝ Ⓝ

✦ *Math Journal 1, p. 23*

STUDENT PAGE

Suggestions

How much is

- 1 nickel and 2 pennies? (Count 5, 6, 7; 7¢)
- 2 nickels and 4 pennies? (Count 5, 10, 11, 12, 13, 14; 14¢)
- 3 nickels and 4 pennies? (Count 5, 10, 15, 16, 17, 18, 19; 19¢)
- 4 nickels? (Count 5, 10, 15, 20; 20¢)
- 4 nickels and 3 pennies? (Count 5, 10, 15, 20, 21, 22, 23; 23¢)

Do more problems if needed. When you feel that the children are ready to work on their own, have them complete the journal page independently or with their partners. They may use their coins to help them solve the problems.

Point out that in Problems 4 and 5, children are to write the total value of each set of coins and also show these amounts using fewer coins. They can use the circles on their Pattern-Block Templates to help them draw the coins.

 Adjusting the Activity If children are experiencing difficulty, have them replace each nickel with 5 pennies and then count the total number of pennies. You might also suggest that children write the value of each coin above its picture before trying to find the total value of the set of coins. In Problems 4 and 5, where nickels and pennies are mixed up, suggest that children rearrange the coins on their slates or on a piece of scratch paper to make counting easier.

 ONGOING ASSESSMENT
As children complete the journal page, check to see that they are assigning the correct value to each coin. Dimes are introduced in Lesson 3.11, so children should be fairly comfortable with pennies and nickels by then.

Briefly go over the answers.

Ongoing Learning & Practice

◆ Playing *Penny-Nickel Exchange*

PARTNER ACTIVITY

Partners put 20 pennies and 10 nickels in a pile. This is the bank.

Players take turns. At each turn, a player rolls a die and collects the number of pennies shown on the die from the bank. Whenever players have at least 5 pennies, they say "Exchange!" and trade 5 of their pennies for a nickel in the bank. The game ends when there are no more nickels in the bank. The player who has more nickels wins. If players have the same number of nickels, the player with more pennies wins.

Penny-Nickel Exchange

 Adjusting the Activity Have more skilled children play with a larger bank and two dice.

◆ Math Boxes 2.10 (*Math Journal 1,* p. 24)

INDEPENDENT ACTIVITY

 Mixed Review This journal page provides opportunities for cumulative review or assessment of concepts and skills.

◆ Home Link 2.10 (*Math Masters,* p. 172)

Home Connection Children practice finding total amounts and representing given amounts using alternative coin combinations.

Math Boxes 2.10

1. How many?

~HH~ ~HH~ ~HH~ IIII

___19___

2. Draw the hour hand.

3 o'clock

3. Record the total amount.

Ⓟ Ⓟ Ⓟ Ⓟ Ⓟ Ⓟ

___6___ ¢

Use Ⓟ and Ⓝ to show this amount with fewer coins.

Ⓝ Ⓟ

4. Count up by 2s.

0,	2,	4
6,	8,	10
12,	14,	16
18,	20	

→ *Math Journal 1,* p. 24

Pennies and Nickels

Home Link 2.10

Family Note

First graders do not always know how to represent an amount with the fewest number of coins. That's okay. At this stage, the important thing is that your child understands that 5 pennies can be exchanged for 1 nickel.

In a few days, we are going to set up a "store" in our classroom. Some children will take on the role of shopkeeper, others the role of shopper. Please send some old, inexpensive items (such as rulers, toy cars, stickers, or a ball and jacks) to school for us to use in our store. Thank you!

Please return this Home Link to school tomorrow.

1. Tell or show someone at home how many nickels you get for 10 pennies. 2 nickels

2. For each problem, write how much the coins are worth. Use Ⓟ and Ⓝ to show the amount with fewer coins.

penny	nickel
1¢	5¢
1 cent	5 cents

Example Ⓟ Ⓟ Ⓟ Ⓟ Ⓟ Ⓟ Ⓟ is the same as Ⓝ Ⓟ Ⓟ.

This is 7 cents.

a. Ⓟ Ⓟ Ⓟ Ⓟ Ⓟ Ⓟ Ⓟ Ⓟ Ⓟ Ⓟ Ⓟ is the same as Ⓝ Ⓝ Ⓟ

This is ___11___ cents.

b. Ⓝ Ⓟ Ⓟ Ⓟ Ⓟ Ⓟ Ⓟ is the same as Ⓝ Ⓝ Ⓟ

This is ___11___ cents.

◆ *Math Masters,* p. 172

STUDENT PAGE

HOME LINK MASTER

3 Options for Individualizing

◆ ENRICHMENT Playing *Coin Top-It*

PARTNER ACTIVITY   15–30 min

This game is for 2 players. Each player cuts seven 3" by 5" index cards in half and draws (or stamps) a combination of nickels and pennies on each card. Players can use the circles on their Pattern-Block Templates to help them draw the coins. Each player should make a card for each of 7 through 20 cents.

Combine both sets of cards. Mix them and place them in a stack, facedown. Each player draws a card and counts the coins shown on the card. The player with the larger amount takes both cards. In case of a tie, players take two more cards. The player with the larger amount then takes all of the cards. The game ends when all of the cards in the stack have been played. The winner is the player who took more cards.

Adjusting the Activity When making the card decks, children can write the amounts on one side of the cards, using cent notation.

When playing with such a deck, the cards should be put in a stack with the coin side facing up. When players draw a card, the coin side should remain facing up. After they have decided which card shows the larger amount, players turn the cards over to check that they have not made a mistake.

Children who are more skilled can play with cards having larger amounts

◆ EXTRA PRACTICE Minute Math

SMALL-GROUP ACTIVITY   5–15 min

To offer children more experience with finding the values of various combinations of nickels and pennies, see the following pages in *Minute Math:*

Measurement: pp. 65–67

PLANNING AHEAD

For an optional activity that begins in Lesson 2.13, ask children to bring some old items from home to be used to set up a classroom "store."

2.11 Number Models

OBJECTIVE To introduce number models for change-to-more situations.

summaries	materials

1 Teaching the Lesson

The activities that lead to the introduction of number models are a continuation of the Mental Math and Reflexes routine in which children do a listening count. Children play *Penny-Drop Addition*. They represent each turn orally and then with a number model. [Operations and Computation; Patterns, Functions, and Algebra]

- ☐ Home Link 2.10
- ☐ container
- ☐ pennies
- *See* **Advance Preparation**

2 Ongoing Learning & Practice

Children practice counting combinations of nickels and pennies and comparing amounts by solving *Nickel/Penny Grab* problems. [Measurement and Reference Frames; Numeration]

Children practice and maintain skills through Math Boxes and Home Link activities.

- ☐ *Math Journal 1*, pp. 25 and 26
- ☐ Home Link Master (*Math Masters,* p. 173)
- ☐ 8 nickels and 20 pennies per partnership

3 Options for Individualizing

Extra Practice Children play *Penny Cup* and write a number model to represent each turn. [Operations and Computation; Patterns, Functions, and Algebra]

Reteaching Children complete number models by counting craft sticks. [Operations and Computation; Patterns, Functions, and Algebra]

Extra Practice Children solve problems involving change-to-more situations. [Operations and Computation]

- ☐ pennies; cup; slate
- ☐ half-sheets of paper; number-model cards
- ☐ 20 craft sticks; number cards
- ☐ *Minute Math*®, pp. 8 and 9
- *See* **Advance Preparation**

Additional Information

Advance Preparation For the *Penny-Drop Addition* game in Part 1, you will need a container, such as a can or a pan, so that pennies dropped into it will make a clear, distinct sound.

For the Reteaching activity in Part 3, you need to write a different number model on each of six 4" by 12" construction-paper or tagboard strips. *For example:*

$3 + 4 = $ _____	$2 + 7 = $ _____	$5 + 1 = $ _____
$3 + 6 = $ _____	$8 + 1 = $ _____	$3 + 5 = $ _____

Vocabulary • **add** • **plus** • **number model**

Getting Started

Mental Math and Reflexes

Draw a *pennies* unit box on the board. Drop a selected number of pennies, one at a time, into a container out of children's view. Children count the pennies to themselves as they hear them drop. When the last penny has been dropped, they write the total number of pennies on their slates. Then empty the container and repeat this routine several times, until most children get the correct count.

Have children who want to use slates or scratch paper make a tally mark for each penny that is dropped and then count the tallies.

Unit
pennies

Home Link 2.10
Follow-Up

Briefly go over the answers.

1 Teaching the Lesson

✦ Introducing *Penny-Drop Addition*

WHOLE-CLASS ACTIVITY

1. Begin by doing a "stop-and-start" penny drop.

   ▷ Drop 5 pennies into a container, one at a time. Ask how many pennies are in the container. 5 pennies

   ▷ Tell children that you will drop 3 more pennies into the container and that their job is to figure out how many pennies are in the container after you have dropped in the 3 additional pennies.

   ▷ Drop the 3 pennies. Have children write the total number of pennies on their slates. 8 pennies

   ▷ If some children did not get the correct total, repeat the routine: Drop 5 pennies. Then, as you drop an additional 3 pennies, children count in unison: 6, 7, 8.

   ▷ Summarize what took place with a change-to-more diagram. (See margin.)

   ▷ Point out that another way to say "3 more" is to say "**add** 3."

   ▷ Repeat this routine using different numbers of pennies, until most children get the correct count each time.

2. Next, introduce a variation of this routine. Tell children ahead of time what you are going to do before you start dropping the pennies and ask them to predict the total number of pennies that will be in the container. As you

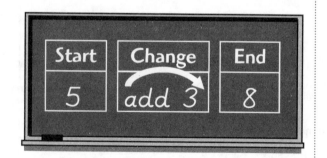

Start	Change	End
5	add 3	8

describe the problem, write what you are going to do on the board. For example:

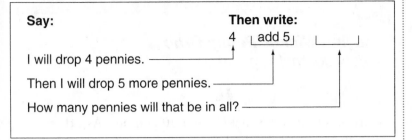

Say: **Then write:**

I will drop 4 pennies.

Then I will drop 5 more pennies.

How many pennies will that be in all?

> ▷ List some of children's answers on the board. Then do a penny drop to check their answers: Drop 4 pennies; children count. Drop 5 more pennies; children count on. Write the total on the answer blank. 9 pennies

> ▷ Repeat this routine using other pairs of numbers.

◆ Introducing Number Models

WHOLE-CLASS ACTIVITY

Tell the class that in mathematics, we can use "shorthand" for what we have been writing on the board. For the word *add*, we can write the symbol +. The + sign is read **plus.** (Write the + sign and the word *plus* next to it on the board.) We can write the = sign in front of the answer. The = sign is read *is equal to.* (Write the = sign and *is equal to* next to it.)

Illustrate the use of these symbols with an example:

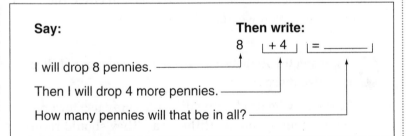

Say: **Then write:**

I will drop 8 pennies.

Then I will drop 4 more pennies.

How many pennies will that be in all?

> ▷ After doing the penny drop, write the answer on the answer blank: 8 + 4 = _12_ .

> 8 + 4 = 12 is called a **number model.**

> ▷ Do a few more penny drops. You or a volunteer can write a number model on the board, or you may ask children to write number models on their slates.

Language Arts Link

Discuss with children the meaning of the word *shorthand,* and ask them if they can think of other examples of people using symbols for words or phrases. Some examples: $ means *dollar,* ¢ means *cent.* In *Everyday Mathematics,* ℗ means *penny* and Ⓝ means *nickel.*

NOTE: Keep in mind that this is children's first exposure to number models. For most children, it will take repeated exposures before they internalize this concept.

STUDENT PAGE

Nickel/Penny Grab Record Sheet

Round 1

We started with ____ Ⓝ and ____ Ⓟ for a total of ____ ¢.

I grabbed ____ Ⓝ and ____ Ⓟ.

My partner grabbed ____ Ⓝ and ____ Ⓟ.

I have ____ ¢. My partner has ____ ¢.

Who has more? _____

Round 2

We started with ____ Ⓝ and ____ Ⓟ for a total of ____ ¢.

I grabbed ____ Ⓝ and ____ Ⓟ.

My partner grabbed ____ Ⓝ and ____ Ⓟ.

I have ____ ¢. My partner has ____ ¢.

Who has more? _____

Round 3

We started with ____ Ⓝ and ____ Ⓟ for a total of ____ ¢.

I grabbed ____ Ⓝ and ____ Ⓟ.

My partner grabbed ____ Ⓝ and ____ Ⓟ.

I have ____ ¢. My partner has ____ ¢.

Who has more? _____

✦ *Math Journal 1, p. 25*

Math Boxes 2.11

1. Count the coins.

Ⓝ Ⓝ Ⓟ

____11____ ¢

2. Count up by 5s.

10,   15,   20,

25 , 30 , 35 ,

40 , 45

3. Complete the table.

Before	Number	After
11	12	13
13	14	15
15	16	17
17	18	19

4. Draw the hour hand.

2 o'clock

✦ *Math Journal 1, p. 26*

Ongoing Learning & Practice

✦ Playing *Nickel/Penny Grab*
(*Math Journal 1*, p. 25)

PARTNER ACTIVITY

Partners take out 8 nickels and 20 pennies. Ask them to calculate the total value of these coins and to describe what they did to find the answer. Expect solution strategies like the following:

▷ First, I found out how much 8 nickels are worth. I counted by 5s and got 40 cents. Then I counted on by 1s until I had counted all of the pennies. I got a total of 60 cents.

▷ I started with 20 because that's how much 20 pennies are worth. Then I counted on by 5s and got 60 cents.

▷ I figured that 20 pennies is the same as 4 nickels, so 8 nickels and 20 pennies is the same as 12 nickels. I counted by 5s twelve times and got 60 cents.

Write 60¢ on the board. Have children record the numbers of nickels and pennies they will use and their total value in their journals.

Next, have one partner mix the coins. Then, child A grabs a handful, and child B takes what is left. Partners help each other find the total value of their coins in order to see whose "grab" is worth more.

They record the totals in their journals and circle the name of the person who grabbed more.

Adjusting the Activity Children who are more skilled may use more coins.

Children who are having difficulty may use fewer coins or only pennies. Either way, they should record this information in their journals.

✦ Math Boxes 2.11 (*Math Journal 1*, p. 26)

INDEPENDENT ACTIVITY

Mixed Review This journal page provides opportunities for cumulative review or assessment of concepts and skills.

◆ Home Link 2.11 (*Math Masters*, p. 173)

Home Connection Children find the value of combinations of nickels and pennies and compare the amounts of money.

Reminder: Again ask children to bring old items from home for the School Store, if you want to use the optional Enrichment activity that is outlined in Lesson 2.13.

3 Options for Individualizing

◆ EXTRA PRACTICE Writing Number Models

PARTNER ACTIVITY   15–30 min

Draw a unit box on the board with the word *pennies* written in it. (See margin.)

Play the *Penny-Cup* game that was introduced in Lesson 2.8. At each turn, players write a number model on their slates. For example, if there are 4 pennies under the cup and 6 pennies on top, a number model might be $4 + 6 = 10$. (When playing with 10 pennies, the sum of the two numbers of pennies will always be 10.)

ONGOING ASSESSMENT
Instead of having children use slates, have them record their number models on half-sheets of paper. Collect and date the papers.

◆ RETEACHING Acting Out Number Models

SMALL-GROUP ACTIVITY   15–30 min

Children, working in groups of 6, solve the number models on number-model cards (see Advance Preparation) with the help of craft sticks. They place craft sticks above the given numbers on the number-model cards, or they place craft sticks above the answer spaces. Then they take turns reading their number models to the group.

◆ EXTRA PRACTICE Minute Math

SMALL-GROUP ACTIVITY   15–30 min

To offer children more experience with change-to-more situations, see the following pages in *Minute Math*:

Basic Routines: pp. 8 and 9

Nickel/Penny Grab

Home Link 2.11

Family Note In class, we have been playing *Nickel/Penny Grab*. Ask your child to tell you how to play. The game provides practice in counting combinations of pennies and nickels and then comparing amounts of money. If your child is having trouble doing this, use real coins to model the problems. Another way to help your child is to trade nickels for pennies and then count the pennies.

We will be doing a lot of work with money exchanges and with counting money. But do not expect your child to master these skills at this time.

Please return this Home Link to school tomorrow.

Sabine and Tony played *Nickel/Penny Grab*. They played 3 games. Here is what happened:

Game 1: Sabine grabbed 2 nickels and 7 pennies.

She had ___17___ ¢.

Tony grabbed 3 nickels and 1 penny. He had ___16___ ¢.

Circle who grabbed more: (Sabine) or **Tony**

Game 2: Sabine grabbed 2 nickels and 6 pennies.

She had ___16___ ¢.

Tony grabbed 3 nickels and 5 pennies. He had ___20___ ¢.

Circle who grabbed more: **Sabine** or (Tony)

Game 3: Sabine grabbed 4 nickels and 8 pennies.

She had ___28___ ¢.

Tony grabbed 3 nickels and 10 pennies. He had ___25___ ¢.

Circle who grabbed more: (Sabine) or **Tony**

◆ *Math Masters*, p. 173

Unit

pennies

NOTE: This activity is a good one to use with children who are working to acquire proficiency in English, as well as native English speakers.

2.12 Subtraction Number Models

OBJECTIVE To extend number models to change-to-less situations.

summaries	materials

1 Teaching the Lesson

Cups are placed standing up. Some are knocked over, and children figure out how many are left standing. This routine is represented first with a change-to-less diagram, then with words, and finally with a number model for the oral description. [Operations and Computation; Patterns, Functions, and Algebra]

☐ Home Link 2.11
☐ 20 paper cups
☐ slate (optional)
***See* Advance Preparation**

2 Ongoing Learning & Practice

Children practice simple addition facts by counting on in *High Roller.* [Numeration; Operations and Computation]

Children practice and maintain skills through Math Boxes and Home Link activities.

☐ *Math Journal 1*, p. 27
☐ Home Link Master (*Math Masters*, p. 174)
☐ 2 dice per partnership or small group
☐ demonstration clock (optional)

3 Options for Individualizing

Enrichment Children practice solving simple addition and subtraction expressions. [Operations and Computation; Patterns, Functions, and Algebra]

Extra Practice Children solve change-to-less problems. [Operations and Computation; Patterns, Functions, and Algebra]

☐ number cards
☐ *Minute Math*®, pp. 8, 9, 16, 80, and 94

Additional Information

Advance Preparation For Part 1, you will need about 20 paper cups. Also, if overhead nickels and pennies are available, you will find them useful for Mental Math and Reflexes.

Vocabulary • subtract • minus

Getting Started

Mental Math and Reflexes

Display coin combinations using overhead nickels and pennies, if available. If not, use Ⓟs and Ⓝs on the board. Children write the total value of each collection on their slates. *Suggestions:*

- 1 nickel and 3 pennies 8¢
- 2 nickels and 5 pennies 15¢
- 2 nickels and 9 pennies 19¢
- 3 nickels and 1 penny 16¢

Home Link 2.11 Follow-Up

Briefly go over the answers to the problems involving the 3 games of *Nickel/Penny Grab.* Have children share their strategies.

Teaching the Lesson

◆ Introducing Subtraction Number Models

WHOLE-CLASS ACTIVITY

This activity is similar to the routine used in Lesson 2.11 to introduce number models for change-to-more situations.

1. Do the following demonstration:

   ▷ Place 9 paper cups standing up in a row.

   How many cups are standing up? 9

   ▷ Knock over 4 of the cups.

   How many cups did I knock over? 4

   How many are left standing up? 5

   ▷ Summarize what took place with a change-to-less diagram:

Start	Change	End
9	4 less	5

   Point out that another way to say "4 less" is to say "**subtract** 4."

   ▷ Repeat this routine a few more times. Each time, start with a different number of cups. You might ask volunteers to knock over the cups each time.

2. Next, introduce a variation of this routine. Tell children what you are going to do before you start knocking over cups, and ask them to predict how many cups will be left standing up. As you describe the problem, write what you are going to do on the board. For example:

Say: **Then write:**

7 |subtract 3| |____|

I will place 7 cups standing up. ———

Then I will knock over 3 cups. ———

How many cups will be left standing up? 4 ———

   ▷ List some of children's answers on the board. Then do the cup knock-over to check children's answers. Write the number of cups that are left standing up on the answer blank.

How many cups are left standing up?

3. Tell the class that for the word *subtract,* we can write the symbol –. The – symbol is read **minus.** (Write the – sign and the word *minus* next to it on the board.) Illustrate the use of these symbols with an example:

Say: **Then write:**

$$12 \quad -5 \quad =\underline{\qquad}$$

I will place 12 cups standing up.

Then I will knock over 5 cups.

How many cups will be left standing? 7

NOTE: Please keep in mind that children are not expected to master writing number models at this time. This is an early exposure to the concept of number models. There will be many future opportunities to reinforce these ideas.

▷ After children have predicted the number of cups standing, knock 5 cups over to check their answers. Write the number of cups that are left standing in the answer blank. A number model to describe this problem is $12 - 5 = 7$.

▷ Do a few more examples, starting with a different number of cups each time. You or a volunteer can write a number model on the board each time; or you may ask children to write number models on their slates.

2 Ongoing Learning & Practice

◆ Playing *High Roller*

PARTNER ACTIVITY 👬

This game can be played by 2 players or in small groups. Players take turns. One player rolls 2 dice. The player keeps the die with the larger number (the High Roller) and throws the other die again. The player then counts on from the number rolled on the first die to get the sum of the two dice.

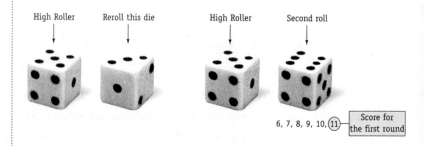

High Roller   Reroll this die   High Roller   Second roll

6, 7, 8, 9, 10, ⑪ — Score for the first round

◆ Math Boxes 2.12 (*Math Journal 1*, p. 27)

INDEPENDENT ACTIVITY

Mixed Review This journal page provides opportunities for cumulative review or assessment of concepts and skills.

◆ Home Link 2.12 (*Math Masters*, p. 174)

Home Connection Children practice telling time to the hour. Briefly review telling time to the hour on the demonstration clock, if necessary.

Reminder: Once again, ask children to bring old items from home for the School Store, if you plan to use the optional Enrichment activity that is introduced in Lesson 2.13.

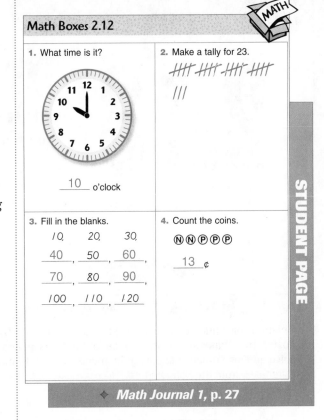

Math Boxes 2.12

1. What time is it?

_____10_____ o'clock

2. Make a tally for 23.

HHT HHT HHT HHT
///

3. Fill in the blanks.

10, *20,* *30,*
40, *50,* *60,*
70, *80,* *90,*
100, *110,* *120*

4. Count the coins.

Ⓝ Ⓝ Ⓟ Ⓟ Ⓟ

_____13_____ ¢

◆ *Math Journal 1*, p. 27

STUDENT PAGE

---

3 Options for Individualizing

◆ ENRICHMENT Playing *Who Am I Thinking Of?*

SMALL-GROUP ACTIVITY **15–30 min**

Give each child a number card. The number on the card is that child's "name" for the game. Pick a number and write clues about that number on the board. For example, for the number 5, you might write $1 + 4$, $7 - 2$, and $0 + 5$. Children raise their hands if the clues fit their numbers.

◆ EXTRA PRACTICE Minute Math

SMALL-GROUP ACTIVITY **15–30 min**

To offer children more experience with change-to-less situations, see the following pages in *Minute Math*:

Basic Routines: pp. 8, 9, and 16
Number Stories: pp. 80 and 94

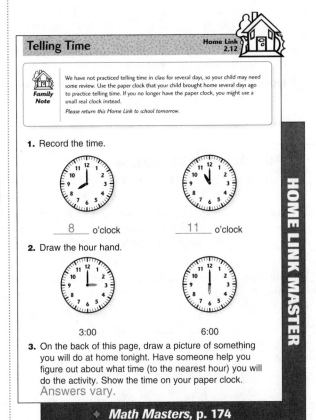

Telling Time

Home Link 2.12

Family Note We have not practiced telling time in class for several days, so your child may need some review. Use the paper clock that your child brought home several days ago to practice telling time. If you no longer have the paper clock, you might use a small real clock instead.

Please return this Home Link to school tomorrow.

1. Record the time.

_____8_____ o'clock   _____11_____ o'clock

2. Draw the hour hand.

3:00   6:00

3. On the back of this page, draw a picture of something you will do at home tonight. Have someone help you figure out about what time (to the nearest hour) you will do the activity. Show the time on your paper clock.
Answers vary.

◆ *Math Masters*, p. 174

HOME LINK MASTER

2.13

Number Stories

OBJECTIVES To practice making up and solving number stories; and to review counting money.

summaries	materials
1 Teaching the Lesson	
Children solve number stories based on a School Store Mini-Poster. They make up number stories for their classmates to solve and also practice counting the money needed to make purchases from the School Store. [Operations and Computation; Measurement and Reference Frames]	☐ *Math Journal 1*, pp. 28 and 29 ☐ Home Link 2.12 ☐ tool-kit coins
2 Ongoing Learning & Practice	
Children write the times shown on clock faces. [Measurement and Reference Frames] Children practice and maintain skills through Math Boxes and Home Link activities.	☐ *Math Journal 1*, p. 30 ☐ Teaching Master (*Math Masters*, p. 14) ☐ Home Link Master (*Math Masters*, p. 175) ***See* Advance Preparation**
3 Options for Individualizing	
Enrichment Children simulate running and shopping at a Classroom Store. [Measurement and Reference Frames] **Language Diversity** Children act out number models. [Numeration; Operations and Computation]	☐ 2 boxes ☐ large cards ☐ objects from home (optional) ***See* Advance Preparation**

Additional Information

Advance Preparation For Part 2, make a copy of *Math Masters*, page 14. Draw an hour hand and a minute hand to show a time on the hour on each clock face. Then run off 1 copy per child. Keep the original for later use.

For the Language Diversity activity in Part 3, you will need two large boxes. Make 2 large cards, one with a + sign on it and one with a − sign. Put the cards in one of the boxes–the "operator" box. Make another large card with an = sign on it. Put that card in the other box–the "equalizer" box. Also, put large number cards in the box.

For the optional Enrichment activity in Part 3, you will need a class bank, from which money can be taken for making purchases at the Classroom Store. Children should not use their tool-kit coins, because they are needed in lessons. Have children bring objects from home to sell in the Classroom Store.

Getting Started

Mental Math and Reflexes

Practice "stop and start" counting. Count by 10s; stop; point to a new child or group; count on from there by 5s; stop; point to a new child or group; count on from there by 1s. This skill will be used in counting combinations of dimes, nickels, and pennies in Unit 3.

Home Link 2.12 Follow-Up

Briefly review the answers. Have a few children share the activities they chose and the times they recorded for those activities.

---

1 Teaching the Lesson

◆ Solving Number Stories (*Math Journal 1*, p. 28)

WHOLE-CLASS ACTIVITY

Write *cents* in a unit box on the board. Ask children to turn to the School Store Mini-Poster on journal page 28.

Make up a few number stories based on the items on the School Store Mini-Poster, and have children solve the number-problem stories, using whatever methods make sense to them: using counters or pennies to act out the story; drawing doodles, tallies, or pictures; counting on fingers; and so on.

Give children a couple of minutes to solve each problem. Then have children share their solution strategies as you record their answers and strategies on the board. Some children may suggest a number model for a story, but do not expect children to be able to do so at this time.

Below are some sample problems and some sample solution strategies. Choose from these samples or make up your own.

• How much less does the eraser cost than the scissors?
3¢ less (Possible strategies: "I lined up 10 pennies for the cost of the scissors and 7 pennies for the cost of the eraser. I put them in pairs and found that the scissors still had 3 pennies left over." "I started with 7¢ and counted up to 10¢—that's 3¢." Possible number models: 10 − 7 = 3 or 7 + 3 = 10.)

School Store Mini-Poster 1

crayon 9¢

scissors 10¢

ball 25¢

gum 1¢

pencil 18¢

candy 5¢

eraser 7¢

STUDENT PAGE

↓ *Math Journal 1*, p. 28

Ⓟ Ⓟ Ⓟ Ⓟ Ⓟ Ⓟ Ⓟ
| | | | | | |
Ⓟ Ⓟ Ⓟ Ⓟ Ⓟ Ⓟ Ⓟ Ⓟ Ⓟ Ⓟ

10 − 7 = _____
7 + _____ = 10

Using pennies to represent the difference between the cost of the eraser and the cost of the scissors

- You want to buy a pencil and an eraser. How much money do you need? 25¢ (Possible strategy: "I made 18 tallies for the cost of the pencil and 7 tallies for the cost of the eraser. Then I counted the tallies: There were four 5s and five tallies, so I counted 5, 10, 15, 20, 21, 22, 23, 24, 25." Possible number model: $18 + 7 = 25$.)

- You have a nickel. You buy 3 pieces of gum. How much money do you have left? 2¢ (Possible strategies: "A nickel is worth 5 cents, so I drew 5 pennies. Then I crossed out the 3 pennies I used to pay for the gum. I had 2 pennies left." "The gum costs 3¢. I counted up to 5¢: 4¢, 5¢. That's 2 more cents." Possible number models: $5 - 3 = 2$ or $3 + 2 = 5$.)

- You have 8 cents. How much more money do you need to buy a crayon? 1¢ (Possible strategy: "I put up 8 fingers. I had to count one more to get to 9. I need one more penny." Possible number models: $8 + 1 = 9$ or $9 - 8 = 1$.)

- How much more does a pencil cost than a piece of candy? 13¢ more (Possible strategy: "I put out 3 nickels and 3 pennies for the pencil. I put out a nickel for the candy. I took out a nickel from the pencil pile and a nickel from the candy pile. Then I still had 2 nickels and 3 pennies left for the pencil—that's 13¢." Possible number models: $18 - 5 = 13$ or $5 + 13 = 18$.)

- You have 2 nickels. You want to buy the ball. How much more money do you need? 15¢ (Possible strategy: "I put 2 nickels in one pile—that's how much I have. I know that there are 5 nickels in 25¢, so I put 5 nickels in another pile—that's how much I need. I know the two piles must be the same when I finish. So I need 3 more nickels—that's 15¢." Possible number models: $25 = 10 + 15$ or $25 - 10 = 15$.)

When you think children are ready, have them make up problems for the class to solve.

◆ Solving More Number Stories
(*Math Journal 1*, pp. 28 and 29)

PARTNER ACTIVITY 👥

Partners complete journal page 29. Encourage them to model problems with coins, pictures, doodles, and tallies—whatever will help. Circulate and assist children who are having difficulty.

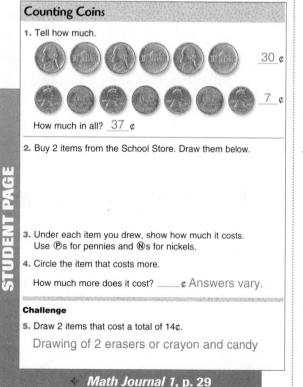

Counting Coins

1. Tell how much.

30 ¢

7 ¢

How much in all? 37 ¢

2. Buy 2 items from the School Store. Draw them below.

3. Under each item you drew, show how much it costs. Use Ⓟs for pennies and Ⓝs for nickels.

4. Circle the item that costs more.

How much more does it cost? _____ ¢ Answers vary.

Challenge

5. Draw 2 items that cost a total of 14¢.

Drawing of 2 erasers or crayon and candy

◆ *Math Journal 1*, p. 29

ONGOING ASSESSMENT

Check on each child's ability to show correct coin combinations for the cost of each item in Problem 2. If children have trouble showing the amounts with nickels and pennies, first have them show the amounts using only pennies. Then have them exchange pennies for nickels.

When most children have completed the problems, briefly go over the answers.

Ongoing Learning & Practice

◆ Telling Time (*Math Masters*, p. 14)

INDEPENDENT ACTIVITY

Use your demonstration clock to go through the hours of the day. Stop at each hour and have children tell the time. When you have something new on your classroom schedule, identify the activity after children have said the hour—for example, at 10 o'clock, we have a snack; at about 12 o'clock, we have lunch; between 3 and 4 o'clock, we go home.

Children work on their own or with their partners to fill in the times suggested in your discussion.

◆ Math Boxes 2.13 (*Math Journal 1*, p. 30)

INDEPENDENT ACTIVITY

Mixed Review This journal page provides opportunities for cumulative review or assessment of concepts and skills.

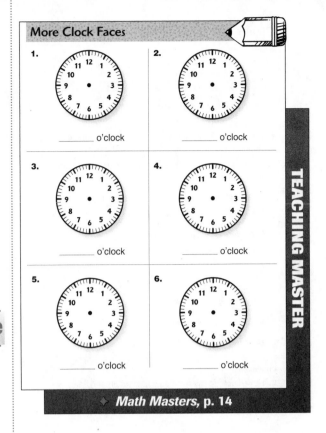

✦ *Math Masters, p. 14*

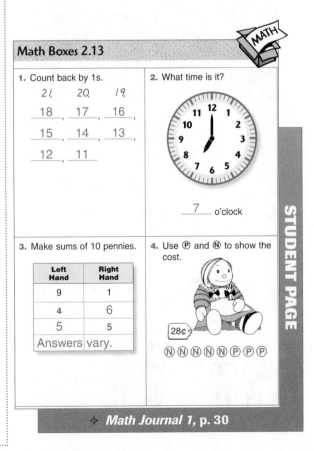

✦ *Math Journal 1, p. 30*

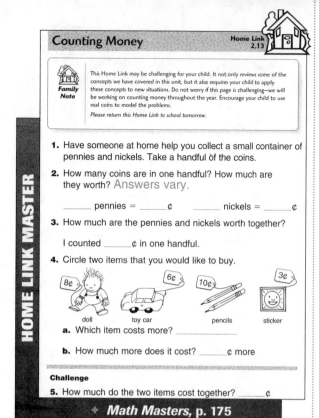

Counting Money

HOME LINK MASTER

1. Have someone at home help you collect a small container of pennies and nickels. Take a handful of the coins.

2. How many coins are in one handful? How much are they worth? **Answers vary.**

   _____ pennies = _____ ¢   _____ nickels = _____ ¢

3. How much are the pennies and nickels worth together?

   I counted _____ ¢ in one handful.

4. Circle two items that you would like to buy.

   8¢ doll   toy car   6¢   10¢ pencils   3¢ sticker

   a. Which item costs more? _____

   b. How much more does it cost? _____ ¢ more

   Challenge

5. How much do the two items cost together? _____ ¢

   ✦ *Math Masters,* p. 175

Children enjoy being customers and shopkeepers in the Classroom Store.

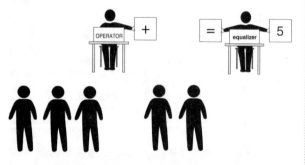

Players use + and = to act out a number story.

✦ Home Link 2.13 (*Math Masters,* p. 175)

Home Connection Children solve several problems that involve counting combinations of pennies and nickels. They are encouraged to use real coins to model the problems.

3 Options for Individualizing

✦ ENRICHMENT The Classroom Store

SMALL-GROUP ACTIVITY 15–30 min

Use items children have brought from home to simulate running a store. Teachers who have done this activity find that children enjoy the hands-on money experience of shopping at the Classroom Store.

Run the store for a few minutes a couple of days per week.

✦ LANGUAGE DIVERSITY Acting Out Number Models

SMALL-GROUP ACTIVITY 15–30 min

Players act out the meanings of addition and subtraction operations, using the +, −, and = symbols.

One child is the "Operator" and sits at the Operator box. Another is the "Equalizer" and sits at the Equalizer box.

Tell a number story about children at a party. For example: *There were 3 children at a birthday party.* (You might use children's names to personalize the story.) Have the 3 children come and stand to the left of the operator. *Two more children came.* Have 2 children stand to the right of the Operator (between the Operator and the Equalizer). Then ask the Operator: *Which sign do you need?* The Operator holds up the + sign. *Equalizer, how many people are at the birthday party now?* The Equalizer holds up the = sign in the hand closest to the Operator and the appropriate number card (5) in the other hand.

For subtraction, start with a given number of children at the party and then have some children leave to go home.

 Adjusting the Activity You can extend this activity by having children make up number stories. Consider reversing the order of the Equalizer and Operator. This will result in number models like 5 = 3 + 2.

2.14
Unit 2 Review and Assessment

OBJECTIVE To review and assess children's progress on the material covered in Unit 2.

1 Assess Progress

learning goals

2a Developing Goal Calculate the values of various combinations of pennies and nickels. **(Lessons 2.10–2.13)**

2b Developing Goal Find complements of 10. **(Lessons 2.3, 2.10, and 2.12)**

2c Developing Goal Solve simple addition and subtraction number stories. **(Lessons 2.6–2.8, 2.10, 2.12, and 2.13)**

2d Developing/Secure Goal Count up and back by 1s on the number grid. **(Lessons 2.1–2.4)**

2e Developing/Secure Goal Tell time to the nearest hour. **(Lessons 2.5, 2.6, and 2.13)**

2f Developing/Secure Goal Exchange pennies for nickels. **(Lessons 2.9–2.11 and 2.13)**

2g Secure Goal Count by 2s to 20. Count by 5s to 50. **(Lessons 2.2, 2.4, 2.7, 2.9, 2.10, and 2.13)**

activities

❑ Written Assessment, Problems 3–5

❑ Slate Assessment, Problem 6

❑ Slate Assessment, Problems 3 and 6

❑ Oral Assessment, Problem 5
❑ Slate Assessment, Problem 1

❑ Oral Assessment, Problem 6
❑ Written Assessment, Problems 1 and 2

❑ Written Assessment, Problem 5

❑ Oral Assessment, Problems 1–3

materials

❑ Teaching Master (*Math Masters*, p. 18; 1 half-sheet per child)

❑ Assessment Master (*Math Masters*, p. 304)

❑ slate

❑ Home Link 2.13

❑ pennies and nickels

❑ demonstration clock

2 Build Background for Unit 3

summaries

Children practice and maintain skills through Math Boxes and Home Link activities.

materials

❑ *Math Journal 1*, p. 31

❑ Home Link Masters (*Math Masters*, pp. 176–179)

Each **learning goal** listed above indicates a level of performance that might be expected at this point in the *Everyday Mathematics* K–6 curriculum. For a variety of reasons, the levels indicated may not accurately portray your class's performance.

Additional Information

Advance Preparation For additional information on assessment for Unit 2, see the *Assessment Handbook,* pages 39–41. For assessment checklists, see *Math Masters,* pages 330, 331, and 355–358.

Getting Started

Home Link 2.13 Follow-Up
Ask a few children to tell how many nickels and pennies they grabbed. Then have the class calculate how much those sets of coins are worth.

NOTE: Many of these assessment suggestions relate to learning goals that have been addressed in the previous unit. Now is a good time to evaluate children's progress toward those goals.

 Assess Progress

✦ Oral and Slate Assessments

WHOLE-GROUP ACTIVITY

If the suggested problems below are not appropriate for your class's level of performance, adjust the numbers (or the problems themselves) to better assess your children's abilities.

Oral Assessment Suggestions

1. Count up by 2s, starting with 0; with 10; with 16. **Goal 2g**

2. Count up by 5s, starting with 0; with 20; with 35; with 40. **Goal 2g**

3. Stop-and-start count by 5s and then by 1s. For example: Count by 5s to 35. Stop. Then count by 1s from 36 to 42. **Goal 2g**

4. Count up and back by 1s on the number line. Start with 0; with 8; with 15; with 19.

5. Count up and back by 1s on the number grid. Start with 0; with 17; with 28; with 35. **Goal 2d**

6. Tell the time shown on the demonstration clock. (Show the following: 3 o'clock; 8 o'clock; 11 o'clock; 5 o'clock; 2 o'clock.) **Goal 2e**

Slate Assessment Suggestions

1. On your number grid ...**Goal 2d**

    ▷ Put your finger on 7. Count forward 5 spaces. Where did you end up? 12

    ▷ Put your finger on 3. Count forward 10 spaces. Where did you end up? 13

    ▷ Put your finger on 14. Count back 6 spaces. Where did you end up? 8

2. Make tally marks for the number of pennies you hear fall into the can. (Drop 8 pennies; 12 pennies; 15 pennies.)

3. Solve these number stories: **Goal 2c**

▷ Michael was juggling with 4 balls. He dropped a ball. How many balls were still in the air? 3 balls

▷ Wilma had 8 dimes in her piggy bank. Then her mom gave her 4 dimes for helping with the dishes. Wilma put those 4 dimes in her piggy bank. How many dimes did Wilma have in her piggy bank then? 12 dimes

▷ Lisa bought a pencil for 4 cents and an eraser for 6 cents. How much money did Lisa spend? 10 cents

4. Which number is 1 more than 9? 10 1 more than 14? 15 1 more than 18? 19 1 more than 26? 27

5. Which number is 1 less than 7? 6 1 less than 12? 11 1 less than 18? 17 1 less than 26? 25

6. Mary had 10 pennies. She left 4 pennies showing on the table. She put the rest under her cup. How many pennies did Mary put under her cup? 6 pennies **Goals 2b and 2c**

◆ Written Assessment (*Math Masters*, p. 304)

INDEPENDENT ACTIVITY

Read the problems with the class. If appropriate, complete the page together—that is, wait for children to complete a problem before reading the next one to them. You may want to do an example with the class for each of the problems.

If children can work independently, have them complete the page alone or with partners. Circulate and assist as children work.

• What time is it? (Problem 1) **Goal 2e**

• Draw the hour hand and the minute hand. (Problem 2) **Goal 2e**

• How much money has Dorothy saved? (Problem 3) **Goal 2a**

• How much money has Frank saved? (Problem 4) **Goal 2a**

• How much money has Phyllis saved? (Problem 5) **Goal 2a**

• Show the same amount with fewer coins. Draw Ⓟs and Ⓝs on the back of this page. (Problem 5) **Goal 2f**

Unit 2 Checking Progress

1. What time is it?

         5 o'clock   9 o'clock

2. Draw the hour hand and the minute hand.

         4 o'clock   8 o'clock

3. How much money has Dorothy saved? 17 ¢

Ⓝ Ⓝ Ⓝ Ⓟ Ⓟ

4. How much money has Frank saved? 15 ¢

Ⓟ Ⓟ Ⓝ Ⓟ Ⓟ Ⓝ

5. How much money has Phyllis saved? 16 ¢

Ⓟ Ⓝ Ⓟ Ⓝ Ⓟ Ⓟ Ⓟ

Show the same amount with fewer coins. Draw Ⓟs and Ⓝs on the back of this page.

◆ *Math Masters*, p. 304

ASSESSMENT MASTER

◆ ALTERNATIVE ASSESSMENT OPTION
Play *Two-Fisted Penny Addition*

PARTNER ACTIVITY

Use this game from Lesson 2.3 to assess children's understanding of sums of 10, as well as their skill in counting objects (rational counting).

On half-sheets of paper, children record their starting numbers of pennies. Then they make two columns—one for Player A and one for Player B. For each round, they record each player's total in the correct column.

Have each child count his or her own total and then guess how many the partner is holding. Check to see whether children can successfully make this prediction. You can collect and date the half-sheet records.

◆ ALTERNATIVE ASSESSMENT OPTION
Find 2-Addend Combinations for Sums of 10

INDEPENDENT ACTIVITY

Use this activity from Lesson 2.4 to assess how children are progressing with simple addition facts for sums of 10.

On half-sheets of paper, have children work individually or with their partners to list all of the possible combinations of two numbers whose sum is 10. Collect and date these record sheets.

◆ ALTERNATIVE ASSESSMENT OPTION
Play *Nickel/Penny Grab* (*Math Masters,* p. 18)

PARTNER ACTIVITY

Use this activity from Lesson 2.11 to assess children's skill with counting nickels and pennies.

Partners combine their tool-kit coins. At each turn, a child:

1. Grabs a handful of coins, guesses how much money this is, and records the guess on *Math Masters,* page 18.

2. Counts the coins and records the actual total.

3. Exchanges all nickels for pennies and counts the total number of pennies.

Nickel/Penny Grab **Record Sheet**

1. Grab a handful of coins. Guess how much money you grabbed. Record your guess.

   I guess my total is _____ cents. Answers vary.

2. Count the coins.

   I have _____ nickels. I have _____ pennies.

   That's _____ cents in all.

3. Trade your nickels for pennies.

   Now I have _____ pennies.

- -

Name _____ Date _____

Nickel/Penny Grab **Record Sheet**

1. Grab a handful of coins. Guess how much money you grabbed. Record your guess.

   I guess my total is _____ cents. Answers vary.

2. Count the coins.

   I have _____ nickels. I have _____ pennies.

   That's _____ cents in all.

3. Trade your nickels for pennies.

   Now I have _____ pennies.

◆ *Math Master,* p. 18

TEACHING MASTER

2 Build Background for Unit 3

♦ **Math Boxes 2.14** (*Math Journal 1*, p. 31)

INDEPENDENT ACTIVITY

Mixed Review This journal page provides opportunities for cumulative review or assessment of concepts and skills.

♦ **Home Link 2.14: Unit 3 Family Letter**
(*Math Masters*, pp. 176–179)

Home Connection This Home Link is a four-page newsletter that introduces parents and guardians to Unit 3's topics and terms. The letter also offers ideas for home-based mathematics activities that are supportive of the classroom work.

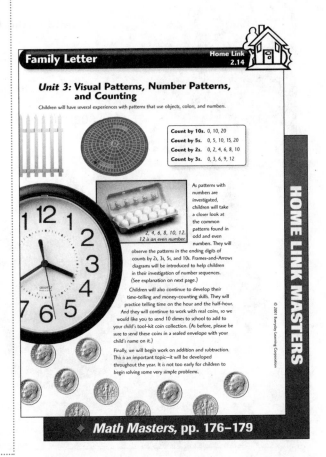

Math Boxes 2.14

1. Draw the hour hand.

6 o'clock

2. Record the total amount.

Ⓝ Ⓝ Ⓟ Ⓟ Ⓟ Ⓟ

__15__ ¢

Use Ⓝ to show this amount with fewer coins.

Ⓝ Ⓝ Ⓝ

3. Complete the table.

Before	Number	After
7	8	9
9	10	11
19	20	21
28	29	30

4. Count up by 2s.

2, 4, 6,

8, 10, 12,

14, 16, 18,

20, 22,

Math Journal 1, p. 31

STUDENT PAGE

Family Letter

Home Link 2.14

Unit 3: Visual Patterns, Number Patterns, and Counting

Children will have several experiences with patterns that use objects, colors, and numbers.

Count by 10s.	0, 10, 20
Count by 5s.	0, 5, 10, 15, 20
Count by 2s.	0, 2, 4, 6, 8, 10
Count by 3s.	0, 3, 6, 9, 12

*2, 4, 6, 8, 10, 12.
12 is an even number.*

As patterns with numbers are investigated, children will take a closer look at the common patterns found in odd and even numbers. They will observe the patterns in the ending digits of counts by 2s, 3s, 5s, and 10s. Frames-and-Arrows diagrams will be introduced to help children in their investigation of number sequences. (See explanation on next page.)

Children will also continue to develop their time-telling and money-counting skills. They will practice telling time on the hour and the half-hour. And they will continue to work with real coins, so we would like you to send 10 dimes to school to add to your child's tool-kit coin collection. (As before, please be sure to send these coins in a sealed envelope with your child's name on it.)

Finally, we will begin work on addition and subtraction. This is an important topic—it will be developed throughout the year. It is not too early for children to begin solving some very simple problems.

Math Masters, pp. 176–179

HOME LINK MASTERS

© 2001 Everyday Learning Corporation

Unit 3
Visual Patterns, Number Patterns, and Counting

overview

One of the most important topics in mathematics is the study of predictable patterns. Since patterns are predictable, it is usually possible to state a rule that describes each pattern. This rule can then be used to extend the pattern. Much of Unit 3 focuses on number patterns: odd and even numbers, patterns in number lines, number grids, and number sequences. Number patterns will be revisited throughout the year.

This unit also continues the steady development of some important first grade topics: Telling time is extended to times on the half-hour, dimes are added to children's existing collections of coins to be counted, and work is begun on solving simple addition and subtraction problems.

contents

UNIT

3

learning goals in perspective

learning goals	links to the past	links to the future
3a **Beginning/Developing** Complete Frames-and-Arrows diagrams. **(Lessons 3.8, 3.9, and 3.11)**	Children had experience with number sequencing in Kindergarten.	The Frames-and-Arrows routine will be used throughout first grade and will extend into second and third grade to incorporate more than one rule and to use a variety of concepts.
3b **Developing** Identify and complete patterns. **(Lessons 3.1–3.5, 3.13, and 3.14)**	Beginning in Kindergarten, children worked with patterns including calendar patterns, even and odd, and skip counting by 2s, 5s, and 10s. Children used calculators, number lines and number grids to explore patterns.	Finding patterns in a variety of situations is emphasized throughout the grades. Identifying patterns is key to determining solutions for "What's My Rule?" and Frames-and-Arrows problems. *(Related Grade 1 lessons: 4.10, 5.2, 5.11, 5.12, 6.1, 6.8, 7.1, 9.1, 9.2, 9.3)*
3c **Developing** Solve simple addition and subtraction problems by skip counting on the number line and the number grid. **(Lessons 3.3–3.7 and 3.9)**	Number lines and number grids are part of *Kindergarten Everyday Mathematics.* Children used them for skip counting and to explore addition and subtraction. *(Related Grade 1 lessons: 1.2, 2.1)*	In later lessons this year, the number line will be compared to the scale on a thermometer, and extended to include negative numbers. Number grids continue to be used in addition and subtraction, and for place value. *(Related Grade 1 lessons: 4.1, 4.9, 5.11, 6.1)*
3d **Developing** Identify numbers as even or odd. **(Lessons 3.2–3.5, 3.13, and 3.14)**	Children were introduced to even and odd numbers in Kindergarten.	Children will continue to work with odd and even number patterns in second and third grade.
3e **Developing** Know the value of pennies, nickels, and dimes, and calculate the values of combinations of these coins. **(Lessons 3.2, 3.4, and 3.10–3.13)**	Children were introduced to pennies, nickels, and dimes in Kindergarten. In Unit 1, practice with skip counting by 5s and 10s helped prepare children to count coins. In Unit 2, children practiced counting pennies and nickels. *(Related Grade 1 lessons: 1.7, 1.11, 2.9–2.10)*	Children will continue to practice counting and using money throughout the grades. *(Related Grade 1 lessons: 6.9, 8.1, 8.2, 8.5, 8.7, 8.8)*
3f **Developing** Tell time to the nearest half-hour. **(Lessons 3.5, 3.7, and 3.8)**	In Kindergarten, children began telling time to the nearest hour, and were introduced to the minute hand. In Unit 2 telling time to the hour was reviewed. *(Related Grade 1 lessons: 2.5, 2.6)*	Children will continue to practice telling time to the nearest half-hour in Unit 4, and work with the minute and second hands in Unit 6. *(Related Grade 1 lessons: 4.8, 6.10, 6.11)*
3g **Developing Goal** Solve simple number stories. **(Lessons 3.6 and 3.11–3.13)**	Children began telling and solving number stories in Kindergarten. *(Related Grade 1 lesson: 2.13)*	Throughout the grades, children will continue to create and solve number stories. *(Related Grade 1 lessons: 5.6–5.11, 8.4)*

assessment
ongoing • product • periodic

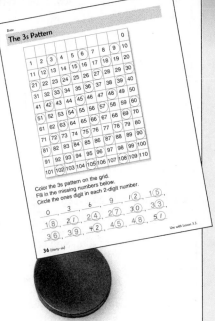

✔ Informal Assessment

Math Boxes These *Math Journal* pages provide opportunities for cumulative review or assessment of concepts and skills.

Ongoing Assessment: Kid Watching Use the Ongoing Assessment suggestions in the following lessons to make quick, on-the-spot observations about children's understanding of:
• Numeration **(Lessons 3.2, 3.5, and 3.6)**
• Operations and Computation **(Lessons 3.6, 3.11, 3.12, and 3.14)**
• Measurement and Reference Frames **(Lesson 3.7)**
• Patterns, Functions, and Algebra **(Lessons 3.1 and 3.8)**

Portfolio Ideas Samples of children's work may be obtained from the following assignments:
• Exchanging Coins **(Lesson 3.11)**
• Identify and Complete Patterns **(Lesson 3.15)**

✔ Unit 3 Review and Assessment

Oral and Slate Assessments Use oral or slate assessments during Lesson 3.15 to assess children's progress toward the following learning goals: **Goals 3c, 3f, and 3g**

Written Assessment Use a written review during Lesson 3.15 to assess children's progress toward the following learning goals: **Goals 3a, 3b, 3c, 3d, 3e, and 3f**

Performance/Group Assessment Use a small-group activity in Lesson 3.15 to assess children's progress toward the following learning goals: **Goals 3b, 3e, and 3f**

assessment handbook

For more information on how to use different types of assessment in Unit 3, see the Assessment Overview on pages 48–51 in the *Assessment Handbook*. The following Assessment Masters can be found in the *Math Masters* book:

> • Unit 3 Checking Progress, p. 305
> • Unit 3 Class Checklist, p. 332
> • Unit 3 Individual Profile of Progress, p. 333
> • Class Progress Indicator, p. 358
> • Math Logs, pp. 362–364
> • Self-Assessment Forms, pp. 365–366
> • Interest Inventory, p. 361

problemsolving

A process of modeling everyday situations using tools from mathematics

Encourage children to use a variety of strategies when attacking a given problem—and to explain those strategies. *Strategies children might use in this unit:*

- Acting out the problem
- Using physical models
- Using a number line
- Identifying and using patterns
- Using a graph
- Using a diagram

Four Problem-Solving REPRESENTATIONS

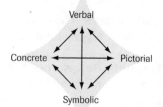

Lessons that teach *through* problem solving, not just *about* problem solving.

Lesson	Activity	Lesson	Activity
3.1	Creating patterns with craft sticks	3.8	Solving-frames-and-arrows problems
3.2	Creating and continuing child patterns; even and odd	3.11	Exchanging pennies, nickels, and dimes
3.4	Exploring even and odd number patterns with coins	3.13	Answering questions and interpreting data on a line plot
3.5	Finding patterns on the number grid	3.14	Using parts-and-total diagram to solve problems
3.6	Introducing addition and subtraction on the number line		

For more information about problem solving in *Everyday Mathematics,* see the *Teacher's Reference Manual,* pp. 197–208.

cross-curricularlinks

social studies

- Children share magnifying lenses for a closer inspection of a dime. **(Lesson 3.11)**
- Discuss different currencies and monetary systems found around the world. **(Lesson 3.11)**

language

- Discuss the origin of the word *dime* and other words that have the same Latin root. **(Lesson 3.11)**

meeting INDIVIDUAL needs

UNIVERSAL ACCESS

◆ RETEACHING

The following features provide additional instructional support:

Adjusting the Activity
- **Lesson 3.1, Part 2**
- **Lesson 3.2, Part 1**
- **Lesson 3.6, Parts 1, 3**
- **Lesson 3.9, Part 1**
- **Lesson 3.12, Parts 1, 3**

Options for Individualizing
- **Lesson 3.5** Counting Hops on the Number Line
- **Lesson 3.10** Playing *Penny-Nickel Exchange*
- **Lesson 3.11** Exchanging Coins

◆ ENRICHMENT

The following features suggest enrichment and extension activities:

Adjusting the Activity
- **Lesson 3.2, Part 1**
- **Lesson 3.6, Part 3**
- **Lesson 3.7, Part 1**
- **Lesson 3.9, Part 1**
- **Lesson 3.10, Part 1**
- **Lesson 3.11, Part 1**
- **Lesson 3.12, Part 1**

Options for Individualizing
- **Lesson 3.1** Making Patterns with Colored Chalk
- **Lesson 3.3** Exploring the 4s Pattern
- **Lesson 3.6** Making Up and Solving Penny Stories
- **Lesson 3.7** Ordering Clock by Time Displayed
- **Lesson 3.11** Playing *Coin Top-It*
- **Lesson 3.12** Playing *Dime-Nickel-Penny Grab*
- **Lesson 3.14** Exploring Sums of Even and Odd Numbers

◆ LANGUAGE DIVERSITY

The following feature suggests ways to support children who are acquiring proficiency in English:

Adjusting the Activity
- **Lesson 3.3, Part 1**

◆ MULTIAGE CLASSROOM

The following chart lists related activities from the *Kindergarten Teacher's Guide to Activities* and lessons from Grade 2 that can help you meet your instructional needs:

Grade K Pages	39 103 187	200	141 174 222	200 162 234 270	10 84 198	198	191 192 254– 257	99 248– 253	248– 253	120 130 140	142 143 172	172	24 176	226 277
Grade 1 Lessons	3.1	3.2	3.3	3.4	3.5	3.6	3.7	3.8	3.9	3.10	3.11	3.12	3.13	3.14
Grade 2 Lessons	7.6 9.7 10.7	1.11 7.1 7.5	1.9 1.11 72	7.1 7.6 10.7	7.1		1.3 3.3 12.2	2.10 3.6	2.10 3.6	1.11	3.7 10.1– 10.6	3.8 10.1– 10.6	3.5 6.3 7.7	2.2– 2.5 4.2

m*aterials*

lesson	math masters pages	manipulative kit items	other items
3.1	Teaching Master, p. 19 (optional) Teaching Master, p. 20 Home Link Master, p. 180	Pattern-Block Template 16 craft sticks per partnership number cards 0–10	construction paper colored chalk
3.2	Home Link Master, p. 181	slate Class Number Line	40 pennies per partnership nickels
3.3	transparency of Teaching Master, p. 21 (optional) Teaching Masters, pp. 21–22 Home Link Master, p. 182 ***See* Advance Preparation, p. 178.**		colored marking pens (optional) laminated Number Grid

3.4	Teaching Master, p. 23
	   per group (optional)
	Teaching Masters, pp. 24–26
	Home Link Master, p. 183
		per small group:
		  double-9 dominoes
		  pattern blocks
		  Pattern-Block Template
			materials for a math game

3.5	Home Link Master, p. 184 Teaching Master, p. 27 (optional)	Class Number Line	took-kit clock large number line ***See* Advance Preparation, p. 187.**
3.6	Home Link Master, p. 185	slate	tool-kit pennies

3.7	Home Link Masters,
	  pp. 186 and 187
		clock-face stamps (optional)	hour-hand-only demonstration clock
			demonstration clock
			tool-kit clock
			3" by 5" index cards cut in half
			  (optional)

3.8	transparency of Teaching Master, p. 28 (optional) Teaching Master, pp. 14 and 28 Home Link Masters, pp. 188 and 189 ***See* Advance Preparation, p. 201.**		semi-permanent chalk (optional) tool-kit clock
3.9	transparency of Teaching Master, p. 28 (optional) Home Link Master, p. 190 ***See* Advance Preparation, p. 206**		
3.10	Home Link Master, p. 191		calculator overhead calculator (optional) pennies and nickels
3.11	Teaching Master, p. 29 Home Link Masters, pp. 192 and 193		tool-kit coins overhead coins (optional) 1 magnifying glass per group calculator
3.12	Teaching Master, p. 30 Home Link Master, p. 194	slate 2 dice per partnership	overhead coins (optional) tool-kit coins
3.13	Home Link Master, p. 195		stick-on notes
3.14	Teaching Master, pp. 24 and 31–32 Home Link Master, p. 196	slate double-9 dominoes	resealable plastic bag paper plate and counters (optional) ***See* Advance Preparation, p. 231.**
3.15	Teaching Master, p. 28 Assessment Masters, pp. 305 and 306 Home Link Masters, pp. 197–200	slate craft sticks pattern blocks die	tool-kit clock and coins

planning tips

Pacing

Pacing depends on a number of factors, such as children's individual needs and how long your school has been using *Everyday Mathematics*. At the beginning of Unit 3, review your Content by Strand Poster to help you set a monthly pace.

SEPTEMBER	OCTOBER	NOVEMBER

◄─── MOST CLASSROOMS ───►

Using the Projects

Project 4 will help your children get ready for the holidays. Use geometric shapes to create designs for gift wrap or greeting cards. The Projects can be found at the back of this book.

Home Communication

Share Home Links 3.1–3.14 with families to help them understand the content and procedures in this unit. At the end of the unit, use Home Link 3.15 to introduce Unit 4. Supplemental information can be found in the *Home Connection Handbook*.

NCTM Standards

Standard	1	2	3	4	5	6	7	8	9	10
Unit 3 Lessons	2-6, 8-12, 14	1-5, 8-10, 14	1, 4	4-7, 11, 12	13	1-14	1-14	1-14	1-14	1-14

Content Standards
1 Number and Operation
2 Patterns, Functions, and Algebra
3 Geometry and Spatial Sense
4 Measurement
5 Data Analysis, Statistics, and Probability

Process Standards
6 Problem Solving
7 Reasoning and Proof
8 Communication
9 Connections
10 Representations

PRACTICE *through* Games

Everyday Mathematics uses games to help children develop good fact power and other math skills.

- Practice numeration in *Before and After* **(Lesson 3.1)**
- Find equivalent coin combinations in *Penny-Nickel Exchange* **(Lessons 3.2 and 3.10)**
- Practice adding coins with *Coin Top-It* **(Lesson 3.11)**
- Review coin exchange and numeration in *Coin-Dice* **(Lessons 3.12 and 3.15)**
- Practice addition and number comparison in *Dime-Nickel-Penny Grab* **(Lesson 3.12)**
- Practice addition skills with *Domino Top-It* **(Lesson 3.14)**

The notes below highlight the major content ideas presented in Unit 3. These notes may help you establish instructional priorities.

Patterns All Around (Lessons 3.1 and 3.4)

The main thrust of these lessons is to help children become aware that there are shapes or combinations of shapes and colors that can be arranged in regular ways according to patterns.

The lessons focus on simple patterns so that children can see how predictable the patterns are. These patterns should be merely a starting point to sensitize children to more complex patterns in their everyday world. For example, patterns around the classroom or school include grilles on light fixtures, panes in windows, wire or slats in fences, the array of milk cartons in a box or crate, floor or ceiling tiles, and patterns in magazine or newspaper pictures and advertisements. Encourage children to look for and bring examples of patterns to school.

Visual patterns make fine recreational exercises at any time and are very helpful in building both aesthetic sensibilities and intuition about geometry.

Odd and Even Number Patterns (Lessons 3.2 and 3.4)

An understanding of odd and even numbers can lead children to generalizations of mathematical importance. For example, when an odd number of things is paired or shared between two people, there will always be one thing left over. From this understanding, children may begin to observe relationships such as the following:

▷ The sum of two even numbers is always an even number—the pieces remain paired.

▷ The sum of two odd numbers is also always an even number—the two leftover pieces can be paired up.

▷ The sum of an even number and an odd number is always an odd number—the leftover piece cannot be paired.

> **Kevin:** Odd numbers are neat. They always have a middle.
>
> **Father:** What?
>
> **Kevin:** See (pointing to the third of five sticks in a row), always something in the middle. But with even numbers (removing the third stick from the row), there is just a space in the middle.

Odd numbers of people or things are often seen as a nuisance since they spoil equal sharing or make it impossible to get the same number of players on two teams. But consider the insight (see previous page) reported by the parent of a first grader. Mathematicians would recognize this observation to be a nice "theorem." As children work with data, they will find that this property of odd numbers makes identifying a "middle value" easier. Not many children can express such pattern-based properties, even if they "see" and "feel" them. But children often "know" things long before they can say or write them.

									0
1	2	3	4	5	6	7	8	9	10
11	12	13	14	15	16	17	18	19	20
21	22	23	24	25	26	27	28	29	30
31	32	33	34	35	36	37	38	39	40
41	42	43	44	45	46	47	48	49	50
51	52	53	54	55	56	57	58	59	60
61	62	63	64	65	66	67	68	69	70
71	72	73	74	75	76	77	78	79	80
81	82	83	84	85	86	87	88	89	90
91	92	93	94	95	96	97	98	99	100
101	102	103	104	105	106	107	108	109	110

Number-Grid Patterns (Lesson 3.3)

Much use is made of number grids because these grids are so effective in showing the patterns in our number system. For example, by coloring the results of various counts on the number grid, counting patterns become apparent.

In future lessons, number grids will also be quite useful for illustrating place-value concepts and for solving addition and subtraction problems.

Number Lines (Lessons 3.5 and 3.6)

Number lines were introduced in *Everyday Mathematics* in Kindergarten. Lesson 3.5 focuses on number-line concepts that children have worked with but may not have talked about in specific terms:

▷ The marks on any number line are equally spaced, but the spacing need not be the same on all number lines.

▷ Number lines can be vertical, horizontal, diagonal, or of any other orientation.

▷ Number lines can begin and end with any numbers—they need not begin with zero.

▷ The arrow at each end of a number line indicates that a number line can go on forever in either direction. Therefore, the line may show both positive and negative numbers.

Number lines are particularly important in this unit as a visual device that can be used for solving simple addition and subtraction problems. In Lesson 3.5, children practice counting up and back by 1s, starting at any number. In Lesson 3.6, these "hops" on the number line are related to addition and subtraction. For example, to solve the problem 3 + 5 = ___, start at 3 on the number line and count up 5 hops. You end on 8, which is the answer to the problem.

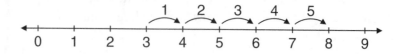

Number lines do have limitations. As numbers become larger, number lines become cumbersome when stretched along a wall of the classroom; and it is nearly impossible to print long number lines in children's books without breaking them into chunks. On the other hand, number grids fit nicely on a page or on a classroom poster. Number grids may be used in the same way as number lines: Children can count up and back from any number on the grid, thus using it as an aid for addition and subtraction. Later, children will learn to add and subtract 2-digit numbers on the number grid without having to count by 1s. For example, to add 37 to a number, they can simply count down 3 rows and then count 7 spaces. This procedure leads to an addition algorithm in which the tens are added first and then the ones.

NOTE: The *Everyday Mathematics* authors prefer number grids with spaces for a few negative numbers before zero and a few numbers after 100. The grids in children's math journals permit numbers from −9 to 110.

Time and Money (Lessons 3.7, 3.11, and 3.12)

These lessons continue where Lessons 2.5–2.10 left off. The purpose of introducing time and money incrementally is to give children time to practice what has been introduced before adding new elements.

Lesson 3.7 extends telling time to the nearest half-hour. Continue to practice estimating time, using the hour-hand-only clock.

Lesson 3.11 adds dimes to children's tool-kit coin collections. As in Unit 2, the material first focuses on coin exchanges as a prerequisite for counting collections of dimes, nickels, and pennies. It is most efficient to count the coins with the greatest value (dimes) first, and then the nickels, and finally the pennies. This should not be too difficult since children have already practiced counting by 10s, 5s, and 1s.

Dollars-and-cents notation is introduced in Lesson 3.11 as a first exposure to decimals. Children should have no difficulty with amounts that are 1 dollar or more. Expect many children to make errors with amounts that are less than 1 dollar, especially with amounts that are less than 10 cents. Children may write $0.5 or $0.50 for 5 cents. But don't worry; they will get it right following repeated exposures.

Frames and Arrows (Lessons 3.8 and 3.9)

The Frames-and-Arrows diagram is one of several formats used for showing regular sequences of numbers. It allows for many variations and experiences in problem solving. Frames-and-Arrows diagrams consist of three basic elements:

▷ **Frames** in which numbers are written or can be written.

▷ **Arrows** that link the frames. These arrows represent a consistent pattern or rule for progressing from one frame to the next.

▷ A **rule box** that identifies the pattern or rule for the arrows.

In a given problem, some or all of the frames may be blank, or the rule may not be shown. Children use the information provided to find the missing parts. In Lesson 3.8, the rule is given and children apply the rule to find the numbers that belong in the blank frames. In Lesson 3.9,

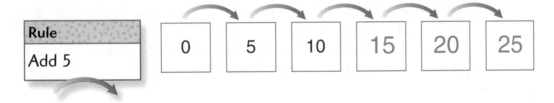

the numbers in the frames are given, and children find the rule that dictates the sequence of numbers. Problems in which the first frame is blank are avoided, because these kinds of problems involve applying the rule in the opposite direction.

Counting with the Calculator (Lesson 3.10)

To help children learn to count with calculators by using the ⊜ key, they are taught that the calculator must be programmed. There are three elements that must be entered first: the starting number, an indication of whether the calculator is to count up ⊕ or down ⊖ from the starting number, and the number the calculator is to count by.

Calculator counts will be used as an aid in solving number-sequence problems and to observe place-value digit patterns.

Data Day (Lesson 3.13)

This lesson continues children's experience with collecting, organizing, displaying, and analyzing data. In Units 1 and 2, children collected and recorded various kinds of data on tally charts. In this lesson, they collect data about the class's favorite color and display the data using a line plot. Line plots are similar to tally charts, but they look very much like bar graphs. As such, they are useful interim steps to the introduction of bar graphs.

Problem Solving (Lessons 3.11–3.13)

The Mental Math and Reflexes problems in these lessons consist of parts-and-total number stories. As with the change-to-more and change-to-less problems in Unit 2, display a parts-and-total diagram to summarize each problem situation. It is important that this not be done until after children have had a chance to share their solution strategies. Use the diagrams as a way to summarize the discussions.

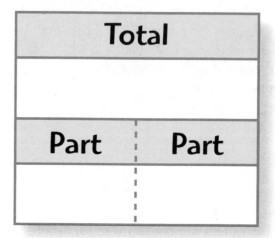

Domino-Dot Patterns and Domino Combinations
(Lesson 3.14)

Domino combinations are used in preparation for the study of fact families, which will be introduced in Lesson 6.3. Here, the focus is on addition facts. Children observe that three numbers can be associated with any domino: the number of dots on each half of the domino and the total number of dots. When viewed in this way, dominoes are examples of parts-and-total situations. Some children may observe this relationship, but it need not be discussed unless someone brings it up.

> ### For **additional information** on the following topics, see the *Teacher's Reference Manual:*
>
> - calculators
> - data collection, organization, and analysis
> - money
> - number grids, scrolls, and lines
> - odd and even number patterns
> - operations and use classes
> - sequences
> - teaching problem solving
> - time
> - visual patterns

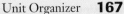

3.1 Visual Patterns

OBJECTIVE To explore and extend visual patterns.

---

summaries   materials

1 Teaching the Lesson

Children explore and create their own patterns using craft sticks. They also look for patterns in the classroom.
[Patterns, Functions, and Algebra; Geometry]

- ☐ *Math Journal 1*, p. 32
- ☐ Class Number Line
- ☐ Pattern-Block Template
- ☐ 16 craft sticks per partnership
- ☐ masking tape or magnets (optional)

2 Ongoing Learning & Practice

Children play *Before and After* to practice identifying the number that is 1 less and the number that is 1 more than a given number. [Numeration; Operations and Computation]

Children practice and maintain skills through Math Boxes and Home Link activities.

- ☐ *Math Journal 1*, p. 33
- ☐ Home Link Master (*Math Masters*, p. 180)
- ☐ Teaching Master (*Math Masters*, p. 19; optional)
- ☐ number cards 0–10 (1 deck per partnership)

3 Options for Individualizing

Extra Practice Children make colored patterns out of cutout diamond shapes. [Patterns, Functions, and Algebra; Geometry]

Enrichment Children identify and extend patterns using colored chalk. [Patterns, Functions, and Algebra]

Extra Practice Children review patterns in counting.
[Numeration]

- ☐ Teaching Master (*Math Masters*, p. 20)
- ☐ crayons or colored pencils
- ☐ scissors
- ☐ glue or paste
- ☐ construction paper
- ☐ colored chalk
- ☐ *Minute Math*®, p. 31

Additional Information
Vocabulary • **pattern**

Getting Started

Mental Math and Reflexes

1. Children count up and back by 2s in unison as you point to the Class Number Line.
   - Start at 0 and count up by 2s to 40. 0, 2, 4, ..., 40
   - Then count back by 2s, starting at 30. 30, 28, 26, ... Stop at 0 and ask children if they can figure out what will happen if you continue to count back by 2s. You will name negative numbers. Children might notice that the numbers that come before 0 are in the opposite order from the numbers that come after 0. Children should not be expected to know about negative numbers at this time, but some children will enjoy this venture into new territory.

2. Children count up and back by 2s in unison as you point to the Class Number Grid Poster.
   - Start at 0 and count up by 2s to 40. 0, 2, 4, ..., 40
   - Then count back by 2s, starting at 30. 30, 28, 26, ... *How is counting by 2s on the number grid the same as counting by 2s on the number line?* You land on the same numbers. *How is it different?* Instead of going from left to right in a straight line, you go to the end of a row and then to the beginning of the next row. Children may notice that you land in the same columns in each row. Acknowledge that this is correct, but do not emphasize this at this time.

1 Teaching the Lesson

◆ Introducing Visual Patterns

WHOLE-CLASS ACTIVITY

Display a simple craft-stick pattern on the overhead (or by attaching the sticks with masking tape or magnets to the board). *For example:*

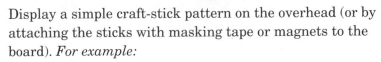

Record the pattern on the board with vertical and horizontal marks: |— | —

Ask children to figure out what comes next. | Then add a vertical mark to the pattern on the board.

Repeat this routine using another pattern. *For example:*

Tell children that these are examples of **patterns.** Ask children to describe what they think a pattern is. It's something that happens over and over. It's something that allows you to predict what will come next.

Invite children to propose other craft-stick patterns. Display these patterns on the overhead or on the board. Ask the class to describe each pattern and to tell what comes next to continue the pattern.

ONGOING ASSESSMENT
At this early stage, children's descriptions of patterns may be awkward or incomplete. It doesn't matter; praise their attempts regardless.

NOTE: Many *Everyday Mathematics* teachers and children have enjoyed making a Patterns Museum by displaying patterns children find at home and in their everyday world. The exhibits can begin with patterns you and children observe in the classroom, responses to Home Link 3.1, and some responses you collect from some of the Explorations.

NOTE: Keep a classroom pool of extra craft sticks handy in case some children devise elaborate patterns for which they need more craft sticks.

◆ Finding Patterns in the Classroom

WHOLE-CLASS ACTIVITY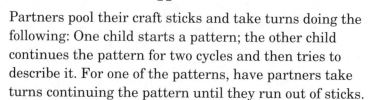

Ask children to point out and describe any patterns they observe in the classroom. Floor tiles, light fixtures, and so on Explain that patterns are a part of our world. Some patterns are simple; others are complex. Patterns are everywhere.

◆ Creating Craft-Stick Patterns

PARTNER ACTIVITY

Partners pool their craft sticks and take turns doing the following: One child starts a pattern; the other child continues the pattern for two cycles and then tries to describe it. For one of the patterns, have partners take turns continuing the pattern until they run out of sticks.

Remind children of partner etiquette: "Guide, Check, Praise." Doing so will help to keep these pattern games from becoming competitive and will also help prevent less successful attempts from being criticized.

◆ Extending Patterns (*Math Journal 1*, p. 32)

PARTNER ACTIVITY

Children extend visual patterns and then create their own patterns for their partners to extend.

2 Ongoing Learning & Practice

◆ Playing *Before and After* (*Math Masters*, p. 19)

PARTNER ACTIVITY

This game is for 2 players and is played with a deck of cards consisting of four of each card numbered 1–10. Directions are found on *Math Masters*, page 19.

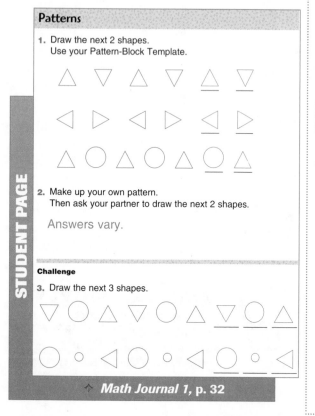

Patterns

1. Draw the next 2 shapes.
   Use your Pattern-Block Template.

2. Make up your own pattern.
   Then ask your partner to draw the next 2 shapes.

   Answers vary.

Challenge

3. Draw the next 3 shapes.

Math Journal 1, p. 32

STUDENT PAGE

Adjusting the Activity If you wish to decrease the level of difficulty, have children play with the 0–6 cards only. Or have each child start with only 3 cards in a hand instead of 6.

◆ Math Boxes 3.1 (*Math Journal 1*, p. 33)

INDEPENDENT ACTIVITY

 Mixed Review This journal page provides opportunities for cumulative review or assessment of concepts and skills.

◆ Home Link 3.1 (*Math Masters*, p. 180)

 Home Connection Children find patterns in their homes and then draw the patterns. Children are encouraged to look for articles of clothing that have one or more patterns on them and to wear those clothes to school the next day.

Before and After

Materials	❑ cards 0–10 (4 of each number)
Players	2

Directions

1. Mix the cards.
2. Deal 6 cards to each player.
3. Put 2 cards down side by side and faceup.
4. Put the rest of the cards facedown in a stack.
5. Take turns. When it is your turn:
   - Look for any number in your hand that comes *before* or *after* one of the faceup numbers. Put it on top of the faceup number. Play as many cards as you can.
   - Take as many cards as you need from the stack so that you have 6 cards again.
   - If you can't play any cards when it is your turn, take 2 cards from the stack. Place them faceup on top of the 2 faceup cards. Try to play cards from your hand again. If you still can't, your turn is over.
6. The game is over when:
   - There are no more cards left in the stack
   - No one can play any more cards
7. The player holding fewer cards at the end wins.

◆ *Math Masters*, p. 19

TEACHING MASTER

Math Boxes 3.1

1. Draw the hour hand.

4 o'clock

2. Count up by 2s.

<u>6</u> , <u>8</u> , <u>10</u> ,

<u>12</u> , <u>14</u> , <u>16</u> ,

<u>18</u> , <u>20</u> , <u>22</u> ,

<u>24</u> , <u>26</u>

3. Draw dice dots for 6.

4. Record the total.

Ⓝ Ⓟ Ⓟ Ⓟ Ⓟ Ⓟ Ⓟ

<u>11</u> ¢

Use Ⓟ and Ⓝ to show this amount with fewer coins.

Ⓝ Ⓝ Ⓟ

STUDENT PAGE

✦ *Math Journal 1*, p. 33

Patterns

Family Note Patterns are so important in mathematics that mathematics is sometimes called the "Science of Patterns." Help your child identify patterns in and around your home and in the outside world.

Some suggestions for places to look for patterns:

· floor tiles   · carpeting   · window panes
· curtains   · wallpaper   · fences

Please return this Home Link to school tomorrow.

1. Find at least two patterns in your home. Draw the patterns you find.

Answers vary.

2. If you have articles of clothing (such as a shirt or a pair of socks) that have patterns on them, please wear those clothes to school tomorrow!

✦ *Math Masters*, p. 180

HOME LINK MASTER

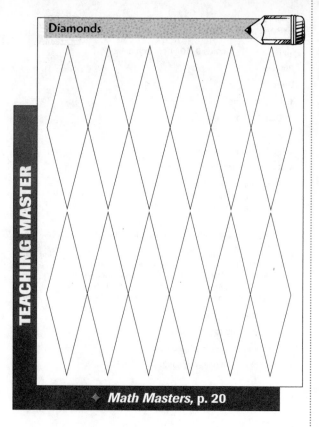

Diamonds

Math Masters, p. 20

3 Options for Individualizing

✦ EXTRA PRACTICE Making Colored Patterns
(*Math Masters*, p. 20)

INDEPENDENT ACTIVITY 👤   15–30 min ⏰

Children color the diamonds on the master in two colors (for example, the top row red and the bottom row blue). Then they cut out the shapes, make one or two patterns, and glue or paste their shape patterns onto construction paper. Collect the patterns and use them to make a bulletin-board display.

Example of a pattern

✦ ENRICHMENT Making Patterns with Colored Chalk

WHOLE-CLASS ACTIVITY   5–15 min

Using colored chalk, start a sequential pattern on the board. Then have children tell you how to continue it. Write the words in the colors that children name, or use one color for horizontal marks and another color for vertical shapes, or draw shapes with each kind of shape a different color.

Ask children to suggest other color patterns. Draw the patterns on the board.

✦ EXTRA PRACTICE Minute Math

SMALL-GROUP ACTIVITY   5–15 min

To offer children more experience with patterns, see the following page in *Minute Math:*

Counting: p. 31

3.2 Even and Odd Number Patterns

OBJECTIVE To explore even and odd number patterns.

summaries	materials

1 Teaching the Lesson

Children are introduced to even and odd numbers by pairing members of groups of various sizes. Children use the pairing procedure to determine whether a randomly chosen number of pennies is odd or even. Children also explore even and odd number patterns and practice identifying even and odd numbers. [Patterns, Functions, and Algebra; Numeration]

- ☐ *Math Journal 1*, p. 34
- ☐ Home Link 3.1
- ☐ slate
- ☐ pennies (40 per partnership)
- ☐ Class Number Line

2 Ongoing Learning & Practice

Children play *Penny-Nickel Exchange* [Measurement and Reference Frames; Numeration]

Children practice and maintain skills through Math Boxes and Home Link activities.

- ☐ *Math Journal 1*, p. 35
- ☐ Home Link Master (*Math Masters*, p. 181)
- ☐ pennies and nickels

3 Options for Individualizing

Extra Practice Children determine whether the number of children who are present is an even or odd number. [Numeration; Patterns, Functions, and Algebra]

Extra Practice Children model even and odd numbers. [Numeration; Patterns, Functions, and Algebra]

Extra Practice Children count up and back by 1s to find missing numbers between given numbers. [Numeration; Patterns, Functions, and Algebra]

- ☐ *Minute Math®*, pp. 28 and 29

Additional Information
Vocabulary • **even number** • **odd number**

Getting Started

Mental Math and Reflexes

Children skip count on the number grid on the journal inside back cover.

- Count up by 2s from 26 to 60.
- Count back by 5s from 35 to 0 and from 100 to 70.
- Count back by 10s from 100 to 0.
- Count up by 5s from 0 to 50 and from 35 to 85.
- Count up by 10s from 0 to 100.

Home Link 3.1 Follow-Up

Children display and tell about the patterns on their Home Links and on their clothing.

Pairs	Not All Pairs
2	3
4	5
6	7
8	9
10	11

✦ Introducing Even and Odd Numbers

WHOLE-CLASS ACTIVITY

For this demonstration, children are called to the front of the room, one at a time.

Start a table on the board with columns labeled *Pairs* and *Not All Pairs*. Ask two children to come to the front of the room. Two children make a pair, so write the number 2 in the *Pairs* column. (Leave a blank line above the 2, to be filled in later.)

Invite another child to the front of the room. Ask whether there is another child standing with whom this child can be paired. No, this child is temporarily the "odd person out." Keep this activity playful!

Write 3 in the *Not All Pairs* column.

Call another child to the front of the room. This child can be paired with the third child, so now each child has a partner. Write 4 in the *Pairs* column.

Continue calling children one at a time, until there are 10 children (5 pairs) in line. With each new child, record the total number of children in the appropriate column of the table. (You may want to remind children of the first grade chant: "2, 4, 6, 8, first graders are really great!")

• In which column would you write 11? In the *Not All Pairs* column

Tell the class that whenever each child standing can be paired with another child, the total number of children is called an **even number.** Replace the word *Pairs* with the word *Even* in the heading in the table. Then tell the class that when there is a child who cannot be paired with another child, the total number of children standing is called an **odd number.** Replace *Not All Pairs* with *Odd* in the heading.

✦ Exploring Even and Odd Number Patterns

PARTNER ACTIVITY

Divide the class into partnerships and have partners pool their pennies. Each partnership should have 40 pennies. One partner grabs a fistful of pennies; the other partner takes the rest. Children count their pennies and write the totals on their slates. Then they arrange their pennies in pairs and decide whether the total number of pennies is an even number or an odd number. They report their results for you to record in the table.

 Adjusting the Activity If children are having difficulty, have each partnership use only 20 pennies.

 ONGOING ASSESSMENT
Check to make sure that children realize when they have made all possible pairs with their pennies. This lesson deals with even and odd numbers for the first time, so expect that many children may have difficulty with this concept.

When all children have reported their results, bring the class together to explore the patterns in the numbers in the table. Make sure that the following concepts are discussed:

▷ Even numbers end in 0, 2, 4, 6, or 8. Odd numbers end in 1, 3, 5, 7, or 9. (Circle the ones digits in the numbers in the table.)

▷ Even numbers are counts by 2s, starting with 0.

▷ If you know an even number, you know that its two neighbors—the number that comes before it and the number that comes after it—are odd numbers. *For example:* 8 is an even number, so 7 and 9—its neighbors—are both odd numbers. Try to elicit recognition of this pattern by referring to the Class Number Line.

▷ If you know an odd number, you know that its two neighbors are even numbers. *For example:* 9 is an odd number, so 8 and 10—its neighbors—are both even numbers. Again, refer to the Class Number Line.

Ask: *Do you think that 1 is an even number or an odd number? Why?* It is an odd number because it comes before 2, which is an even number. *What about 0?* 0 is an even number because it comes before 1, which is an odd number.

Write 0 and 1 in the first line of the table.

NOTE: The pairing definition for even numbers does not apply to the number zero, since 0 objects cannot be paired. In later grades, children will learn that a number is even if, when it is divided by 2, the remainder is 0. Using this definition, 0 is an even number, since $0 \div 2$ has a remainder of 0.

Even	Odd
0	1
2	3
4	5
6	7
8	9
10	11

Odd and Even Patterns

Label **odd** or **even**. How many ☐s?

Example

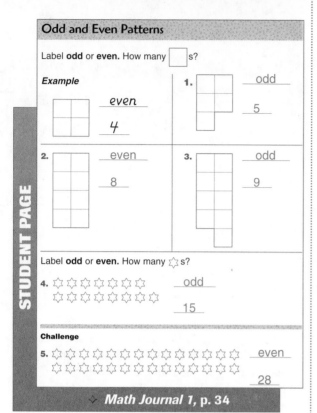

even
4

1. odd
5

2. even
8

3. odd
9

Label **odd** or **even**. How many ☆s?

4. odd
15

Challenge

5. even
28

Math Journal 1, p. 34

On the board, draw a "circle of digits" for even and odd numbers.

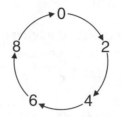 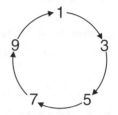

As you point to the digits, lead the class in a choral recitation of the even and odd numbers into the forties or beyond.

 Adjusting the Activity To extend this activity, write some large numbers on the board and ask whether they are even numbers or odd numbers. How can children tell? By looking at the ones digit

---

 Identifying Even and Odd Numbers
(*Math Journal 1*, p. 34)

INDEPENDENT ACTIVITY

Children determine whether numbers of squares and stars are even or odd and write the number near each arrangement. Circulate and help as needed.

Math Boxes 3.2

1. Make a tally for 25.

HHT HHT HHT HHT
HHT

2. Write the number that is one more.

8   9

14   15

19   20

28   29

3. Make sums of 10 pennies.

Left Hand	Right Hand
3	7
4	6
2	8
Answers	vary.

4. Count up by 1s.

36, 37, 38,

39, 40, 41,

42, 43, 44,

45, 46

Math Journal 1, p. 35

---

2 Ongoing Learning & Practice

 Playing *Penny-Nickel Exchange*

PARTNER ACTIVITY

Children practice money skills by playing *Penny-Nickel Exchange*. For detailed instructions, see Lesson 2.10.

 Math Boxes 3.2 (*Math Journal 1*, p. 35)

INDEPENDENT ACTIVITY

Mixed Review This journal page provides opportunities for cumulative review or assessment of concepts and skills.

✦ Home Link 3.2 (*Math Masters*, p. 181)

Home Connection Children count the number of people in their homes. They record this number and tell if it is odd or even. After telling someone about odd and even numbers, they record some examples.

3 Options for Individualizing

✦ EXTRA PRACTICE Is the Number of Children Present an Even or Odd Number?

WHOLE-CLASS ACTIVITY   5–15 min

Have everyone line up with a partner. If there is an odd number of children and someone does not have a partner, that child goes to the end of the line.

• Is the number of children who are here today odd or even?

To count the number of children present, partners count aloud by 2s, starting from the front of the line: 2, 4, 6, 8, … If there is a single child, he or she counts last.

• Is the number of *people* who are in our room right now odd or even?

✦ EXTRA PRACTICE Modeling Even and Odd Numbers

WHOLE-CLASS ACTIVITY 5–15 min

Have five children come to the front of the room. The first child holds up two fingers, one from each hand. Say together, "Two fingers." Ask if this is an odd or even number of fingers. Even—they make a pair. Now the next child holds up two fingers, while the first child continues to hold up two fingers. *Even or odd?* even Continue in this way. If time allows, add more children to the group.

Have the last child hold up one finger. *Even or odd?* odd

✦ EXTRA PRACTICE Minute Math

SMALL-GROUP ACTIVITY 5–15 min

To offer children more experience with counting up and back, see the following pages in *Minute Math*:

Counting: pp. 28 and 29

Odd and Even Numbers   Home Link 3.2

>
> **Family Note**
> As children learn about the concept of odd and even numbers, extend this activity to include the number of people at home or the numbers of various objects, such as chairs, windows, videos, and books on a shelf.
> *Please return this Home Link to school tomorrow.*

1. Count the number of people in your home.

   There are _____ people in my home.

   Is this number **even** or **odd**? _____

2. Tell someone at home about odd and even numbers.

   Write some **odd** numbers here: ____, ____, ____, ____

   Write some **even** numbers here: ____, ____, ____, ____

3. Count the number of a type of object in your home. Write the number and the type of object.

   There are _____ _____ in my home.

   Is this number **even** or **odd**? _____
   Answers vary.

✦ *Math Masters*, p. 181

HOME LINK MASTER

NOTE: Use this routine at other times; for example, when children are lining up.

3.3 Number-Grid Patterns

OBJECTIVE To explore skip-counting patterns on the number grid.

summaries	materials
1 Teaching the Lesson	
Children explore the patterns in counts by 2s, 5s, 10s, and 3s on the number grid and in the ones digits of 2-digit numbers. [Numeration; Patterns, Functions, and Algebra]	☐ *Math Journal 1*, p. 36 ☐ Home Link 3.2 ☐ Class Number Line ☐ Teaching Master transparency (*Math Masters*, p. 21), or a laminated number grid (optional) ☐ colored marking pens (optional) ☐ crayons or colored pencils ***See* Advance Preparation**
2 Ongoing Learning & Practice	
Children classify numbers of things in the classroom as odd or even. [Numeration; Patterns, Functions, and Algebra] Children practice and maintain skills through Math Boxes and Home Link activities.	☐ *Math Journal 1*, p. 37 ☐ Home Link Master (*Math Masters*, p. 182)
3 Options for Individualizing	
Enrichment Children explore the pattern in counts by 4s on the number grid. [Numeration; Patterns, Functions, and Algebra] **Extra Practice** Children complete number sequences. [Numeration; Patterns, Functions, and Algebra]	☐ Teaching Masters (*Math Masters*, pp. 21 and 22)

Additional Information

Advance Preparation You will need an overhead transparency of a number grid. If you do not have an overhead projector, make a large, laminated number grid and use it with water-based, colored marking pens, which are easily erasable. Also, mount a class-size number grid in a prominent place.

Vocabulary • **column** • **diagonal** • **row**

Vocabulary (teacher) • **multiples**

Getting Started

Children count hops in unison on the Class Number Line.

- Start at 8. Count the number of hops to 11. 3
- Start at 1. Count the number of hops to 8. 7

Children solve problems like the ones below using the number line on the inside back cover of their journals. They record their answers on their slates.

Count the hops from

- 4 to 10. 6   • 5 to 17. 12
- 9 to 18. 9   • 12 to 18. 6

Note: Circulate as children count on their number lines. Watch for children who include the starting number in their counts—their answers will be 1 more than the correct answer.

Home Link 3.2 Follow-Up

Tally how many children have odd or even numbers of people living at home.

Have children share some of the even and odd numbers they recorded. Write their numbers in two columns on the board—labeled *Even* and *Odd*—as instructed by children. Review the first grade chant ("2, 4, 6, 8, first graders are really great!") to remind children of the ones digits for even numbers—and perhaps amend the chant to include 0. Then name the remaining digits: These are the ones digits in odd numbers. Check the ones digit in each number on the board to make sure that each number is recorded in the correct column.

What are the largest even and odd numbers children wrote?

1 Teaching the Lesson

✦ Exploring Skip-Counting Patterns on a Number Grid

WHOLE-CLASS ACTIVITY

Use either an overhead transparency of a number grid or a laminated number grid. Children count by 5s, one child at a time, in turn. Mark the 5s count (**multiples** of 5) on the number grid with colored dots. Once a pattern begins to emerge, ask if there is a way to find the numbers in the 5s count on the number grid without actually counting. The numbers in the 5s count are found in the 5s and 10s columns.

Make a list of the first few 5s counts and circle their ones digits. Ask children to describe the pattern in the ones digits. The numbers 5 and 0 alternate.

- How many numbers does it take for the pattern to be repeated? 2

Use different-color dots to repeat this routine with 2s and 10s counts. (If you don't have different-color markers, use different marks, such as dots, checks, and crosses, for each set of counts.) Children should observe the following:

▷ The 2s are found in the 2s, 4s, 6s, 8s, and 10s **columns;** the 10s are found only in the 10s column.

The 3s Pattern

									0
1	2	3	4	5	6	7	8	9	10
11	12	13	14	15	16	17	18	19	20
21	22	23	24	25	26	27	28	29	30
31	32	33	34	35	36	37	38	39	40
41	42	43	44	45	46	47	48	49	50
51	52	53	54	55	56	57	58	59	60
61	62	63	64	65	66	67	68	69	70
71	72	73	74	75	76	77	78	79	80
81	82	83	84	85	86	87	88	89	90
91	92	93	94	95	96	97	98	99	100
101	102	103	104	105	106	107	108	109	110

Color the 3s pattern on the grid.
Fill in the missing numbers below.
Circle the ones digit in each 2-digit number.

0, 3, 6, 9, 12, 15,
18, 21, 24, 27, 30, 33,
36, 39, 42, 45, 48, 51

STUDENT PAGE

✧ *Math Journal 1*, p. 36

▷ The 2s end in the digits 2, 4, 6, 8, or 0; all 10s end in 0.

▷ The 2s pattern in the ones digits is repeated every five numbers.

Ask which numbers have been marked more than once. The 10s; this shows that all 10s are also in counts by 5s and 2s.

✦ Exploring the 3s Pattern (*Math Journal 1,* p. 36)

SMALL-GROUP ACTIVITY

Children work in small groups. Ask all group members to do the following:

1. Make light marks for the counts by 3s on the number grid on page 36 in your journal.
2. Check with other children in your group to see if everyone agrees. Then color the 3s pattern on your grid.
3. List the numbers you have colored at the bottom of the page.
4. Circle the ones digits in your list.
5. Study the colored number patterns on your grid and talk about what you have discovered with other children in your group.

Bring the class together and have volunteers tell about the patterns that their groups discovered.

Possible patterns might include the following:

▷ The colored numbers fall on **diagonal** lines.

▷ The colored numbers follow a "down 1, back 1" pattern.

▷ The pattern repeats every three **rows.**

▷ Every column has some colored numbers. (The 2s, 5s, and 10s were only in certain columns.)

▷ The 3s count alternates between odd and even numbers.

▷ The ones digits in the colored numbers start repeating after 30.

Adjusting the Activity If necessary, help non-native English speakers to use such terms as *pattern, repeat,* and *diagonal.*

To extend this activity, describe the number pattern in the diagonal that starts with 9 in the first row and goes down and left. Counts by 9s

2 Ongoing Learning & Practice

✦ Even/Odd Number Patterns

WHOLE-CLASS DISCUSSION

Ask about numbers of people or things around the room. For example: *Is the number of teachers in this room odd or even? The number of doors? The number of children at the front table?*

✦ Math Boxes 3.3 (*Math Journal 1*, p. 37)

INDEPENDENT ACTIVITY

 Mixed Review This journal page provides opportunities for cumulative review or assessment of concepts and skills.

✦ Home Link 3.3 (*Math Masters*, p. 182)

 Home Connection Children use the number line to find the distance between two numbers. They count the number of hops from one number to another.

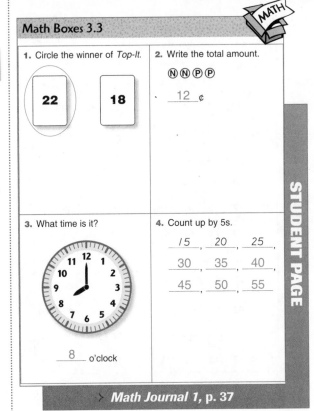

Math Boxes 3.3

1. Circle the winner of *Top-It.*

22   18

2. Write the total amount.

Ⓝ Ⓝ Ⓟ Ⓟ

___12___ ¢

3. What time is it?

___8___ o'clock

4. Count up by 5s.

_15_, _20_, _25_,
_30_, _35_, _40_,
_45_, _50_, _55_

Math Journal 1, p. 37

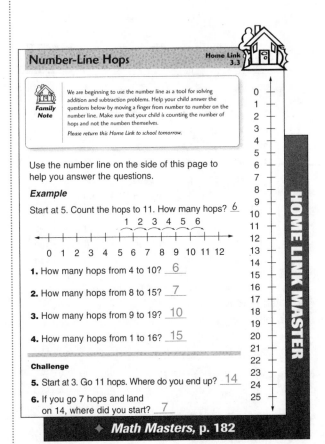

Number-Line Hops

Home Link 3.3

Family Note We are beginning to use the number line as a tool for solving addition and subtraction problems. Help your child answer the questions below by moving a finger from number to number on the number line. Make sure that your child is counting the number of hops and not the numbers themselves.
Please return this Home Link to school tomorrow.

Use the number line on the side of this page to help you answer the questions.

Example

Start at 5. Count the hops to 11. How many hops? _6_

1 2 3 4 5 6
0 1 2 3 4 5 6 7 8 9 10 11 12

1. How many hops from 4 to 10? _6_

2. How many hops from 8 to 15? _7_

3. How many hops from 9 to 19? _10_

4. How many hops from 1 to 16? _15_

Challenge

5. Start at 3. Go 11 hops. Where do you end up? _14_

6. If you go 7 hops and land on 14, where did you start? _7_

0 1 2 3 4 5 6 7 8 9 10 11 12 13 14 15 16 17 18 19 20 21 22 23 24 25

Math Masters, p. 182

Vertical Number Grid

									0
1	2	3	④	5	6	7	⑧	9	10
11	⑫	13	14	15	⑯	17	18	19	㉑
21	22	23	㉔	25	26	27	㉘	29	30
31	㉜	33	34	35	㊱	37	38	39	㊵
41	42	43	㊹	45	46	47	㊽	49	50
51	52	53	54	55	56	57	58	59	60
61	62	63	64	65	66	67	68	69	70
71	72	73	74	75	76	77	78	79	80
81	82	83	84	85	86	87	88	89	90
91	92	93	94	95	96	97	98	99	100
101	102	103	104	105	106	107	108	109	110
111	112	113	114	115	116	117	118	119	120

◆ *Math Masters*, p. 21

---

3 Options for Individualizing

◆ ENRICHMENT Exploring the 4s Pattern
(*Math Masters*, p. 21)

INDEPENDENT ACTIVITY   5–15 min

Children shade the 4s pattern up to 48 on the number grid on *Math Masters*, page 21. Ask them to see if they can figure out how to shade the rest of the grid without counting. Which patterns do they see in the number grid? Expect answers such as the following:

▷ There are 3 unshaded squares at the beginning of every other row.

▷ There is 1 unshaded square at the beginning of every other row.

▷ Not every column has a shaded square.

▷ In columns where there are shaded squares, every other square is shaded.

◆ EXTRA PRACTICE Filling in Missing Numbers in a Number Sequence
(*Math Masters*, p. 22)

INDEPENDENT ACTIVITY   5–15 min

Children use a number grid to help them complete number sequences.

Number Sequences

									0
1	②	3	4	⑤	6	7	⑧	9	10
11	12	13	⑭	15	16	17	18	19	20
21	22	㉓	24	25	26	27	28	29	30
31	㉜	33	34	35	36	37	38	39	40
41	42	43	㊹	45	46	47	48	49	50
51	52	㊳	54	55	56	57	58	59	60
61	62	63	64	65	66	67	68	69	70
71	72	73	74	75	76	77	78	79	80
81	82	83	84	85	86	87	88	89	90
91	92	93	94	95	96	97	98	99	100
101	102	103	104	105	106	107	108	109	110

Color the following numbers on the number grid.

Fill in the rest of the numbers below. Use the grid to help you.

Circle the ones digit in each 2-digit number.

2 , 5 , 8 , 1① , 1④ , 1⑦ , 2⓪ ,
2③ , 2⑥ , 2⑨ , 3② , 3⑤ , 3⑧ , 4① ,
4④ , 4⑦ , 5⓪ , 5③ , 5⑥ , 5⑨ , 6②

◆ *Math Masters*, p. 22

TEACHING MASTER

3.4
EXPLORATIONS

Exploring Even & Odd Numbers, Covering Shapes, and Patterns

OBJECTIVES To identify even and odd numbers; to cover shapes with pattern blocks; and to create and continue repeating patterns.

summaries

materials

1 Teaching the Lesson

Exploration A: Children sort dominoes according to whether the numbers of dots on the two sides are both even, both odd, or mixed. [Numeration; Patterns, Functions, and Algebra]

Exploration B: Children cover shapes with pattern blocks in various ways. [Patterns, Functions, and Algebra; Geometry]

Exploration C: Children create and continue repeating patterns, using pattern blocks. [Geometry; Patterns, Functions, and Algebra]

☐ Home Link 3.3

Exploration A: Per small group:
☐ Teaching Master (*Math Masters*, p. 23, p. 24)
☐ 1 set of double-9 dominoes

Exploration B: Per small group:
☐ Teaching Masters (*Math Masters*, pp. 25 and 26)
☐ pattern blocks
☐ Pattern-Block Template
☐ crayons

Exploration C: Per small group:
☐ pattern blocks

***See* Advance Preparation**

2 Ongoing Learning & Practice

Children play a math game. [Numeration; Measurement and Reference Frames]

Children practice and maintain skills through Math Boxes and Home Link activities.

☐ *Math Journal 1*, p. 38
☐ Home Link Master (*Math Masters*, p. 183)
☐ materials for a math game

3 Options for Individualizing

Extra Practice Children practice money exchanges.
[Numeration; Measurement and Reference Frames]

☐ *Minute Math®*, p. 66

Additional Information

Advance Preparation Explorations A, B, and C are best done in small groups. Plan to spend most of your time with children working on Exploration A.

Math Masters, page 23 gives directions for the Exploration A activity. You may want to place copies of this master at the appropriate workstations if a teacher's aide or volunteer is helping children with this activity. *Math Masters*, pages 24, 25, and 26 are required because children will use them to record their work.

Getting Started

Mental Math and Reflexes

Children count spaces in unison on the Class Number Grid Poster.
- Start at 12. Count the number of spaces to 20. 8
- Start at 6. Count the number of spaces to 18. 12

Children use the number grid in their journals to solve problems like the ones below. They record their answers on their slates.

- Count the spaces from 39 to 48 9; 37 to 52 15; 45 to 61 16; 36 to 50 14.

Note: Watch for children who include the starting numbers in their counts. Their answers will be 1 more than the correct answers.

- How is counting on the number grid similar to counting on the number line? You count 1 space or hop each time you move to the next number.

- How is it different? On the number grid, when you come to the end of a row, you go to the first box in the next row.

Home Link 3.3 Follow-Up

Have children share their strategies for solving the Challenge problems. A typical answer to the second Challenge problem: "I tried starting at 3 and found that 7 hops did not get me to 14. Then I tried 10 and found that 7 hops took me too far. I started at 8 and that got me close. I went 1 hop too far. So I moved back to 7 to start. Then it worked."

1 Teaching the Lesson

Plan to spend most of your time with the group that is working on Exploration A. You may also need to help other children get started on the other Explorations.

◆ Exploration A: Sorting Dominoes by Odd and Even Numbers of Dots
(*Math Masters*, pp. 23 and 24)

SMALL-GROUP ACTIVITY

Children work in groups of 4. Each workstation should have a copy of *Math Masters*, page 23 and a set of 55 dominoes, up to and including double-9s. Give each child a copy of *Math Masters*, page 24, and have children write their names at the top.

Assign tasks to each member of the group as follows:

▷ One child finds all the dominoes that have an even number of dots on both sides.

▷ One child finds all the dominoes that have an odd number of dots on both sides.

▷ The other two children find all the dominoes that have an even number of dots on one side and an odd number of dots on the other side.

When they have finished, children circle which kind of dominoes they have sorted on *Math Masters*, page 24.

TEACHING MASTER

Domino Sort

Materials
- ☐ 1 set of dominoes
- ☐ *Math Masters*, page 24

1. Work in a group of four.

   - One person finds all the dominoes with an even number of dots on both sides.

   - Another person finds all the dominoes with an odd number of dots on both sides.

   - The other two people find all the dominoes with an odd number of dots on one side and an even number of dots on the other side.

2. Record the dominoes in your pile on page 24. Write the number of dots on each side of each domino. Do not draw dots.

   Example

   | 2 | 4 | | 5 | 1 | | 3 | 0 |

   both even   both odd   one odd, one even

   The two people who sorted dominoes with even and odd numbers of dots need their own Record Sheets. They should share the work.

3. Count the dominoes in each pile.

   When you have finished this activity, give page 24 to your teacher.

◆ *Math Masters*, p. 23

Then children record the dominoes they have sorted: They write numbers for the numbers of dots, rather than draw the dots. The two children who were assigned to sort dominoes with an even number on one side and an odd number on the other side should share the recording task: Each child should record about half the dominoes on his or her recording sheet. The answer blank under each domino will be filled in in Lesson 3.14, so save the children's work.

Finally, children in each group count how many of each kind of domino there are in each of the three groups. There are 15 dominoes with even numbers on both sides. There are 15 dominoes with odd numbers on both sides. There are 25 dominoes with both even numbers and odd numbers.

◆ Exploration B: Covering Shapes with Pattern Blocks (*Math Masters,* pp. 25 and 26)

SMALL-GROUP ACTIVITY

Using pattern blocks, children work together to cover each shape on *Math Masters,* pages 25 and 26. They use their Pattern-Block Templates and crayons to record each configuration of pattern blocks. Each child then uses pattern blocks to make his or her own shape and records this new configuration of blocks.

◆ Exploration C: Exploring Patterns with Pattern Blocks

SMALL-GROUP ACTIVITY

One child begins a pattern with pattern blocks. The other children in the group take turns continuing the pattern. Children also take turns starting a pattern.

A group drawing can be made of some of the patterns by tracing the blocks or by using a Pattern-Block Template.

---

2 | 4

Children record the number of dots on the dominoes they have sorted.

NOTE: Collect *Math Masters,* page 24 from each child. These masters will be used in an Options for Individualizing activity in Lesson 3.14.

Adjusting the Activity If children have difficulty, one team of two children can find and record all the dominoes with even numbers on both sides and a second team of two children can find and record all the dominoes with odd numbers on both sides. Group members can work together to check and record the remaining dominoes. Each team then takes one domino at a time from those remaining and checks that it has an odd number of dots on one side and an even number of dots on the other side.

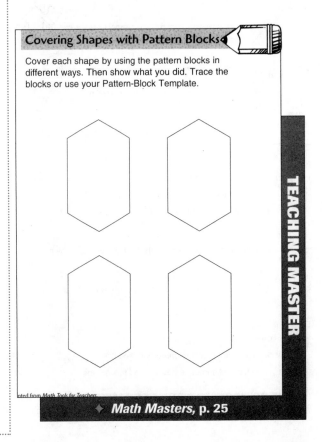

Covering Shapes with Pattern Blocks

Cover each shape by using the pattern blocks in different ways. Then show what you did. Trace the blocks or use your Pattern-Block Template.

Math Masters, p. 25

TEACHING MASTER

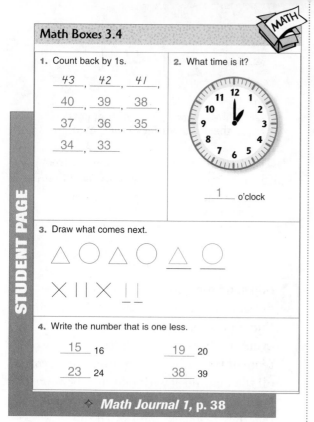

Math Boxes 3.4

1. Count back by 1s.

43 , 42 , 41 ,

40 , 39 , 38 ,

37 , 36 , 35 ,

34 , 33

2. What time is it?

1 o'clock

3. Draw what comes next.

△ ◯ △ ◯ △ ◯

✕ ‖ ✕ ‖ ‖

4. Write the number that is one less.

15 16   19 20

23 24   38 39

Math Journal 1, p. 38

STUDENT PAGE

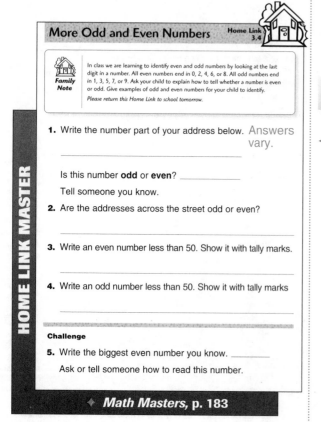

More Odd and Even Numbers

Home Link 3.4

Family Note

In class we are learning to identify even and odd numbers by looking at the last digit in a number. All even numbers end in 0, 2, 4, 6, or 8. All odd numbers end in 1, 3, 5, 7, or 9. Ask your child to explain how to tell whether a number is even or odd. Give examples of odd and even numbers for your child to identify.

Please return this Home Link to school tomorrow.

1. Write the number part of your address below. Answers vary.

_____

Is this number **odd** or **even**? _____
Tell someone you know.

2. Are the addresses across the street odd or even?

_____

3. Write an even number less than 50. Show it with tally marks.

_____

4. Write an odd number less than 50. Show it with tally marks

_____

Challenge

5. Write the biggest even number you know. _____
Ask or tell someone how to read this number.

Math Masters, p. 183

HOME LINK MASTER

---

2 Ongoing Learning & Practice

◆ Playing a Math Game

PARTNER ACTIVITY

Depending on their needs, children can play *Before and After* (see Lesson 3.1), *Two-Fisted Penny Addition* with 10 to 20 pennies (see Lesson 2.3), or *Penny-Nickel Exchange* (see Lesson 2.10).

◆ Math Boxes 3.4 (*Math Journal 1*, p. 38)

INDEPENDENT ACTIVITY

Mixed Review This journal page provides opportunities for cumulative review or assessment of concepts and skills.

◆ Home Link 3.4 (*Math Masters*, p. 183)

Home Connection Children tell whether their addresses and the addresses across the street from their homes are represented by odd or even numbers. They also use tallies to show an even and an odd number.

3 Options for Individualizing

◆ EXTRA PRACTICE Minute Math

SMALL-GROUP ACTIVITY 5–15 min

To offer children more experience with money exchanges, see the following page in *Minute Math*:

Measurement: p. 66

3.5 Counting on the Number Line

OBJECTIVES To review basic number-line concepts; and to practice counting on the number line.

summaries	materials

1 Teaching the Lesson

Children skip count up and back by 2s, 5s, 10s, and 3s on the number line and use it to do choral counts. They also practice counting up and back by 1s on the number line, from 0 and from other numbers. [Measurement and Reference Frames; Numeration]

- ☐ *Math Journal 1*, pp. 39 and 40
- ☐ Home Link 3.4
- ☐ tool-kit clock
- ☐ Class Number Line or Teaching Master transparency (*Math Masters*, p. 27; optional)

2 Ongoing Learning & Practice

Children create and continue patterns. [Patterns, Functions, and Algebra]

Children practice and maintain skills through Math Boxes and Home Link activities.

- ☐ *Math Journal 1*, p. 41
- ☐ Home Link Master (*Math Masters*, p. 184)

3 Options for Individualizing

Reteaching Children step off counting problems on a large, on-the-floor number line. [Numeration; Measurement and Reference Frames]

Extra Practice Children review skip counting. [Numeration]

- ☐ large number line
- ☐ *Minute Math®*, pp. 28, 29, and 31

See Advance Preparation

Additional Information

Advance Preparation For the optional Reteaching activity in Part 3, make a large number line on the floor of your classroom. This can be done with paper cut into 4-inch strips or with masking tape. The number line should go from 0 to at least 20. If there is not enough space in the classroom, you might do this activity in the hallway with small groups.

Vocabulary • number line • negative number

Getting Started

Mental Math and Reflexes

Have children show times on the hour on their tool-kit clocks. Review the position of the hour hand when the time is exactly on the hour.

1. Move the hour hand so that it points to 5 and ask what time the clock shows.

2. Move the hour hand so that it points about halfway between 8 and 9. Ask about what time the clock shows. Repeat several times. Emphasize the use of estimation language: With the hour hand between two numbers, we say the time using phrases like *about ___, almost ___, just before ___, a little after ___,* and *between ___ and ___.*

Home Link 3.4 Follow-Up

List the addresses of several children. *How can you tell whether these large numbers are even or odd?* If the ones digit is 0, 2, 4, 6, or 8, then the number is even. If the ones digit is 1, 3, 5, 7, or 9, then the number is odd. Children tell whether each of the addresses on the board is even or odd. Depending on where children live, there may be a pattern in the house numbers. *Are all the numbers on one side of the street even numbers? Are all the numbers on the opposite side odd numbers?*

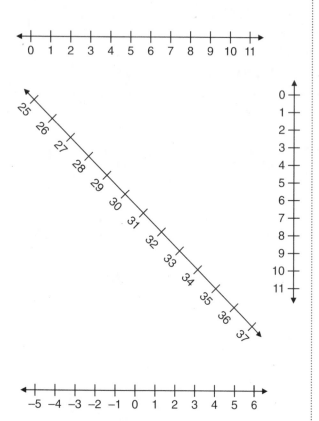

1 Teaching the Lesson

✦ Reviewing Basic Number-Line Concepts

WHOLE-CLASS DISCUSSION

Sketch a variety of **number lines** on the board.

Use these number lines to discuss some of their features. *For example:*

▷ Number lines can go in any direction—left to right, up and down, or slanted.

▷ The arrows at the beginning and end of a number line show that the number line goes on forever in both directions.

▷ A number line can start with any number.

▷ A number line can extend to the left of, or below, zero. Numbers on the below-zero part of the number line are called **negative numbers** and are written with a "–" symbol before the number. Remind children of below-zero temperatures on thermometers.

NOTE: Because a number line extends infinitely in both directions, it is not possible to draw all of it. When we draw a number line, we are really drawing only a part of the number line—a line that extends infinitely.

◆ Reviewing Skip Counting on Number Lines
(*Math Journal 1*, p. 39)

WHOLE-CLASS ACTIVITY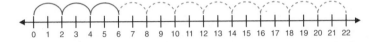

Use the Class Number Line or a transparency of *Math Masters*, page 27 to demonstrate how to show counts by 2s with arcs. Children follow along, showing counts by 2s on the first number line on the journal page. Then, on their own, they show counts by 5s, 10s, and 3s on the other number lines.

When children have completed the number-line counts, they count up and back by 2s, 5s, 10s, and 3s, in unison. They follow along on their number lines, using their fingers to hop from one number to the next.

◆ Counting Hops Up and Back on the Number Line (*Math Journal 1*, p. 40)

WHOLE-CLASS ACTIVITY

The purpose of this routine is to prepare children for addition and subtraction on the number line, a topic that will be addressed in the next lesson.

Children use the number line on the inside back cover of their journals to count hops on the number line. Use the Class Number Line or a transparency of *Math Masters*, page 27 to review the answers.

Suggestions

- Start at 0. Count up 5 hops. Where do you end up? At 5 Count up 3 more hops. Where do you end up? At 8

- Start at 0. Count up 3 hops. Where do you end up? At 3 Count up 7 more hops. Where do you end up? At 10

- Start at 3. Count up 7 hops. Where do you end up? At 10

- Start at 0. Count up 9 hops. Then count back 2 hops. Where do you end up? At 7

- Start at 0. Count up 12 hops. Then count back 7 hops. Where do you end up? At 5

- Start at 12. Count back 7 hops. Where do you end up? At 5

- Start at 6. Count up to 10. How many hops are there from 6 to 10? 4 hops

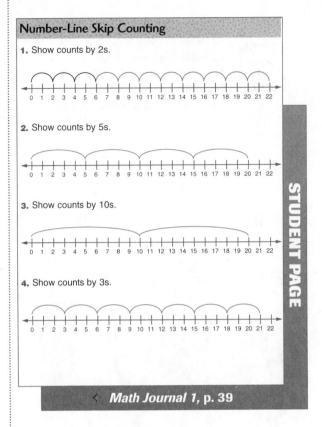

Math Journal 1, p. 39

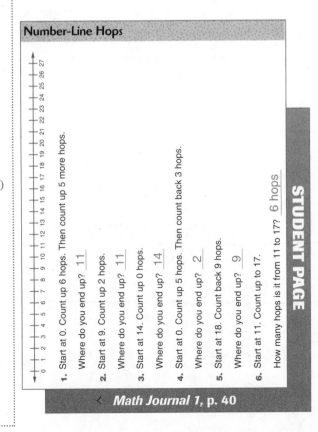

Math Journal 1, p. 40

Some children may notice that counting up 3 hops, starting at 0, and then counting 7 more hops gives the same result as counting up 7 hops, starting at 3. Similarly, counting up 12 hops, starting at 0, and then counting back 7 hops gives the same result as counting back 7 hops, starting at 12.

Pose additional problems as needed. When you feel that children are ready to work on their own, ask them to complete journal page 40.

Children act out the pattern, "one hand up, two hands up, no hands up, one hand up, two hands up, no hands up."

2 Ongoing Learning & Practice

◆ Creating and Continuing Patterns

WHOLE-CLASS ACTIVITY

Line up a group of children in a pattern. For example, the first child might raise his or her left hand; the second, two hands; the third, no hands; the fourth, his or her left hand; the fifth, two hands; and so on. Ask the class first to identify the next child in the pattern and then to describe the pattern in general. Repeat using other patterns (for example, stand, squat, stand, squat, and so on) and other groups of children.

◆ Math Boxes 3.5 (*Math Journal 1*, p. 41)

INDEPENDENT ACTIVITY

Mixed Review This journal page provides opportunities for cumulative review or assessment of concepts and skills.

STUDENT PAGE

Math Boxes 3.5

1. Count up by 2s.

_12_ , _14_ , _16_

_18_ , _20_ , _22_

_24_ , _26_ , _28_

_30_ , _32_

2. Write the total amount.

Ⓝ Ⓝ Ⓝ Ⓟ

_16_ ¢

3. Draw the hour hand.

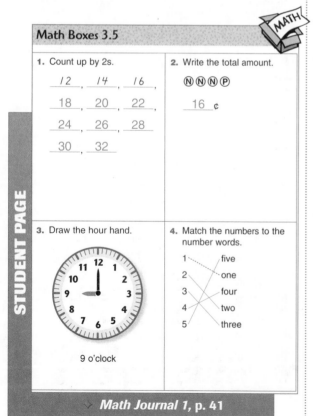

9 o'clock

4. Match the numbers to the number words.

```
1 ········· five
2 ········· one
3 ········· four
4 ········· two
5 ········· three
```

Math Journal 1, p. 41

◆ Home Link 3.5 (*Math Masters*, p. 184)

Home Connection Children tell someone what they know about number lines. They show how they can count by 10s, 5s, 2s, and 3s on a number line, beginning at zero. They record their counts and tell about each pattern.

Number Lines and Counting
Home Link 3.5

Family Note Listen as your child tells you about number lines and counts. Be sure he or she records the numbers counted. Provide several objects, such as pennies or dried beans, for your child to use to count by 10s, 5s, 2s, and 3s.
Please return this Home Link to school tomorrow.

Tell someone at home what you know about number lines and counting patterns.

Count by 10s, 5s, 2s, and 3s. Begin at 0 each time.

Then go back and circle all the odd numbers on the number line.

Count by 10s. 0, __10__ , __20__

Count by 5s. 0, __5__ , __10__ , __15__ , __20__

Count by 2s. 0, __2__ , __4__ , __6__ , __8__

Count by 3s. 0, __3__ , __6__ , __9__ , __12__

0
①
2
③
4
⑤
6
⑦
8
⑨
10
⑪
12
⑬
14
⑮
16
⑰
18
⑲
20

HOME LINK MASTER

◆ *Math Masters*, p. 184

---

3 Options for Individualizing

◆ RETEACHING Counting Hops on the Number Line

WHOLE-CLASS ACTIVITY   5–15 min

Ask questions, such as the following, and have children step along the number line to check their answers:

- How many hops do you think you need to take to get from 7 to 12? *5 hops*
- From 3 to 11? *8 hops*
- From 15 to 10? *5 hops*
- From 4 to 20? *16 hops*

◆ EXTRA PRACTICE Minute Math

SMALL-GROUP ACTIVITY   5–15 min

To offer children more experience with skip counting, see the following pages in *Minute Math:*

Counting: pp. 28, 29, and 31

3.6 Adding and Subtracting on the Number Line

OBJECTIVE To introduce addition and subtraction on the number line.

summaries	materials
1 Teaching the Lesson	
Children use the number line to solve simple addition and subtraction problems. [Measurement and Reference Frames; Operations and Computation]	□ *Math Journal 1*, p. 42 □ Home Link 3.5 □ slate
2 Ongoing Learning & Practice	
Children practice and maintain skills through Math Boxes and Home Link activities.	□ *Math Journal 1*, p. 43 □ Home Link Master (*Math Masters*, p. 185)
3 Options for Individualizing	
Enrichment Children make up and solve penny stories. [Measurement and Reference Frames; Operations and Computation] **Extra Practice** Children become familiar with addition and subtraction facts. [Operations and Computation]	□ tool-kit pennies □ slate (optional) □ *Minute Math*®, pp. 10 and 15

Additional Information

Today's Mental Math and Reflexes activity may take longer than usual. Take the time necessary to complete it. It is an important part of the problem-solving strand in *Everyday Mathematics*.

Getting Started

Mental Math and Reflexes

Tell "change to more" and "change to less" number stories, and have children solve them any way they can: by using counters, by drawing pictures, by making doodles, by counting on their fingers, and so on. Also have children share solution strategies after each problem. Then summarize each solution by drawing the appropriate "change" diagram on the board *but only after children have had a chance to share what they did to solve the problem.* (See Lesson 2.7 for information about change diagrams.) Ask someone to suggest a number model for each story.

- Bruno was 5 years old when he got his first bicycle. He is 2 years older now. How old is Bruno now? 7 years old
- Leo's sunflower plant was about 4 inches tall the first time he measured it. It has grown about 4 inches. About how tall is Leo's plant now? About 8 inches tall
- Sue had a 12-piece puzzle. She dropped it and lost 4 pieces. How many pieces does she still have? 8 pieces
- Mel used to watch TV for 5 hours a week. Now she is learning to play the violin, and she practices an hour every day. So now Mel watches TV 2 hours less a week. How many hours a week does Mel watch TV now? 3 hours a week

Home Link 3.5 Follow-Up

Go over the answers. Discuss the odd/even number patterns in each sequence of numbers.

1 Teaching the Lesson

◆ Introducing Addition on the Number Line

WHOLE-CLASS ACTIVITY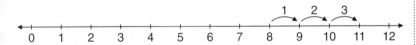

Pose the following number story:

• Cynthia had 8 model cars. Then she got 3 more model cars for her birthday. How many model cars does Cynthia have now? 11 model cars

After children have solved the problem in the story, demonstrate how to use the number line to find the answer. You might say something like the following:

• I'll start at 8. This shows that Cynthia had 8 model cars. Now I'll count up 3 hops. This shows that she got 3 more model cars. I've landed on 11. That's how many model cars Cynthia has now.

Then write a number model for the problem on the board: $8 + 3 = 11$.

Use the following routine to practice adding on the number line:

1. Write an addition problem on the board. $5 + 7 =$ ____

2. Have children use the number line on the inside back cover of their journals to find the answer.

3. Have children write the answer on their slates.

4. Ask a child to show the class how to find the answer using the Class Number Line.

5. Complete the addition problem. $5 + 7 = \underline{\ 12\ }$

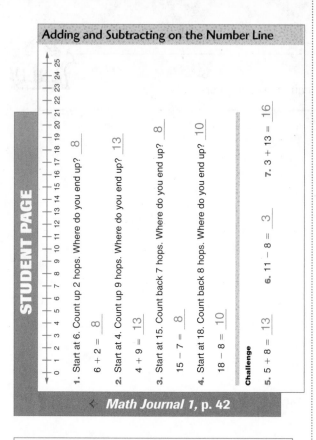

Adding and Subtracting on the Number Line

STUDENT PAGE

1. Start at 6. Count up 2 hops. Where do you end up? __8__

   6 + 2 = __8__

2. Start at 4. Count up 9 hops. Where do you end up? __13__

   4 + 9 = __13__

3. Start at 15. Count back 7 hops. Where do you end up? __8__

   15 − 7 = __8__

4. Start at 18. Count back 8 hops. Where do you end up? __10__

   18 − 8 = __10__

Challenge

5. 5 + 8 = __13__   6. 11 − 8 = __3__   7. 3 + 13 = __16__

Math Journal 1, p. 42

NOTE: If necessary, discuss the meaning of the word *dozen*.

 Adjusting the Activity If children are having difficulty with the problems on journal page 42, have them use counters and then describe each problem in words before solving it on the number line.

 ONGOING ASSESSMENT
Note the strategies that children are using to solve the problems. Encourage all children to use the number line and suggest that they check their work with counters, tallies, or pictures.

Suggestions

6 + 4 = ____   Start at 6. Count up 4 hops.
End up on 10. Complete: 6 + 4 = __10__

2 + 9 = ____   Start at 2. Count up 9 hops.
End up on 11. Complete: 2 + 9 = __11__

15 + 0 = ____   Start at 15. Count up 0 hops.
End up on 15. Complete: 15 + 0 = __15__

◆ Introducing Subtraction on the Number Line

WHOLE-CLASS ACTIVITY

Pose the following number story:

• Ali bought a dozen eggs at the store. Then on his way home, he dropped the egg carton, and 5 of the eggs broke. How many eggs did not break? 7 eggs

After children have solved the number story, ask if someone can show how to use the number line to find the answer. Start at 12 on the number line. Count back 5 hops. You end up on 7. That's how many eggs did not break.

Then write a number model for the problem on the board: 12 − 5 = 7.

Follow the same routine you used for addition to practice subtracting on the number line.

Suggestions

9 − 4 = ____   Start at 9. Count back 4 hops.
End up on 5. Complete: 9 − 4 = __5__

13 − 6 = ____   Start at 13. Count back 6 hops.
End up on 7. Complete: 13 − 6 = __7__

12 − 1 = ____   Start at 12. Count back 1 hop.
End up on 11. Complete: 12 − 1 = __11__

Finally, do a couple of mixed problems before children solve problems on their own in their journals.

8 + 8 = ____   Start at 8. Count up 8 hops.
End up on 16. Complete: 8 + 8 = __16__

15 − 9 = ____   Start at 15. Count back 9 hops.
End up on 6. Complete: 15 − 9 = __6__

◆ Adding and Subtracting on the Number Line
(*Math Journal 1*, p. 42)

INDEPENDENT ACTIVITY

Children complete the page individually or with a partner, while you circulate and assist as needed. Be sure to reserve time to go over the answers.

2 Ongoing Learning & Practice

◆ **Math Boxes 3.6** (*Math Journal 1*, p. 43)

INDEPENDENT ACTIVITY

Mixed Review This journal page provides opportunities for cumulative review or assessment of concepts and skills.

◆ **Home Link 3.6** (*Math Masters*, p. 185)

Home Connection Children use the number line to solve simple addition and subtraction problems. They start at a given number, count up or back a given number of steps, and then tell where they ended up.

3 Options for Individualizing

◆ **ENRICHMENT** Making Up and Solving Penny Stories

PARTNER ACTIVITY 5–15 min

Each partnership needs one set of tool-kit pennies. The first partner tells a penny story. For example: "Lucy had 7 pennies. She lost 3 pennies. How many pennies does Lucy have left?"

The other partner solves the story with hops on the number line. The first partner checks the answer by using pennies to model the story.

Adjusting the Activity If you think children are able to do so, encourage them to write number models for the number stories on their slates.

◆ **EXTRA PRACTICE** Minute Math

SMALL-GROUP ACTIVITY 5–15 min

To offer children more experience with addition and subtraction, see the following pages in *Minute Math:*

Basic Routines: pp. 10 and 15

1. Draw the hour hand.

5 o'clock

2. Odd or even?

odd   even

odd   even

3. Complete the table.

Before	Number	After
24	25	26
28	29	30
32	33	34
36	37	38
39	40	41

4. Count up by 10s.

20, 30, 40,

50, 60, 70,

80, 90, 100,

110, 120

STUDENT PAGE

◆ *Math Journal 1*, p. 43

More Number-Line Hops

Home Link 3.6

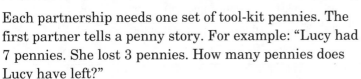

Family Note We are beginning to work with number models like 3 + 2 = 5 and 8 − 5 = 3. We are solving them by counting up and back on the number line. Ask your child to show you how to do this. If your child has trouble with the Challenge problems, make up number stories that use these numbers. For example, for 7 + 3 = ___, you might make up the following story: "You have 7 pennies. I give you 3 more. How many pennies do you have now?" Your child can use real pennies to find the answer.

Please return this Home Link to school tomorrow.

Use the number line to help you solve these problems.

1. Start at 4. Count up 3 hops. Where do you end up? 7   4 + 3 = 7

2. Start at 12. Count back 5 hops. Where do you end up? 7   12 − 5 = 7

3. Start at 11. Count back 6 hops. Where do you end up? 5   11 − 6 = 5

4. Start at 14. Count up 2 hops. Where do you end up? 16   14 + 2 = 16

Challenge

5. 7 + 3 = 10   **6.** 6 − 5 = 1

7. 2 + 10 = 12   **8.** 9 − 7 = 2

0
1
2
3
4
5
6
7
8
9
10
11
12
13
14
15
16
17
18
19
20
21
22
23
24
25

HOME LINK MASTER

◆ *Math Masters*, p. 185

3.7 Telling Time to the Half-Hour

OBJECTIVES To review basic concepts of telling time; and to tell time to the hour and the half-hour.

summaries	materials
1 Teaching the Lesson	
Children review what they have learned about how to tell time on an analog clock. They are introduced to and practice telling time to the half-hour. [Measurement and Reference Frames]	☐ *Math Journal 1*, p. 44 ☐ Home Link 3.6 ☐ hour-hand-only demonstration clock ☐ tool-kit clock ☐ demonstration clock
2 Ongoing Learning & Practice	
Children fill in missing numbers on number lines. [Numeration; Patterns, Functions, and Algebra] Children practice and maintain skills through Math Boxes and Home Link activities.	☐ *Math Journal 1*, pp. 45 and 46 ☐ Home Link Masters (*Math Masters*, pp. 186 and 187)
3 Options for Individualizing	
Enrichment Children practice telling time to the hour and the half-hour. [Measurement and Reference Frames] **Extra Practice** Children review telling time. [Measurement and Reference Frames]	☐ tool-kit clock ☐ clock-face stamps (optional) ☐ 3" by 5" index cards, cut in half (optional) ☐ *Minute Math*®, p. 71

Additional Information
Vocabulary • **half-past (the hour)**

Getting Started

Mental Math and Reflexes

Use the following routine to add and subtract on the number grid:

1. Write an addition or subtraction problem on the board.

2. Children use the number grid in their journals to find the answer.

3. Children write the answer on their slates.

Suggestions 12 + 7 = ___19___   23 + 8 = ___31___   41 + 10 = ___51___

28 – 5 = ___23___   17 – 9 = ___8___   35 – 10 = ___25___

Home Link 3.6 Follow-Up

Go over the answers. Ask several children to demonstrate on the Class Number Line or on a transparency of *Math Masters*, page 185 how to solve the problems.

Teaching the Lesson

◆ Revisiting Telling Time on an Analog Clock

WHOLE-CLASS ACTIVITY

1. Use your demonstration clock as you discuss the following questions:

   - Which is the hour hand? Which is the minute hand? The hour hand is the shorter hand. The minute hand is the longer hand.

   - In which direction do the hands move? Review the term *clockwise*.

   - How long does it take for the minute hand to go all the way around the clock face? 1 hour, or 60 minutes

   - How long does it take for the hour hand to go all the way around the clock face? 12 hours

   - When the minute hand points to the 12, what does the hour hand point to? One of the numbers on the clock face. This is the number that tells the hour.

2. Practice telling time to the hour.

   ▷ Show a time to the hour on the demonstration clock and ask children to say the time.

   ▷ Name a time on the hour and ask children to show it on their tool-kit clocks.

3. Practice estimating the time, using an hour-hand-only clock.

   ▷ Move the hour hand so that it points to the 5. *About what time is it?* About 5 o'clock

   ▷ Move the hour hand so that it points halfway between the 6 and the 7. *About what time is it?* Between 6 o'clock and 7 o'clock

Repeat this routine a few more times. Move the hour hand to various positions and ask children to tell about what time it is. Remind them to use phrases like *about _____, almost _____, just before _____, a little after _____,* and *between _____ and _____.*

If some children can tell time using the terms *half, quarter,* and so on, praise them by telling them that those are excellent ways of saying the "between" times.

NOTE: Be consistent in saying *about* when stating a time. Remind children that telling time is an estimate: Clocks may be set differently; we don't know exactly where the hand is pointing; and by the time we say or write a time, it is already a little later!

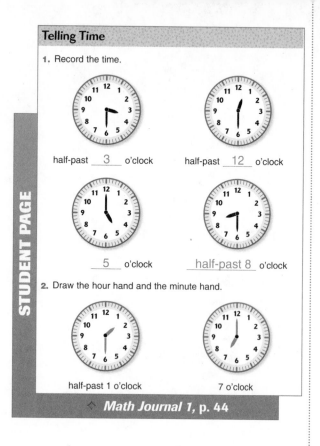

Telling Time

1. Record the time.

half-past ___3___ o'clock   half-past ___12___ o'clock

___5___ o'clock   _half-past 8_ o'clock

2. Draw the hour hand and the minute hand.

half-past 1 o'clock   7 o'clock

Math Journal 1, p. 44

NOTE: Use the activities in this lesson often during the next few weeks. Encourage children to set their tool-kit clocks to estimate the time of some activity during the day, such as recess, lunch, or music. Occasionally set the hour-hand-only display clock to match the hour hand on the classroom clock and call on children to estimate the time. Keep in mind that mastery of telling-time skills happens rapidly for some children and slowly for others.

✦ Introducing Telling Time to the Half-Hour
(*Math Journal 1*, p. 44)

WHOLE-CLASS ACTIVITY

Set your demonstration clock to 4 o'clock.

• If I move the minute hand halfway around the clock, which number will the hand point to? 6

Ask children to watch the hour hand as you move the minute hand to the 6. Mention that the hour hand now points halfway between the 4 and the 5, so the time shown is between 4 o'clock and 5 o'clock. To be exact, it is half an hour after 4 o'clock. We say that it is "**half-past** 4 o'clock," "half-past 4," or "four-thirty."

Use the following routine to practice telling time to the half-hour:

1. Show a time on the demonstration clock with the minute hand pointing to the 6.

2. Have children show the same time on their tool-kit clocks.

3. Have children tell what time is shown on the clock.

As a variation, give the class times to the half-hour and ask children to show those times on their clocks. Also mix in a few times on the hour.

Adjusting the Activity To extend this activity, use the demonstration clock to show a time that is half-past the hour, for example, half-past 5. Then ask what time it will be in *another* half-hour. 6 o'clock Model the answer by moving the minute hand forward a half-hour. Then move the minute hand back to where it was and ask what time it was a half-hour *earlier*. 5 o'clock Again model the answer on the demonstration clock by moving the minute hand back a half-hour.

When you feel that children have had sufficient practice, have them complete the journal page independently or with a partner. When children have completed the page, briefly review the answers with them.

ONGOING ASSESSMENT
Watch for children who are having trouble displaying times on their tool-kit clocks. Ask them to tell you which numbers the hour hand and the minute hand are pointing to each time as they set their clocks.

2 Ongoing Learning & Practice

◆ Finding Missing Numbers on Number Lines
(*Math Journal 1*, p. 45)

INDEPENDENT ACTIVITY

Children practice counting skills using number-line patterns.

◆ Math Boxes 3.7 (*Math Journal 1*, p. 46)

INDEPENDENT ACTIVITY

Mixed Review This journal page provides opportunities for cumulative review or assessment of concepts and skills.

◆ Home Link 3.7 (*Math Masters*, pp. 186 and 187)

Home Connection Children practice telling time to the nearest hour and half-hour. Family members are asked to talk with the child about the times of several daily events.

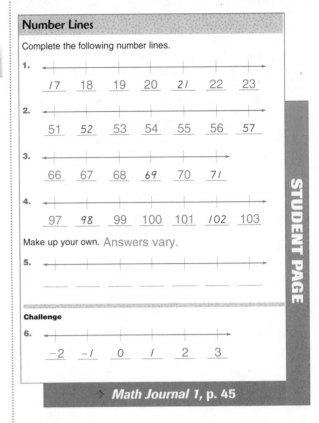

Number Lines

Complete the following number lines.

1. $\quad$ _17_ _18_ _19_ _20_ _21_ _22_ _23_

2. $\quad$ _51_ _52_ _53_ _54_ _55_ _56_ _57_

3. $\quad$ _66_ _67_ _68_ _69_ _70_ _71_

4. $\quad$ _97_ _98_ _99_ _100_ _101_ _102_ _103_

Make up your own. Answers vary.

5.

Challenge

6. $\quad$ _−2_ _−1_ _0_ _1_ _2_ _3_

STUDENT PAGE

➔ *Math Journal 1*, p. 45

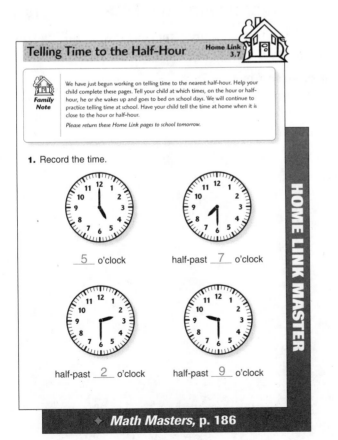

Telling Time to the Half-Hour   Home Link 3.7

Family Note — We have just begun working on telling time to the nearest half-hour. Help your child complete these pages. Tell your child at which times, on the hour or half-hour, he or she wakes up and goes to bed on school days. We will continue to practice telling time at school. Have your child tell the time at home when it is close to the hour or half-hour.

Please return these Home Link pages to school tomorrow.

1. Record the time.

_5_ o'clock

half-past _7_ o'clock

half-past _2_ o'clock

half-past _9_ o'clock

HOME LINK MASTER

◆ *Math Masters*, p. 186

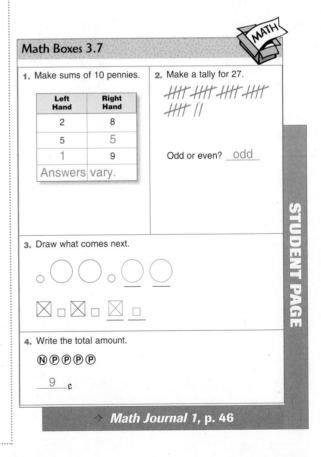

Math Boxes 3.7

1. Make sums of 10 pennies.

Left Hand	Right Hand
2	8
5	5
1	9
Answers	vary.

2. Make a tally for 27.

HHT HHT HHT HHT
HHT II

Odd or even? _odd_

3. Draw what comes next.

4. Write the total amount.

N P P P P

_9_ ¢

STUDENT PAGE

➔ *Math Journal 1*, p. 46

Lesson 3.7   **199**

HOME LINK MASTER

Challenge

2. Draw the hour hand and the minute hand to show the time.

This is the time I wake up in the morning on a school day.

This is the time I go to bed at night before a school day.

Answers vary.

◆ *Math Masters*, **p. 187**

3 Options for Individualizing

◆ ENRICHMENT Ordering Clocks by Time Displayed

SMALL-GROUP ACTIVITY   5–15 min

Collect the tool-kit clocks from a small group of children and set the clocks to different times. Then distribute the clocks—one to each child—and have children in the group work together to put the clocks in consecutive order.

Variation

Use five index cards cut in half. Stamp a clock face on each card and ask children to draw the minute hand pointing to 12 or 6. Then have them draw the hour hand for a time of their choosing. Remind them that the position of the hour hand depends on the position of the minute hand. Finally, have children put the cards in consecutive order.

◆ EXTRA PRACTICE Minute Math

SMALL-GROUP ACTIVITY   5–15 min

To offer children more experience with telling time, see the following page in *Minute Math:*

Measurement: p. 71

3.8 Introduction to the Frames-and-Arrows Routine

OBJECTIVE To introduce the Frames-and-Arrows routine.

summaries	materials

1 Teaching the Lesson

Children complete Frames-and-Arrows diagrams in which the arrow rule and the first number are both given. [Patterns, Functions, and Algebra; Operations and Computation]	☐ *Math Journal 1*, p. 47 ☐ Home Link 3.7 ☐ Teaching Master transparency (*Math Masters*, p. 28; optional) ☐ semipermanent chalk (optional)

2 Ongoing Learning & Practice

Children practice telling time on the hour and the half-hour. [Measurement and Reference Frames] Children practice and maintain skills through Math Boxes and Home Link activities.	☐ *Math Journal 1*, p. 48 ☐ Teaching Master (*Math Masters*, p. 14) ☐ Home Link Masters (*Math Masters*, pp. 188 and 189) ☐ tool-kit clock ***See* Advance Preparation**

3 Options for Individualizing

Extra Practice Children practice completing Frames-and-Arrows diagrams. [Patterns, Functions, and Algebra; Operations and Computation] **Extra Practice** Children review basic addition and subtraction. [Measurement and Reference Frames; Operations and Computation]	☐ Teaching Master (*Math Masters*, p. 28) ☐ Pattern-Block Template (optional) ☐ *Minute Math*®, pp. 10, 16, and 79–81 ***See* Advance Preparation**

Additional Information

Advance Preparation For Part 2, on a copy of *Math Masters*, page 14, write some times on the hour and the half-hour. Then make a copy of this master for each child. To individualize the first Extra Practice activity in Part 3, make 2 versions of *Math Masters*, page 28. Prepare one master for children who are struggling and another master for children who are doing well.

▷ For struggling students, fill in problems like the following:
  Rule: +1 **Frames:** 5, 6, blank, 8, blank
  Rule: Count back by 1s **Frames:** 10, 9, blank, blank, 6
  Rule: +3 **Frames:** 8, 11, blank, blank, 20
  Rule: Add 5 **Frames:** 10, 15, blank, blank, 30
  Rule: Subtract 2 **Frames:** 16, blank, blank, 10, blank

▷ For children who are doing well, fill in problems like the following:
  Rule: Add 10 **Frames:** 20, 30, blank, 50, blank
  Rule: Subtract 5 **Frames:** 30, blank, blank, 15, blank
  Rule: [leave blank] **Frames:** 15, 18, 21, blank, blank
  Rule: [leave blank] **Frames:** blank, 9, 13, blank, blank
  Rule: [leave blank] **Frames:** blank, blank, 4, 2, blank

Vocabulary • **Frames-and-Arrows diagram** • **arrow rule** • **frame** • **arrow**

Getting Started

Mental Math and Reflexes

In Lesson 3.10, children will be introduced to skip counting with a calculator. In preparation for this, it is important to begin posing skip-counting problems using a "start at/count by" template. The template names three pieces of information needed to program a calculator for skip counting. You can write the template on the board and then write the appropriate information for each problem.

Pose problems such as the following on the board. Children count in unison as they follow along on the number grid in their journals.

Start at:	7	13	28	20	80	5
Count:	up	up	back	up	back	up
By:	1s	5s	2s	10s	10s	3s

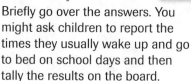

Home Link 3.7 Follow-Up

Briefly go over the answers. You might ask children to report the times they usually wake up and go to bed on school days and then tally the results on the board.

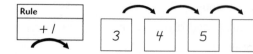

Teaching the Lesson

◆ Introducing the Frames-and-Arrows Routine

WHOLE-CLASS DISCUSSION AND ACTIVITY

Use a transparency of *Math Masters,* page 28, or, if an overhead projector is not available, draw a Frames-and-Arrows diagram on the board (see margin). (Use semipermanent chalk to draw the frames, the arrows, and the rule box. Use regular chalk to write the rule in the rule box and the numbers in the frames.)

Discuss the following features of the diagram:

▷ The diagram is called a **Frames-and-Arrows diagram.**

▷ A Frames-and-Arrows diagram has three parts: a rule, called an **arrow rule;** several **frames;** and **arrows** that lead from one frame to the next. In this particular diagram, the arrow rule is "Count up by 1s." Some of the frames have numbers in them; other frames are empty.

▷ To solve a Frames-and-Arrows problem, use the arrow rule to fill in the empty frames.

With the help of children, fill in the missing numbers in the empty frames. Explain that counting up by 1s is like *adding* 1 to each number to get the next number. For example: $3 + 1 = 4$, $4 + 1 = 5$, $5 + 1 = 6$, and so on. Another way to state the arrow rule is to write "Add 1" or "+1."

Adjusting the Activity If children are having difficulty, they may benefit from acting out the rule with counters.

Display the following Frames-and-Arrows diagram and ask children to help you fill in the missing numbers:

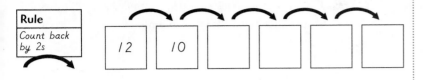

Adjusting the Activity If necessary, use hops on the Class Number Line or on the number line on the transparency of *Math Masters,* page 27 to count back by 2s as children follow on the number line on the inside back cover of their journals.

Mention that counting back by 2s is like *subtracting* 2 from each number to get the next number. *For example:* 12 – 2 = 10, 10 – 2 = 8, 8 – 2 = 6, and so on. Another way to state the arrow rule is to write "Subtract 2" or "–2."

Repeat this routine with several more problems. Keep the rules simple, and always provide the starting numbers. Children should use their number lines if they need to.

Suggestions

Rule	First Frames	Missing Frames
Count up by 1s	15, 16, 17	18, 19, 20
Count up by 2s	8, 10, 12	14, 16, 18
Count back by 1s	15, 14, 13	12, 11, 10
Add 10	10, 20, 30	40, 50, 60
Subtract 2	13, 11, 9	7, 5, 3
* Count back by 5s	25, 20, 15	10, 5, 0
* Subtract 3	18, 15, 12	9, 6, 3

* Denotes a Challenge problem

Ask children to make up Frames-and-Arrows problems for the class to solve.

◆ Solving Frames-and-Arrows Problems
(*Math Journal 1,* p. 47)

PARTNER ACTIVITY 👥

Partners work together to solve the problems. Encourage children to help each other and check each other's work. They should use the number line to help them with the more difficult problems.

Adjusting the Activity This lesson is children's first exposure to the Frames-and-Arrows routine. It focuses on the simplest kind of Frames-and-Arrows diagram, in which the rule is known and the first number is given. In the next lesson, children will solve more difficult problems. If you think children are ready, you may want to challenge them now with one or two problems in which all the numbers are given and the rule is missing. In this kind of problem, children are to find the rule. For example:

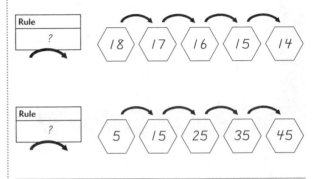

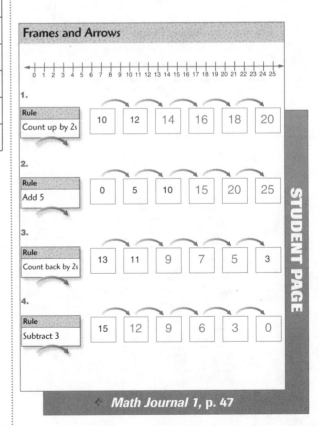

Math Journal 1, p. 47

Math Boxes 3.8

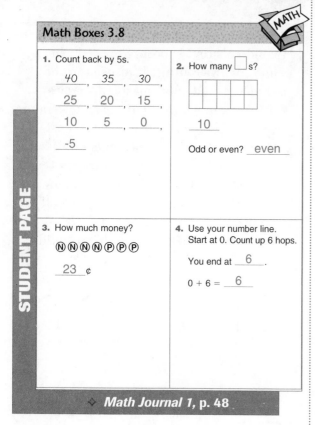

1. Count back by 5s.

40 , 35 , 30 ,

25 , 20 , 15 ,

10 , 5 , 0 ,

-5

2. How many ☐s?

10

Odd or even? even

3. How much money?

Ⓝ Ⓝ Ⓝ Ⓟ Ⓟ Ⓟ

23 ¢

4. Use your number line.
Start at 0. Count up 6 hops.

You end at 6 .

0 + 6 = 6

STUDENT PAGE

◆ *Math Journal 1, p. 48*

ONGOING ASSESSMENT

Check the journal page to see that children are applying the rule correctly to each of the frames. Throughout the year, they will get much more practice with these problems.

2 Ongoing Learning & Practice

◆ Telling Time (*Math Masters*, p. 14)

INDEPENDENT ACTIVITY

Distribute a copy of *Math Masters*, page 14 to each child. Have children work individually or with a partner to record various times on the hour and half-hour. They can display times on their tool-kit clocks for reinforcement.

◆ Math Boxes 3.8 (*Math Journal 1*, p. 48)

INDEPENDENT ACTIVITY

Mixed Review This journal page provides opportunities for cumulative review or assessment of concepts and skills.

◆ Home Link 3.8 (*Math Masters*, pp. 188 and 189)

Home Connection Children complete Frames-and-Arrows diagrams. An extended Family Note on the Home Link explains these diagrams.

HOME LINK MASTER

Frames-and-Arrows Diagrams

Home Link 3.8

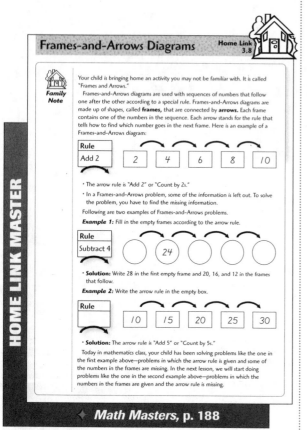

Family Note

Your child is bringing home an activity you may not be familiar with. It is called "Frames and Arrows."

Frames-and-Arrows diagrams are used with sequences of numbers that follow one after the other according to a special rule. Frames-and-Arrows diagrams are made up of shapes, called **frames**, that are connected by **arrows**. Each frame contains one of the numbers in the sequence. Each arrow stands for the rule that tells how to find which number goes in the next frame. Here is an example of a Frames-and-Arrows diagram:

Rule
Add 2
2 4 6 8 10

• The arrow rule is "Add 2" or "Count by 2s."
• In a Frames-and-Arrows problem, some of the information is left out. To solve the problem, you have to find the missing information.

Following are two examples of Frames-and-Arrows problems.

Example 1: Fill in the empty frames according to the arrow rule.

Rule
Subtract 4
 24

• **Solution:** Write 28 in the first empty frame and 20, 16, and 12 in the frames that follow.

Example 2: Write the arrow rule in the empty box.

Rule
 10 15 20 25 30

• **Solution:** The arrow rule is "Add 5" or "Count by 5s."

Today in mathematics class, your child has been solving problems like the one in the first example above—problems in which the arrow rule is given and some of the numbers in the frames are missing. In the next lesson, we will start doing problems like the one in the second example above—problems in which the numbers in the frames are given and the arrow rule is missing.

◆ *Math Masters, p. 188*

3 Options for Individualizing

✦ EXTRA PRACTICE Solving Frames-and-Arrows Problems (*Math Masters*, p. 28)

INDEPENDENT ACTIVITY   **5–15 min**

Distribute copies of *Math Masters*, page 28 according to children's needs. (*See* Advance Preparation.)

Also, you or the class can create your own Frames-and-Arrows problems. Use the Pattern-Block Template to draw frames.

✦ EXTRA PRACTICE Minute Math

SMALL-GROUP ACTIVITY   **5–15 min**

To offer children more experience with addition and subtraction, see the following pages in *Minute Math:*

Basic Routines: pp. 10 and 16
Number Stories: pp. 79–81

PLANNING AHEAD
Before you begin Lesson 3.11, each child should bring 10 dimes to school.

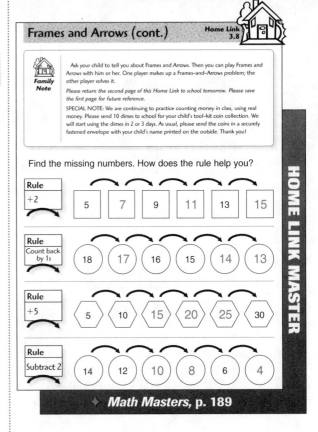

 Math Masters, p. 189

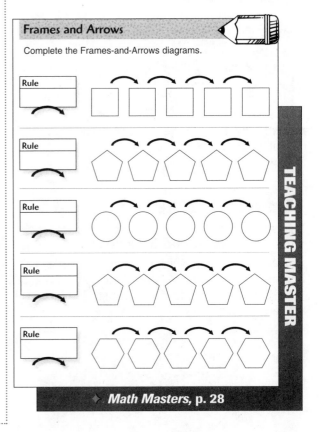

 Math Masters, p. 28

3.9 More Frames-and-Arrows Problems

OBJECTIVE To introduce Frames-and-Arrows problems in which the "arrow rule" is missing.

summaries	materials
1 Teaching the Lesson	
In Lesson 3.8, children were introduced to Frames-and-Arrows problems in which the arrow rule and the first few numbers are given; their task was to find the missing numbers. In the current lesson, children complete Frames-and-Arrows diagrams in which a sequence of numbers is given and they are to find the rule. [Patterns, Functions, and Algebra; Operations and Computation]	□ *Math Journal 1,* p. 49 □ Home Link 3.8 □ Teaching Master transparency (*Math Masters,* p. 28; optional)
2 Ongoing Learning & Practice	
Children solve addition problems with the help of a number grid. [Numeration; Operations and Computation] Children practice and maintain skills through Math Boxes and Home Link activities.	□ *Math Journal 1,* pp. 50 and 51 □ Home Link Master (*Math Masters,* p. 190)
3 Options for Individualizing	
Extra Practice Children practice solving Frames-and-Arrows problems and discuss the similarity between Frames-and-Arrows problems and skip counting on the number line. [Patterns, Functions, and Algebra; Operations and Computation] **Extra Practice** Children solve simple addition and subtraction problems. [Operations and Computation]	□ *Minute Math*®, pp. 10, 15, 16, 39, and 46

Getting Started

Mental Math and Reflexes
Pose problems in which children count up and back on their number grids, starting at any number. Use the "start at/count by" template, introduced in Lesson 3.8, to present each problem.

Home Link 3.8 Follow-Up
Briefly go over the answers.

Teaching the Lesson

✦ Finding the Arrow Rule
(*Math Masters,* p. 28)

WHOLE-CLASS ACTIVITY

Before you proceed to problems in which children are to find the missing rule, do a few problems like the ones in Lesson 3.8, in which the rule and the first few numbers are given. (Write the problems on the board, or use a transparency of *Math Masters,* page 28.)

> **Adjusting the Activity** If necessary, help children make the connection between these Frames-and-Arrows problems and the number-grid patterns they explored in Lesson 3.3. Display a number grid with the counting patterns marked for children to use as they solve the Frames-and-Arrows problems.

When you feel that children are ready, pose the following problem:

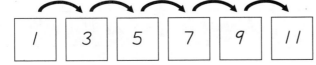

Ask children if they can guess the rule. Let several children make suggestions. There is more than one way to express the rule (for example: "Count up by 2s," "Add 2," "2 more," and "+2"), so encourage children to suggest various statements of the rule.

Continue with several other problems in which the rule is missing. (Write a question mark in the rule box each time.) Children should use the number grid on the inside back cover of their journals if they have trouble figuring out a pattern.

> **Adjusting the Activity** If children are having difficulty, ask those who cannot state the missing rule if they can give the number for the next frame. Extending a pattern is often easier than stating the rule for it.

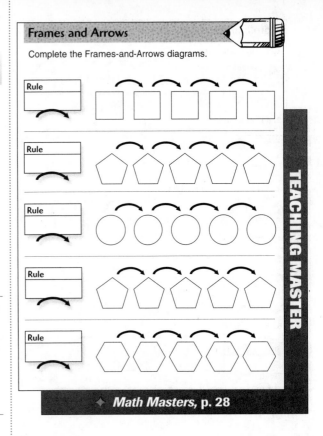

Frames and Arrows

Complete the Frames-and-Arrows diagrams.

✦ *Math Masters, p. 28*

Suggestions

Rule	First Frames	Missing Frames
Count up by 2s	7, 9, 11	13, 15, 17
Count back by 2s	12, 10, 8	6, 4, 2
Add 3	4, 7, 10	13, 16, 19
−10	60, 50, 40	30, 20, 10

Suggestions

Frames	Missing Rules
2, 4, 6, 8, 10, 12	Count up by 2s, or add 2
15, 14, 13, 12, 11, 10	Count back by 1s, or subtract 1
3, 6, 9, 12, 15, 18	Count up by 3s, or add 3
15, 13, 11, 9, 7, 5	Count back by 2s, or subtract 2
20, 30, 40, 50, 60, 70	Count up by 10s, or add 10

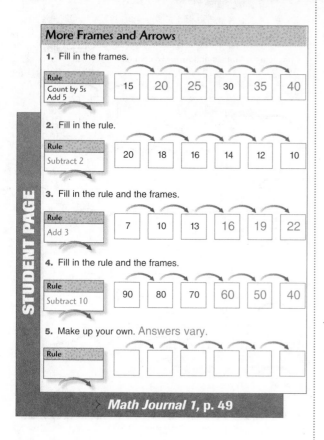

More Frames and Arrows

1. Fill in the frames.

Rule
Count by 5s
Add 5

15 | 20 | 25 | 30 | 35 | 40

2. Fill in the rule.

Rule
Subtract 2

20 | 18 | 16 | 14 | 12 | 10

3. Fill in the rule and the frames.

Rule
Add 3

7 | 10 | 13 | 16 | 19 | 22

4. Fill in the rule and the frames.

Rule
Subtract 10

90 | 80 | 70 | 60 | 50 | 40

5. Make up your own. Answers vary.

Rule

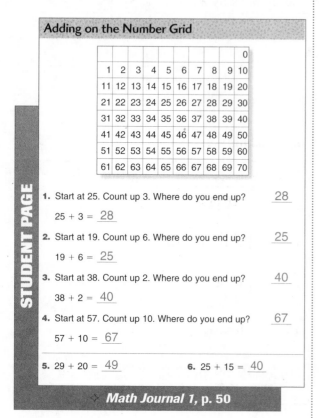

Adding on the Number Grid

									0
1	2	3	4	5	6	7	8	9	10
11	12	13	14	15	16	17	18	19	20
21	22	23	24	25	26	27	28	29	30
31	32	33	34	35	36	37	38	39	40
41	42	43	44	45	46	47	48	49	50
51	52	53	54	55	56	57	58	59	60
61	62	63	64	65	66	67	68	69	70

1. Start at 25. Count up 3. Where do you end up? 28

   25 + 3 = 28

2. Start at 19. Count up 6. Where do you end up? 25

   19 + 6 = 25

3. Start at 38. Count up 2. Where do you end up? 40

   38 + 2 = 40

4. Start at 57. Count up 10. Where do you end up? 67

   57 + 10 = 67

5. 29 + 20 = 49   6. 25 + 15 = 40

◆ Making up Frames-and-Arrows Problems
(*Math Masters,* p. 28)

WHOLE-CLASS ACTIVITY

Ask children to make up their own Frames-and-Arrows problems. Since the simplest problems are those in which the rule and the first number are both given, begin with these. Then encourage children to suggest more difficult problems.

 Adjusting the Activity To extend this activity, suggest that children make up problems in which the first frame is empty. This makes the problem more challenging because it requires working backward to fill in the first frame.

◆ Solving Frames-and-Arrows Problems
(*Math Journal 1,* p. 49)

PARTNER ACTIVITY

Partners work together to solve the problems. Encourage them to help each other and to check each other's work. They should use a number line to help them with the more difficult problems.

Ongoing Learning & Practice

◆ Adding on the Number Grid (*Math Journal 1,* p. 50)

INDEPENDENT ACTIVITY

Children use the number grid on the inside back cover of their journals to solve addition problems.

◆ Math Boxes 3.9 (*Math Journal 1,* p. 51)

INDEPENDENT ACTIVITY

 Mixed Review This journal page provides opportunities for cumulative review or assessment of concepts and skills.

◆ Home Link 3.9 (*Math Masters,* p. 190)

 Home Connection Children find the missing rules in Frames-and-Arrows problems. Family members may want to refer back to the Home Link 3.8 Family Note to review the Frames-and-Arrows routine.

3 Options for Individualizing

✦ EXTRA PRACTICE Skip Counting on the Number Line

WHOLE-CLASS ACTIVITY 👥👥👥 5–15 min

Children use the number line on the inside back cover of their journals to count hops on the number line. As they do so, list each number they land on.

Suggestions

- Start at 0. Count up by 3s. 0, 3, 6, 9, 12, 15, …
- Start at 5. Count up by 5s. 5, 10, 15, 20, 25, 30, …
- Start at 20. Count back by 2s. 20, 18, 16, 14, 12, 10, …

Help children make the connection between skip counting on the number line and completing number sequences in Frames-and-Arrows problems by recording the above number-line counts in a Frames-and-Arrows diagram. For the first problem above, the rule would be "Count by 3s" or "Add 3," and the frames would contain 0, 3, 6, 9, 12, and so on.

✦ EXTRA PRACTICE Minute Math

SMALL-GROUP ACTIVITY 👥👥👥 5–15 min

To offer children more experience with addition and subtraction, see the following pages in *Minute Math:*

Basic Routines: pp. 10, 15, and 16

Operations: pp. 39 and 46

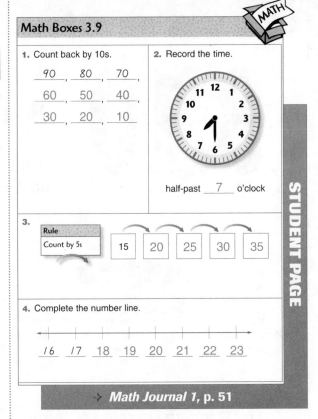

→ *Math Journal 1, p. 51*

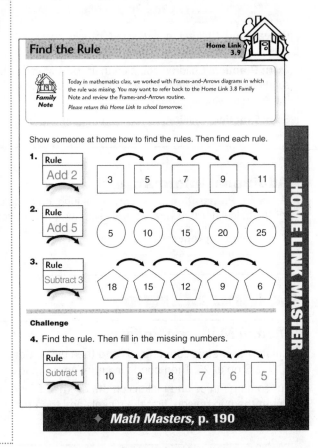

✦ *Math Masters, p. 190*

3.10 Counting with a Calculator

OBJECTIVE To introduce counting up and back on the calculator.

summaries	materials

1 Teaching the Lesson

Children learn to count up and back using a calculator.
[Numeration; Operations and Computation]

- ☐ *Math Journal 1*, p. 52
- ☐ Home Link 3.9
- ☐ calculator
- ☐ overhead calculator (optional)

2 Ongoing Learning & Practice

Children solve subtraction problems with the help of a number grid. [Operations and Computation; Numeration]

Children practice and maintain skills through Math Boxes and Home Link activities.

- ☐ *Math Journal 1*, pp. 53 and 54
- ☐ Home Link Master (*Math Masters*, p. 191)

3 Options for Individualizing

Reteaching Children play *Penny-Nickel Exchange*.
[Measurement and Reference Frames; Numeration]

Extra Practice Children count on their calculators to check solutions to Frames-and-Arrows problems. [Numeration; Patterns, Functions, and Algebra]

Extra Practice Children review counting up and back.
[Numeration]

- ☐ *Math Journal 1*, p. 49
- ☐ pennies and nickels
- ☐ calculator
- ☐ *Minute Math®*, pp. 5, 27, 29, and 31

Additional Information

Advance Preparation Most basic four-function calculators provide for counting up and back. Read the instruction manual for the calculator that your class is using for a description of the counting (constant) function.

Vocabulary • program

Getting Started

Mental Math and Reflexes

Do stop-and-start counts by 5s and then by 1s. Count by 5s beginning with 0. Stop at 25. Then continue counting by 1s to 29.

Put some pennies and nickels on the overhead (or draw them on the board). Count them in unison, first the nickels and then the pennies.

Repeat as time allows.

Home Link 3.9 Follow-Up

Children share their strategies for figuring out the missing rules.

Teaching the Lesson

◆ Counting Up and Back with a Calculator

WHOLE-CLASS ACTIVITY

Tell children that they are going to learn how to use a calculator to count.

Review some of the basic rules for using calculators:

▷ Do not drop or throw calculators.

▷ It is easier to use a calculator when you place it on a firm, flat surface.

▷ Pressing the middle of a key helps to make sure that only one key is pressed at a time.

▷ Use only your finger to press a key. Do not use a pencil to press a key.

Write the following information on the board:

Start at:	0
Count:	up
By:	2s

Before the calculator can start counting, you must **program** it. This means that you must get it ready to count. Describe how to program the calculator to count up by 2s, as children follow along on their calculators:

1. Press ON/C . This clears your calculator.

2. Press 0. This is the *starting number.*

3. Press the ⊕ key. This tells the calculator to count *up.*

4. Press 2. This tells the calculator to *count by 2s.*

Now the calculator is ready to start counting by 2s. Direct the class to do the following:

• Without clearing your calculator, press the ⊜ key. Which number is in the calculator display? 2

• Without clearing your calculator, press the ⊜ key again. Which number is in the display now? 4

• Continue to press the ⊜ key. (Each time, the class calls out the number in the display.)

NOTE: Some people suggest that it is efficient to use the nonwriting hand for calculator keying while keeping the writing hand available for recording. In a playful, challenging way, see if children can do the counts using their nonwriting hands.

Repeat the procedure, this time counting up by 5s, starting at 0. Write the following information on the board:

Start at: 0
Count: up
By: 5s

You or a volunteer describes how to program the calculator to count by 5s, as the class follows along.

1. Press ON/C. This clears the calculator.

2. Press 0. This is the *starting number*.

3. Press the ⊕ key. This tells the calculator to count *up*.

4. Press 5. This tells the calculator to *count by 5s*.

Now children press the ⊜ key repeatedly and call out the numbers in the display, in unison.

Next, write the information for counting back by 1s, starting at 12, on the board:

Start at: 12
Count: back
By: 1s

Describe how to program the calculator, as children follow along.

1. Press ON/C. This clears the calculator.

2. Press 12. This is the *starting number*.

3. Press the ⊖ key. This tells the calculator to count *back*.

4. Press 1. This tells the calculator to *count by 1s*.

• How is programming the calculator to count back different from programming it to count up? To count up, press the ⊕ key; to count back, press the ⊖ key.

Now children press the ⊜ key repeatedly to ascertain that the calculator is counting back by 1s from 12.

 Adjusting the Activity To extend this activity, ask children: *What happens when you press the ⊜ key after 0 has been displayed?* You get –1. *Continue to do this several times. What are these numbers called?* Negative numbers

Do a few more counts back from a given number on the calculator.

✦ Counting Up, Starting from Any Number

WHOLE-CLASS ACTIVITY

Ask someone to supply the information for counting up by 2s, starting at 5. Write it on the board, as follows:

> Start at: 5
> Count: up
> By: 2s

Give children a couple of minutes to try to program their calculators to do this count. Press ⟨ON/C⟩ 5 ⊕ 2 Children should press the ⊜ key a few times to check that they have programmed their calculators correctly. Have a volunteer describe what he or she did as the class follows along.

- How is programming the calculator to count up from 5 different from programming it to count up from 0? To count up from 0, enter 0 before pressing the ⊕ key; to count up from 5, enter 5 before pressing the ⊕ key.

Do a few more counts up, starting with a number other than 0.

✦ Counting with a Calculator
(*Math Journal 1*, p. 52)

INDEPENDENT ACTIVITY

Children count up by 2s and back by 3s on their calculators. They mark their counts on a number grid and identify the numbers that occur in both counts. They observe that the numbers that occur in both counts are counts by 6s.

ONGOING ASSESSMENT
Check to make sure that children first clear their calculators; then enter the starting number followed by ⊕ or ⊖ (depending on whether they are counting up or back); and finally enter the number they are counting by. Although children began counting on a calculator in Kindergarten, it may take some practice for them to become good at it.

Calculator Counts

									0
⊗1	2	③	⤫4	⑤	6	⊗7	8	9	10
⑪	12	⑬	14	⑮	16	⑰	18	⑲	20
㉑	22	㉓	24	㉕	26	㉗	28	29	30
㉛	32	㉝	34	㉟	36	㊲	38	39	40
㊶	42	⊗43	44	㊺	46	㊼	48	⊗49	50

Do the following counts on a calculator:

1. Start at: 1
   Count: up
   By: 2s

   Circle these numbers on the grid.

2. Start at: 49
   Count: back
   By: 3s

   Mark these numbers on the grid with an X.

Challenge

3. List the numbers that have a circle and an X.

   _1_, _7_, _13_, _19_, _25_, _31_, _37_, _43_, _49_

   These are counts by _6s_.

✦ *Math Journal 1,* p. 52

STUDENT PAGE

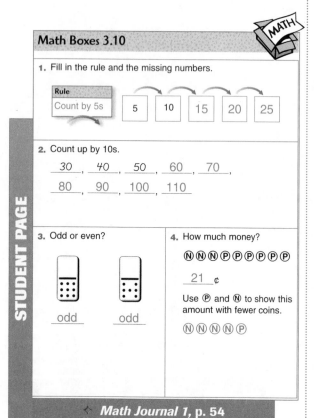

Subtracting on the Number Grid

									0
1	2	3	4	5	6	7	8	9	10
11	12	13	14	15	16	17	18	19	20
21	22	23	24	25	26	27	28	29	30
31	32	33	34	35	36	37	38	39	40
41	42	43	44	45	46	47	48	49	50
51	52	53	54	55	56	57	58	59	60
61	62	63	64	65	66	67	68	69	70

1. Start at 35. Count back 2. Where do you end up?   <u>33</u>

   $35 - 2 =$ <u>33</u>

2. Start at 27. Count back 5. Where do you end up?   <u>22</u>

   $27 - 5 =$ <u>22</u>

3. Start at 48. Count back 10. Where do you end up?   <u>38</u>

   $48 - 10 =$ <u>38</u>

4. Start at 65. Count back 15. Where do you end up?   <u>50</u>

   $65 - 15 =$ <u>50</u>

5. $52 - 20 =$ <u>32</u>   6. $46 - 16 =$ <u>30</u>

Math Journal 1, p. 53

2 Ongoing Learning & Practice

◆ Subtracting on the Number Grid
(*Math Journal 1*, p. 53)

INDEPENDENT ACTIVITY

Children use the number grid on this journal page to solve subtraction problems.

◆ Math Boxes 3.10 (*Math Journal 1*, p. 54)

INDEPENDENT ACTIVITY

Mixed Review This journal page provides opportunities for cumulative review or assessment of concepts and skills.

◆ Home Link 3.10 (*Math Masters,* p. 191)

Home Connection Children look closely at a dime and determine some dime exchanges. They are asked to bring 10 dimes to school to add to their tool-kit coin collections.

Math Boxes 3.10

1. Fill in the rule and the missing numbers.

   Rule
   Count by 5s

   | 5 | 10 | 15 | 20 | 25 |

2. Count up by 10s.

   <u>30</u>, <u>40</u>, <u>50</u>, <u>60</u>, <u>70</u>,
   <u>80</u>, <u>90</u>, <u>100</u>, <u>110</u>

3. Odd or even?

   <u>odd</u>   <u>odd</u>

4. How much money?

   Ⓝ Ⓝ Ⓝ Ⓟ Ⓟ Ⓟ Ⓟ Ⓟ Ⓟ

   <u>21</u> ¢

   Use Ⓟ and Ⓝ to show this amount with fewer coins.

   Ⓝ Ⓝ Ⓝ Ⓝ Ⓟ

Math Journal 1, p. 54

3 Options for Individualizing

◆ RETEACHING Playing *Penny-Nickel Exchange*

PARTNER ACTIVITY    **5–15 min**

Children practice money skills by playing *Penny-Nickel Exchange.* For detailed instructions, see Lesson 2.10.

◆ EXTRA PRACTICE Checking Frames-and-Arrows Problems with a Calculator
(*Math Journal 1*, p. 49)

INDEPENDENT ACTIVITY   **15–30 min**

Children use their calculators to check the Frames-and-Arrows problems on journal page 49. The first frame tells children which number to start with; the rule tells whether to enter $\oplus$ or $\ominus$ and which number to enter to count by.

◆ EXTRA PRACTICE Minute Math

SMALL-GROUP ACTIVITY   **5–15 min**

To offer children more experience with counting up and back, see the following pages in *Minute Math*:

Basic Routines: p. 5

Counting: pp. 27, 29, and 31

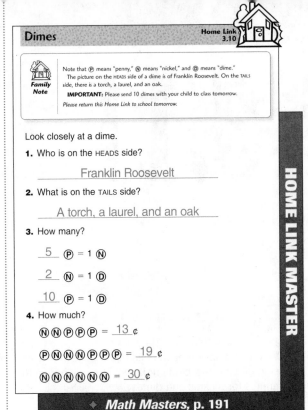

Math Masters, p. 191

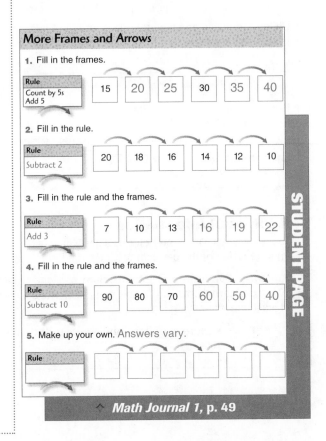

Math Journal 1, p. 49

3.11 Dimes

OBJECTIVES To introduce the dime; to introduce dollars-and-cents notation; and to practice exchanging pennies, nickels, and dimes.

summaries	materials

1 Teaching the Lesson

Children explore dimes. They figure out how much money the class would have if each child had a dime and write the total using dollars-and-cents notation. They exchange their tool-kit pennies for nickels and dimes. [Measurement and Reference Frames; Numeration]

- ☐ *Math Journal 1*, p. 55
- ☐ Home Link 3.10
- ☐ tool-kit coins
- ☐ overhead coins (optional)
- ☐ 10 dimes
- ☐ 1 magnifying lens per 4–5 children
- ☐ calculator

See **Advance Preparation**

2 Ongoing Learning & Practice

Children practice completing Frames-and-Arrows diagrams. [Patterns, Functions, and Algebra; Operations and Computation]

Children practice and maintain skills through Math Boxes and Home Link activities.

- ☐ *Math Journal 1*, pp. 56 and 57
- ☐ Home Link Masters (*Math Masters*, pp. 192 and 193)
- ☐ calculator

3 Options for Individualizing

Reteaching Children grab handfuls of pennies and exchange each handful for as few dimes and nickels as possible. [Measurement and Reference Frames; Numeration]

Enrichment Children play *Coin Top-It*. [Measurement and Reference Frames; Numeration]

- ☐ Teaching Master (*Math Masters*, p. 29)
- ☐ tool-kit coins

Additional Information

Today's Mental Math and Reflexes activity may take longer than usual. Take the time necessary to complete it. It is an important part of the problem-solving strand in *Everyday Mathematics*.

Advance Preparation Display the Story of Money Poster. (See Advance Preparation in Lesson 2.8.) Each child will need 10 dimes. Have extras (preferably real ones) available for children who did not bring any to school. Each small group will need at least one magnifying lens.

Vocabulary • **dime** • **dollars-and-cents notation** • **decimal point**

Getting Started

Mental Math and Reflexes

Tell parts-and-total number stories, and have children solve them any way they can (by using counters, by drawing pictures, and so on) and write the answers on their slates. Also have children share solution strategies after each problem. Summarize each solution by drawing a parts-and-total diagram on the board, *but only after children have had a chance to share what they did to solve the problem.*

Suggestions

- Rich bought 4 batteries for his radio on Monday. He played it all week. He had to buy 8 more batteries on Friday. How many batteries did Rich buy that week? 12 batteries
- Diane walked 2 blocks to meet Linda on her way to school. The two girls then walked another 4 blocks to get to school. How far did Diane walk to get to school? 6 blocks
- Liz read 5 books in the month of April. She read 6 more books in the month of May. How many books did Liz read altogether during those two months? 11 books

Children having difficulty can use counters to model the problems. Ask children who are doing well to write number models for the problems.

Total	
12	
Part	Part
4	8

Home Link 3.10 Follow-Up

Children share magnifying lenses for a closer inspection of what's on a dime.

1 Teaching the Lesson

◆ Introducing Dollars-and-Cents Notation

WHOLE-CLASS ACTIVITY

Remind children that a **dime** is worth 10 cents. Ask them how many nickels they would get in exchange for 1 dime. 2 nickels For 2 dimes? 4 nickels

 Language Link Explain that the word *dime* comes from the Latin word *decima*, which means *tenth*. Ask if children know other words that have the same root (for example: *decade, decimeter, decibel,* and *decimal*). If appropriate, encourage children not born in this country to describe the coins used in the countries of their birth.

Fill in the "Dime" column on your Story of Money Poster (see margin).

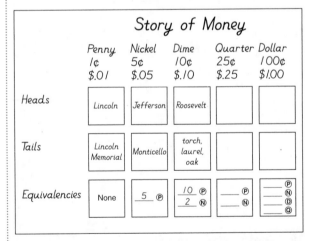

Story of Money				
Penny 1¢ $.01	Nickel 5¢ $.05	Dime 10¢ $.10	Quarter 25¢ $.25	Dollar 100¢ $1.00
Heads Lincoln	Jefferson	Roosevelt		
Tails Lincoln Memorial	Monticello	torch, laurel, oak		
Equivalencies None	5 ℗	10 ℗ / 2 ℕ	___ ℗ / ___ ℕ	℗ / ℕ / Ⓓ / Ⓠ

NOTE: Dimes are a metal sandwich—the coating is made of a combination of nickel and copper; the middle is copper. Franklin Roosevelt, who is pictured on the heads side, was president from 1933 until he died in 1945.

Pose the following problem:

- If every child in our class had one dime, how much money would our class have in all?

To solve the problem, have the class count by 10s (10 cents, 20 cents, 30 cents, ...), with each child saying one of the 10-counts, until all children have had a turn. For example, if there are 25 children in your class, the count will reach 250 cents. You might want to point to the numbers on the number grid (as high as it goes) as you do this count. Children have not yet had much experience with counts over 100, so expect that some children may falter as the count gets higher.

Start the count again. This time, when children get to 100 cents, tell them to say *1 dollar,* since there are 100 cents in 1 dollar. As they continue, instead of saying *110 cents,* they say *1 dollar and 10 cents,* and so on.

Record both final counts on the board: 250 cents = 2 dollars and 50 cents (or whichever amount applies to your class). Then write the final amount using **dollars-and-cents notation:** $2.50. Discuss how to interpret this notation:

- The symbol "$" stands for the word *dollar.*
- The dot (or period) after the 2 is called a **decimal point.**
- The number before the decimal point shows the number of dollars; the numbers after the decimal point show the number of cents.

Ask children to suggest things that cost about that much money.

Demonstrate how to enter this amount in a calculator:

▷ Clear the calculator. Then press ② ⊙ ⑤ ⓪.

Write several amounts, each greater than one dollar, in dollars-and-cents notation on the board. Have children read the amounts and enter them into their calculators. Remind them to clear their calculators before they enter each new amount.

Social Studies Link

Discuss with children the monetary systems found in other countries. Encourage class members who are familiar with coins from other countries to share their experiences. (For information on foreign currency, consult a world almanac or the business section of a Sunday newspaper.)

◆ Exchanging Pennies and Nickels for Dimes
(*Math Journal 1*, p. 55)

Draw 3 nickels on the board using an Ⓝ to represent each nickel. Have children take out 3 nickels from their tool-kit coin collections. Ask them to arrange their nickels into two groups so that there are 2 nickels in one group and 1 nickel in the other group. (Model this with overhead coins, if they're available.)

Ⓝ Ⓝ   Ⓝ

Next, have children exchange 2 of the nickels for 1 dime. On the board, draw a Ⓓ under the two nickels to represent 1 dime and draw 1 Ⓝ next to it. Explain that 1 dime and 1 nickel are worth the same amount as 3 nickels, or 15 cents. Point to the dime and the nickel as you count together: *10 cents, 15 cents*.

Ⓝ Ⓝ   Ⓝ
⎵
Ⓓ   Ⓝ

Next, draw 18 pennies on the board using a Ⓟ to represent each penny. Have children take out 18 pennies. Ask them to show how they would pay for something that costs 18 cents, using fewer coins. 1 dime, 1 nickel, 3 pennies If children show an exchange that does not consist of the *fewest* number of coins, ask them whether they can exchange any more pennies for nickels or any more nickels for dimes. Draw a diagram like the one shown below to summarize the exchange, and point to the coins as you count together: *10 cents, 15 cents, 16 cents, 17 cents, 18 cents*.

Ⓟ Ⓟ Ⓟ Ⓟ Ⓟ   Ⓟ Ⓟ Ⓟ Ⓟ Ⓟ   Ⓟ Ⓟ Ⓟ Ⓟ Ⓟ   Ⓟ Ⓟ Ⓟ
⎵   ⎵   ⎵
Ⓝ   Ⓝ   Ⓝ   Ⓟ Ⓟ Ⓟ
⎵⎵⎵⎵⎵⎵⎵
Ⓓ   Ⓝ   Ⓟ Ⓟ Ⓟ

Do a few more examples with the class, as needed. Children then work independently or in partnerships to complete the journal page.

Adjusting the Activity If necessary, have children model the problems and make their exchanges using their tool-kit coins. It helps if they keep their coins grouped according to their value, as you did in the whole-class examples.

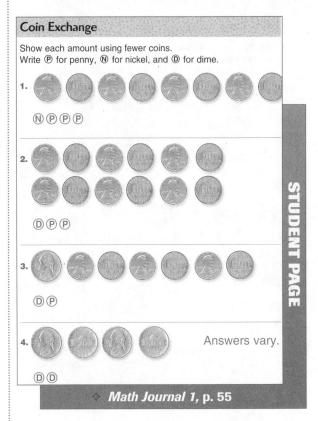

Coin Exchange

Show each amount using fewer coins.
Write Ⓟ for penny, Ⓝ for nickel, and Ⓓ for dime.

1. Ⓝ Ⓟ Ⓟ Ⓟ

2. Ⓓ Ⓟ Ⓟ

3. Ⓓ Ⓟ

4. Ⓓ Ⓓ
   Answers vary.

Math Journal 1, p. 55

STUDENT PAGE

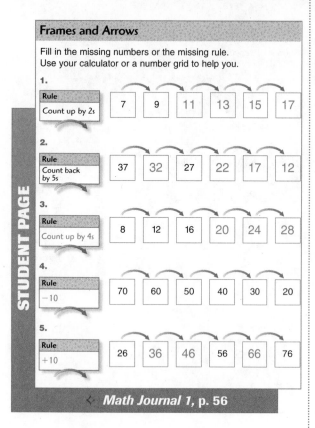

Frames and Arrows

Fill in the missing numbers or the missing rule.
Use your calculator or a number grid to help you.

1.
Rule: Count up by 2s
| 7 | 9 | 11 | 13 | 15 | 17 |

2.
Rule: Count back by 5s
| 37 | 32 | 27 | 22 | 17 | 12 |

3.
Rule: Count up by 4s
| 8 | 12 | 16 | 20 | 24 | 28 |

4.
Rule: −10
| 70 | 60 | 50 | 40 | 30 | 20 |

5.
Rule: +10
| 26 | 36 | 46 | 56 | 66 | 76 |

Math Journal 1, p. 56

Ongoing Learning & Practice

◆ **Completing Frames-and-Arrows Diagrams**
(*Math Journal 1,* p. 56)

INDEPENDENT ACTIVITY

Children solve Frames-and-Arrows problems. They use their calculators to help them count.

◆ **Math Boxes 3.11** (*Math Journal 1,* p. 57)

INDEPENDENT ACTIVITY

Mixed Review This journal page provides opportunities for cumulative review or assessment of concepts and skills.

◆ **Home Link 3.11** (*Math Masters,* pp. 192 and 193)

Home Connection Children practice exchanging pennies for nickels and dimes and finding the fewest number of coins for a given amount.

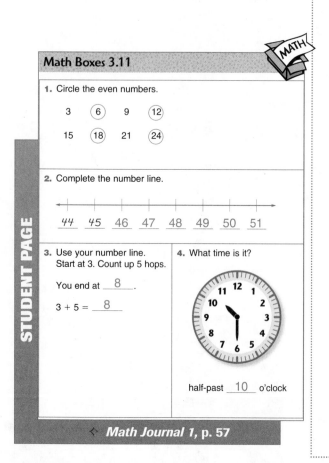

Math Boxes 3.11

1. Circle the even numbers.

   3 (6) 9 (12)

   15 (18) 21 (24)

2. Complete the number line.

   44 45 46 47 48 49 50 51

3. Use your number line. Start at 3. Count up 5 hops.

   You end at ___8___.

   3 + 5 = ___8___

4. What time is it?

   half-past ___10___ o'clock

Math Journal 1, p. 57

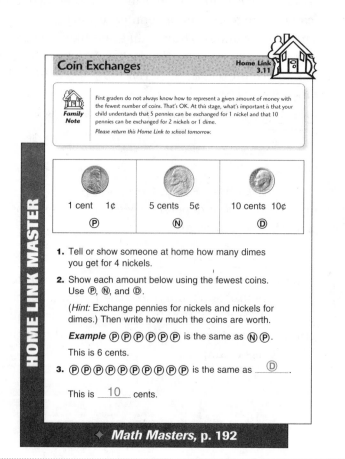

Coin Exchanges

Home Link 3.11

Family Note First graders do not always know how to represent a given amount of money with the fewest number of coins. That's OK. At this stage, what's important is that your child understands that 5 pennies can be exchanged for 1 nickel and that 10 pennies can be exchanged for 2 nickels or 1 dime.

Please return this Home Link to school tomorrow.

| 1 cent 1¢ (P) | 5 cents 5¢ (N) | 10 cents 10¢ (D) |

1. Tell or show someone at home how many dimes you get for 4 nickels.

2. Show each amount below using the fewest coins. Use (P), (N), and (D).

   (*Hint:* Exchange pennies for nickels and nickels for dimes.) Then write how much the coins are worth.

   Example (P)(P)(P)(P)(P)(P) is the same as (N)(P).

   This is 6 cents.

3. (P)(P)(P)(P)(P)(P)(P)(P)(P)(P) is the same as ___(D)___.

   This is ___10___ cents.

Math Masters, p. 192

3 Options for Individualizing

✦ RETEACHING Exchanging Coins
(*Math Masters*, p. 29)

PARTNER ACTIVITY   15–30 min

Partners combine their tool-kit pennies. One partner grabs a handful of pennies. Partners then work together to count the total number of pennies grabbed and to record the total amount in the first column of the table on *Math Masters*, page 29. Then they exchange those pennies for as many dimes (pennies in groups of 10) and nickels (pennies in groups of 5) as possible. They record the final number of each coin (dimes, nickels, and pennies) in the next three columns of the table. Repeat as time allows, with partners taking turns grabbing pennies.

Variation
Have children first trade as many pennies as possible for nickels and record the number of each coin on the master. Then have them trade as many nickels as possible for dimes and again record the total number of each coin on the master.

ONGOING ASSESSMENT
Collect *Math Masters*, page 29 from each partnership and check to make sure that children have made correct exchanges. Watch for children who do not end up with the fewest numbers of coins.

Portfolio Ideas

✦ ENRICHMENT Playing *Coin Top-It*

PARTNER ACTIVITY   15–30 min

Children practice addition skills by playing *Coin Top-It*. For detailed instructions, see Lesson 2.10. Adjust the level of difficulty of the cards by adding harder combinations to the deck.

Coin Exchanges (cont.)
Home Link 3.11

4. P P P P P P P P P P P P is the same

as ___D P P___.

This is __12__ cents.

5. N P P P P P P P P P is the same

as ___D P P P P___.

This is __14__ cents.

Challenge

6. N N N P P P P P P P P P is the

same as __D D N__.

This is __25__ cents.

7. N P N P N P P is the same as ___D D___.

This is __20__ cents.

✦ *Math Masters*, p. 193

Coin Exchanges Record

Grab a handful of pennies. Write the number of pennies you grabbed.

Trade as many of the pennies as you can for dimes. Trade as many of the leftover pennies as you can for nickels. Write the numbers of dimes, nickels, and pennies you have in the next 3 columns of the table.

Pennies Grabbed	Dimes	Nickels	Pennies

✦ *Math Masters*, p. 29

3.12 Counting Dimes, Nickels, and Pennies

OBJECTIVE To find the values of collections of dimes, nickels, and pennies.

summaries	materials
1 Teaching the Lesson	
Children count collections of dimes, nickels, and pennies. [Measurement and Reference Frames; Numeration]	□ *Math Journal 1*, p. 58 □ Home Link 3.11 □ slate □ overhead coins (optional) □ tool-kit coins
2 Ongoing Learning & Practice	
Children practice and maintain skills through Math Boxes and Home Link activities.	□ *Math Journal 1*, p. 59 □ Home Link Master (*Math Masters*, p. 194)
3 Options for Individualizing	
Extra Practice Children play *Coin-Dice*. [Measurement and Reference Frames; Numeration] **Enrichment** Children play *Dime-Nickel-Penny Grab*. [Measurement and Reference Frames; Numeration] **Extra Practice** Children practice finding the values of various coin combinations and making exchanges. [Measurement and Reference Frames; Numeration]	□ Teaching Master (*Math Masters*, p. 30) □ 2 dice per partnership □ tool-kit coins □ *Minute Math*®, pp. 22, 65–67, 69, and 70

Getting Started

Mental Math and Reflexes

Tell parts-and-total number stories. Children solve them any way they can (by using counters, drawing pictures, and so on) and write the answers on their slates. Have children share solution strategies after each problem. Summarize each solution by drawing a parts-and-total diagram on the board, *but only after children have had a chance to share what they did to solve the problem.* If children are doing well, challenge them to write number models for the problems.

• Megan's cat, Alice, had 3 female kittens and 4 male kittens. How many kittens did Alice have in all? 7 kittens

• Brian has 12 toy cars. His sister Bernice has 14 toy cars. When they play together with their toy cars, how many do they have in all? 26 toy cars

• Jake and Theresa were playing *Penny Grab*. Jake grabbed 14 pennies. Theresa was left with 6 pennies. How many pennies did they have? 20 pennies

• Janine has 5 pairs of blue socks and 5 pairs of red socks. How many pairs of socks does she have in all? 10 pairs of socks
Challenge: How many socks is that? 20 socks

Teaching the Lesson

◆ Counting Collections of the Same Kind of Coin

WHOLE-CLASS ACTIVITY

Children take a certain number of one kind of coin. They write the total value of the coins on their slates, using cents notation. They return one group of coins before taking the next.

Suggestions

- Take out 12 pennies. Write the amount. 12¢

- Take out 4 nickels. Write the amount. 20¢ (After children have answered, have them count the coins in unison: *5 cents, 10 cents, 15 cents, 20 cents.*)

- Take out 7 dimes. Write the amount. 70¢ (Count the coins: *10 cents, 20 cents, …, 70 cents.*)

Continue practicing as needed.

 Adjusting the Activity To extend the activity, ask questions such as: *How many dimes are in 70 cents? In 90¢? In $1.10?*

◆ Counting Combinations of Dimes, Nickels, and Pennies

WHOLE-CLASS ACTIVITY

To review counting nickels and pennies:

1. Have four children come up to the front of the room, each bringing a nickel.

2. Have three children come up, each bringing a penny.

3. Have the seven children form a line, with the "nickels" at the left end of the line (facing the rest of the class), followed by the "pennies." The "nickels" then hold up 5 fingers each and the "pennies" 1 finger each.

4. Walk behind the children and tap each one on the head as the class counts together. 5, 10, 15, 20, 21, 22, 23

5. Draw Ⓝ Ⓝ Ⓝ Ⓝ Ⓟ Ⓟ Ⓟ on the board. Write "23¢" next to the coin drawings. Then write the same amount

Adjusting the Activity If children are having difficulty, first do the routine on page 223 using dimes and pennies, and then dimes and nickels, before continuing with the routine at the right that uses all three kinds of coins (dimes, nickels, and pennies).

using dollars-and-cents notation: "$0.23." The 0 before the decimal point shows that there are 0 dollars. $0.23 is read *23 cents.*

To introduce counting dimes, nickels, and pennies:

1. Have three children come up to the front of the room, each bringing a dime.

2. Have two children come up, each bringing a nickel.

3. Have four children come up, each bringing a penny.

4. Have the nine children form a line, with the "dimes" at the left end of the line (facing the rest of the class), followed by the "nickels" and then the "pennies." The "dimes" hold up 10 fingers each, the "nickels" 5 fingers each, and the "pennies" 1 finger each.

5. Walk behind the children and tap each one on the head as the class counts together. 10, 20, 30, 35, 40, 41, 42, 43, 44

6. Draw ⒟ ⒟ ⒟ Ⓝ Ⓝ Ⓟ Ⓟ Ⓟ Ⓟ on the board. Write "44¢" next to the coin drawings. *How would you write 44¢ in dollars-and-cents notation?* $0.44

◆ Counting Combinations of Dimes, Nickels, and Pennies (*Math Journal 1,* p. 58)

WHOLE-CLASS ACTIVITY

For these exercises, use overhead pennies, nickels, and dimes, if they are available, or draw the coins on the board. Children count their own coins and write the total value of each combination on their slates, using either cents or dollars-and-cents notation. Write the answers on the board, both in cents and dollars-and-cents notation. Children then count the coins in unison.

Suggestions

• What is the value of 4 dimes and 3 pennies? 43¢, or $0.43 (Count: *10 cents, 20 cents, 30 cents, 40 cents, 41 cents, 42 cents, 43 cents.*)

• What is the value of 2 dimes and 2 nickels? 30¢, or $0.30 (Count: *10 cents, 20 cents, 25 cents, 30 cents.*)

• What is the value of 3 dimes, 1 nickel, and 2 pennies? 37¢, or $0.37 (Count: *10 cents, 20 cents, 30 cents, 35 cents, 36 cents, 37 cents.*)

• What is the value of 2 dimes, 3 nickels, and 7 pennies? 42¢, or $0.42 (Count: *10 cents, 20 cents, 25 cents, 30 cents, 35 cents, 36 cents, 37 cents, 38 cents, 39 cents, 40 cents, 41 cents, 42 cents.*)

How Much Money?

How much money? Use your coins.

Example

	Ⓟ	Ⓝ	Ⓓ
	1¢	5¢	10¢
	$0.01	$0.05	$0.10
	a penny	a nickel	a dime

_35_ ¢ or $ _0.35_

How much money? Use your coins.

1. $ 0.20

2. $ 0.46

3. 75 ¢

4. ⒟ ⒟ Ⓝ Ⓝ Ⓝ Ⓟ Ⓟ $ 0.37

Adjusting the Activity To extend this activity, have children trade in some of the coins so that they end up with as few coins as possible for each given amount.

Do more problems like these, as needed. Children then work independently or in partnerships to complete the journal page. They should use their coins to model the problems.

 Adjusting the Activity If children are having difficulty with the journal page, have them write the amount that each coin is worth above or below the coin and/or show the value of each coin by drawing tally marks.

Briefly go over the answers.

 ONGOING ASSESSMENT
Although children should be fairly comfortable with pennies and nickels by now, expect that many children may still find penny, nickel, and dime combinations difficult to calculate. Children will continue to practice finding the total values of such combinations in future lessons.

Ongoing Learning & Practice

◆ Math Boxes 3.12 (*Math Journal 1*, p. 59)

INDEPENDENT ACTIVITY

 Mixed Review This journal page provides opportunities for cumulative review or assessment of concepts and skills.

◆ Home Link 3.12 (*Math Masters*, p. 194)

 Home Connection Children calculate the values of various combinations of pennies, nickels, and dimes and record their answers using dollars-and-cents notation.

Math Boxes 3.12

1. Write the number for:
   HHT HHT HHT HHT HHT HHT
   HHT HHT //

   _42_

   Odd or even? _even_

2. Use your number grid. Start at 52. Count back 8.

   You end at _44_.

   52 − 8 = _44_

3. Complete the number line.

   _9_ _10_ _11_ _12_ _13_ _14_ _15_ _16_

4.
Rule				
−4	24	20	16	12	8

✧ Math Journal 1, p. 59

Counting Coins 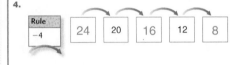 Home Link 3.12

 Family Note We have begun to count coin combinations consisting of pennies, nickels, and dimes. We are also starting to use dollars-and-cents notation. Help your child with the problems on this page. The Challenge problem is difficult because the coins are in no particular order. It might help to sort real coins into groups of like coins (all dimes together, all nickels together, all pennies together) before counting. If your child has trouble recording the amounts in dollars-and-cents notation, don't worry—this is a skill we will continue to work on throughout the year.
Please return this Home Link to school tomorrow.

1 cent 1¢ $0.01 (P)	5 cents 5¢ $0.05 (N)	10 cents 10¢ $0.10 (D)

How much money? Write each answer in cents and in dollars-and-cents.

1. (D)(N)(N)(N)   _25_ ¢ or $ _0.25_

2. (D)(D)(N)(N)(N)(N)   _45_ ¢ or $ _0.45_

3. (D)(N)(N)(P)(P)(P)   _23_ ¢ or $ _0.23_

4. (D)(D)(N)(N)(N)(P)(P)   _37_ ¢ or $ _0.37_

Challenge

5. (P)(P)(N)(P)(D)(N)(N)(D)(N)   _43_ ¢ or $ _0.43_

✧ Math Masters, p. 194

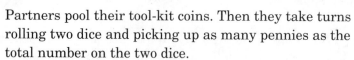

Options for Individualizing

◆ EXTRA PRACTICE Playing *Coin-Dice*

PARTNER ACTIVITY   15–30 min

Partners pool their tool-kit coins. Then they take turns rolling two dice and picking up as many pennies as the total number on the two dice.

Each player makes exchanges at the end of his or her turn—5 pennies for a nickel, 5 pennies and 1 nickel for a dime, 2 nickels for a dime, or 10 pennies for a dime.

To pick up the last coins, the total number on the two dice must match the total value of the remaining coins.

> **Adjusting the Activity** If children are not yet ready to work with dimes, restrict the game to pennies and nickels only.

◆ ENRICHMENT Playing *Dime-Nickel-Penny Grab* (*Math Masters*, p. 30)

PARTNER ACTIVITY   15–30 min

Partners play with 10 dimes, 8 nickels, and 20 pennies. After they mix the coins together, one player grabs a handful, and the other player takes the coins that are left. The players help each other figure out who took more.

◆ EXTRA PRACTICE Minute Math

SMALL-GROUP ACTIVITY   5–15 min

To offer children more experience with finding the values of various combinations of dimes, nickels, and pennies, see the following pages in *Minute Math:*

Basic Routines: p. 22

Measurement: pp. 65–67, 69, and 70

PLANNING AHEAD

In Lesson 3.14, children will need the dominoes from *Math Journal 1,* Activity Sheets 3 and 4. If you have a paper cutter, you or an aide can do the cutting ahead of time. Children's dominoes may be stored in resealable plastic bags with children's identification numbers on them. It is well worth taking the time to provide each child with his or her own set of dominoes, since dominoes are a valuable tool for memorizing the basic addition facts.

Dime-Nickel-Penny Grab

Play with 10 dimes, 8 nickels, and 20 pennies.

Mix the coins. One player grabs a handful. The other player takes what is left.

Round 1

I grabbed _____ (D), _____ (N), and _____ (P).

My partner grabbed _____ (D), _____ (N), and _____ (P).

I have _____¢. My partner has _____¢.

Who has more? _____

Round 2

I grabbed _____ (D), _____ (N), and _____ (P).

My partner grabbed _____ (D), _____ (N), and _____ (P).

I have _____¢. My partner has _____¢.

Who has more? _____

Round 3

I grabbed _____ (D), _____ (N), and _____ (P).

My partner grabbed _____ (D), _____ (N), and _____ (P).

I have _____¢. My partner has _____¢.

Who has more? _____

◆ *Math Masters, p. 30*

3.13

Data Day

OBJECTIVE To introduce line plots.

summaries	materials
1 Teaching the Lesson	
Children each decide which of four colors is their favorite. Then they tally the class's choices. Finally, they record each of their choices on a stick-on note and use all the notes to make a line plot. [Data and Chance]	☐ Home Link 3.12 ☐ stick-on note
2 Ongoing Learning & Practice	
Children fill out a blank calendar for the month, identify the even and odd numbers on the calendar, and observe even/odd number patterns in the rows, columns, and diagonals. [Measurement and Reference Frames; Patterns, Functions, and Algebra] Children practice and maintain skills through Math Boxes and Home Link activities.	☐ *Math Journal 1,* pp. 60 and 61 ☐ Home Link Master (*Math Masters,* p. 195)
3 Options for Individualizing	
Extra Practice Children collect information about a topic of their choice and display it on a line plot. [Data and Chance] **Extra Practice** Children compare numbers. [Numeration]	☐ stick-on notes ☐ *Minute Math®,* p. 38

Additional Information
Vocabulary • line plot

Getting Started

Home Link 3.12 Follow-Up

As you go over the answers, record them on the board in both cents notation and dollars-and-cents notation.

If you want to extend the activity, have children find the fewest number of coins to represent each total.

Mental Math and Reflexes

Tell number stories: change-to-more or change-to-less stories and parts-and-total stories. Children solve the problems any way they can (by using counters, drawing pictures, and so on) and write the answers on their slates. They share solution strategies after each problem. Summarize each solution by drawing an appropriate diagram on the board, *but only after children have shared what they did to solve the problem.*

Do not force a number story into a particular mold. Do not say there is a "best" diagram for a problem. For example, in the first story below, one child may think of change: Karl "started" with 12 tickets and then won 9 more. Another child may think of the tickets won in the first game as one part of a total and the tickets won in the second game as another part of a total.

Suggestions

- Karl went to the video arcade. He won 12 tickets at the first game he played. He won another 9 tickets at the second game. How many tickets did he win altogether? 21 tickets
- Melinda has 19 stamps in her stamp album. Her friend John gave her 5 more stamps. How many stamps does Melinda have now? 24 stamps
- Gabriela bought a dozen doughnuts. She and her sister Claudia ate 5 of them. How many doughnuts do the two girls have left? 7 doughnuts (You may need to remind children that there are 12 items in a dozen.)
- **Challenge:** There are 16 children in Emily's gymnastics class. Nine of the children are girls. How many of the children are boys? 7 of the children are boys.

To extend this activity, have children write number models for the problems.

Color	Tallies
Blue	
Red	
Green	
Yellow	

1 Teaching the Lesson

◆ Making a Line Plot

WHOLE-CLASS ACTIVITY

Give each child one stick-on note.

Each child indicates his or her favorite color by writing *B* on the stick-on note if the favorite color is blue, *R* if it is red, *G* if it is green, and *Y* if it is yellow.

Make a tally chart on the board (see margin). Ask children, one at a time, which of the four colors they like best—blue, red, green, or yellow. You or a volunteer tallies the responses.

Children then count the tally marks to determine which color is the class's favorite color.

Tell the class that another way to show the results of the survey is to make a **line plot.** To make a line plot of the class's favorite colors:

1. Draw a horizontal line on the board and label it as shown below.

2. Have children come up to the board, one at a time, and attach their stick-on notes to the board in columns above their favorite colors. Help them make vertical columns with no overlap between the notes.

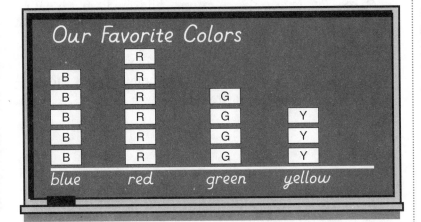

NOTE: Line plots are used extensively to organize and display data. A line plot shows data by using checks, Xs, or stick-on notes. A line plot can be thought of as a rough sketch of a bar graph.

- Which column has the most stick-on notes?

- Which column has the fewest stick-on notes?

- Can you tell which color is our class's favorite color without counting the notes? How?

② Ongoing Learning & Practice

◆ Looking for Even/Odd Number Patterns in a Calendar (*Math Journal 1*, p. 60)

PARTNER ACTIVITY

Children fill in a blank calendar page for the month. They circle the even numbers and check off the odd numbers. They look for even/odd number patterns and discuss them with their partners.

Briefly bring the class together to share the patterns partners have discovered. Even and odd numbers alternate in each row and in each column. Diagonals are all even or all odd. The pattern is like a checkerboard.

Calendar Patterns

Fill out the calendar for this month.

Month _____

Sunday	Monday	Tuesday	Wednesday	Thursday	Friday	Saturday

Circle all the even numbers.
Make a ✓ next to each odd number.
Look for patterns in the even and odd numbers.
Discuss the patterns with your partner.

Math Journal 1, p. 60

STUDENT PAGE

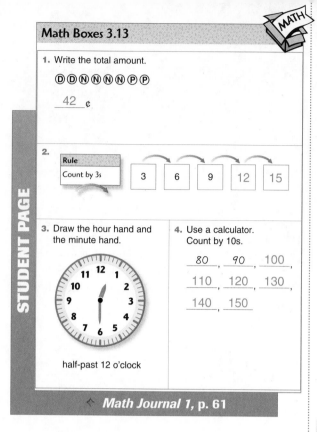

Math Boxes 3.13

1. Write the total amount.

Ⓓ Ⓓ Ⓝ Ⓝ Ⓝ Ⓟ Ⓟ

__42__ ¢

2.

Rule					
Count by 3s	3	6	9	12	15

3. Draw the hour hand and the minute hand.

half-past 12 o'clock

4. Use a calculator. Count by 10s.

__80__, __90__, __100__,

__110__, __120__, __130__,

__140__, __150__

◆ **Math Boxes 3.13** (*Math Journal 1*, p. 61)

INDEPENDENT ACTIVITY

 Mixed Review This journal page provides opportunities for cumulative review or assessment of concepts and skills.

◆ **Home Link 3.13** (*Math Masters,* p. 195)

Home Connection Children discuss a data set with someone at home. (Have children draw the first letter of the class's favorite color on their Home Links with that color crayon to help them remember what the class's favorite color is.)

3 Options for Individualizing

◆ **EXTRA PRACTICE** **Making a Line Plot**

WHOLE-CLASS ACTIVITY 15–30 min

Make line plots for other categories of information, such as favorite foods, favorite books, or favorite songs. Follow the same model as the one used in today's lesson, using stick-on notes to construct the line plot.

◆ **EXTRA PRACTICE** **Minute Math**

SMALL-GROUP ACTIVITY 5–15 min

To offer children more experience with comparing numbers, see the following page in *Minute Math:*

Counting: p. 38

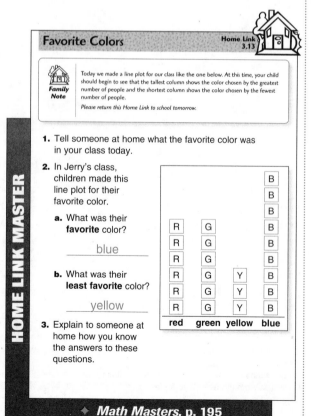

Favorite Colors

Home Link 3.13

Family Note Today we made a line plot for our class like the one below. At this time, your child should begin to see that the tallest column shows the color chosen by the greatest number of people and the shortest column shows the color chosen by the fewest number of people.

Please return this Home Link to school tomorrow.

1. Tell someone at home what the favorite color was in your class today.

2. In Jerry's class, children made this line plot for their favorite color.

   a. What was their **favorite** color?

   __blue__

   b. What was their **least favorite** color?

   __yellow__

3. Explain to someone at home how you know the answers to these questions.

R	G		B
R	G		B
R	G		B
R	G	Y	B
R	G	Y	B
R	G	Y	B
red	**green**	**yellow**	**blue**

3.14

Domino Addition

OBJECTIVES To explore domino-dot patterns; and to practice all the basic addition facts.

summaries	materials
1 Teaching the Lesson	
Children look for patterns in the representation of even and odd numbers on dominoes. They use parts-and-total diagrams to find the total numbers of dots on dominoes. Then they play *Domino Top-It* to practice finding sums of dots. [Patterns, Functions, and Algebra; Operations and Computation]	☐ *Math Journal 1,* p. 62 ☐ Home Link 3.13 ☐ double-9 dominoes from *Math Journal 1,* Activity Sheets 3 and 4 ☐ resealable plastic bag ☐ slate ☐ paper plate and counters (optional) ***See* Advance Preparation**
2 Ongoing Learning & Practice	
Children practice and maintain skills through Math Boxes and Home Link activities.	☐ *Math Journal 1,* p. 63 ☐ Home Link Master (*Math Masters,* p. 196) ☐ Teaching Masters (*Math Masters,* pp. 31 and 32)
3 Options for Individualizing	
Enrichment Children find the sums of the dots on the dominoes they sorted in Exploration A in Lesson 3.4. Then they look for even/odd patterns in the sums. [Patterns, Functions, and Algebra; Operations and Computation] **Extra Practice** Children solve simple addition facts. [Operations and Computation]	☐ Teaching Master (*Math Masters,* p. 24) ☐ *Minute Math®,* p. 10 ***See* Advance Preparation**

Additional Information

Advance Preparation For Part 1, children will need the set of dominoes from *Math Journal 1,* Activity Sheets 3 and 4. If children cut the dominoes apart, help those who are having difficulty. If you have a paper cutter, you or an aide can do the cutting ahead of time. Children's dominoes may be stored in resealable plastic bags with children's identification numbers on them. It is well worth taking the time to provide each child with his or her own set of dominoes, since dominoes are a valuable tool for memorizing the basic addition facts.

For the optional Enrichment activity in Part 3, children will need their copies of *Math Masters,* page 24, which they completed as part of Exploration A in Lesson 3.4.

Getting Started

Mental Math and Reflexes

Lead children in the special first grade chant: "2, 4, 6, 8, first graders are really great!"

Ask children to name the first five even numbers. Record them on the board. Do the same for the first five odd numbers. Remind children that a number is even if it ends in 0, 2, 4, 6, or 8 and that it is odd if it ends in 1, 3, 5, 7, or 9.

Dictate some numbers. Children write them on their slates. Then they write *E* if the number is even and *O* if it is odd.

Home Link 3.13 Follow-Up

Ask children to describe how they figured out the answers to the questions.

NOTE: The game of dominoes is played in many countries around the world. Invite any non-native English speakers in your class to say the words for *dominoes* in their native languages. If possible, make a chart listing all of these words.

1 Teaching the Lesson

◆ Exploring Dot Patterns on Halves of Dominoes

WHOLE-CLASS ACTIVITY

Ask children to use their cutout dominoes to do the following:

1. Find all the dominoes that have at least one blank half (a side with no dots). There should be 10 of these one-blank-half dominoes. Except for the double-zeros domino, each of these one-blank-half dominoes should have some dots on the other half.

2. Line up these 10 blank-on-one-half dominoes in order from 0 dots to 9 dots on one side.

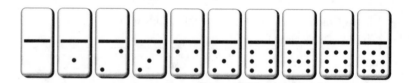

3. Separate these 10 dominoes into two groups: dominoes with an even number of dots on one side and dominoes with an odd number of dots on one side.

4. Look for patterns in the dots in each of these two groups. Try to find a common pattern in all the dominoes in each group. Talk it over with your partner.

Children share the patterns they found. If no one brings it up, point out that dominoes with an odd number of dots on one side have a dot in the middle and that dominoes with an even number of dots on one side have no dot in the middle.

◆ Introducing Number Combinations on Entire Dominoes, Not on Isolated Halves

WHOLE-CLASS ACTIVITY

Draw a 3│5 domino on the board. Point out that this domino shows two numbers: one number on each half of the domino. Then point out that there is a third number that corresponds to each domino—and that number is the total number of dots on *both* halves of the domino. Draw a parts-and-total diagram with 3 and 5 as the parts and 8 as the whole. Point out that the domino has a part with 3 dots and a part with 5 dots—and that the whole domino has 8 dots.

Part	Part
3	5
Total	
8	

Ask several children to choose a domino, hold it up, and name the three numbers associated with that domino. Draw a parts-and-total diagram for each domino you discuss. Keep doing this until it is clear that most children grasp the concept.

Then draw some dominoes on the board. For each domino, children write the three numbers on their slates.

◆ Playing *Domino Top-It*

PARTNER ACTIVITY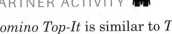

Domino Top-It is similar to *Top-It*. At first, limit the game to two players and have players use the sets of cutout dominoes from *Math Journal 1,* Activity Sheets 3 and 4.

NOTE: The double-9 set of dominoes contains all the basic addition facts. Encourage children to play the game often as a way of building recognition of and quick responses to these basic facts.

Directions

1. Place all the dominoes facedown on the table.

2. Each player turns over a domino and finds the total number of dots.

3. The player with the larger total takes both dominoes. In case of a tie, each player takes another facedown domino—and the player with the larger total then takes all the faceup dominoes.

4. Play continues until all the dominoes have been played. The player who has more dominoes wins.

NOTE: *Math Journal 1,* Activity Sheet 3 includes dominoes 0│0 through 0│6, 1│1 through 1│6, 2│2 through 2│6, 3│3, and 3│4. *Math Journal 1,* Activity Sheet 4 includes dominoes 0│7 through 0│9, 1│7 through 1│9, 2│7 through 2│9, 3│5 through 3│9, 4│4 through 4│6, 5│5, 5│6, and 6│6.

Paper plates divided into sections may help children count the total number of domino dots.

Adjusting the Activity If children are struggling with this activity, limit the set of dominoes to those on Activity Sheet 3. (See note above.) Also, give each child a paper plate, divided into three sections (two quarter-sections and one half-section). Children put as many counters in each smaller section as there are dots on the two sides of the domino. Then they move the counters into the larger section and count the total.

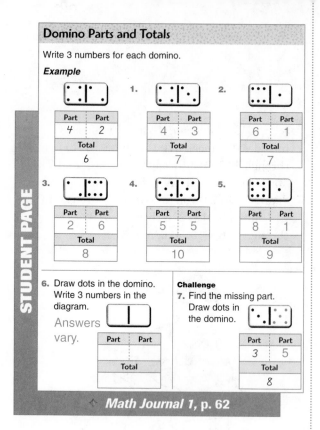

Domino Parts and Totals

Write 3 numbers for each domino.

Example

Example domino: dots 4 and 2

Part	Part
4	2
Total	
6	

1.

Part	Part
4	3
Total	
7	

2.

Part	Part
6	1
Total	
7	

3.

Part	Part
2	6
Total	
8	

4.

Part	Part
5	5
Total	
10	

5.

Part	Part
8	1
Total	
9	

6. Draw dots in the domino. Write 3 numbers in the diagram.

Answers vary.

Part	Part
Total	

Challenge

7. Find the missing part. Draw dots in the domino.

Part	Part
3	5
Total	
8	

Math Journal 1, p. 62

◆ **Finding the Total Numbers of Dots on Dominoes** (*Math Journal 1*, p. 62)

INDEPENDENT ACTIVITY

Children use parts-and-total diagrams to find the total numbers of dots on dominoes.

NOTE: The Challenge problem on this page suggests the use of dominoes to model subtraction facts.

ONGOING ASSESSMENT

As children work on the journal page, check to make sure that they are recording the correct number for each "part" and the correct number for the "total." If necessary, have children act out the problems with counters and a paper plate, as described in the "Adjusting the Activity" note on page 233.

2 Ongoing Learning & Practice

◆ **Math Boxes 3.14** (*Math Journal 1*, p. 63)

INDEPENDENT ACTIVITY

Mixed Review This journal page provides opportunities for cumulative review or assessment of concepts and skills.

◆ **Home Link 3.14** (*Math Masters*, p. 196)

Home Connection Children teach their families how to play *Domino Top-It*. Send copies of *Math Masters*, pages 31 and 32 home along with Home Link 3.14. Children can also play with real dominoes if they have them at home.

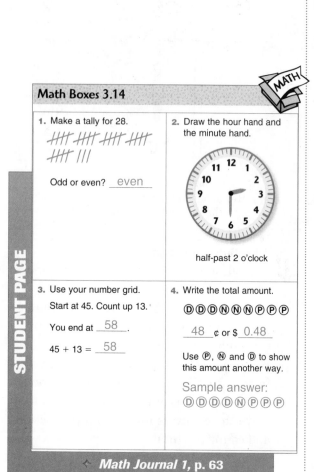

Math Boxes 3.14

1. Make a tally for 28.

~~HHT HHT HHT HHT~~
~~HHT~~ III

Odd or even? **even**

2. Draw the hour hand and the minute hand.

half-past 2 o'clock

3. Use your number grid. Start at 45. Count up 13.

You end at __58__.

45 + 13 = __58__

4. Write the total amount.

Ⓓ Ⓓ Ⓓ Ⓝ Ⓝ Ⓝ Ⓟ Ⓟ Ⓟ

__48__ ¢ or $ __0.48__

Use Ⓟ, Ⓝ and Ⓓ to show this amount another way.

Sample answer:
Ⓓ Ⓓ Ⓓ Ⓓ Ⓝ Ⓟ Ⓟ Ⓟ

Math Journal 1, p. 63

Options for Individualizing

◆ ENRICHMENT Exploring Sums of Even and Odd Numbers (*Math Masters*, p. 24)

SMALL-GROUP ACTIVITY 5–15 min

Children work in the same groups as in Exploration A in Lesson 3.4. Pass out the copies of *Math Masters,* page 24 that you collected during Lesson 3.4. Children record the total number of dots on each of the dominoes.

Bring the class together to discuss the following questions:

• If each side of a domino has an even number of dots, is the total number of dots an even number or an odd number? An even number

• If each side of a domino has an odd number of dots, is the total number of dots an even number or an odd number? An even number

• If a domino has an odd number of dots on one side and an even number of dots on the other side, is the total number of dots an even number or an odd number? An odd number

◆ EXTRA PRACTICE Minute Math

SMALL-GROUP ACTIVITY 5–15 min

To offer children more experience with addition facts, see the following page in *Minute Math:*

Basic Routines: p. 10

Domino Top-It Home Link 3.14

 Family Note Today your child examined dot patterns on dominoes and learned a game played with dominos. The relationship between the numbers represented by the dots on each domino part and those on the entire domino is useful for work with basic facts. *Domino Top-It* is a great game for helping your child practice basic addition facts.

Show someone at home how to play *Domino Top-It.* Use a set of real dominoes, if you have one. Or use the dominoes on the sheets your teacher gave you.

Directions

1. If you have real dominoes, turn them facedown on the table.

   If you are using paper dominoes, put them facedown in a stack.

2. Each player turns over a domino.

   If you are using paper dominoes, take one from the top of the stack.

3. The player with the larger total number of dots takes both dominoes.

   In case of a tie, each player turns over another domino. The player with the larger total takes all the dominoes that are faceup.

4. The game is over when all the dominoes have been played.

   The player who has more dominoes wins the game.

◆ *Math Masters,* p. 196

Domino Sort Record Sheet

Circle the kind of domino you are sorting.

both even   both odd   one odd, one even

◆ *Math Masters,* p. 24

3.15 Unit 3 Review and Assessment

OBJECTIVE To review and assess children's progress on the material covered in Unit 3.

1 Assess Progress

learning goals

3a **Beginning/Developing Goal** Complete Frames-and-Arrows diagrams. **(Lessons 3.8, 3.9, and 3.11)**

3b **Developing Goal** Identify and complete patterns. **(Lessons 3.1–3.5, 3.13, and 3.14)**

3c **Developing Goal** Solve simple addition and subtraction problems by skip counting on the number line and the number grid. **(Lessons 3.3–3.7 and 3.9)**

3d **Developing Goal** Identify numbers as even or odd. **(Lessons 3.2–3.5, 3.13, and 3.14)**

3e **Developing Goal** Know the values of ℗, Ⓝ, Ⓓ, & calculate the values of combinations of these coins. **(Lessons 3.2, 3.4, 3.10–3.13)**

3f **Developing Goal** Tell time to the nearest half-hour. **(Lessons 3.5, 3.7, and 3.8)**

3g **Developing Goal** Solve simple number stories. **(Lessons 3.6, 3.11–3.13)**

activities

❏ Written Assessment, Problem 4

❏ Written Assessment, Problem 4

❏ Oral Assessment, Problems 1, 2, and 3
❏ Slate Assessment, Problem 1
❏ Written Assessment, Problem 5

❏ Slate Assessment, Problem 5
❏ Written Assessment, Problem 2

❏ Written Assessment, Problem 3

❏ Written Assessment, Problem 1
❏ Oral Assessment, Problem 4

❏ Slate Assessment, Problem 3

materials

☐ Teaching Master (*Math Masters,* p. 28)
☐ Assessment Masters (*Math Masters,* pp. 305, 306)

☐ slate; tool-kit clock
☐ tool-kit coins; craft sticks

☐ pattern blocks; die
☐ Home Link 3.14

2 Build Background for Unit 4

summaries

Children practice and maintain skills through Math Boxes and Home Link activities.

materials

☐ *Math Journal 1,* p. 64
☐ Home Link Masters (*Math Masters,* pp. 197–200)

Each **learning goal** listed above indicates a level of performance that might be expected at this point in the *Everyday Mathematics* K–6 curriculum. For a variety of reasons, the levels indicated may not accurately portray your class's performance.

Additional Information

Advance Preparation For additional information on assessment for Unit 3, see the *Assessment Handbook,* pages 42–45. For assessment checklists, see *Math Masters,* pages 332, 333, and 355–358.

Getting Started

Home Link 3.14 Follow-Up
Ask if there are any questions about *Domino Top-It.*

1 Assess Progress

◆ Oral and Slate Assessments

WHOLE-CLASS ACTIVITY

If the suggested problems below are not appropriate for your class's level of performance, adjust the numbers or the problems themselves to better assess your children's abilities.

Oral Assessment Suggestions

1. Count up by 2s on your number line. Start at 0.
   Goal 3c

2. On the number grid … **Goal 3c**

   Count up by 5s, starting at 10; starting at 45.

   Count back by 5s, starting at 30; starting at 100.

   Count up by 10s, starting at 0; starting at 50.

   Count back by 10s, starting at 50; starting at 100.

3. Do start-and-stop counts by 5s to 40. 5, 10, 15, …, 40
   Stop. Now count by 1s to 46. 41, 42, …, 46 **Goal 3c**

4. Show 5 o'clock on your tool-kit clock. Show 9 o'clock;
   2 o'clock; half-past 3 o'clock; eleven-thirty; half-past
   1 o'clock. **Goal 3f**

Slate Assessment Suggestions

1. On your number grid … **Goal 3c**

   Start at 8. Count up 3 spaces. Where did you end up?
   11

   Start at 12. Count up 7 spaces. Where did you end up?
   19

   Start at 23. Count up 12 spaces. Where did you end
   up? 35

   Start at 15. Count back 9 spaces. Where did you end
   up? 6

   Start at 20. Count back 12 spaces. Where did you end
   up? 8

> NOTE: Many of these assessment suggestions relate to learning goals that have been addressed in previous units. Now is a good time to evaluate children's progress toward those goals.

2. Make tally marks to show 10; 14; 17.

3. Solve these number stories: **Goal 3g**

   ▷ Vickie was keeping track of how many games of *Domino Top-It* she won. On Monday, she played 10 games and won 7. On Wednesday, she played 10 more games and won 5. How many games did Vickie win in all? 12 games

   ▷ Jasmine loves to draw flowers. She taped 9 drawings to the refrigerator and another 7 on her closet door. How many drawings in all does Jasmine have on display? 16 drawings

   ▷ Rodney's puppy, Spot, weighed 3 pounds when Rodney's family brought him home. Six months later, Spot weighed 15 pounds more. How much did Spot weigh after six months? 18 pounds

   ▷ Mark's dad was running a 26-mile marathon. Mark took a picture of his dad at the 20-mile marker. This meant that his dad had run 20 miles so far. How many more miles did Mark's dad have to run? 6 more miles

4. Write the number that is …

   1 more than 7. 8

   1 more than 16. 17

   1 more than 20. 21

   1 more than 29. 30

   1 less than 5. 4

   1 less than 14. 13

   1 less than 27. 26

   1 less than 40. 39

5. Write 8, 12, and 17 on your slate. Now circle the odd number. 17 **Goal 3d**

   Write 9, 14, and 22 on your slate. Now circle the odd number. 9 **Goal 3d**

6. Write the following amounts in dollars-and-cents notation:

   2 dollars and 50 cents $2.50

   3 dollars and 25 cents $3.25

   1 dollar and 5 cents $1.05

   75 cents $0.75

   14 cents $0.14

◆ Written Assessment
(*Math Masters,* pp. 305 and 306)

INDEPENDENT ACTIVITY

Read the problems with the class. If appropriate, complete the page together—that is, wait for children to complete a problem before reading the next one to them. You may want to do an example with the class of each kind of problem.

- Tell the time. (Problem 1) **Goal 3f**
- Circle the odd numbers. (Problem 2) **Goal 3d**
- How much money is this? Show the same amount using fewer coins. (Problem 3) **Goal 3e**
- Complete the diagrams. (Problem 4) **Goals 3a and 3b**
- Use your number grid to help you solve the following problems. (Problem 5) **Goal 3c**

If children in your class can work independently, have them complete these pages alone or with a partner. Circulate and assist as children work.

◆ ALTERNATIVE ASSESSMENT OPTION
Identify and Complete Patterns

PARTNER ACTIVITY

To assess children's progress on identifying and completing patterns, have children work in partnerships. One child starts a pattern with craft sticks. The other child completes the pattern. Each partnership can record its patterns on a half-sheet of paper for you to collect.

Variation

One child uses pattern blocks to begin a pattern; the other child continues the pattern. Children can record their patterns on half-sheets of paper by using their Pattern-Block Templates or by tracing the actual blocks.

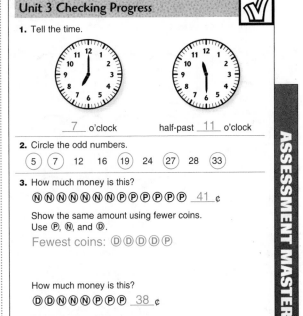

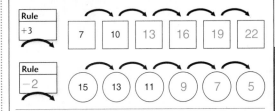

♦ *Math Masters,* p. 306

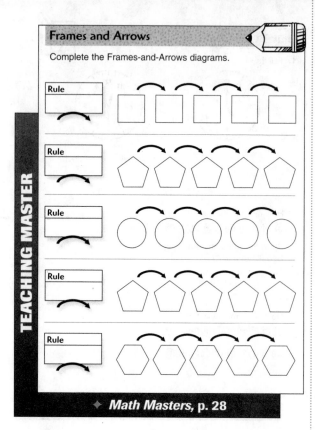

Frames and Arrows

Complete the Frames-and-Arrows diagrams.

Math Masters, p. 28

✦ ALTERNATIVE ASSESSMENT OPTION
Play *Coin-Dice*

PARTNER ACTIVITY

Use this activity from Lesson 3.12 to assess how children are progressing with exchanges of pennies, nickels, and dimes and with counting collections of such coins.

✦ ALTERNATIVE ASSESSMENT OPTION
Complete Frames-and-Arrows Diagrams
(*Math Masters,* p. 28)

INDEPENDENT ACTIVITY

Use this activity from Lesson 3.8 to assess children's progress with extending number sequences. Fill in the master with a set of problems of varying degrees of difficulty. Choose problems that are appropriate for your class.

✦ ALTERNATIVE ASSESSMENT OPTION
Order Clocks

SMALL-GROUP ACTIVITY

Use this activity from Lesson 3.7 to assess children's progress with telling time and with putting times in sequence.

Work with small groups of children. Assign each child a time to show on his or her tool-kit clock. The time should be to the nearest hour or half-hour. Then have the children work together to order their clocks from the earliest time to the latest.

2 Build Background for Unit 4

◆ **Math Boxes 3.15** (*Math Journal 1*, p. 64)

INDEPENDENT ACTIVITY

 Mixed Review This journal page provides opportunities for cumulative review or assessment of concepts and skills.

◆ **Home Link 3.15: Unit 4 Family Letter**
(*Math Masters*, pp. 197–200)

Home Connection This Home Link is a four-page newsletter that introduces parents and guardians to Unit 4's topics and terms. The letter also offers ideas for home-based mathematics activities that are supportive of the classroom work.

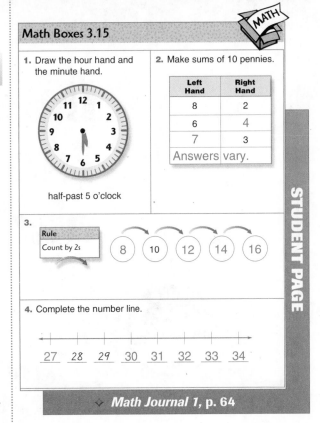

Math Journal 1, p. 64

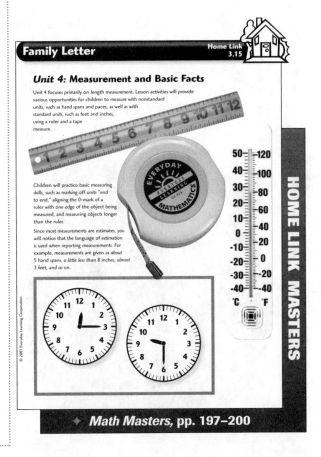

Math Masters, pp. 197–200

Unit **4**
Measurement and Basic Facts

overview

In this unit, children work with linear measures and review and extend their use of thermometers and clocks. They measure in nonstandard units, such as digits and hand spans, as well as in the U.S. customary units of inches and feet. They use rulers and tape measures to practice measuring classroom objects and themselves.

Children begin the important work of achieving "automaticity" (automatic recall) of the basic addition facts.

Also, two routines are introduced in this unit that will continue throughout first grade. First, children will begin to add numbers to their number scrolls. This activity will provide number-writing practice and increased understanding of place value. The second routine that is introduced in this unit is the Math Message, which will be used through sixth grade.

contents

UNIT
4

learning goals in perspective

learning goals	links to the past	links to the future
4a **Beginning/Developing Goal** Use standard units for measuring length. **(Lessons 4.3–4.7)**	In Kindergarten children used both nonstandard and standard units to measure length.	In later grades, measurement activities will be extended to acquaint children with equivalent units and to show how decimals and fractions are connected to measurement. In second grade, fractional units are extended to include $\frac{1}{8}$ of an inch. *(Related Grade 1 lesson: 6.6)*
4b **Developing Goal** Find simple sums and missing addends. **(Lessons 4.1, 4.2, 4.5–4.9, 4.11, and 4.12)**	Children did simple addition and missing-addend activities in Kindergarten. *(Related Grade 1 lessons: 2.3, 2.11, 3.6, 3.14)*	Units 5 and 6 focus on developing fact power. Addition will also be practiced through games and in a variety of problem-solving situations throughout first grade. *(Related Grade 1 lessons: 5.9–5.11, 6.1, 6.3–6.5, 6.7, 6.8, 7.2)*
4c **Developing Goal** Calculate the values of coin combinations. **(Lessons 4.3 and 4.10)**	In Unit 3, children practiced counting pennies, nickels, and dimes. *(Related Grade 1 lessons: 1.11, 2.8–2.10, 3.2, 3.4, 3.12, 3.13)*	Children will continue to practice counting and using money throughout the grades. *(Related Grade 1 lessons: 6.9, 8.1, 8.2, 8.5)*
4d **Developing Goal** Solve simple number stories. **(Lessons 4.3, 4.6, 4.7, and 4.9)**	Children began telling and solving number stories in Kindergarten and have continued in first grade. *(Related Grade 1 lessons: 1.13, 2.13)*	Throughout the grades, children will continue to create and solve number stories. *(Related Grade 1 lessons: 5.6–5.8, 8.4)*
4e **Developing/Secure Goal** Order and compare numbers to 22. **(Lessons 4.1, 4.5, 4.8, 4.11, and 4.12)**	Children began ordering and comparing numbers in Kindergarten, and they play games such as *Number Squeeze* and *Top-It* in first grade. *(Related Grade 1 lessons: 1.2–1.6, 1.6, 1.7, 1.10, 2.11, 2.12, 3.13)*	Comparisons are fundamental for understanding many mathematical relationships, number stories, and for analyzing data. Children will make comparisons of many types throughout the grades. *(Related Grade 1 lessons: 5.3, 5.6–5.8, 9.5, 9.7)*
4f **Developing/Secure Goal** Tell time to the nearest half-hour. **(Lessons 4.4, 4.5, 4.8, and 4.9)**	In Kindergarten, children began telling time to the nearest hour and were introduced to the minute hand. In Unit 2, telling time to the hour was reviewed; and in Unit 3 the half-hour was introduced. *(Related Grade 1 lessons: 2.5, 2.6, 3.7)*	Children will continue to practice telling time throughout Grades 1 and 2. Children will work with the minute and second hands in Unit 6. *(Related Grade 1 lessons: 6.10, 6.11)*

assessment
ongoing • product • periodic

✓ Informal Assessment

Math Boxes These *Math Journal* pages provide opportunities for cumulative review or assessment of concepts and skills.

Ongoing Assessment: Kid Watching Use the Ongoing Assessment suggestions in the following lessons to make quick, on-the-spot observations about children's understanding of:
- Numeration **(Lesson 4.10)**
- Operations and Computation **(Lessons 4.11 and 4.12)**
- Measurement and Reference Frames **(Lessons 4.1, 4.3–4.6, 4.8, and 4.9)**
- Patterns, Functions, and Algebra **(Lesson 4.10)**

Portfolio Ideas Samples of children's work may be obtained from the following assignments:
- Reading a Thermometer **(Lesson 4.1)**
- Making a Storybook Timeline **(Lesson 4.9)**
- Draw domino number families **(Lesson 4.11)**

✓ Unit 4 Review and Assessment

Math Message Use the problem in Lesson 4.13 to assess children's progress toward the following learning goal: **Goal 4b**

Oral and Slate Assessments Use oral or slate assessments during Lesson 4.13 to assess children's progress toward the following learning goals: **Goals 4c, 4d, 4e, and 4f**

Written Assessment Use a written review during Lesson 4.13 to assess children's progress toward the following learning goals: **Goals 4a, 4b, 4c, and 4f**

Performance/Group Assessment Use a small-group activity in Lesson 4.13 to assess children's progress toward the following learning goals: **Goals 4a, 4b, and 4e**

assessment handbook

For more information on how to use different types of assessment in Unit 4, see the Assessment Overview on pages 46–48 in the *Assessment Handbook*. The following Assessment Masters can be found in the *Math Masters* book:

- Unit 4 Checking Progress, pp. 307 and 308
- Unit 4 Class Checklist, p. 334
- Unit 4 Individual Profile of Progress, p. 335
- Class Progress Indicator, p. 358
- Math Logs, pp. 362–364
- Self-Assessment Forms, pp. 365 and 366
- Interest Inventory, p. 361

problemsolving

A process of modeling everyday situations using tools from mathematics

Encourage children to use a variety of strategies when attacking a given problem—and to explain those strategies. *Strategies children might use in this unit:*

- Using logical reasoning
- Acting out the problem
- Modeling with manipulatives
- Using a diagram
- Making a graph
- Using estimation
- Using a number line

Four Problem-Solving REPRESENTATIONS

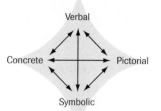

Lessons that teach *through* problem solving, not just *about* problem solving

Lesson	Activity	Lesson	Activity
4.2	Deciding how to measure lengths with nonstandard units	4.9	Making timelines
4.3	Deciding how to get nearly the same measurement when two people measure the same object	4.7	Measuring heights, making a line plot and a bar graph, finding the "typical" height
4.5	Solving number stories	4.10	Making a number scroll
4.5	Estimating the length of an object	4.11	Finding sums using dominoes

For more information about problem solving in *Everyday Mathematics,* see the *Teacher's Reference Manual,* pp. 197–208.

cross-curricularlinks

literature

- Read *How Big Is a Foot?* by Rolf Myller, in which a carpenter learns the benefits of using standard measurement while making a bed for the queen. **(Lesson 4.3)**

- Read *Inch by Inch* by Leo Lionni, a book about an inchworm who measures parts of different birds. **(Lesson 4.4)**

art and literature

- Draw number combinations for 10 using *Anno's Counting House* by Mitsumasa Anno as a model. **(Lesson 4.11)**

science and literature

- Plant bean seeds and read *Jack and the Beanstalk.* **(Lesson 4.5)**

meeting INDIVIDUAL needs

◆ RETEACHING

The following features provide additional instructional support:

Adjusting the Activity
- **Lesson 4.1**, Part 1
- **Lesson 4.2**, Part 1
- **Lesson 4.3**, Part 1
- **Lesson 4.5**, Part 1
- **Lesson 4.7**, Part 2
- **Lesson 4.8**, Part 1
- **Lesson 4.9**, Part 1
- **Lesson 4.11**, Part 1

Options for Individualizing
- **Lesson 4.2** Measuring with Stacking Cubes
- **Lesson 4.4** Measuring with Cubes and Comparing with a Ruler
- **Lesson 4.10** Constructing a Class Number Grid

◆ ENRICHMENT

The following features suggest enrichment and extension activities:

Adjusting the Activity
- **Lesson 4.1**, Part 1
- **Lesson 4.4**, Part 1
- **Lesson 4.5**, Part 1
- **Lesson 4.7**, Parts 1, 3
- **Lesson 4.8**, Part 1
- **Lesson 4.10**, Part 1
- **Lesson 4.11**, Part 3

Options for Individualizing
- **Lesson 4.3** Naming Things That Are about 1 Foot Long, 2 Feet Long, and So On
- **Lesson 4.4** Introducing the Yard
- **Lesson 4.5** Starting the *Jack and the Beanstalk* Project
- **Lesson 4.6** Making a Measurement Book
- **Lesson 4.7** Making an Inch Collection
- **Lesson 4.9** Making a Storybook Timeline
- **Lesson 4.12** Playing a Variation of *Shaker Addition Top-It*
- **Lesson 4.12** Playing *High Roller* to 20

◆ MULTIAGE CLASSROOM

The following chart lists related activities from the *Kindergarten Teacher's Guide to Activities* and lessons from Grade 2 that can help you meet your instructional needs:

Grade K Pages	24	12 14 43	136– 139 146– 151	146 151	146 151	146 151	13 100 184	191– 192 254– 257	160	222	226 277	226 277
Grade 1 Lessons	4.1	4.2	4.3	4.4	4.5	4.6	4.7	4.8	4.9	4.10	4.11	4.12
Grade 2 Lessons	1.1 1.13 4.4	9.2	9.1 9.2	9.1 9.2	9.1– 9.4	9.1– 9.6	1.13 3.4 3.5	1.3 3.3 12.2	12.3	1.9 7.2	2.2– 2.5 2.8	1.4 2.2– 2.5

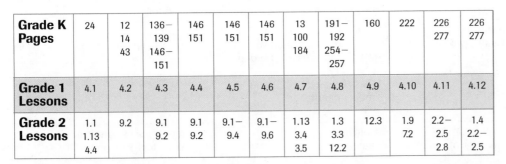

materials

lesson	math masters pages	manipulative kit items	other items
4.1	Home Link Masters, pp. 201 and 202 Teaching Masters, pp. 33 and 34	dominoes outdoor thermometer Class Thermometer Poster	**See Advance Preparation, p. 254**
4.2	Home Link Master, p. 203	slate	small items of various lengths pennies half-sheets of paper
4.3	Home Link Master, p. 204 Teaching Master, p. 35		construction paper pennies, nickels, and dimes *How Big Is a Foot?* by Rolf Myller
4.4	Home Link Master, p. 205 Teaching Masters, pp. 36–38 **See Advance Preparation, p. 270**		foot-long foot from Lesson 4.3 1-inch objects; yardstick small objects 1-inch stacking cubes
4.5	Home Link Master, p. 206 transparency of Teaching Master, p. 40 **See Advance Preparation, p. 276**	dominoes 6 inch ruler	*Jack and the Beanstalk* plastic foam cup or half-pint milk carton soil; bean or sunflower seeds dowel rod or 14" stick ties for supporting plant
4.6	Home Link Master, p. 207	tape measure; ruler	quarter-sheets of paper
4.7	Home Link Master, p. 208 Teaching Masters, pp. 41–43	tape measure; ruler geoboards; rubber bands base-10 blocks dominoes per partnership number cards 0–18	stick-on notes **See Advance Preparation, p. 285**
4.8	Home Link Master, p. 209 Teaching Master, p. 14 **See Advance Preparation, p. 291**	dominoes clock-face stamp (optional)	demonstration clock tool-kit clock pennies 3" by 5" index cards, cut in half (optional)
4.9	Home Link Master, p. 210 Teaching Master, p. 14 transparency of Teaching Master, p. 44 (optional) **See Advance Preparation, p. 296**	slate	tool-kit clock demonstration clock 24-hour timeline
4.10	Home Link Master, p. 211 Teaching Master, pp. 39 and 45–48	base-10 blocks	calculator (optional) stick or cardboard tube stick-on notes *Time Match* cards **See Advance Preparation, p. 301**
4.11	Home Link Master, p. 212 Teaching Master, p. 49	slate two dice base-10 blocks	calculator *Anno's Counting House* by Mitsumasa Anno
4.12	Home Link Master, p. 213 Teaching Masters, pp. 50 and 51 (optional)	base-10 blocks 2 six-sided dice and two polyhedral dice per group craft sticks Class Number Grid Poster rubber bands die	calculator resealable bags
4.13	Home Link Masters, pp. 214–217 Assessment Masters, pp. 307, 308	dominoes slate	tool-kit clocks and coins slate; tool-kit rulers

planning tips

Pacing

Pacing depends on a number of factors, such as children's individual needs and how long your school has been using *Everyday Mathematics.* At the beginning of Unit 4, review your Content by Strand Poster to help you set a monthly pace.

OCTOBER	NOVEMBER	DECEMBER

← MOST CLASSROOMS →

Home Communication

Share Home Links 4.1–4.12 with families to help them understand the content and procedures in this unit. At the end of the unit, use Home Link 4.13 to introduce Unit 5. Supplemental information can be found in the *Home Connection Handbook.*

NCTM Standards

Standard	1	2	3	4	5	6	7	8	9	10
Unit 4 Lessons	1, 2, 5–12	10	7, 10	1–11	7	1–12	1–12	1–12	1–12	1–12

Content Standards
1 Number and Operation
2 Patterns, Functions, and Algebra
3 Geometry and Spatial Sense
4 Measurement
5 Data Analysis, Statistics, and Probability

Process Standards
6 Problem Solving
7 Reasoning and Proof
8 Communication
9 Connections
10 Representations

PRACTICE *through* Games

Everyday Mathematics uses games to help children develop good fact power and other math skills.

- Practice addition and comparison in *Domino Top-It* **(Lessons 4.1, 4.5, and 4.8)**
- Practice addition and subtraction with *Two-Fisted Penny Addition* **(Lessons 4.2 and 4.8)**
- Practice money-exchanging skills with *Coin-Dice* **(Lesson 4.3)**
- Practice telling time in *Time Match* **(Lessons 4.4 and 4.10)**
- Practice addition facts in *High Roller* **(Lessons 4.11 and 4.12)**
- Practice addition facts in *Shaker Addition Top-It* **(Lesson 4.12)**

unit 4 content highlights

The notes below highlight the major content ideas presented in Unit 4. These notes may help you establish instructional priorities.

Math Message (Lesson 4.1)

Beginning with Lesson 4.1, a **Math Message** is included as a part of each lesson. Some Math Messages review previously covered topics; others are tasks for children to complete in preparation for one or more lesson activities. Many teachers use the Math Message as a routine to help start the day. Children should complete the Math Message before the start of the lesson.

You need to decide how you will display the Math Messages and how you will expect children to respond to the messages. Read about Math Messages in the Management Guide section of the *Teacher's Reference Manual*.

Although the *Teacher's Lesson Guide* provides daily suggestions for Math Messages, you are encouraged to write your own messages based on the needs of your students and the particularities of your classroom and your school.

NOTE: Certainly in the beginning of the year, and probably throughout much of the year, you may need to read each day's Math Message to the class.

Measurement and Reference Frames

Although reference frames (such as clocks, calendars, timelines, and thermometers) often make use of measures, numbers in reference frames mean different things and are used differently from measures. For example, ordinary arithmetic is seldom meaningful when applied to numbers from reference frames: 30°F is not "twice as warm" as 15°F; 3:00 P.M. plus 2:00 P.M. is not 5:00 P.M.

Knowledge about the reference frame itself is needed to make sense of the numbers in it. For example, the year 2001 on the standard United States calendar does not mean 2001 on the Jewish calendar, the Muslim calendar, or the Chinese calendar.

Measurements are never negative, but there are many negative numbers in reference frames.

Be as clear and as correct as you can in what you say in class about measurement and reference frames, but you need not and should not make a fuss about the distinctions with children; these issues will get sorted out with experience.

For more information about measurement and reference frames, see Essays 6 and 7 in the *Teacher's Reference Manual*.

Reading a Thermometer (Lesson 4.1)

Most people think of temperatures as measures, but temperatures are actually numbers that are being used in different number-line reference systems. There is an arbitrary zero (where a saturated salt solution freezes in the Fahrenheit system and pure water freezes in the Celsius system), and temperatures are measured above and below that zero. Also, the value of one *degree* is different. There are 180 degrees from freezing to boiling water in the Fahrenheit system; 100 degrees from freezing to boiling water in the Celsius system.

In Unit 1, children color-coded daily temperature readings and began reading temperatures to the nearest ten degrees. In this lesson, children begin reading temperatures to the nearest two degrees. As with other measures, encourage children to report temperatures using phrases like *between __ and __ degrees Fahrenheit* or *almost __ degrees Fahrenheit*. Only the Fahrenheit scale is used in first grade; the Celsius scale will be introduced in second grade.

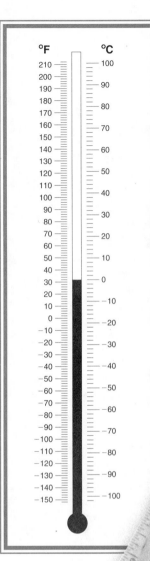

Nonstandard Linear Measures (Lesson 4.2)

Children measure the lengths of various classroom objects using such units as digits (finger widths), hands, paces, and arm spans. As they perform this activity, children learn that basic measuring techniques, whether with standard or nonstandard units, require placing the units end to end, without gaps, in a straight line and then labeling the resulting measure with whichever unit was used, such as "Juan's foot" or "Beth's hand."

Measurements are approximations. The object being measured never corresponds exactly to marked intervals, so a measurement is taken to the nearer unit. Thus, the development of "estimation" vocabulary using terms like *about, almost, a little more, a little less,* and so on is encouraged. Another reason for considering measurements as approximations is that the tools we use to measure things are imprecise.

Personal "Foot" and Standard Foot (Lesson 4.3)

Children use tracings of their feet to measure the lengths of objects around the room. Then they compare the measurements of the objects and find that they get different numbers of feet for measurements of the same objects since children don't all have the same size feet! A "foot-long foot" (with the standard U.S. customary foot unit) is then used to measure the same objects to get the same measures, thus emphasizing the need for standard units.

The Inch (Lesson 4.4)

The inch is introduced as a standard unit for measuring objects smaller than a foot and for measuring objects whose lengths are "between feet." Children use inch rulers with the half-inches marked to help them

when measuring to the nearest inch. Children also use rulers marked in sixteenths—even though fractions of an inch are not used at this time—because most "everyday" rulers are marked in this way.

Measuring Tools and Standards for Measures
(Lessons 4.5 and 4.6)

Measuring tools provide ways to attach numbers to many common and uncommon things. Much of modern industry and technology depends on using accurate measures that are standardized throughout the world.

Tape measures and rulers, along with weighing scales and balances, are among the first tools used by children. If children are using retractable tape measures, teaching and enforcing the "2-inch, no-zap rule" (do not "zap" the tape measure until less than 2 inches are showing) will extend the life of these tools. Just as carpenters, doctors, and other workers respect and take care of the tools they use, children should learn to respect and care for the tools in their tool kits.

In these two lessons, children estimate the total length of an object to begin to develop a sense of the length of a foot and of an inch. They also "estimate" to measure to the nearest foot or inch.

Explorations (Lesson 4.7)

In this lesson, you should direct the measuring and recording of children's heights. (This activity will also be done later in the school year so that children can find out how much they have grown.) The data (heights) from this activity are used to make a bar graph to find a "typical" height for a first grader.

Another activity provides for children's exploration of base-10 blocks. Time spent getting familiar with the blocks is important, since the blocks will be used for developing place-value concepts and for early work with computational algorithms.

Telling Time to the Quarter-Hour (Lesson 4.8)

This lesson refines children's skill in telling time. Notice that times continue to be reported with phrases that suggest approximation: *about, between, almost.* Also, note that digital notation is not yet introduced, since work with the division of the hour into 60 minutes has not yet been addressed.

Timelines (Lesson 4.9)

These devices for showing when events took place are intended to help children begin to develop a sense of longer periods of time. Children make timelines for a 24-hour day, for the first half of the school year, and for their lives to date.

Number Scrolls (Lesson 4.10)

Many teachers have found the activity of filling in blank number grids to be a fruitful exercise both for number-writing practice and for increased intuition about how our base-10 place-value system works. This activity can be continued in small doses over several weeks or many weeks, depending on the interest of the group or of individual children in extending their scrolls.

The *Everyday Mathematics* authors and developers believe it is important that the scroll-writing activity be open-ended and fun for children and that competition over who "scrolls" the furthest not be allowed to mar the enjoyment and learning that occur when children perform this exercise at different levels.

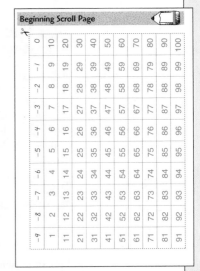

Beginning Scroll Page

Introducing Fact Power (Lesson 4.11)

This lesson begins children's work toward "automaticity" (automatic recall) of basic facts. *Everyday Mathematics* provides practice and drill in several formats, such as games, choral responses, and paper-and-pencil work, in relatively brief sessions throughout the year.

Good Fact Habits (Lesson 4.12)

Lessons designed to build instant recall of the basic facts appear throughout the *Everyday Mathematics* program. The regular class routine includes games to practice basic facts at each grade level. This lesson introduces *Shaker Addition Top-It*. In addition to playing mathematics games, the choral-response routine provides for frequent practice of basic facts.

For **additional information** on the following topics, see the *Teacher's Reference Manual:*

- basic facts
- clocks
- games for practice
- length
- measurement
- number grids
- number scrolls
- reference frames
- rulers and tape measures
- temperature

4.1 Math Message and Reading a Thermometer

OBJECTIVES To introduce the Math Message routine; to review thermometers; and to read temperatures to the nearest two degrees.

summaries	materials

1 Teaching the Lesson

Children review the features of a thermometer and how it works. They learn how to read a thermometer that has marks for every two degrees. [Measurement and Reference Frames; Numeration]	☐ *Math Journal 1*, p. 65 ☐ outdoor thermometer ☐ Class Thermometer Poster ☐ slate (optional) ***See** Advance Preparation*

2 Ongoing Learning & Practice

Children play *Domino Top-It*. [Operations and Computation; Numeration] Children practice and maintain skills through Math Boxes and Home Link activities.	☐ *Math Journal 1*, p. 66 ☐ Home Link Masters (*Math Masters*, pp. 201 and 202) ☐ dominoes

3 Options for Individualizing

Extra Practice Children number the 2-degree marks on a thermometer marked with multiples of 10. They read temperatures by placing mercury "strips" on their thermometers. [Measurement and Reference Frames; Numeration]	☐ Teaching Masters (*Math Masters*, pp. 33 and 34) ***See** Advance Preparation*

Additional Information

Background Information Read about Math Messages in the *Teacher's Reference Manual*.

Advance Preparation For Part 1, record the actual temperature as part of the Math Message. Position the Class Thermometer Poster so that, during the lesson, you can display Side B. You may want to lightly color the different zones on Side B to match those on Side A. Also, uncover the marks between 10s on the Fahrenheit scale of the outdoor thermometer, but keep the Celsius scale covered with masking tape. The outdoor thermometer should resemble the thermometer pictured on journal page 65.

For the optional Extra Practice activity in Part 3, write multiples of 10 at the appropriate marks on the thermometer on *Math Masters*, page 33. Use multiples for temperatures common to your location—for example, 30° to 60° or 60° to 90°. Then make a copy of the master for each child and cut out the mercury strips, or have children cut them out.

Vocabulary • **Math Message** • **thermometer** • **temperature** • **mercury** • **degree** • **Fahrenheit**

Getting Started

Mental Math and Reflexes

Count up and back by 2s. Begin by starting at multiples of 10. Then continue by starting at even numbers that are not multiples of 10.

Math Message

Today's temperature is (insert today's temperature). *What is the color zone for today's temperature? Look at the Class Thermometer Poster.* (You can also refer children to the thermometer on *Math Journal 1,* page 65.)

---

1 Teaching the Lesson

✦ Introducing the Math Message Routine

WHOLE-CLASS DISCUSSION

Explain the routine you will use for your daily **Math Message.**

1. Tell the children that the Math Message will give them a task to complete each day.

2. Show the specific place in the classroom where the Math Message will appear.

3. Tell children when to complete the task, discuss how their answers might be recorded, and tell them where to put responses on days when answers are to be handed in.

When beginning to use the Math Message routine, many teachers read the message aloud, and the class works on it together. As the year progresses and children learn to read independently, the Math Message routine should become a more independent routine. Help children develop that independence by using rebuses or pictures as you write the Math Messages. At times, you might need to supplement a written message with an oral explanation.

✦ Math Message Follow-Up

WHOLE-CLASS DISCUSSION

Have children answer today's Math Message question. Review the color zones on the Class Thermometer Poster by asking questions like those on the next page.

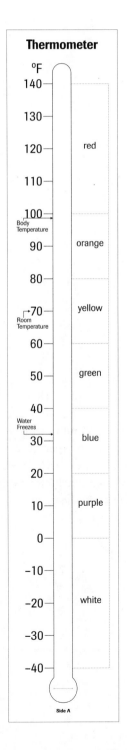

Thermometer

°F

140 —
130 —
120 — red
110 —
100 — Body Temperature
90 — orange
80 —
70 — Room Temperature — yellow
60 —
50 — green
40 —
Water Freezes
30 — blue
20 —
10 — purple
0 —
−10 —
−20 — white
−30 —
−40 —

Side A

- Which color zone names a hot temperature? Orange or red

- Which color zone names a cold temperature? Blue, purple, or white

- Name some temperatures that would be in the green zone. Any temperature between 40° and 60°

- What might you be wearing if the temperature were in the orange zone? Warm-weather clothing, such as T-shirts and shorts

◆ Reviewing Thermometers and How to Read Them

WHOLE-CLASS DISCUSSION

Ask questions like the following to review how thermometers work:

- What is a **thermometer** used for? Measuring temperature

- What is **temperature**? A measurement of how cold or hot something is

- How does a thermometer measure temperature? The **mercury,** or colored alcohol, in the glass tube goes up when the air, or a person's or thing's temperature, gets warmer and goes down when the temperature gets colder.

- How is the temperature reported? The temperature is reported as the number of **degrees** indicated by a thermometer. The number next to the mark closest to the top of the mercury names the number of degrees.

- What does °F at the top of the thermometer mean? Degrees **Fahrenheit.** The "°" symbol means degrees, and the F means Fahrenheit. It names the unit of temperature measures.

- How is the Class Thermometer like the Class Number Line? They both have evenly spaced marks that represent numbers.

- How is the Class Thermometer different from the Class Number Line? Numbers on the thermometer are marked only at the 10s. Also, there are no arrows at either end of the thermometer as there are on the number line.

NOTE: You might mention that another unit for temperature measures is °C (degrees Celsius). Fahrenheit and Celsius are different scales for measuring temperatures. A scale is a number line made by choosing a cold point and a hot point and then marking a number of equal spaces between them.

✦ Reading Temperatures to the Nearest Ten Degrees

WHOLE-CLASS ACTIVITY

Set the red ribbon on the Class Thermometer Poster to show various temperatures, and then have children report the temperatures to the nearest ten degrees.

▷ Start with temperatures that are multiples of 10 and then temperatures between multiples of 10. Set the ribbon close to multiples of 10 and continue to make the readings more difficult as appropriate.

▷ Remind children to name temperatures using phrases like *between __ and __ degrees Fahrenheit, almost __ degrees Fahrenheit,* and *about halfway between __ and __ degrees Fahrenheit.*

Position the red ribbon at, or near, temperatures that are multiples of 10.

Adjusting the Activity To extend the activity, have children write temperatures on their slates.

✦ Reading Temperatures to the Nearest Two Degrees (*Math Journal 1*, p. 65)

WHOLE-CLASS ACTIVITY

Turn over the Class Thermometer Poster to show Side B.

1. Discuss how the thermometer shown on this side is the same as, yet different from, the one on the other side. The only difference is that this thermometer has nine marks between the 10s.

2. Ask children if they can guess what the shorter marks stand for. Numbers that are not written that name temperatures between multiples of 10. (You might relate these marks to marks between the numbered marks on other measuring tools children may have seen, such as rulers and bath scales.)

3. Explain how to find out which numbers the extra marks stand for. Pick two numbers on the thermometer; for example, 40 and 50.

   ▷ Point out that there are 10 spaces from 40 to 50 on the thermometer, just as there are 10 spaces from 40 to 50 on the Class Number Line. Each mark stands for 1 degree.

   ▷ Count from 40 to 50 on the thermometer with children. Ask them which numbers they said at the larger of the extra marks. Help children understand that the larger marks name even numbers between 40 and 50.

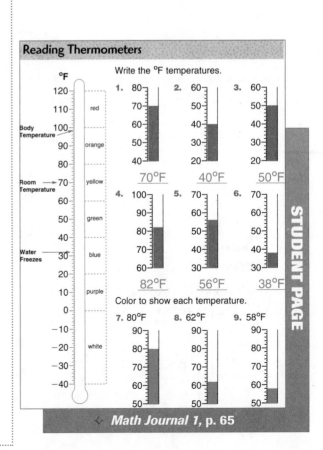

ONGOING ASSESSMENT

This is the first time children are formally asked to read a thermometer to the nearest two degrees. At this time, most children should be able to read temperatures to the nearest 10 degrees using language like *a little more than* and *about halfway between*. Children will continue to practice reading temperatures to the nearest two degrees throughout the year.

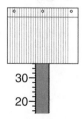

A sheet of paper can make it easier to read temperatures.

4. Have children practice reading temperatures that are multiples of 2. Set the red ribbon on the Class Thermometer Poster to a temperature, and have the class count the number of degrees in unison by starting with the largest multiple of 10 and then counting up by 2s. Repeat as time allows.

5. Children complete the problems on the journal page on their own or with a partner. For Problems 1–6, remind children to label their answers °F since the numbers stand for "degrees Fahrenheit." Circulate and assist as children color the mercury to show temperatures in Problems 7–9.

Adjusting the Activity If children are having difficulty completing the problems on the journal page, use a piece of paper to align the top of the mercury with the number on the scale. Position the paper from the top of the thermometer so that both the mercury column and the number scale are visible below the paper.

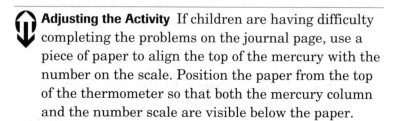

Ongoing Learning & Practice

✦ Comparing Numbers while Playing *Domino Top-It*

PARTNER ACTIVITY 👥

This is a variation of the *Top-It* game first introduced in Lesson 1.6. This game is for two or three players.

Rules

1. Place the dominoes facedown on the table.

2. Each child chooses a domino and compares the total number of dots to the total number on his or her partner's dominoes.

3. The child with the larger total takes the dominoes chosen for that turn. Ties are settled by another draw.

4. The game ends when time is up or when all dominoes have been drawn.

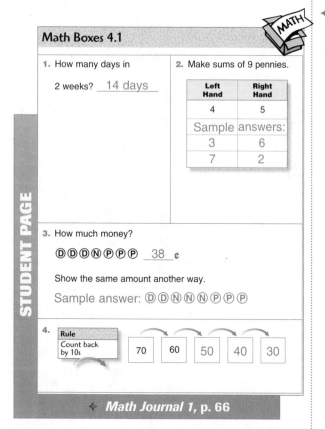

STUDENT PAGE

Math Boxes 4.1

1. How many days in

   2 weeks? __14 days__

2. Make sums of 9 pennies.

Left Hand	Right Hand
4	5
Sample	answers:
3	6
7	2

3. How much money?

   ⒟⒟Ⓝ🅟🅟🅟   __38__ ¢

   Show the same amount another way.

   Sample answer: ⒟⒟ⓃⓃⓃ🅟🅟🅟

4. **Rule** Count back by 10s

   70 60 50 40 30

✦ *Math Journal 1, p. 66*

258 Unit 4 *Measurement and Basic Facts*

◆ Math Boxes 4.1 (*Math Journal 1,* p. 66)

INDEPENDENT ACTIVITY

Mixed Review This journal page provides opportunities for cumulative review or assessment of concepts and skills.

◆ Home Link 4.1 (*Math Masters,* pp. 201 and 202)

Home Connection Children complete Frames-and-Arrows diagrams to practice counting by 2s. They also read temperatures to the nearest ten degrees.

3 Options for Individualizing

◆ EXTRA PRACTICE Reading a Thermometer
(*Math Masters,* pp. 33 and 34)

INDEPENDENT ACTIVITY   **15–30 min**

Children fill in the missing numbers (between the multiples of 10 that you provide on *Math Masters,* page 33), as represented by the interval marks. Then children cut out each of the eight mercury strips on *Math Masters,* page 34 and place them on the labeled thermometer as shown below. Children write the corresponding temperature for each strip.

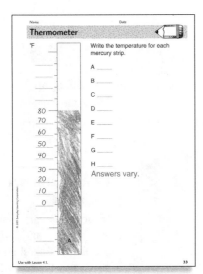

Check to be sure that the bottom of the strip aligns with the bottom of the thermometer.

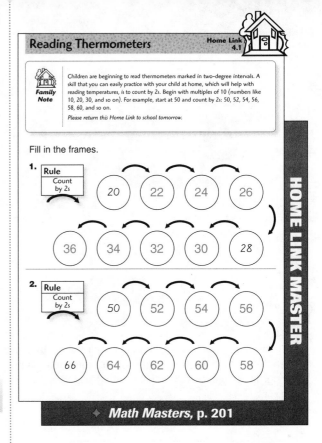

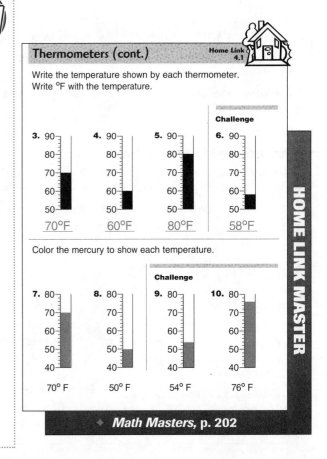

4.2 Nonstandard Linear Measures

OBJECTIVE To measure and compare lengths using nonstandard units.

summaries

materials

1 Teaching the Lesson

Children learn how to use parts of their bodies to measure lengths of objects. They also compare their heights to the heights of objects in the classroom. [Measurement and Reference Frames; Numeration]

- ☐ *Math Journal 1*, pp. 67 and 68
- ☐ Home Link 4.1
- ☐ slate
- ☐ small items of various lengths
- **See Advance Preparation**

2 Ongoing Learning & Practice

Children continue the *Two-Fisted Penny Addition* activity. [Numeration; Operations and Computation]

Children practice and maintain skills through Math Boxes and Home Link activities.

- ☐ *Math Journal 1*, pp. 69–72
- ☐ Home Link Master (*Math Masters*, p. 203)
- ☐ pennies

3 Options for Individualizing

Reteaching Children use cubes to practice measuring length. [Measurement and Reference Frames]

Extra Practice Children compare the lengths of various objects. [Measurement and Reference Frames; Numeration]

- ☐ small objects of various lengths
- ☐ half-sheets of paper; crayons
- **See Advance Preparation**

Additional Information

Advance Preparation For Parts 1 and 3, gather small objects of various lengths for children to measure. Objects might include a piece of chalk, a pencil, a drinking straw, a ruler, the Pattern-Block Template, a book, and so on.

Vocabulary • **unit** • **measure** • **length** • **digit** • **hand** • **hand span** • **yard** • **cubit** • **arm span**

Getting Started

Mental Math and Reflexes

- *Count up by 5s, beginning with 75. Count back by 5s, beginning with 150.*
- *On the number grid, count up by 10s, beginning with 33. Count back by 10s, beginning with 87.*

Math Message

How would you tell someone how far it is across the playground, using only your body or part of your body to describe the distance?

(Consider using another distance: the distance across the classroom.)

Home Link 4.1 Follow-Up

Review answers to the Frames-and-Arrows and temperature problems. Ask children to share strategies for solving the two Challenge problems.

Teaching the Lesson

✦ Math Message Follow-Up

WHOLE-CLASS DISCUSSION

Ask children to share how they would describe the distance and which body parts they would use. For example, they might use arm lengths, foot lengths, steps, or hops as **units.** To **measure** the distance is to compare the body part to the distance. The measurement of the distance is the number of times a particular body part is used to go the distance. Caution children that these body parts must be marked off "end to end"; leaving spaces between body parts will not result in an accurate measurement.

✦ Measuring Things with Fingers, Hands, Feet, and Arms (*Math Journal 1,* p. 67)

WHOLE-CLASS ACTIVITY

Using journal page 67 as a reference, explain that for centuries people used their bodies and parts of their bodies as units to tell about how long something is from end to end (**length**) or about how far one place is from another. Today the class will do the same.

Children take turns coming to the front of the class and measuring various items. The rest of the children make tallies on their slates, or orally count in unison, to help keep track of how many units are marked off. They record the measurements on journal page 67.

When measuring, children might use **digits** (finger widths), **hands,** or **hand spans** (outstretched fingers) for small items, such as a pencil or a book. Children might use feet, paces, historical **yards, cubits** (forearms), or **arm spans** (fathoms) for larger objects, such as the board or a bulletin board, a rug, a desk, or a table. Help children mark off the units end to end without leaving gaps.

Discuss the use of smaller units (digits, hands) to measure smaller items and larger units (feet, paces, fathoms) to measure larger items.

NOTE: Children will measure and record digits, hands, spans and other historic units in Lesson 4.6, after they have more experience using rulers and tape measures.

My Body and Units of Measure

Measure some objects. Record your measurements.

Unit	Picture	Object	Measurements
digit		Answers vary.	about ____ digits
yard			about ____ yards
hand			about ____ hands
pace			about ____ paces
cubit			about ____ cubits
arm span (or fathom)			about ____ arm spans
foot			about ____ feet
hand span			about ____ hand spans

Math Journal 1, p. 67

STUDENT PAGE

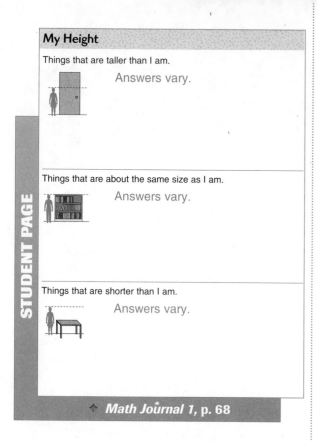

My Height

Things that are taller than I am.

Answers vary.

Things that are about the same size as I am.

Answers vary.

Things that are shorter than I am.

Answers vary.

Math Journal 1, p. 68

NOTE: Since most measurements are estimates, encourage children to report measurements using words like *about, almost, a little more than, a little less than,* and so on.

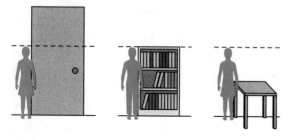

For things starting at floor level, help children mark either their own heights or the height of an object, using their hands, and then make comparisons to shorter and taller objects.

Children work in partnerships to measure objects in the room. Have several partnerships measure the same object using different units. For example: one partnership measures a desk in digits, another measures the desk in hand spans, and another measures it in "steps" by removing shoes and measuring.

Follow up with a brief discussion comparing measurements. For example: the partnership that measured a desk with digits reports its measurement (such as 62 digits). Then the partnership that measured the same object with hand spans reports its measurement (such as 26 spans).

Discuss why there are such differences in the measurements.

▷ Different partnerships used different units.

▷ There may have been gaps between units or accidental overlapping of units when measuring.

▷ Even if the same units (such as digits, hands, or arm spans) were used, the units are nonstandard because people have different-size bodies.

It is important that you and children use the unit labels, as well as estimation words like *about* or *nearly.* For example: *about* 5 Tony digits; *nearly* 2 Diana hands; *a little shorter than* 3 Josh arm spans; *about* 6 Paulo feet; and so on.

◆ Comparing Individual Heights to Things in the Classroom (*Math Journal 1,* p. 68)

INDEPENDENT ACTIVITY

Children find things that are taller (longer) than, shorter than, and about the same height as they are. They record the names or pictures of these things on journal page 68 for discussion now or later.

Adjusting the Activity If children are not adept at comparing the lengths and heights of objects to their own heights, have them directly compare the lengths side by side from a common base. Or, you might cut pieces of string the same lengths as children's heights for comparing lengths and heights of objects not resting on the floor.

Ongoing Learning & Practice

◆ *Two-Fisted Penny Addition* **Using 8 Pennies and 18 Pennies** (*Math Journal 1*, pp. 70–72)

INDEPENDENT ACTIVITY

This activity begins a systematic record of splits of numbers from 5 to 20 as a means of developing readiness for learning the basic addition/subtraction facts and the commutative property of addition. Whenever this activity is used, agree with children on a number not yet recorded in their journals. Encourage them to find and record all of the splits of that number.

◆ **Math Boxes 4.2** (*Math Journal 1*, p. 69)

INDEPENDENT ACTIVITY

Mixed Review This journal page provides opportunities for cumulative review or assessment of concepts and skills.

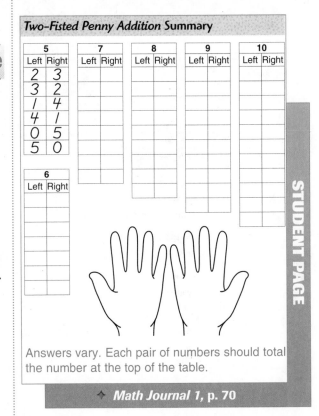

Two-Fisted Penny Addition Summary

5 Left	5 Right	7 Left	7 Right	8 Left	8 Right	9 Left	9 Right	10 Left	10 Right
2	3								
3	2								
1	4								
4	1								
0	5								
5	0								

6 Left	6 Right

Answers vary. Each pair of numbers should total the number at the top of the table.

✦ *Math Journal 1, p. 70*

▼ Tables continue on journal page 72.

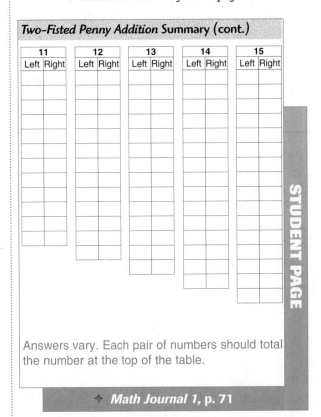

Two-Fisted Penny Addition Summary (cont.)

11 Left	11 Right	12 Left	12 Right	13 Left	13 Right	14 Left	14 Right	15 Left	15 Right

Answers vary. Each pair of numbers should total the number at the top of the table.

✦ *Math Journal 1, p. 71*

Math Boxes 4.2

1. Use your number grid.

   Start at 48. Count up 15.

   You end at ___63___.

   48 + 15 = ___63___

2. Draw the hands.

   half-past 8 o'clock

3. Circle the winner of *Domino Top-It*.

4. Most popular pet ___cat___

   How many like snakes?

   ___1 student___

   Favorite Pets, Mrs. Lee's Class

   snake dog cat bird fish

✦ *Math Journal 1, p. 69*

Home Link 4.2 *(Math Masters, p. 203)*

Home Connection Children measure their beds with their hand spans. They record the measurements and make drawings of their beds. Children will discover that they each get different measurements.

LEFT PANEL

HOME LINK MASTER

Measuring with Hand Spans   Home Link 4.2

Family Note

In today's lesson, we measured objects using nonstandard units like digits (finger widths), hands, fathoms, and hand spans.

One of our discoveries is that we get different measurements for the same object if different people do the measuring using these units. We will continue this investigation, eventually realizing that standard units, such as feet and inches, provide us with more reliable measurements. Help your child measure his or her bed using hand spans. The drawing below shows a hand span.

Please return this Home Link to school tomorrow.

Measure your bed with your hand span.

1. How many hand spans across is it?

About _____ hand spans

2. How many hand spans long is it?

About _____ hand spans

3. Draw a picture of your bed.

Answers vary.

◆ *Math Masters, p. 203*

---

3   Options for Individualizing

◆ RETEACHING   Measuring with Stacking Cubes

SMALL-GROUP ACTIVITY    15–30 min

Provide a group of objects for children to measure using stacking cubes. Cubes should be stacked and placed next to the object, so that the base of the cube stack aligns with one of its edges. On a half-sheet of paper, children can draw the object and record how many "cubes" long it is.

◆ EXTRA PRACTICE   Arranging Objects by Length

SMALL-GROUP ACTIVITY   5–15 min

Display a group of objects. Ask a volunteer to pick one object. Have another child select an object that is longer than, shorter than, or about the same length as the object the volunteer is holding. Children can compare the objects side by side from a common base, or edge. They can also measure each object with a cube stack and use the stack to check relative lengths.

PLANNING AHEAD

For upcoming optional activities, get Rolf Myller's *How Big Is a Foot?* to read to children when you teach Lesson 4.3, Leo Lionni's *Inch by Inch* to read when you teach Lesson 4.4, and any version of *Jack and the Beanstalk* to read in Lesson 4.5.

4.3

Personal "Foot" and Standard Foot

OBJECTIVES To measure with a nonstandard unit and the standard foot; and to understand the need for standard units.

summaries	materials
1 Teaching the Lesson	
Children measure objects with their personal feet and with a standard foot. [Measurement and Reference Frames]	☐ *Math Journal 1*, p. 73 ☐ Home Link 4.2 ☐ Teaching Master (*Math Masters*, p. 35; 2 per child) ☐ construction paper ☐ scissors ***See* Advance Preparation**
2 Ongoing Learning & Practice	
Children play *Coin-Dice*. [Measurement and Reference Frames; Numeration] Children practice and maintain skills through Math Boxes and Home Link activities.	☐ *Math Journal 1*, p. 74 ☐ Home Link Master (*Math Masters*, p. 204) ☐ pennies, nickles, and dimes
3 Options for Individualizing	
Enrichment Children estimate and measure to identify objects that are about one foot long, about two feet long, and so on. [Measurement and Reference Frames] **Extra Practice** Children listen to and discuss *How Big Is a Foot?* [Measurement and Reference Frames]	☐ *How Big Is a Foot?* by Rolf Myller (optional) ***See* Advance Preparation**

Additional Information

Advance Preparation For Part 1, each child will need a piece of construction paper large enough on which to trace her or his foot. Cut 1-foot strips of construction paper if you wish to give children additional feet to use when measuring with the standard foot-long foot. Each child also will need 2 copies of the foot-long foot from *Math Masters*, page 35. One copy will be used in class, and the second copy will be taken home to be used in the Home Link activity.

For the optional Extra Practice activity in Part 3, obtain the book *How Big Is a Foot?* by Rolf Myller (Young Yearling, 1991).

Vocabulary • **foot** • **standard foot**

Getting Started

Mental Math and Reflexes

Tell "change to more" and "change to less" number stories, and have children solve them any way they can, sharing solution strategies after solving each problem. Summarize each solution by drawing a "change" diagram and by writing a number model. If children are able, ask volunteers to complete the diagrams or write the number models. Although children should not be expected to do either of these things at this time, this is an opportunity to revisit these developing skills. *Suggestions:*

- Marcia woke up to find that it was 28° Fahrenheit. By lunchtime, it was 33° Fahrenheit. How much did the temperature go up? 5°F Do you think Marcia wore a coat to school? yes Why? She would be cold without one.

- Leo saw that it was raining. He noticed that it was 35° Fahrenheit. An hour later, the rain turned into snow and the temperature had dropped to 25° Fahrenheit. How much colder was it? 10°F colder Why do you think the rain turned to snow? The temperature fell below 32°F.

- The coldest temperature Thursday night was 22°F. By morning, the temperature had warmed up 7°F. What was the temperature Friday morning? 29°F

- One hot August day, Justin noticed that the thermometer outside showed 90°F. He decided to go swimming when the temperature reached 95°F. The water in the pool was 85°F. How much did the temperature go up before Justin decided to jump in the pool? 5°F

Math Message

A tall person and a short person measured the same thing with their **feet.** *Why might they get different answers?*

Home Link 4.2 Follow-Up

Volunteers share how they measured their beds. *Why do you think different children might get different hand-span measures?* Their beds may be different sizes, and their hands are probably different sizes.

My Foot and the Standard Foot

Measure two objects with the cutout of your foot. Draw pictures of the objects, or write their names.

1. I measured

Answers vary.

It is about _____ _____ feet.
(your name)

2. I measured

It is about _____ _____ feet.
(your name)

Measure two objects with the foot-long foot. Sometimes it is called the *standard foot.*

3. I measured

It is about _____ feet.

4. I measured

It is about _____ feet.

Math Journal 1, p. 73

---

1 Teaching the Lesson

◆ Math Message Follow-Up

WHOLE-CLASS ACTIVITY

Invite children to share their answers to the Math Message problem. Then tell them that you will measure to see why people get different answers. Their feet are different lengths.

1. Starting in a corner, measure heel to toe the number of teacher-feet for a marked distance along a wall. As you measure, have children count off the steps. Have them observe that you are leaving no gaps between your feet. Record the total number of teacher-feet.

2. Next, have a child step off the same distance. Make sure that the child leaves no gaps. Record the total in child-feet. Use the child's name, such as, "Jane-feet."

3. Discuss who got the larger total number of units. Informally develop the idea that it takes more small units than large units to measure something.

◆ Measuring with Construction-Paper Cutouts of Children's Feet (*Math Journal 1*, p. 73)

PARTNER ACTIVITY

Pass out the construction paper, one piece per child. Partners help each other trace one foot on the paper, either with shoes on or in stocking feet. Then each partner cuts out the foot and writes his or her name on it.

Partners use their foot cutouts to measure tables, the board, a desk, and so on. Then each partner names or draws each object on journal page 73 and records how many "(my name)-feet" long each object is. They record two of these measurements in Problems 1 and 2.

ONGOING ASSESSMENT
Watch for children who are
- overlapping units.
- leaving gaps between units.
- not naming the measurement to the nearest unit.

Bring the group together and compare children's personal foot-length measurements. Children with different-size foot tracings will get different foot measurements for the same item. Hint at a standardization of measurement by asking what people might do to get nearly the same number when they measure the same thing.

◆ Measuring with a Standard Foot-Long Foot (*Math Journal 1*, p. 73 and *Math Masters*, p. 35)

PARTNER ACTIVITY

Children cut out the foot-long foot from copies of *Math Masters*, page 35. You may want to give children additional "feet" by cutting 1-foot strips of construction paper.

Partners choose something to measure. They each independently and carefully measure that object until they agree on a number that is close; for example, "a little more than 2 feet." Objects will usually be longer or shorter than a whole number of feet.

Children develop their measuring skills.

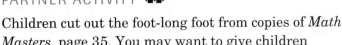 **Adjusting the Activity** If children are having difficulty using just one foot cutout to measure, help individual children cut out four or five feet from construction paper. Each child can then practice lining up the feet—without gaps and without overlapping—to measure objects. When each child is ready, have him or her work on measuring with two feet, and then finally with only one foot.

NOTE: Overlapping and leaving gaps between units may cause differences in measurements for the same items.

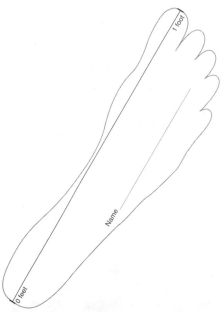

Foot-Long Foot from *Math Masters*, p. 35

Math Boxes 4.3

1. Complete the table.

Before	Number	After
27	28	29
34	35	36
39	40	41
100	101	102

2. Show 26¢.

Use Ⓓ, Ⓝ, and Ⓟ.

Sample answer:

Ⓓ Ⓓ Ⓝ Ⓟ

3. Count back by 2s.

36, 34, 32,

30, 28, 26,

24, 22, 20,

18, 16

4. What is the temperature today?

Answers vary. °F

Odd or even?

Answers vary.

STUDENT PAGE

Children record two of their measurements, using a **standard foot,** in Problems 3 and 4 on journal page 73. As always with measurements, encourage children to use the language of approximation: *about* x *feet, a little less than* y *feet,* or *about halfway between* x *and* y *feet.*

Briefly discuss why children think partners were able to find a number to agree on when they were using the foot-long foot. Because they were measuring with a tool that was the same length

Have children fold and save their foot-long feet and their own foot tracings for use in today's Home Link and in Lesson 4.4.

2 Ongoing Learning & Practice

◆ Playing *Coin-Dice*

PARTNER ACTIVITY

Children practice making coin exchanges by playing *Coin-Dice.* For instructions, see Lesson 3.12.

◆ Math Boxes 4.3 (*Math Journal 1,* p. 74)

INDEPENDENT ACTIVITY

Mixed Review This journal page provides opportunities for cumulative review or assessment of concepts and skills.

◆ Home Link 4.3 (*Math Masters,* p. 204)

Home Connection Children take home a copy of *Math Masters,* page 35, *Foot-Long Foot.* Using different-color crayons, they trace each family member's foot onto the foot-long foot and then compare the foot lengths of family members.

The Foot-Long Foot

Home Link 4.3

Family Note

To help us investigate the measuring unit "feet," please help your child trace each family member's foot using different-color crayons.
Please return this Home Link to school tomorrow.

Compare the foot-long foot to the feet of members of your family.

Here is what you do:

1. Trace each person's foot onto the foot-long foot. Use a different-color crayon for each person's foot.

2. Label each traced foot with the person's name.

3. Talk about why it is not a good idea for people to use their own feet for measuring things.

HOME LINK MASTER

3 Options for Individualizing

◆ **ENRICHMENT** Naming Things That Are
about 1 Foot Long, 2 Feet Long, and So On

INDEPENDENT ACTIVITY   15–30 min

Children identify things that they think are about 1 foot
long, 2 feet long, and so on. They check their estimates by
measuring.

◆ **EXTRA PRACTICE** Discussing *How Big Is a Foot?*

WHOLE-CLASS ACTIVITY   5–15 min

Literature Link If the book *How Big Is a Foot?* by
Rolf Myller (Young Yearling, 1991) is available
and time permits, share it with the class. Discuss why the
first bed was too small for the queen. Use the apprentice's
idea that "three King's feet wide" and "three apprentice's
feet wide" are not the same to point out the need for
standard measurement units.

4.4

The Inch

OBJECTIVES To introduce the inch as a standard unit of length; and to measure to the nearest inch.

summaries	materials

1 Teaching the Lesson

Children measure using 1-inch objects and then measure to the nearest inch with a 1-foot ruler. [Measurement and Reference Frames]

- ☐ *Math Journal 1*, p. 75
- ☐ Home Link 4.3
- ☐ Teaching Master (*Math Masters*, p. 36); scissors
- ☐ foot-long foot from Lesson 4.3
- ☐ 1-inch objects
- ☐ *Inch by Inch* by Leo Lionni (optional)

***See* Advance Preparation**

2 Ongoing Learning & Practice

Children play *Time Match* to practice telling time. [Measurement and Reference Frames]

Children practice and maintain skills through Math Boxes and Home Link activities.

- ☐ *Math Journal 1*, p. 76
- ☐ Home Link Master (*Math Masters*, p. 205)
- ☐ 24 *Time Match* cards per group from Teaching Masters (*Math Masters*, pp. 37 and 38)
- ☐ clock-face stamp (optional)

***See* Advance Preparation**

3 Options for Individualizing

Enrichment Children are introduced to the yard and learn that there are 3 feet in a yard. [Measurement and Reference Frames]

Extra Practice Children paste their foot tracings onto the standard foot. [Measurement and Reference Frames]

Reteaching Children measure with cubes to help develop skill in the use of a ruler. [Measurement and Reference Frames]

- ☐ yardstick
- ☐ foot tracing and foot-long foot from Lesson 4.3
- ☐ paste or glue
- ☐ 1-inch stacking cubes
- ☐ small objects

Additional Information

Advance Preparation For the Math Message, draw on the board a line segment three or four inches longer than three feet, or place masking tape of a similar length on the floor or wall. Also, gather enough 1-inch square pattern blocks (or other objects one inch across) so that each partnership can have at least eight. As an alternative, children can use the distance across their index and middle fingers to approximate 1 inch.

For Part 2, each group of two or three children needs a deck of 24 cards to play *Time Match* (*Math Masters*, pages 37 and 38). Save the decks of cards for reuse in Lesson 4.10.

Optional: To create your own deck of cards, cut twelve 3" by 5" index cards in half. On 12 of the cards, stamp a clock face. Fill in appropriate times on the clock faces and write the same times in words on the other 12 cards.

Vocabulary • inch • nearest inch • in.

Getting Started

Mental Math and Reflexes

Dictate amounts of money less than $1 for children to show with their tool-kit coins. Have them show amounts like 38¢, 42¢, 63¢, and 76¢.

Math Message

How long is this line segment? Use your foot-long foot to measure it. A bit longer than 3 feet

Home Link 4.3 Follow-Up

Did anyone find a person with a foot-long foot? Probably not *Should people use their own feet as a measurement unit?* No; it might give a good estimate, but each person might get a different measurement.

1 Teaching the Lesson

✦ Math Message Follow-Up

WHOLE-CLASS DISCUSSION

Discuss children's measurements. Ask them what they did about the part of the line segment that extends beyond 3 feet. *How would you describe the length of that part?* Less than a foot; part of a foot Ask children if they know of rulers other than the foot-long foot that they can use to measure smaller distances. If no one suggests rulers marked off in inches (or centimeters), discuss the need for a unit of measure smaller than the foot.

✦ Introducing the Inch as a Standard Unit of Length (*Math Masters,* p. 36)

WHOLE-CLASS ACTIVITY

1. Review the process of measuring things that are longer than one foot by marking and counting with one foot-long foot cutout or by laying several cutouts end to end.

2. Next, distribute at least eight 1-inch square pattern blocks (or other 1-inch objects) to each partnership. Tell children that the **inch** is a standard unit of length that is shorter than the foot and that each edge of the block (or other object) is 1 inch long.

3. Partners measure several nearby objects—a pencil, a book, and so on—by laying a row of squares next to the object and then counting the squares. The edge of the first square should align with one end of the object. Observe partners' actions and interactions. After a few minutes, bring the class together to share results.

NOTE: This lesson marks the beginning of the development of children's measurement sense for units.

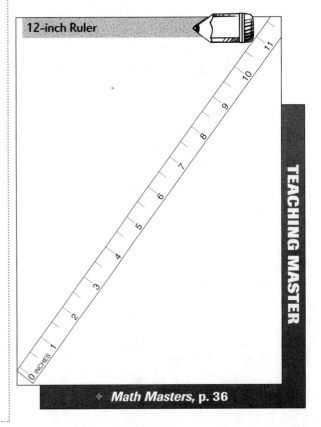

Math Masters, p. 36

TEACHING MASTER

Lesson 4.4   **271**

Literature Link

In *Inch by Inch* by Leo Lionni (Mulberry Books, 1995), an inchworm measures parts of different birds.

4. Then children cut out the 12-inch ruler on *Math Masters*, page 36. (This ruler is labeled in inches and marked in half-inches.) Children match a 1-inch square against a 1-inch space on the ruler. Then they compare the ruler to their foot-long foot and count the number of inches in a foot. 12 inches

Adjusting the Activity If children are ready, you might ask if anyone can guess what the smaller marks on the ruler indicate. Half-inches Children may be able to see that the mark falls halfway along the inch-long object.

✦ Measuring in Inches with the Cutout Ruler
(*Math Journal 1*, p. 75)

WHOLE-CLASS ACTIVITY

Display an object shorter than a foot. Then show how to use the cutout ruler to measure the object:

1. Place the object on or alongside the ruler, with one end at the 0-mark. (Explain that this is like lining objects up side by side to compare their lengths.)

2. Find the inch mark nearest the other end of the object using the mark halfway between whole inches to help you decide. (Children may need several demonstrations and considerable encouragement at this beginning stage of using this measuring tool.)

 ONGOING ASSESSMENT
Watch for children
- who have difficulty reading the nearest inch as the measurement.
- who do not align one end of the object with the 0-mark.

Adjusting the Activity You may want to draw a large "ruler" on the board or use a transparent ruler on an overhead projector to demonstrate how the ruler should be used. Show children how to line up an object at the 0-mark and how to find a measurement to the **nearest inch.**

STUDENT PAGE

Inches

Pick 4 short objects to measure. Draw or name them. Then measure them.

1.

Answers vary.

About _____ inches long

2.

About _____ inches long

3.

About _____ inches long

4.

About _____ inches long

✦ *Math Journal 1*, p. 75

Partners pick four short objects (for example, pencils or calculators) not already measured. They draw or name each object on journal page 75. Then they use their rulers to measure the objects to the nearest inch and record their measurements.

Put a unit box (inches, **in.**) on the board. Circulate and help children to line up one end of the object to be measured with the 0-mark on the ruler and then to read the nearest inch at the other end of the object. Explain that inches give better measurements than feet, but that objects are seldom exactly on an inch mark.

 Adjusting the Activity You may want to have children use crayons to mark the inch marks on their rulers to help them distinguish between the inch and $\frac{1}{2}$ inch marks.

Bring the class together to share results. Then summarize by making the following points:

▷ Standard measures, such as feet and inches, enable different people measuring the same thing to get about the same measures.

▷ Measure by starting at the 0-mark (or end mark, if there is no zero).

▷ If the object being measured is longer than the measuring tool, lay the tool end to end without leaving any gaps.

▷ Few things are an exact number of inches or feet in length. Therefore, descriptions like *between ___ and __ inches (or feet), just past __ inches (or feet), about __ inches (or feet),* or *almost __ inches (or feet)* are good phrases to use.

▷ 12 inches equal 1 foot.

NOTE: A symbol for a unit of measure usually does not end with a period.

The symbol for inches: in.

The symbol for feet: ft

NOTE: Some children may give a measurement to the nearest $\frac{1}{2}$ inch if the end of an object is close to that mark. In second grade, children will measure to the nearest $\frac{1}{2}$ inch using the $\frac{1}{4}$ inch marks on a ruler.

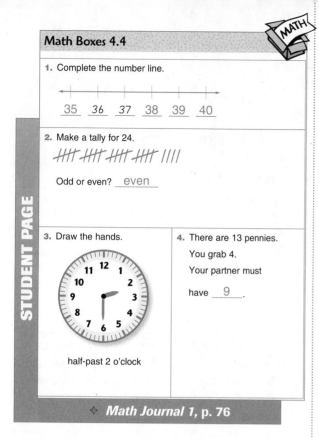

Math Boxes 4.4

STUDENT PAGE

1. Complete the number line.

   35 36 37 38 39 40

2. Make a tally for 24.

   |||| |||| |||| |||| ||||

   Odd or even? __even__

3. Draw the hands.

   half-past 2 o'clock

4. There are 13 pennies.
   You grab 4.
   Your partner must

   have __9__ .

✦ *Math Journal 1, p. 76*

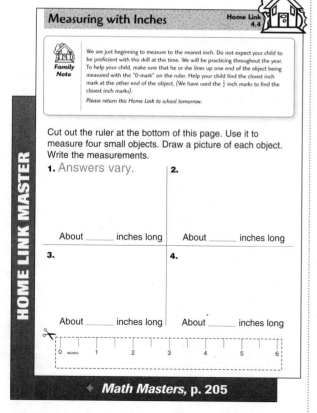

Measuring with Inches

Home Link
4.4

Family Note

We are just beginning to measure to the nearest inch. Do not expect your child to
be proficient with this skill at this time. We will be practicing throughout the year.
To help your child, make sure that he or she lines up one end of the object being
measured with the "0-mark" on the ruler. Help your child find the closest inch
mark at the other end of the object. (We have used the ½ inch marks to find the
closest inch marks).

Please return this Home Link to school tomorrow.

Cut out the ruler at the bottom of this page. Use it to
measure four small objects. Draw a picture of each object.
Write the measurements.

1. Answers vary.   2.

   About ____ inches long   About ____ inches long

3.   4.

   About ____ inches long   About ____ inches long

   ✂
   0 INCHES 1   2   3   4   5   6

✦ *Math Masters, p. 205*

---

2 Ongoing Learning & Practice

✦ Playing *Time Match* (*Math Masters,* pp. 37, 38)

PARTNER ACTIVITY

This game can be played by 2 or 3 players using a
prepared deck of 24 cards. (See Advance Preparation.)

Rules

1. One player mixes the deck and places all 24 cards
   facedown in a 4 by 6 array.

2. Players take turns turning over 2 cards at a time. If
   they match, the player keeps them. If they don't
   match, they are returned facedown to their original
   positions.

3. When all of the cards have been collected, the player
   with the most matches wins.

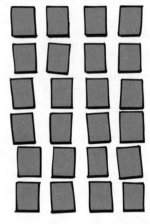

NOTE: If appropriate, pair native English speakers with
non-native English speakers for this activity.

✦ Math Boxes 4.4 (*Math Journal 1,* p. 76)

INDEPENDENT ACTIVITY

Mixed Review This journal page provides
opportunities for cumulative review or
assessment of concepts and skills.

✦ Home Link 4.4 (*Math Masters,* p. 205)

Home Connection Children cut out a ruler,
measure with it, record lengths, and draw
pictures. Children will continue to practice
measuring with a ruler throughout the year.

♦ Math Masters, p. 37

3 Options for Individualizing

♦ ENRICHMENT Introducing the Yard

SMALL-GROUP ACTIVITY ♛♛♛♛   15–30 min

With the children, explore the relationship between feet and yards. Count how many feet it takes to make a yard by lining up 12-inch rulers along a yardstick. Since it takes three 12-inch rulers, a yard is equal to 3 feet. You might even point out that the yardstick shows 36 inches, which is the same as 12 inches + 12 inches + 12 inches on the three rulers.

Ask children to find objects in the room that are longer than a yard and shorter than a yard. Then have them find objects that are about one yard long. Compare the objects to the yardstick to check the estimates.

♦ EXTRA PRACTICE Foot Tracings and Foot-Long Foot Cutouts

INDEPENDENT ACTIVITY (👤)   5–15 min

Children may enjoy pasting their own foot tracings inside the foot-long foot cutouts. These make a nice display.

♦ RETEACHING Measuring with Cubes and Comparing with a Ruler

INDEPENDENT ACTIVITY (👤)   15–30 min

Children use 1-inch stacking cubes to measure a variety of objects that are each shorter than a foot. They then compare the stack of cubes to the ruler to see how many inches long each object is. Remind children to line up the stack with the 0-mark and then to find the mark on the ruler at the end of the stack.

PLANNING AHEAD
Label children's tape measures with their tool-kit numbers for distribution in Lesson 4.6.

3 o'clock	6 o'clock	Half-past 11 o'clock
Half-past 4 o'clock	Half-past 2 o'clock	Half-past 10 o'clock
Half-past 12 o'clock	Quarter-past 5 o'clock	Quarter-before 7 o'clock
Half-past 6 o'clock	Half-past 8 o'clock	8 o'clock

♦ Math Masters, p. 38

TEACHING MASTER

TEACHING MASTER

4.5 The 6-Inch Ruler

OBJECTIVE To estimate and measure the lengths of objects in inches.

summaries	materials

1 Teaching the Lesson

Children discuss the markings on a 6-inch ruler. They use the ruler to measure objects longer than 6 inches. They measure and draw line segments of specified lengths. [Measurement and Reference Frames]

☐ *Math Journal 1*, p. 77

☐ Home Link 4.4

☐ Teaching Master (*Math Masters*, p. 40) (transparency optional)

☐ 6-inch ruler

2 Ongoing Learning & Practice

Children play *Domino Top-It*. [Operations and Computation; Numeration]

Children practice and maintain skills through Math Boxes and Home Link activities.

☐ *Math Journal 1*, p. 78

☐ Home Link Master (*Math Masters*, p. 206)

☐ dominoes

3 Options for Individualizing

Enrichment Children plant bean (or sunflower) seeds and measure the growth of the plants. [Measurement and Reference Frames]

Extra Practice Children measure objects longer than a 6-inch ruler by lining up rulers. [Measurement and Reference Frames]

Extra Practice Children solve problems involving the length of a dollar bill and planting flower bulbs. [Measurement and Reference Frames]

☐ Teaching Master (*Math Masters*, p. 40)

☐ the story *Jack and the Beanstalk;* plastic foam cup or half-pint milk carton; soil; bean (or sunflower) seeds; dowel rod or stick at least 14" long; ties for supporting plant

☐ *Minute Math*®, pp. 86 and 106

Additional Information

Vocabulary • **estimate**

Getting Started

Mental Math and Reflexes

Children use their tool-kit clocks to show times on the hour and half-hour. For example: 5 o'clock, 2:30, half-past 12, and half-past 8.

Math Message

Look at the marks on your 6-inch ruler. Be ready to talk about what the marks might mean.

Home Link 4.4 Follow-Up

Ask a few volunteers to describe the objects they measured and their approximate lengths.

1 Teaching the Lesson

◆ Math Message Follow-Up
(*Math Masters,* p. 40)

WHOLE-CLASS DISCUSSION

Have children identify the inch scale on the 6-inch ruler. Ask if anyone knows what the other scale shows. centimeters Explain that inches are units in what is called the U.S. customary system. Centimeters are units in the metric system, a system of measurement that will be introduced in Unit 6.

On the ruler, or on a transparency of the ruler, point out the subdivisions of the inch scale. Focus on the half-inch mark. In measuring to the nearest inch, the half-inch mark helps the person measuring decide which is the nearest inch. You might ask if anyone knows what the other marks are. Quarter-inch, eighth-inch, sixteenth-inch

◆ Estimating the Length of an Object

WHOLE-CLASS DISCUSSION

So far, children have been measuring objects to the nearest unit by comparing the objects to lengths using their bodies, other objects, and rulers.

Now that they have had some experience measuring with feet and inches, suggest that they **estimate** the length of an object before actually measuring it.

Discuss how reference objects can be used to help make an estimate. For example, tell children that they might use a single square pattern block or the combined width of their forefinger and middle finger as a reference for an inch.

Then, to estimate the total length of an object in inches, explain that they can think, "About how many blocks (or combined finger widths) long is this object?" or "The (object) is between x and y combined finger widths (or blocks) long."

Estimate the length in inches of a few objects with the class. Expect the estimates to be very rough since children are in the early stages of developing measurement sense.

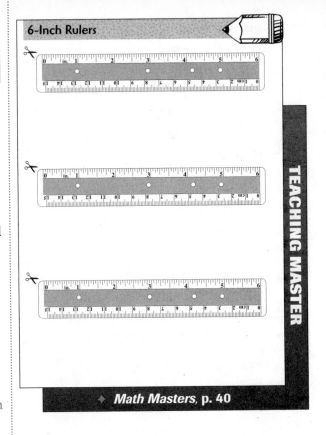

6-Inch Rulers

◆ *Math Masters,* p. 40

Adjusting the Activity To make the inch marks more obvious on the transparency of *Math Masters,* page 40, color over each inch mark with a colored transparency marker. Count up from zero—1 inch, 2 inches, and so on. You might lay an object next to the transparency ruler and review how to measure the length of the object. Review on the overhead how to estimate the length to the nearest inch.

Measuring in Inches

Choose two objects to measure. Estimate each object's length. Measure the objects to the nearest inch.

Object (Name it or draw it)	My Estimate	My Measurement
	about _____ inches	about _____ inches
	about _____ inches	about _____ inches

Measure each line segment.

1.

2. about __5__ inches

about __8__ inches

3. about __3__ inches

4. about __7__ inches

Draw a line segment about

5. 3 inches long _____

6. 5 inches long _____

Math Journal 1, p. 77

Adjusting the Activity If children are able to do so, encourage them to draw line segments involving $\frac{1}{2}$ inches or $\frac{1}{4}$ inches, such as $5\frac{1}{2}$ inches and $3\frac{1}{4}$ inches.

◆ Measuring Objects with the 6-Inch Ruler
(*Math Journal 1*, p. 77)

PARTNER ACTIVITY

Ask children to suggest ways to measure something longer than the 6-inch ruler. Select something to measure, such as the side of a wall calendar. Demonstrate the following:

1. Put the 0-end of the ruler at one edge of the object.

2. Use something like the point of a pencil to mark the point on the object at which the 6-inch end of the ruler falls. Then shift the 0-end of the ruler ahead to this mark. (Or, put the 0-end of a second ruler at the 6-inch end of the first ruler.)

3. Decide on the measure to the nearest inch. For example, by counting on from 6 (6, 7, 8, 9, ...) or by adding (6 + additional inches = ___ inches).

Partners select objects to measure. They draw or name the objects on the top part of journal page 77, estimate the total lengths, and then measure and record the lengths. Circulate and assist.

ONGOING ASSESSMENT
Watch for children

· who do not begin each measure at the 0-mark.

· who can measure objects that are longer than the rulers they are using. Expect that most children will struggle with this activity.

◆ Measuring and Drawing Line Segments
(*Math Journal 1*, p. 77)

WHOLE-CLASS ACTIVITY

Demonstrate on the board or on an overhead projector how to draw a line segment of a specified length. For example, to draw a line segment 4 inches long:

1. Make a dot for the beginning of the line segment.

2. Place the 0-mark of the ruler at the dot, with the inch marks on the ruler going in the direction the line will be drawn.

3. Make a second dot at the 4-inch mark on the ruler.

4. Use the ruler's edge to draw a line to connect the dots.

Partners use their rulers to measure line segments and to draw line segments of specified lengths on the bottom part of journal page 77.

---

2 Ongoing Learning & Practice

◆ Playing *Domino Top-It*

PARTNER ACTIVITY

Children practice addition skills by playing *Domino Top-It*. For detailed instructions, see Lesson 4.1.

◆ Math Boxes 4.5 (*Math Journal 1*, p. 78)

INDEPENDENT ACTIVITY

Mixed Review This journal page provides opportunities for cumulative review or assessment of concepts and skills.

◆ Home Link 4.5 (*Math Masters*, p. 206)

Home Connection Children measure the lengths of objects to the nearest inch using a 6-inch ruler marked in sixteenths.

3 Options for Individualizing

◆ ENRICHMENT Starting the *Jack and the Beanstalk* Project

INDEPENDENT ACTIVITY **15–30 min**

Science and Literature Links Read the story of *Jack and the Beanstalk* to the class before children begin this activity.

Individual children or partners fill their planters (plastic cups or half-pint milk cartons) with soil and plant their bean seeds. (Sunflower seeds also work well.) Then children push their dowels (each about 14 inches long) into the soil and mark where the dowel meets the soil.

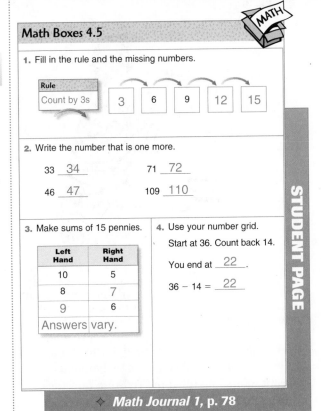

Math Journal 1, p. 78

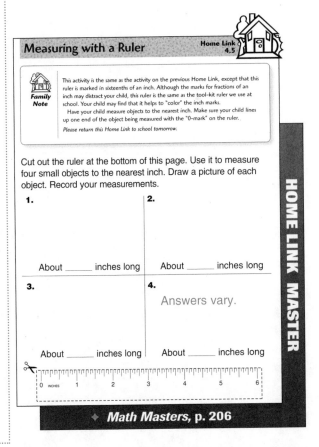

Math Masters, p. 206

The dowels are used for support and to keep the vines growing fairly straight. Children mark the growth point on the dowel each day or two as the seeds begin to sprout and grow. The soil mark is the "zero" point.

NOTE: These plants can be used as gifts later in the year. Simple ribbon bows tied around the containers and filled-in "To/From" gift tags attached to them are nice finishing touches.

The marked dowels become a record of the growth. Children can measure and record the growth using a ruler. Regular watering will be required, of course.

Consider tracking the growth of any plants you may have in the classroom from now until the end of the school year or for some limited amount of time. One way to record height over time is to cut construction paper into 1" by 8" strips. Children stand a strip of construction paper next to the plant and tear off the strip to the same height as the plant. These strips can then be glued onto a bar graph.

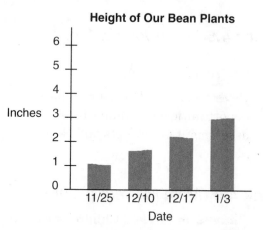

Height of Our Bean Plants

♦ **EXTRA PRACTICE** **Measuring Objects Longer Than 6 Inches** (*Math Masters,* p. 40)

PARTNER ACTIVITY 15–30 min

Make copies of *Math Masters,* page 40. Cut each ruler at exactly the 0-mark and the 6-inch mark.

Partners line up the rulers end to end to measure objects longer than 6 inches. Stress that an object is always measured beginning at the 0-mark. Point out that if children line the rulers up, the 6-inch mark and the 0-mark must match up each time.

 Adjusting the Activity When children seem proficient at using the paper rulers without overlapping or leaving gaps, provide opportunities for them to use the technique from the lesson. For example, they can use the ruler to make a heavy dot with a pencil at the 6-inch mark. Then they move the 0-mark on the ruler to match it with the pencil dot.

♦ **EXTRA PRACTICE** **Minute Math**

SMALL-GROUP ACTIVITY 5–15 min

To offer children more experience with estimating and measuring lengths, see these pages in *Minute Math:*

Number Stories: pp. 86 and 106

4.6

Measuring with a Tape Measure

OBJECTIVE To use a tape measure to measure curved and flat objects in inches.

summaries	materials

1 Teaching the Lesson

Children are introduced to the use of a tape measure to measure curved objects. They practice using a tape measure to measure around and across objects. Children also measure parts of their bodies. [Measurement and Reference Frames]

- ☐ *Math Journal 1*, pp. 79 and 80
- ☐ Home Link 4.5
- ☐ tool-kit tape measure

***See* Advance Preparation**

2 Ongoing Learning & Practice

Children draw domino dot patterns and then find the total number of dots. [Operations and Computation; Patterns, Functions, and Algebra]

Children practice and maintain skills through Math Boxes and Home Link activities.

- ☐ *Math Journal 1*, pp. 81 and 82
- ☐ Home Link Master (*Math Masters*, p. 207)

3 Options for Individualizing

Enrichment Children make a book of objects and their measurements. [Measurement and Reference Frames]

- ☐ quarter-sheets of paper
- ☐ tape measure or ruler

Additional Information

Background Information For information on the "no-zap" tape measure rule, see page 252 of this unit's Content Highlights.

Advance Preparation For Part 1, prepare tape measures for distribution by numbering them with children's tool-kit numbers.

Vocabulary • **tape measure**

Getting Started

Math Message
How could you measure the distance around your neck?

Home Link 4.5 Follow-Up
Ask volunteers to share their measurements. Discuss the use of a 6-inch ruler to measure objects longer than six inches.

Tell "parts-and-total" number stories, and have children solve them any way they can, sharing solution strategies after solving each problem. Summarize each solution by drawing a "parts-and-total" diagram and by writing a number model. *Suggestions:*

• Julie baked a batch of huge chocolate chip cookies. She baked 3 cookies on the first tray and 5 more cookies on the second tray. How many cookies did Julie bake in all? 8 cookies

• Regina was saving her money to buy her favorite CD. She earned $3 for sweeping the floors and another $2 for helping her mom wash the car. How much money did Regina earn for those two jobs? $5

• Henry was playing a game in which you roll a die and collect the number of pennies shown on the die. On his first roll, he collected 4 pennies. On his second roll, he collected 5 more pennies. How many pennies did Henry collect on those two rolls? 9 pennies

• Mark was doing some *Two-Fisted Penny Addition*. When he grabbed the pennies, he had 5 pennies in his right hand and 7 pennies in his left hand. How many pennies did Mark have altogether? 12 pennies

• Alice loves to write stories. During the month of October, Alice wrote 6 stories about her pet cat. During the same month, she wrote 8 stories about her brother Michael. How many stories did Alice write altogether? 14 stories

1 Teaching the Lesson

◆ Math Message Follow-Up

WHOLE-CLASS DISCUSSION

Discuss solutions for the Math Message problem. Possible methods include using a string and then measuring it with a ruler, using a paper ruler, or using a tape measure.

◆ Introducing Tape Measures

WHOLE-CLASS ACTIVITY

Distribute **tape measures** for children to add to their tool kits. Teach (or review) the 2-inch (5-centimeter), no-zap rule (see page 252). Have children look at both sides of the tape measure. Recall the two kinds of units for measuring length (inches and centimeters), which also appear on the 6-inch ruler. Explain that only the inch side will be used in this lesson.

Have children measure a "flat" item to the nearest inch using their tape measures. Possible items to measure include the width of children's desks; a common book, such as math journals; or crayon boxes. Record some results on the board and get general agreement on the measurements.

Measuring Parts of the Body

Record your wrist size below.

1. Wrist
It is about _____ inches.
Answers vary.

Measure these other parts of your body. Work with a partner.

2. Elbow
It is about _____ inches.

3. Neck
It is about _____ inches.

4. Head
It is about _____ inches.

5. Hand span
It is about _____ inches.
Answers vary.

◆ *Math Journal 1,* p. 79

◆ Measuring around and across Things
(*Math Journal 1*, p. 79)

WHOLE-CLASS DISCUSSION

Discuss and demonstrate how tape measures can be used to measure *around* things as well as *across* them. Point out that the item measured need not be "flat."

Ask partners to measure in inches around each other's wrists. Show children how to bring the tape around and read the number nearest the edge of the metal end. Circulate and help. Check techniques. Children record their measurements at the top of journal page 79. Ask whether they think everyone's wrist measurements are about the same. Ask for some measurements and write them on the board.

Talk about the advantages and disadvantages of tape measures compared to rulers, yardsticks, and metersticks.

▷ **Advantages:** Tape measures are easy to store. They bend, so they can be used to measure around things.

▷ **Disadvantages:** The ends of tape measures might be more difficult to line up with the ends of an object. Two people may be needed to stretch and read the tape measure in order to measure longer distances.

Finally, partners measure each other's elbows, necks, heads, and hand spans.

◆ Measuring Parts of the Body
(*Math Journal 1*, p. 80)

PARTNER ACTIVITY

Partners help each other measure, to the nearest inch, the parts of the body listed on journal page 80 and record the results. You might mention that these body parts are the units used in the past (historically) to measure length.

ONGOING ASSESSMENT
Check to see if children

· are using the correct scale (inches).

· are measuring to the nearest inch.

· understand that the end of the measuring tape is used like the 0-mark on a ruler.

Do not expect that children will be proficient with tape measures. Although some children may be doing well, it is likely that most children will need much more practice.

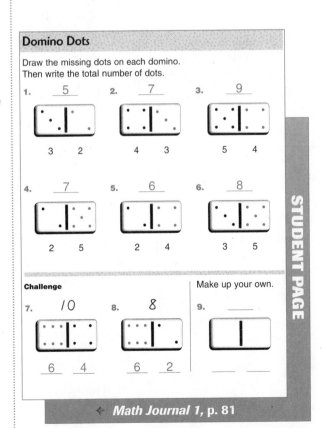

Historical Units of Measure

Measure these parts of your body. Work with a partner.

Historical Unit	Picture	Me
digit (finger width)		about ____ inches Answers vary.
hand		about ____ inches
cubit		about ____ inches
yard		about ____ inches
fathom (arm span)		about ____ inches
pace (heel to toe)		about ____ inches

◆ *Math Journal 1*, p. 80

Domino Dots

Draw the missing dots on each domino. Then write the total number of dots.

1. 5   2. 7   3. 9
    3   2   4   3   5   4

4. 7   5. 6   6. 8
    2   5   2   4   3   5

Challenge   Make up your own.
7. 10   8. 8   9. ____
    6   4   6   2

◆ *Math Journal 1*, p. 81

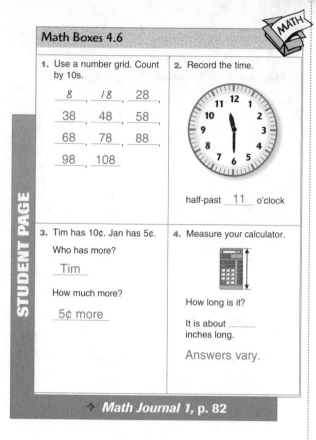

Math Boxes 4.6

1. Use a number grid. Count by 10s.

__8__ , __18__ , __28__ ,

__38__ , __48__ , __58__ ,

__68__ , __78__ , __88__ ,

__98__ , __108__

2. Record the time.

half-past __11__ o'clock

3. Tim has 10¢. Jan has 5¢.

Who has more?

__Tim__

How much more?

__5¢ more__

4. Measure your calculator.

How long is it?

It is about _____ inches long.

Answers vary.

Math Journal 1, p. 82

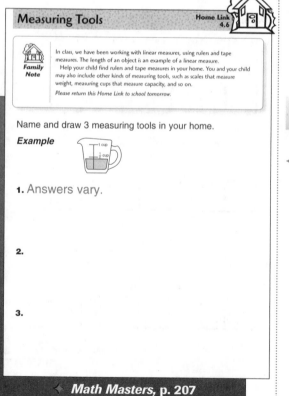

Measuring Tools

Home Link 4.6

Family Note
In class, we have been working with linear measures, using rulers and tape measures. The length of an object is an example of a linear measure.

Help your child find rulers and tape measures in your home. You and your child may also include other kinds of measuring tool, such as scales that measure weight, measuring cups that measure capacity, and so on.

Please return this Home Link to school tomorrow.

Name and draw 3 measuring tools in your home.

Example

1. Answers vary.

2.

3.

Math Masters, p. 207

---

2 Ongoing Learning & Practice

✦ Finding Totals in Domino Dot Patterns
(*Math Journal 1*, p. 81)

INDEPENDENT ACTIVITY

Children draw the given number of dots on half of a domino and then find the total number of dots. Volunteers share strategies for solving the Challenge problems. Remind children of the strategy of thinking, "Which number can I add to 4 to get 10?"

✦ Math Boxes 4.6 (*Math Journal 1*, p. 82)

INDEPENDENT ACTIVITY

Mixed Review This journal page provides opportunities for cumulative review or assessment of concepts and skills.

✦ Home Link 4.6 (*Math Masters*, p. 207)

Home Connection Children name and draw three or more measuring tools they find in their homes, such as rulers, tape measures, scales, and measuring cups.

3 Options for Individualizing

✦ ENRICHMENT Making a Measurement Book

INDEPENDENT ACTIVITY   15–30 min

Children measure a variety of objects. They draw the objects on quarter-sheets of paper and record the lengths of the actual objects on the quarter-sheets.

Depending on children's level of development, this activity could include:

▷ measuring objects longer than their 6-inch rulers.

▷ measuring to the nearest $\frac{1}{2}$ (or even $\frac{1}{4}$) inch.

▷ using their tape measures to measure to the nearest foot-and-inch combination.

4.7 EXPLORATIONS

Exploring Data, Shapes, and Base-10 Blocks

OBJECTIVES To measure children's heights; to make a bar graph; to explore 2-dimensional shapes; and to become familiar with base-10 blocks.

summaries

materials

1 Teaching the Lesson

Exploration A: Children measure their heights and help make a line plot as the measurements are taken. They use the data in the line plot to color a bar graph. (They will measure their heights again in Unit 9.) [Measurement and Reference Frames; Data and Chance]

Exploration B: Children make shapes and designs on a geoboard and record them on dot paper. [Geometry]

Exploration C: Children build structures with base-10 blocks and record how many of each type of block they use. [Numeration]

☐ Home Link 4.6

Exploration A: Per small group:
☐ *Math Journal 1*, p. 83
☐ tape measure
☐ stick-on note

Exploration B: Per small group:
☐ Teaching Master (*Math Masters*, p. 41 or p. 42)
☐ geoboards and rubber bands (colored if possible)

Exploration C: Per small group:
☐ Teaching Master (*Math Masters*, p. 43)
☐ base-10 blocks

See **Advance Preparation**

2 Ongoing Learning & Practice

Children sort dominoes by the total number of dots. [Numeration; Operations and Computation]

Children practice and maintain skills through Math Boxes and Home Link activities.

☐ *Math Journal 1*, p. 84
☐ Home Link Master (*Math Masters*, p. 208)
☐ set of dominoes per partnership
☐ number cards 0–18

See **Advance Preparation**

3 Options for Individualizing

Enrichment Children make drawings of objects that are each about 1 inch long. [Measurement and Reference Frames]

☐ ruler

Additional Information

Advance Preparation For Exploration A, you may want to tape a measuring tape to the door frame or wall to facilitate measuring children's heights. At this time, you may want to use a tape measure showing only inches rather than centimeters. Consider posting and mounting the tape measure in such a way that it can stay up throughout the year.

For Exploration B, make copies of the geoboard dot paper on *Math Masters,* page 41 or page 42 that matches your geoboards.

For Exploration C, gather enough base-10 blocks for each child to have 25 cubes (ones), 12 longs (tens), and 2 flats (hundreds). Make copies of *Math Masters,* page 43 and cut them in half.

For Part 2, each partnership will need a set of dominoes. Use actual dominoes or the cutout dominoes from Lesson 3.14.

Vocabulary • **typical** • **bar graph**

Getting Started

Mental Math and Reflexes

Tell number stories. Have children solve them any way they can, sharing solution strategies after solving them.

You may want to ask children what information in the first two problems is not needed to solve the problems. Encourage children having difficulty to draw pictures or doodles, to count on the number line or number grid, or to use cubes or coins to model the problems.

- Reggie planted bean seeds in 3 milk cartons. He planted 12 bean seeds altogether. After 2 weeks, 10 plants had begun to grow. How many of the seeds did not grow into plants? 2 seeds
- Brian and Nicole went to the zoo. They saw 5 tigers, 8 lions, and 3 giraffes. How many big cats did they see? 13 big cats
- Gerard loved to roll marbles across his bedroom floor. He had 18 marbles when he started. He lost 7 of the marbles. How many marbles did he have left? 11 marbles
- Sarah's favorite kind of cookie is chocolate chip. She and her mom baked one afternoon. Sarah ate 9 cookies. Her brother ate 14 cookies. How many more cookies did her brother eat? 5 more cookies

Math Message

About how many feet tall are most of the first graders in our class?

Home Link 4.6 Follow-Up

Ask volunteers to describe and discuss the use of the measuring tools they found at home.

1 Teaching the Lesson

✦ Math Message Follow-Up

WHOLE-CLASS DISCUSSION

Have children share their estimates. About 4 feet tall You might show on a tape measure or yardstick the lengths that children are suggesting. Mention that another name for the height of most first graders in the class is the **typical** height of a first grader in the class.

Ask for suggestions on how children would check their estimates. Here are a few possibilities:

Measure the heights of all first graders. Then

▷ choose the most frequent height.

▷ choose a number that many heights seem to be close to.

▷ choose one of the heights from the middle if the heights are lined up in order.

▷ measure just one child. (In this case, talk briefly about how one would choose whom to measure.)

You may want to extend the activity by having children estimate how many inches tall a typical first grader is. About 48 inches tall

◆ Exploration A: Measuring Children's Heights and Making a Line Plot (*Math Journal 1,* p. 83)

SMALL-GROUP ACTIVITY 👥👥

Have a volunteer stand straight, with head level, against one of the tape measures you taped to the wall. Demonstrate how to measure the child's height. To help ensure that the measurement is accurate, show children how to use a book held against the wall on top of the head. The measurement is read at the bottom of the book.

You, together with each group, measure the height of each child in the group. When the group agrees on the height of a child, the child records his or her height in the first section of the journal page and on a stick-on note.

Draw a horizontal line on the board. Number the line from 38 to 52 and label it "Inches Tall." Make a line plot by having children attach their stick-on notes above their heights.

NOTE: Children will measure their heights again in Unit 9.

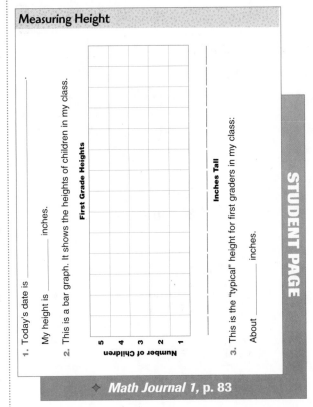

Measuring Height

1. Today's date is _____ .

   My height is _____ inches.

2. This is a bar graph. It shows the heights of children in my class.

   First Grade Heights

   Number of Children

   Inches Tall

3. This is the "typical" height for first graders in my class:

   About _____ inches.

◆ *Math Journal 1,* p. 83

◆ Exploration B: Exploring Shapes on the Geoboard (*Math Masters,* p. 41 or 42)

SMALL-GROUP ACTIVITY 👥👥

Children make different shapes and designs on the geoboard using (colored) rubber bands. Then they copy their favorite designs onto geoboard dot paper.

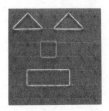

▼7-by-7 geoboard paper is available on *Math Masters,* page 42.

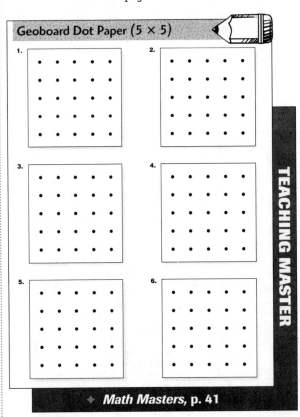

Geoboard Dot Paper (5 × 5)

1.   2.

3.   4.

5.   6.

◆ *Math Masters,* p. 41

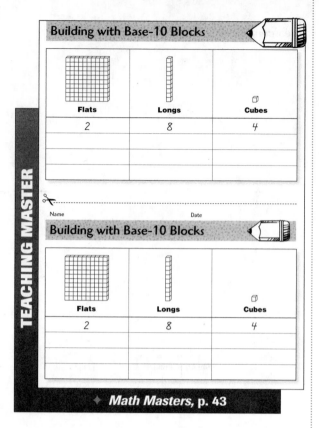

Building with Base-10 Blocks

Flats	Longs	Cubes
2	8	4

Name _____ Date _____

Building with Base-10 Blocks

Flats	Longs	Cubes
2	8	4

◆ *Math Masters, p. 43*

NOTE: The most frequent value in a set of data is called the *mode*. The mode is just one way to describe a set of data.

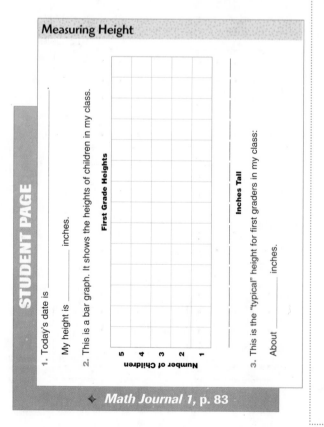

Measuring Height

1. Today's date is _____

My height is _____ inches.

2. This is a bar graph. It shows the heights of children in my class.

First Grade Heights

Number of Children — 1, 2, 3, 4, 5

Inches Tall

3. This is the "typical" height for first graders in my class:

About _____ inches.

◆ *Math Journal 1, p. 83*

◆ Exploration C: Building Structures with Base-10 Blocks (*Math Masters,* p. 43)

SMALL-GROUP ACTIVITY

Children build structures with base-10 blocks. They use flats, longs, and cubes to become familiar with the names, shapes, sizes, and handling of these manipulatives.

Children use the half-page sheet to record how many flats, longs, and cubes they use. (See Advance Preparation.)

◆ Making a Bar Graph and Finding a "Typical" Height (*Math Journal 1,* p. 83)

WHOLE-CLASS ACTIVITY

After all children have been measured, bring the class together to make a **bar graph** using the class line plot of heights.

Review the title of the graph and the labels of the axes. Make sure that children understand their importance.

NOTE: The horizontal axis is a reference line for listing the different heights. The vertical axis is a reference line for the number of children who are a certain height.

Point out that "inches" is the unit that goes with all of the numbers on the bottom axis. Have children fill in the numbers of inches from the line plot.

Together with children, count the number of stick-on notes for each height, and then have children color that number of squares above each height on the graph.

Discuss how the tallest bar on the graph shows a "typical" height for the class. Children record that height in their journals at this time.

Adjusting the Activity You may want to extend this activity by using another way to find a typical height. First list the heights in order and then find the height in the middle of the list. (This description of a data set is called the *median.*)

Ongoing Learning & Practice

◆ Sorting Dominoes by the Total Number of Dots

PARTNER ACTIVITY

Use the following activity to investigate equivalence (many ways of naming the same number):

Partners sort a set of dominoes by the total number of dots (0 to 18) on each domino. Number cards set up as shown in the margin make good labels for grouping the dominoes.

 Adjusting the Activity To help children who are having difficulty, limit the domino set to a double-6 set or to the dominoes found on Activity Sheets 3 and 4 at the back of their journals.

To extend the activity, use two sets of dominoes. After children have finished sorting by total number of dots, have them separate the dominoes back into two sets.

◆ Math Boxes 4.7 (*Math Journal 1,* p. 84)

INDEPENDENT ACTIVITY

Mixed Review This journal page provides opportunities for cumulative review or assessment of concepts and skills.

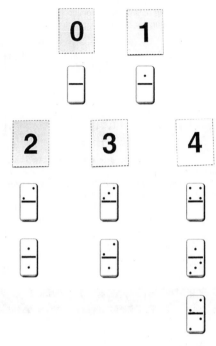

Dominoes sorted by the total number of dots on each domino

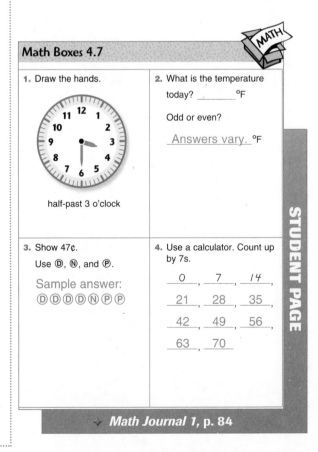

Math Journal 1, p. 84

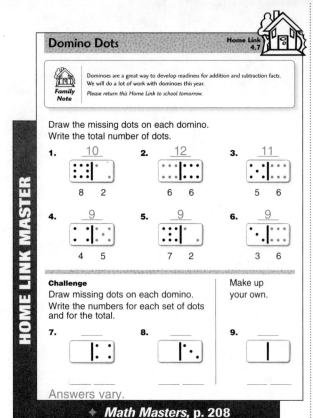

Domino Dots

Home Link
4.7

Family Note Dominoes are a great way to develop readiness for addition and subtraction facts. We will do a lot of work with dominoes this year.
Please return this Home Link to school tomorrow.

Draw the missing dots on each domino.
Write the total number of dots.

1. __10__   2. __12__   3. __11__

   8   2   6   6   5   6

4. __9__   5. __9__   6. __9__

   4   5   7   2   3   6

Challenge

Draw missing dots on each domino.
Write the numbers for each set of dots
and for the total.

Make up
your own.

7. _____   8. _____   9. _____

Answers vary.

◆ *Math Masters*, p. 208

HOME LINK MASTER

◆ **Home Link 4.7** (*Math Masters*, p. 208)

Home Connection Children draw domino dot patterns and record the total number of dots on dominoes.

3 Options for Individualizing

◆ **ENRICHMENT** **Making an Inch Collection**

INDEPENDENT ACTIVITY   **15–30 min**

Children find objects that each measure about an inch in length. They make a record of what they found by drawing the objects on a sheet of paper labeled "About 1 Inch."

Adjusting the Activity To extend the activity, children can make pages for several different lengths; for example, about 3 inches, about 6 inches, and about 1 foot. These pages can be made into a book or a bulletin-board display.

4.8

Telling Time on the Quarter-Hour

OBJECTIVES To review telling time on the hour and half-hour; and to introduce telling time on the quarter-hour.

summaries	materials
1 **Teaching the Lesson**	
Children review the movements of hour and minute hands and telling time on the hour and half-hour. They learn to tell time on the quarter-hour. [Measurement and Reference Frames]	□ *Math Journal 1*, p. 85 □ Home Link 4.7 □ demonstration clock □ tool-kit clock
2 **Ongoing Learning & Practice**	
Children continue to build readiness for the basic addition facts by continuing *Two-Fisted Penny Addition* and by playing *Domino Top-It*. [Numeration; Operations and Computation] Children practice and maintain skills through Math Boxes and Home Link activities.	□ *Math Journal 1*, pp. 70, 72, and 86 □ Home Link Master (*Math Masters*, p. 209) □ pennies □ dominoes
3 **Options for Individualizing**	
Extra Practice Children practice telling time. [Measurement and Reference Frames] **Extra Practice** Children order clocks according to the time displayed. [Measurement and Reference Frames]	□ Teaching Master (*Math Masters*, p. 14) □ tool-kit clock □ 3" by 5" index cards, cut in half (optional) □ clock-face stamp (optional) ***See* Advance Preparation**

Additional Information

Advance Preparation For the first optional activity in Part 3, draw hour and minute hands on *Math Masters*, page 14 to provide children with extra practice. Remember to include the phrases *half-past, quarter-to,* and *quarter-past* when necessary.

Vocabulary • **half-past (the hour)** • **quarter-after, quarter-past (the hour)** • **quarter-before, quarter-to (the hour)**

Getting Started

Mental Math and Reflexes

Do stop-and-start counting by 10s, by 5s, and then by 1s.

Math Message

Draw a picture of a round pizza. Divide the pizza into 2 pieces that are the same size. Then divide the pizza into 4 pieces that are the same size.

Home Link 4.7 Follow-Up

Briefly review children's strategies for solving the domino problems.

1 Teaching the Lesson

◆ Math Message Follow-Up

WHOLE-CLASS DISCUSSION

Have several children share how they divided the pizza they drew into four equal pieces. Ask if anyone knows what one of those pieces is called. Quarter or fourth

◆ Reviewing Hour and Half-Hour Times

WHOLE-CLASS ACTIVITY

Use the demonstration clock to show several times on the hour. Ask children to name each time. Repeat the procedure for several times on the half-hour.

Point out that for exact-hour times it is easy to tell the time with just the hour hand. For the times halfway between hours (the **half-pasts**) and for the other "between" times, we can make a reasonable estimate with just the hour hand, but the minute hand helps us to be more exact.

◆ Telling Time to the Quarter-Hour

WHOLE-CLASS ACTIVITY

▷ Show 10 o'clock on the demonstration clock. Move the minute hand from 12 to 3. *What happened to the hour hand?* It moved part of the way to 11. *About what time does the clock show?* The time is between 10 o'clock and 11 o'clock.

▷ Establish that it takes one-quarter of an hour for the minute hand to move from 12 to 3. Remind children of dividing the pizza into four equal parts. You might suggest that they think of the clock face being divided into four equal parts; each part is a quarter of an hour. We say that the time shown is "about **quarter-after** 10 o'clock," or "about **quarter-past** 10 o'clock."

▷ Move the minute hand to 6. *What happened to the hour hand?* It moved closer to 11; it is about halfway between 10 o'clock and 11 o'clock. Ask a volunteer to tell what time the clock shows now. About half-past 10

▷ Now move the minute hand to 9. *What happened to the hour hand?* It moved still closer to 11. *About what time does the clock show now?* The time is still between 10 o'clock and 11 o'clock, but closer to 11 than to 10.

▷ Move the minute hand from 9 to 12—and then back to 9. Establish that it takes one-quarter of an hour for the minute hand to move from 9 to 12. Ask children if they can guess how we would say the time. About a **quarter-before** 11 o'clock, or about a **quarter-to** 11 o'clock.

Adjusting the Activity You may want to extend the activity by asking the class how many minutes are in $\frac{1}{2}$ hour and in $\frac{1}{4}$ hour. 30 minutes; 15 minutes

---

◆ Practice Telling Time on the Quarter-Hour and Half-Hour (*Math Journal 1,* p. 85)

WHOLE-CLASS ACTIVITY

1. Show a variety of times on the demonstration clock while children say the times: 4 o'clock, quarter-past 4, half-past 4, quarter-to 5, and so on.

2. Name a variety of hour, half-hour, and quarter-hour times while children show them on their tool-kit clocks. Use words to write the times on the board so that children recognize them.

3. Have children complete the journal page.

Adjusting the Activity Label your classroom clock with words on strips of paper. A label next to the three would read "quarter-past" or "quarter-after"; under the six, "half-past"; and next to the nine, "quarter-to" or "quarter-before."

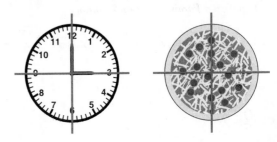

Children can think of a quarter of an hour as a quarter piece of pizza.

NOTE: In this unit, time is still being named and written using words. Digital notation and language will be introduced in Unit 6.

Remember to use *about* when stating the time, and keep reminding children that telling time is always an estimate.

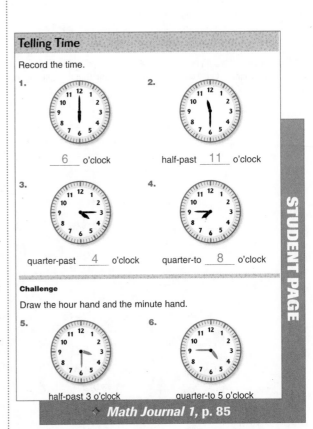

Telling Time

Record the time.

1. 6 o'clock

2. half-past 11 o'clock

3. quarter-past 4 o'clock

4. quarter-to 8 o'clock

Challenge

Draw the hour hand and the minute hand.

5. half-past 3 o'clock

6. quarter-to 5 o'clock

Math Journal 1, p. 85

STUDENT PAGE

Two-Fisted Penny Addition Summary

5		7		8		9		10	
Left	Right	Left	Right	Left	Right	Left	Right	Left	Right
2	3								
3	2								
1	4								
4	1								
0	5								
5	0								

6	
Left	Right

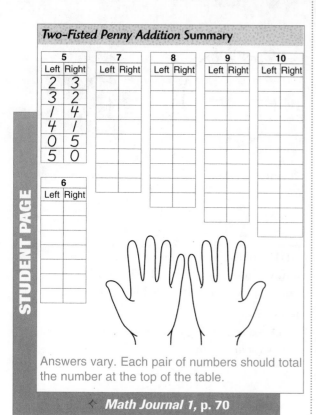

Answers vary. Each pair of numbers should total the number at the top of the table.

Math Journal 1, p. 70

Two-Fisted Penny Addition Summary (cont.)

16		17		18		19		20	
Left	Right	Left	Right	Left	Right	Left	Right	Left	Right

Answers vary.
Each pair of numbers should total the number at the top of the table.

Math Journal 1, p. 72

ONGOING ASSESSMENT

Children should know the difference between the minute hand and the hour hand and have some proficiency with telling time on the half-hour. Expect that many children will still struggle with telling time on the quarter-hour. (Telling time will be practiced throughout the year.)

2 Ongoing Learning & Practice

◆ Playing *Domino Top-It*

PARTNER ACTIVITY

Children practice addition skills by playing *Domino Top-It*. For detailed instructions, see Lesson 3.14.

◆ *Two-Fisted Penny Addition* Using 9 Pennies and 17 Pennies (*Math Journal 1,* pp. 70 and 72)

PARTNER ACTIVITY

Partners record all of the splits for 9 and 17 on journal pages 70 and 72. They pool their pennies to find splits for more than 17 pennies.

◆ **Math Boxes 4.8** (*Math Journal 1,* p. 86)

INDEPENDENT ACTIVITY 👤

Mixed Review This journal page provides opportunities for cumulative review or assessment of concepts and skills.

◆ **Home Link 4.8** (*Math Masters,* p. 209)

Home Connection Children record the times shown on clock faces. This Home Link provides practice in telling time on the quarter-hour.

3 Options for Individualizing

◆ **EXTRA PRACTICE** Telling Time
(*Math Masters,* p. 14)

INDEPENDENT ACTIVITY 👤　　　15–30 min

Children complete the clock faces and write the times on the master introduced in Lesson 2.6.

◆ **EXTRA PRACTICE** Ordering Clocks by the Time They Display

SMALL-GROUP ACTIVITY 👥👥　　15–30 min

Collect the tool-kit clocks from a small group of children and set the clocks to different times. Begin with hours and half-hours. When children are ready, add quarter-hour times. Distribute one clock to each child. Have children work together to order the clocks according to time.

Variation

Use 3" by 5" index cards cut in half, as described in Lesson 3.7.

Math Boxes 4.8

1. Write some odd numbers in this box.

   Sample answers: 11, 17, 3, 9, 21

2. Fill in the rule and the missing numbers.

   Rule
   Count up by 10s

   2　12　22　32　42

3. For each domino:
   Draw the missing dots.
   Find the total number of dots.

   5 + 4 = __9__

   6 + 3 = __9__

4. Measure to the nearest inch.

   It is about __3__ inches long.

   It is about __2__ inches long.

✦ *Math Journal 1,* p. 86

STUDENT PAGE

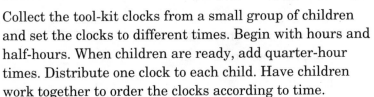

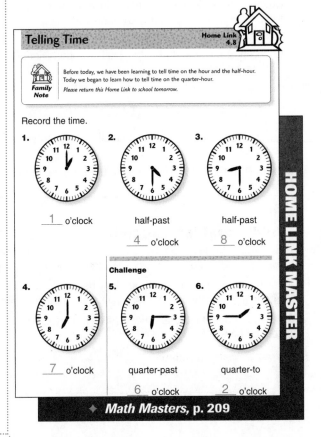

Telling Time　　　　Home Link 4.8

Family Note Before today, we have been learning to tell time on the hour and the half-hour. Today we began to learn how to tell time on the quarter-hour.
Please return this Home Link to school tomorrow.

Record the time.

1.　__1__ o'clock

2.　half-past __4__ o'clock

3.　half-past __8__ o'clock

Challenge

4.　__7__ o'clock

5.　quarter-past __6__ o'clock

6.　quarter-to __2__ o'clock

✦ *Math Masters,* p. 209

HOME LINK MASTER

4.9 Timelines

OBJECTIVE To investigate timelines.

summaries	materials

1 Teaching the Lesson

Children are introduced to timelines by making a 24-hour timeline. They draw pictures for a timeline of the first half of the school year. [Measurement and Reference Frames]

- ☐ *Math Journal 1*, p. 87
- ☐ Home Link 4.8
- ☐ Teaching Master transparency (*Math Masters*, p. 44; optional)
- ☐ slate
- ☐ tool-kit clock
- ☐ demonstration clock
- ☐ 24-hour timeline

***See* Advance Preparation**

2 Ongoing Learning & Practice

Children draw clock hands to practice telling time. They find totals using dominoes and parts-and-total diagrams.
[Measurement and Reference Frames; Operations and Computation]

Children practice and maintain skills through Math Boxes and Home Link activities.

- ☐ *Math Journal 1*, pp. 88 and 89
- ☐ Teaching Master (*Math Masters*, p. 14)
- ☐ Home Link Master (*Math Masters*, p. 210)

***See* Advance Preparation**

3 Options for Individualizing

Enrichment Children make a timeline for a storybook.
[Measurement and Reference Frames]

Extra Practice Children estimate the duration of a minute.
[Measurement and Reference Frames]

- ☐ clock to time one minute

***See* Advance Preparation**

Additional Information

Advance Preparation For Part 1, draw a 24-hour timeline on the board, on two Class Data Pad sheets taped together, or on a transparency made from *Math Masters*, page 44. (The board is preferred since it probably provides the most space.)

For Part 2, fill in times, such as "half-past 7 o'clock," on *Math Masters*, page 14 before making copies. Children will draw clock hands to show the times. Also fill in the appropriate first two digits of the years for the timeline on Home Link 4.9.

For the optional Extra Practice activity in Part 3, obtain a one-minute timer (a stopwatch, kitchen timer, or watch or clock with a second hand).

Vocabulary • **timeline**

Getting Started

Mental Math and Reflexes

Pose problems like the following and have children write their answers on their slates. Encourage children having difficulty to draw pictures or doodles, count on the number line or number grid, or use pennies or counters to help them solve the number stories.

- Janine picked 6 flowers from the garden behind her house and 3 more flowers from the flower bed in front of the house. She had to put them in two vases because they did not fit in one vase. How many flowers did Janine have altogether? 9 flowers
- Sam had 7 video games for the machine hooked up to his TV. One day his brother and a friend played with the games and broke 2 of them. How many working video games did Sam have left? 5 working games
- Ellie collects different kinds of elephants. She has 8 stuffed-animal elephants, 3 elephant statues, and 2 elephant key chains. How many more stuffed elephants than elephant statues does she have? 5 more stuffed elephants
- Frank has 10 baseball cards today. He got 4 cards for his birthday yesterday. How many baseball cards did Frank have before his birthday? 6 baseball cards

Math Message

Show quarter-past 6 on your tool-kit clock.

Home Link 4.8 Follow-Up

Briefly go over the times shown on the clocks. Ask children how the placement of the hour hand helped them figure out the time.

1 Teaching the Lesson

◆ Math Message Follow-Up

WHOLE-CLASS ACTIVITY

Invite children to describe the placement of the hands on their clocks.

Show times on the quarter-hour on the demonstration clock and have children name the time, or name a time on the quarter-hour and have children display it on their clocks.

◆ Introducing Timelines (*Math Masters*, p. 44)

WHOLE-CLASS ACTIVITY

Explain how people use **timelines** to help them keep track of when important events happen. Tell children that a timeline is like a number line on which the numbers name years, hours, or other times.

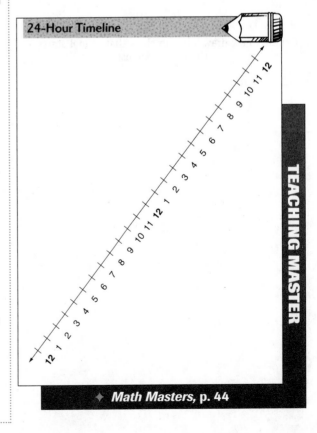

24-Hour Timeline

◆ *Math Masters*, p. 44

TEACHING MASTER

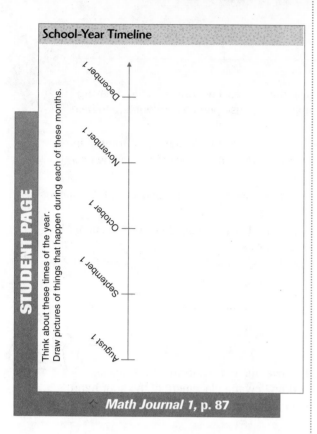

School-Year Timeline

Think about these times of the year.
Draw pictures of things that happen during each of these months.

August 1
September 1
October 1
November 1
December 1

Math Journal 1, p. 87

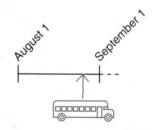

August 1
September 1

Children may draw a bus to show that school starts at
the end of August.

Show the 24-hour timeline. Ask the class how many hours
are in a day. Have children talk about events that usually
occur at various times during the day (get up, school
begins, and so on). Write the names of the events or draw
pictures of them on the timeline. Have children suggest a
picture to represent each activity on the timeline.

You may want to talk informally about the number of
hours in a day and review A.M. and P.M. (introduced in
Lesson 2.6), the number of days in a week, and the
number of days in a month.

 Adjusting the Activity You may want to begin with a
timeline of the activities during a typical school day
and then extend the timeline to before- and after-
school activities.

◆ Making a Timeline (*Math Journal 1,* p. 87)

WHOLE-CLASS ACTIVITY

Help children recall important school-related events that
have taken place since the beginning of the school year.

Ask children if they can think of a reason for the arrow at
the right side of the timeline. It means that the timeline
continues past December 1.

Children draw a picture on the journal page to represent
an event for each month. Suggest that they use the
available space on the page and draw arrows to a point on
the timeline to show whether the event happens at the
beginning, middle, or end of the month.

 ONGOING ASSESSMENT
This is the first time children have worked with
timelines. Children should understand that the
line represents a progression through time.
Expect that children may need guidance in
selecting drawings to portray reasonable activities
for each month noted on the timeline.

Ongoing Learning & Practice

◆ Showing Times on the Quarter-Hour
(*Math Masters*, p. 14)

INDEPENDENT ACTIVITY

Children draw hour and minute hands on clock faces to show times. (See Advance Preparation.)

◆ Domino Parts and Totals
(*Math Journal 1*, p. 88)

INDEPENDENT ACTIVITY

Children use dominoes and parts-and-total diagrams to find totals. Some children may find it helpful to draw a domino-dot pattern above each number.

For the Challenge problems, remind children of the thinking strategy "What number can I add to the given part to get the total?"

◆ Math Boxes 4.9 (*Math Journal 1*, p. 89)

INDEPENDENT ACTIVITY

Mixed Review This journal page provides opportunities for cumulative review or assessment of concepts and skills.

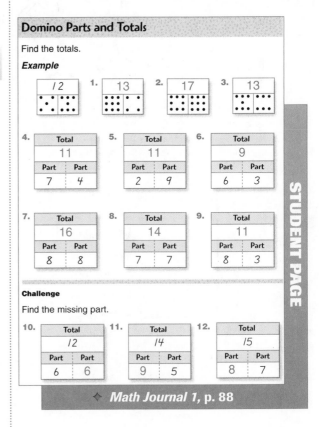

✦ *Math Journal 1*, p. 88

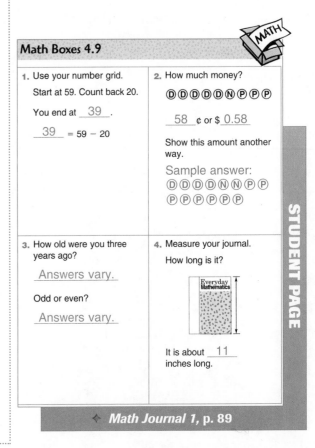

✦ *Math Journal 1*, p. 89

My Timeline

Home Link 4.9

Family Note

Talk about important events that have happened in your family since your child was born. Identify one main event for each year and help your child decide what to draw to represent that event. Use events like the birth of a brother or sister, moving to a new home, and so on.

If you prefer, you can help your child select representative pictures from magazines and tape or glue them in order on this page.

Please return this Home Link to school tomorrow or the day after tomorrow.

Write the years below. Then on the back of this page, draw pictures of important things that happened in your family each year since you were born.

— My 8th birthday
— My 7th birthday
— My 6th birthday
— My 5th birthday
— My 4th birthday
— My 3rd birthday
— My 2nd birthday
— My 1st birthday
— I was born.

◆ *Math Masters, p. 210*

HOME LINK MASTER

◆ Home Link 4.9 (*Math Masters*, p. 210)

Home Connection Children make a timeline of family events since they were born. Consider giving children two days to complete this Home Link.

3 Options for Individualizing

◆ ENRICHMENT Making a Storybook Timeline

INDEPENDENT ACTIVITY   30+ min

Children choose a favorite picture book or fairy tale and make a timeline of the main events in that story. The timeline could represent a number of years, days, or hours, depending on the story.

Portfolio Ideas

◆ EXTRA PRACTICE How Long Is a Minute?

SMALL-GROUP ACTIVITY   15–30 min

This activity appears in Lesson 2.5. You might revisit it now by trying one or more of the following variations:

▷ Stand on one foot for a minute.

▷ See how many times you can hop in a minute.

▷ Tell which seemed longest—sitting, standing, or hopping.

PLANNING AHEAD

Beginning in Lesson 4.10, children should have enough base-10 blocks to work with. Each child will need 25 cubes and 12 longs. If your classroom supply is too small, children can use the base-10 pieces on Activity Sheets 5 and 6 or a combination of blocks and pieces. You or children should cut out the pieces before Lesson 4.10. The pieces can be stored in resealable plastic bags with tool-kit ID numbers on them. As an option, get Mitsumasa Anno's *Anno's Counting House* (Philomel Books, 1982) to use while teaching Lesson 4.11.

4.10

Number Scrolls

OBJECTIVES To introduce scrolls; and to begin making a number scroll for numbers to 100 and beyond.

summaries	materials

1 Teaching the Lesson

Children fill in a 100-number grid, continuing with additional grids for numbers beyond 100, and then make a number scroll. [Numeration; Patterns, Functions, and Algebra]

☐ Home Link 4.9
☐ Teaching Masters (*Math Masters,* pp. 45–46; p. 47 optional)
☐ calculator (optional)
☐ stick or cardboard tube
☐ scissors
☐ tape or glue
***See* Advance Preparation**

2 Ongoing Learning & Practice

Children match base-10 cubes and longs to investigate base-10 block relationships. [Numeration]

Children play *Time Match* to practice telling time. [Measurement and Reference Frames]

Children practice and maintain skills through Math Boxes and Home Link activities.

☐ *Math Journal 1,* p. 90 and Activity Sheets 5 and 6 (optional)
☐ Teaching Masters (*Math Masters,* pp. 39 and 48)
☐ Home Link Master (*Math Masters,* p. 211)
☐ base-10 blocks or pieces
☐ deck of 24 cards from Lesson 4.4
***See* Advance Preparation**

3 Options for Individualizing

Reteaching The class makes a Class Number Grid Poster with numbered stick-on notes. [Numeration; Patterns, Functions, and Algebra]

Extra Practice Children continue filling in number grids and adding them to their number scrolls. [Numeration; Patterns, Functions, and Algebra]

☐ stick-on notes
***See* Advance Preparation**

Additional Information

Advance Preparation For Part 1, obtain a stick (such as a wooden dowel) or a cardboard tube (such as a paper-towel roll) for each child. You may also want to obtain or note examples of scrolls like the following: a pull-down screen, shade, or wall map; a videotape movie with credits that scroll; Chinese or other art scrolls; and so on.

For Part 2, each child will need 25 cubes and 12 longs. Instead of actual base-10 *blocks,* you may want to use the base-10 *pieces* provided on Activity Sheets 5 and 6 at the back of their journals. (See Planning Ahead in Lesson 4.9.) You may want to use *Math Masters,* page 48 as a poster or make one of your own.

Also, add the 12 *Time Match* cards on *Math Masters,* page 39 to each deck of 24 cards used in Lesson 4.4.

For the optional Reteaching activity in Part 3, number 2" by 1" stick-on notes from 1 to 100.

Vocabulary • **scroll** • **long** • **cube** • **base-10 blocks**

Getting Started

Mental Math and Reflexes

Write or show coin combinations on the overhead projector. Children record totals on their slates. If need be, children can use their tool-kit coins to help them figure out the totals.

Extend the activity by asking how much two dimes and four nickels are worth altogether. (Do not show the coin combinations. Keep the exercise oral.) 40 cents

Math Message

What is the largest 3-digit number you know?

Home Link 4.9 Follow-Up

Talk briefly about the timelines made at home. Invite volunteers to explain how they are different from the ones made in class.

---

1 Teaching the Lesson

◆ Math Message Follow-Up

WHOLE-CLASS ACTIVITY

Write some of the children's numbers on the board. Tell children that, during the year, they will learn even larger numbers than the ones they know now. Extend the activity by asking a volunteer to circle the largest and smallest numbers on the board.

◆ Introducing Scrolls

WHOLE-CLASS DISCUSSION

Explain that a **scroll** is a roll of paper or other material, usually with writing or pictures on it. Some examples of scrolls:

▷ a list of names

▷ a pull-down screen

▷ a shade

▷ a wall map

▷ TV or movie credits moving vertically up the screen

▷ the Torah and the Koran (scriptures of the Jewish and Islamic religions, respectively)

▷ some artworks

Show children any samples of scrolls you have gathered. If you have a VCR and a movie videotape in the classroom, you may want to run the credits.

NOTE: Many teachers have found making scrolls to be a fruitful exercise and have continued it over several weeks or longer, depending on children's interest. Scrolls do not fit with the general theme of this unit, but they do need to be started early in the year.

A type of scroll

◆ Filling in a 100-Number Grid
(*Math Masters*, pp. 45 and 46)

PARTNER ACTIVITY

Children begin filling in the 100-number grid on *Math Masters,* page 45. As children discover patterns and shortcuts, let them share these discoveries with the class. If they get stuck deciding which number to write next, encourage them to work with their partners to figure out what to do by using patterns already on the grid.

 Adjusting the Activity Enter a few selected numbers on the number-grid page before children begin working. They can then self-check frequently as they work through the page. If they reach a number that does not agree with what follows next, they can then trace the numbers back to the error.

Remind children that they can also use their calculators by keying in (ON/C) [the number they know] (+) (1) (=) (=) and so on.

Check the rows and completed grids before children go on to a new grid page. Use the Continuing Scroll Page (*Math Masters,* page 46) for additional grids for writing numbers beyond 100. All children should eventually complete several pages.

 ONGOING ASSESSMENT
Expect that children will make mistakes in completing their scroll pages. As they continue with the scrolls, they should begin to use the grid patterns as a means of self-checking and make only minor mistakes, such as accidentally skipping a space or skipping a number. (If the whole class is having difficulty, consider taking a break and doing the Part 3 activity "Constructing a Class Number Grid.")

Some teachers suggest that after most children have written numbers to 200 or 300 (less for some children), they put the scrolls away for a while. When brought out later, the scrolls are like a new activity. For the remainder of the year, allow children to work on their scrolls during independent class time. A Math Message might be: "Do a row (or more) on your number scrolls." Some children enjoy this activity and go beyond 1,000.

Beginning Scroll Page

0	−1	−2	−3	−4	−5	−6	−7	−8	−9
10	9	8	7	6	5	4	3	2	1
20	19	18	17	16	15	14	13	12	11
30	29	28	27	26	25	24	23	22	21
40	39	38	37	36	35	34	33	32	31
50	49	48	47	46	45	44	43	42	41
60	59	58	57	56	55	54	53	52	51
70	69	68	67	66	65	64	63	62	61
80	79	78	77	76	75	74	73	72	71
90	89	88	87	86	85	84	83	82	81
100	99	98	97	96	95	94	93	92	91

TEACHING MASTER

◆ *Math Masters, p. 45*

NOTE: Encourage the use of pencils and frequent checking (with partners or you) to enable quick correction of errors and to avoid disappointment, excess work, and spoiled pages. Supply extra copies of the page in case children need to try again.

Continuing Scroll Page

110	109	108	107	106	105	104	103	102	101
120	119	118	117	116	115	114	113	112	111
130	129	128	127	126	125	124	123	122	121
140	139	138	137	136	135	134	133	132	131
150	149	148	147	146	145	144	143	142	141
160	159	158	157	156	155	154	153	152	151
170	169	168	167	166	165	164	163	162	161
180	179	178	177	176	175	174	173	172	171
190	189	188	187	186	185	184	183	182	181
200	199	198	197	196	195	194	193	192	191
210	209	208	207	206	205	204	203	202	201

Paste/tape here.

TEACHING MASTER

◆ *Math Masters, p. 46*

	303	304	305	306				
	313				317			
	323				327			
	333				337			
	343				347			
	353	354	355	356				
	363				367			
	373					378		
	383						389	
	393							400

Robert filled in numbers in the grid boxes to look like the first letter of his name.

◆ Constructing a Number Scroll
(*Math Masters,* pp. 45 and 46)

WHOLE-CLASS ACTIVITY

After all children complete (and you check) both the Beginning Scroll Page and the first Continuing Scroll Page, stop their number writing and teach them how to glue or tape their grids together. (This activity is repeated as children complete each new continuing scroll page.)

Show the class how to roll the connected sheets into a scroll. The scrolls may be rolled onto a stick (such as a wooden dowel) or onto a cardboard tube (such as a paper-towel roll).

Optional: Have children keep their pages together as a book rather than as a scroll.

Adjusting the Activity For children who are easily completing the grid, suggest that they fill in the next page of the scroll by filling in numbers in the grid boxes to look like the first letter of their name. See the margin for an example.

In order to help children decide which numbers to fill in, consider having them shade the area they want to complete, using a light-color pencil (like yellow or light blue), before they begin.

Children who are able may enjoy the challenge of filling in a grid by starting at 0 and counting back with negative numbers. *Math Masters,* page 47 is a grid with negative numbers in the last row, and 0 is the final number.

ONGOING ASSESSMENT
Shade a particular area of the grid before children begin. When you check children's completed pages, you will be able to tell how well they are able to use the patterns on the number grid based on how well they did filling in the numbers in the unshaded area.

Ongoing Learning & Practice

✦ Exploring Base-10 Blocks
(*Math Masters*, p. 48)

WHOLE-CLASS ACTIVITY

Each child needs 25 cubes and 12 longs for this activity. Show children a **long** and a **cube** so that they know the **base-10 blocks** by name, but do not yet mention how they are related. *Suggested activities:*

▷ Take 14 cubes and a long. Put as many of the cubes as you can in a row next to the long. How many cubes line up next to the long? 10 How many cubes are left over? 4

▷ Take 25 cubes and 5 longs. Put as many of the 25 cubes as you can in rows next to the longs. How many longs do you need? 2 How many cubes are matched to longs? 20 How many cubes are left over? 5 Count the total number of cubes beginning by 10s when they are matched with longs. 10, 20, 21, 22, 23, 24, 25

▷ Continue with other numbers of cubes. Try 19, 16, and 23.

✦ Playing *Time Match* with Quarter-Hours

PARTNER ACTIVITY

This activity is an extension of the game introduced in Lesson 4.4. Each partnership or small group needs to add the 12 cards on *Math Masters*, page 39 to the deck of 24 cards used in Lesson 4.4. The game is played with the same rules.

✦ Math Boxes 4.10 (*Math Journal 1*, p. 90)

INDEPENDENT ACTIVITY

Mixed Review This journal page provides opportunities for cumulative review or assessment of concepts and skills.

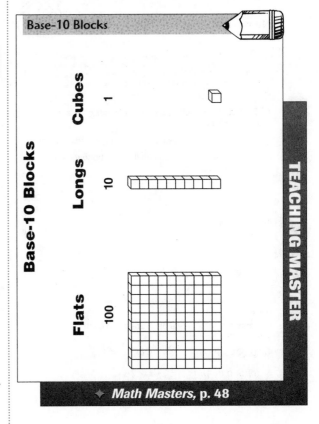

✦ Math Masters, p. 48

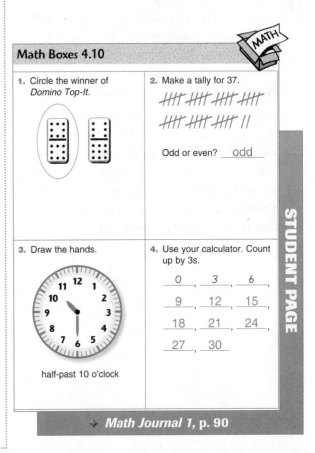

✦ Math Journal 1, p. 90

Number Grids

Family Note
Ordering numbers in a grid is important in identifying number patterns and developing number power. You and your child may want to talk about any patterns in the section of a number grid shown below.
Please return this Home Link to school tomorrow.

1. Tell your family how you filled in number grids and made scrolls.

2. Ask if your family knows about any other kinds of scrolls.

3. Show someone how you can fill in the bottom 3 rows of this number grid.

									100
101	102	103	104	105	106	107	108	109	110
111	112	113	114	115	116	117	118	119	120
121	122	123	124	125	126	127	128	129	130

Review

How much money? Write each answer in cents and dollars-and-cents.

4. Ⓓ Ⓝ Ⓝ Ⓟ Ⓟ Ⓟ __23__ ¢ or $ _0.23_

5. Ⓓ Ⓓ Ⓓ Ⓝ Ⓝ Ⓟ __41__ ¢ or $ _0.41_

◆ *Math Masters*, p. 211

HOME LINK MASTER

Adjusting the Activity To extend the activity, draw a 10-by-10 grid on chart paper with cells large enough to hold the stick-on notes. Then, during the day, individual children can come up and place all of their notes using patterns on the grid.

Have struggling students put up a few stick-on notes early in the process, but have them save more difficult numbers for the end. Some children may need to count by 1s all the way up. Encourage them to use patterns, but accept their counting strategy if necessary.

◆ Home Link 4.10 (*Math Masters*, p. 211)

Home Connection Children tell their families about number grids and number scrolls. They ask family members if they know of other kinds of scrolls. Children fill in a number grid from 100 to 130.

3 Options for Individualizing

◆ RETEACHING Constructing a Class Number Grid

WHOLE-CLASS ACTIVITY 15–30 min

Number 2" by 1" stick-on notes from 1 to 100. While children are out of the room, hide the notes around the classroom. When they return, have them find all of the stick-on notes they can. Consider establishing a rule about how many notes any one child may keep. In a class of 25, each child might keep as many as 6. After that, children can help their classmates find any remaining notes.

When all 100 stick-on notes have been found, each child orders his or her own notes. Have children with notes 1–10 bring those numbers to the front of the room to begin making a number grid. Then have children with numbers 11–20 come up, followed by 21–30, 31–40, and so on. By following your directions, children will complete a number grid.

◆ EXTRA PRACTICE Continuing Work on Number Scrolls

INDEPENDENT ACTIVITY 15–30 min

Have children complete the number-scroll page in a pattern, for example, along the diagonals first, in a checkerboard, or by counts of 3.

Discuss any patterns that children find in the numbers when they have completed the page in one of these ways.

4.11 Introducing Fact Power

OBJECTIVES To introduce addition facts and fact power; and to find addition-fact sums.

summaries	materials
1 Teaching the Lesson	
Children find addition-fact sums using pictures of dominoes. They discuss their strategies. [Operations and Computation]	☐ *Math Journal 1*, p. 91 ☐ Home Link 4.10 ☐ calculator; half-sheets of paper; slate ☐ *Anno's Counting House* by Mitsumasa Anno (optional)
2 Ongoing Learning & Practice	
Children assemble paper thermometers and use them to practice reading and setting Fahrenheit temperatures. [Measurement and Reference Frames] Children practice and maintain skills through Math Boxes and Home Link activities.	☐ *Math Journal 1*, p. 92 ☐ Teaching Master (*Math Masters*, p. 49) ☐ Home Link Master (*Math Masters*, p. 212) ☐ scissors ***See* Advance Preparation**
3 Options for Individualizing	
Extra Practice Children play *High Roller* to practice addition facts. [Operations and Computation]	☐ dice ☐ base-10 cubes and longs (optional)

Additional Information

Advance Preparation For Part 2, list temperatures to the nearest 2 degrees on the board or the Class Data Pad for children to display on their paper thermometers.

Vocabulary • **addition facts** • **sum** • **fact power**

Getting Started

Mental Math and Reflexes

▷ Children count up and back by 10s using the number grid. *What pattern do you see in the numbers on the grid?* Each time you move down a row, the number in the tens place is one more. Each time you move up a row, the number in the tens place is one less.

▷ Children count up and back by 10s using a calculator, saying the numbers aloud as they count. On the board, write the following calculator program (change the program for additional counts as time allows):

Start at:	0	25	38	81	92	157
Count:	Up	Up	Up	Up	Back	Back
By:	10s	10s	10s	10s	10s	10s

Math Message
Draw a domino on a half-sheet of paper. Write the 3 numbers that go with the domino.

Home Link 4.10 Follow-Up
Children share information about scrolls discussed at home.

Teaching the Lesson

✦ Math Message Follow-Up

WHOLE-CLASS ACTIVITY

Draw a blank domino on the board. Ask a volunteer to suggest what to draw in the domino. The class then decides which three numbers go with the domino.

Ask a volunteer to suggest a number model to represent the domino. If no one suggests it, write a possible number model on the board and have children explain what each number represents. For example, for the 3|5 domino, you might write $3 + 5 = 8$.

Then move into a discussion about facts, as described in the activity that follows.

Collect the half-sheets of paper to check how well children understand parts and totals. Expect that most children will know that the two parts and the total make up a number family.

✦ Introducing Addition Facts

WHOLE-CLASS DISCUSSION

Show examples of **addition facts,** each with two 1-digit numbers and a **sum.** Ask a volunteer to explain what he or she thinks an addition fact is. Addition facts are all of the possible sums of two 1-digit numbers. Have children write examples of some addition facts on their slates.

Then write some simple addition facts on the board, leaving off the sums. Have children recite answers together. When they can recite addition-fact sums as easily as reading 1-digit numbers, they will have **"fact power"** for these facts.

Art and Literature Link

Children will be captivated by *Anno's Counting House* by Mitsumasa Anno (Philomel Books, 1982). This wordless book focuses on the number combinations for 10. Using the book as a model, invite children to draw pictures that show number combinations for ten.

✓ ONGOING ASSESSMENT

Watch for children

· who are beginning to recite facts automatically.

· who are able to recall simple +0 and +1 facts.

· who use counters, fingers, number lines, and number grids to calculate answers.

Work with addition facts is just beginning. The class should make significant progress in memorizing +0, +1, +2, and doubles (for example, 4 + 4) facts by the end of the year.

A goal of *Everyday Mathematics* is for children, over time, to develop fact power.

 Adjusting the Activity Encourage children having difficulty to use counters to model each addition fact.

◆ Discussing Fact Power

WHOLE-CLASS DISCUSSION

Addition fact power is the instant recall of sums of 1-digit numbers without stopping to figure them out. Discuss fact power. Include the following points:

▷ Having fact power is like being a good reader. Reading is easier and more enjoyable if you recognize many words immediately, without having to figure them out. The same is true of number facts. Solving problems is easier if you know the sum of any two numbers from 0 to 9 immediately, without having to figure it out.

▷ You can figure out facts you don't know, just as you sound out or decode unfamiliar words, but the goal is not to have to do that.

▷ Some facts lead to other facts. There are not really that many different facts to learn or memorize. You will learn some easy "shortcuts" in later lessons.

▷ Playing number games and practicing will help you build addition fact power.

◆ Finding Sums (*Math Journal 1*, p. 91)

INDEPENDENT ACTIVITY

Children use the pictured dominoes to find the sums for addition facts. Bring the class together to share strategies.

 Adjusting the Activity If children are having difficulty, have them use real dominoes to model each problem. First they find the dominoes that match those on the page. Then they match the dominoes to the problems.

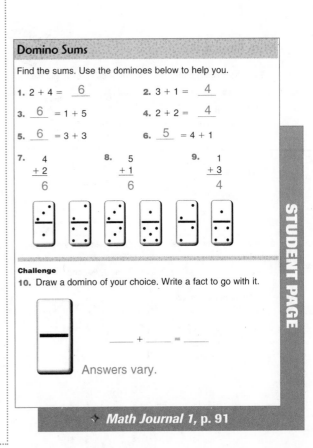

STUDENT PAGE

Domino Sums

Find the sums. Use the dominoes below to help you.

1. 2 + 4 = __6__   2. 3 + 1 = __4__

3. __6__ = 1 + 5   4. 2 + 2 = __4__

5. __6__ = 3 + 3   6. __5__ = 4 + 1

7. 4   8. 5   9. 1
   + 2   + 1   + 3
   ___   ___   ___
    6   6   4

Challenge

10. Draw a domino of your choice. Write a fact to go with it.

___ + ___ = ___

Answers vary.

◆ *Math Journal 1*, p. 91

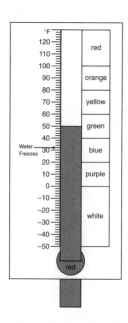

Guide children through the assembly of the paper thermometer on *Math Masters, page* 49. Allow enough time for assembling and color coding.

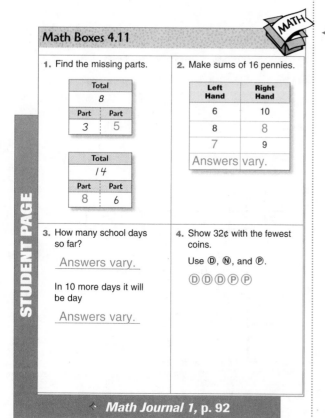

◆ Reading and Setting Temperatures
(*Math Masters,* p. 49)

PARTNER ACTIVITY

Have children follow these steps to assemble their paper thermometers:

1. Color the strip red.

2. Color the thermometer regions to match the color code on the outside class thermometer.

3. Cut out the thermometer and the strip.

4. Make a small cut at the bottom dotted line and insert the indicator strip.

Partners help each other set the indicator strips on their thermometers to temperatures you list on the board or Class Data Pad. (A small piece of removable tape attached to the top of the strip helps when showing the temperatures.) Begin with easy temperatures (multiples of 10) first. At the end of the activity, have children fold their paper thermometers for storage in their tool kits.

NOTE: If appropriate, pair non-native English speakers with native English speakers for this activity.

◆ Math Boxes 4.11 (*Math Journal 1,* p. 92)

INDEPENDENT ACTIVITY

Mixed Review This journal page provides opportunities for cumulative review or assessment of concepts and skills.

✦ Home Link 4.11 (*Math Masters,* p. 212)

Home Connection Children find sums for addition facts pictured with dominoes. This activity continues work with basic addition facts 0 + 0 through 9 + 9.

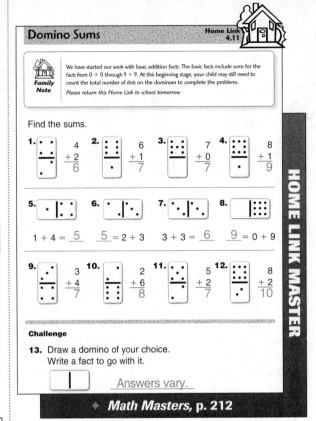

3 Options for Individualizing

✦ EXTRA PRACTICE Playing *High Roller*

PARTNER ACTIVITY 👥 15–30 min 🕐

Children practice addition facts by playing *High Roller*. This game was introduced in Lesson 2.12. It can be played by 2 players or in small groups.

Rules

1. Players take turns. One player rolls 2 dice.

2. The player keeps the die with the larger number (the High Roller) and rolls the other die again.

3. The player then counts on from the number rolled on the first die to get the sum of the 2 dice.

Adjusting the Activity To extend the game, have children take the final total of the dice in each round in base-10 cubes. When they have 10 cubes, they can exchange them for a long. At the end of 10 rounds, they count the total number of cubes they have won, remembering to count 10 cubes for each long. The player with the larger (or smaller) number of cubes wins the game.

Domino Sums

Home Link 4.11

Family Note We have started our work with basic addition facts. The basic facts include sums for the facts from 0 + 0 through 9 + 9. At this beginning stage, your child may still need to count the total number of dots on the dominoes to complete the problems.

Please return this Home Link to school tomorrow.

Find the sums.

1. $\begin{array}{r} 4 \\ +2 \\ \hline 6 \end{array}$ 2. $\begin{array}{r} 6 \\ +1 \\ \hline 7 \end{array}$ 3. $\begin{array}{r} 7 \\ +0 \\ \hline 7 \end{array}$ 4. $\begin{array}{r} 8 \\ +1 \\ \hline 9 \end{array}$

5. $1 + 4 = \underline{5}$ 6. $\underline{5} = 2 + 3$ 7. $3 + 3 = \underline{6}$ 8. $\underline{9} = 0 + 9$

9. $\begin{array}{r} 3 \\ +4 \\ \hline 7 \end{array}$ 10. $\begin{array}{r} 2 \\ +6 \\ \hline 8 \end{array}$ 11. $\begin{array}{r} 5 \\ +2 \\ \hline 7 \end{array}$ 12. $\begin{array}{r} 8 \\ +2 \\ \hline 10 \end{array}$

Challenge

13. Draw a domino of your choice. Write a fact to go with it.

  Answers vary.

✦ *Math Masters,* p. 212

HOME LINK MASTER

Lesson 4.11 **311**

4.12 Good Fact Habits

OBJECTIVE To practice addition facts.

summaries	materials

1 Teaching the Lesson

Children practice addition facts through the use of choral (group) responses and by playing *Shaker Addition Top-It*.
[Operations and Computation]

- ☐ Teaching Master (*Math Masters*, p. 51; optional)
- ☐ Home Link 4.11
- ☐ base-10 blocks or pieces: 25 cubes and 10 longs
- ☐ two 6-sided dice per group
- ☐ two polyhedral dice, marked 0–9, per group (optional)

2 Ongoing Learning & Practice

Children find fact sums for a color-by-number picture.
[Operations and Computation]

They count craft sticks by gathering them into bundles of 10 and then gathering bundles of 10 into a hundreds bundle.
[Numeration]

Children practice and maintain skills through Math Boxes and Home Link activities.

- ☐ *Math Journal 1*, pp. 93 and 94
- ☐ Teaching Master (*Math Masters*, p. 50; optional)
- ☐ Home Link Master (*Math Masters*, p. 213)
- ☐ more than 100 craft sticks
- ☐ rubber bands or resealable bags
- ☐ half-sheet of paper per group

3 Options for Individualizing

Enrichment Children find cumulative totals while playing a variation of *Shaker Addition Top-It* (or *High Rollers* to 20).
[Operations and Computation]

Extra Practice Children solve number stories involving addition facts. [Operations and Computation]

- ☐ die
- ☐ Class Number Grid Poster
- ☐ calculator
- ☐ piece of scratch paper per group
- ☐ *Minute Math®*, pp. 8–11, 16, 39, and 79–82

Getting Started

Mental Math and Reflexes

Make sure that each child has 10 longs and 25 cubes. Have children each take 3 longs and 7 cubes. Then count together, beginning with the longs: 10, 20, 30, 31, 32, 33, 34, 35, 36, 37 Repeat with other numbers of longs and cubes.
Suggestions: 4 longs and 8 cubes; 2 longs and 6 cubes; and so on. Continue as time allows.

Math Message

Fill in a unit box and write 3 addition facts.

Unit

Home Link 4.11 Follow-Up

Discuss solution strategies as needed.

1 Teaching the Lesson

✦ Math Message Follow-Up

WHOLE-CLASS ACTIVITY

Have children share their responses.

Take this opportunity to emphasize that numbers are nearly always about something; unit boxes remind us of that fact and save us the trouble of always writing units to go with the numbers. However, units are often omitted in fact practice, where automatic recall is the goal.

Draw several pictures of dominoes. Have children write an addition fact for each.

✦ Reinforcing Fact Reflexes as "Habits" with Choral Responses

WHOLE-CLASS ACTIVITY

Choral readings have proven to be beneficial for not only beginning readers but primary grade mathematics learners as well. Group responses allow children to participate at their own levels without being put on the spot. More skilled children can lead, while others hear them and are strengthened in areas where they are weak. Establish a lively rhythm, with responses given clearly and simultaneously. Keep group-response activities brief.

Facts to stress now are those with 0, 1, and 2, as well as doubles facts:

▷ $0 + 0 = 0$, $0 + 1 = 1$, $0 + 2 = 2$ (and so on)

▷ $1 + 1 = 2$, $1 + 2 = 3$, $1 + 3 = 4$ (and so on)

▷ $2 + 2 = 4$, $2 + 3 = 5$, $2 + 4 = 6$ (and so on)

▷ $3 + 3 = 6$, $4 + 4 = 8$, $5 + 5 = 10$ (and so on)

✦ Introducing *Shaker Addition Top-It* (*Math Masters,* p. 51)

PARTNER ACTIVITY

This game may be played by 2 to 5 players. Use two 6-sided dice to provide review and practice with facts containing numbers 1 through 6, or two polyhedral dice, marked 0–9, to provide review and practice for all basic addition facts. Begin the game with about 20 pennies or other counters for each small group.

Write Addition Facts

✦ *Math Masters,* p. 51

TEACHING MASTER

Lesson 4.12 **313**

Using polyhedral dice will provide practice for all addition facts.

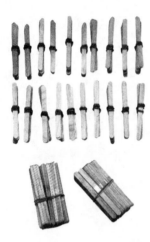

Bundling craft sticks into groups of tens and hundreds

Color by Number

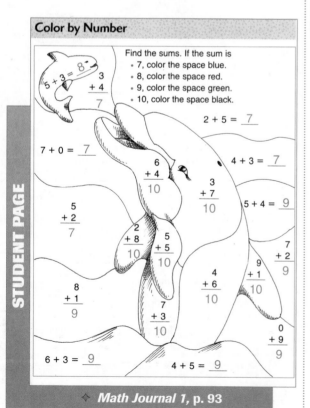

Find the sums. If the sum is
- 7, color the space blue.
- 8, color the space red.
- 9, color the space green.
- 10, color the space black.

$5 + 3 = 8$

$\begin{array}{r} 3 \\ + 4 \\ \hline 7 \end{array}$

$2 + 5 = 7$

$7 + 0 = 7$

$4 + 3 = 7$

$\begin{array}{r} 6 \\ + 4 \\ \hline 10 \end{array}$

$\begin{array}{r} 3 \\ + 7 \\ \hline 10 \end{array}$

$5 + 4 = 9$

$\begin{array}{r} 5 \\ + 2 \\ \hline 7 \end{array}$

$\begin{array}{r} 2 \\ + 8 \\ \hline 10 \end{array}$

$\begin{array}{r} 5 \\ + 5 \\ \hline 10 \end{array}$

$\begin{array}{r} 7 \\ + 2 \\ \hline 9 \end{array}$

$\begin{array}{r} 9 \\ + 1 \\ \hline 10 \end{array}$

$\begin{array}{r} 8 \\ + 1 \\ \hline 9 \end{array}$

$\begin{array}{r} 4 \\ + 6 \\ \hline 10 \end{array}$

$\begin{array}{r} 7 \\ + 3 \\ \hline 10 \end{array}$

$\begin{array}{r} 0 \\ + 9 \\ \hline 9 \end{array}$

$6 + 3 = 9$

$4 + 5 = 9$

◆ Math Journal 1, p. 93

Rules

1. For each round, players take turns shaking and rolling the dice, adding the numbers using any method except a calculator, and stating the sum.

2. Saying the wrong sum disqualifies a player for that round. This encourages children to check every sum, not just their own. A disqualified player may still check others' responses.

3. The player with the highest sum for each round takes a penny or a counter from the pile. If there are ties, each winning player takes a penny or a counter.

4. The player with the most pennies or counters at the end of a given time wins.

ONGOING ASSESSMENT
Expect that many children may still need to add numbers by using counters or by counting with their fingers. The basic addition facts will be continually practiced throughout the year.

(*Math Masters*, page 51 provides spaces in which children can record the facts they are answering as they play the game.)

2 Ongoing Learning & Practice

◆ Coloring by Number
(*Math Journal 1*, p. 93; *Math Masters*, p. 50)

INDEPENDENT ACTIVITY 👤

Children complete the addition facts and color the spaces according to the directions to reveal the picture.

◆ Bundling Craft Sticks

SMALL-GROUP ACTIVITY 👥

Children work in small groups to gather single craft sticks into bundles of 10—and then 10 bundles of 10 into a hundreds bundle. They put sticks into small resealable bags or bundle them together using rubber bands. Once a group finishes, children count how many hundreds, tens, and ones they have, as well as the total number of craft sticks. They record the results on a half-sheet of paper for a group report. Their final task is to unbundle everything for the next group. If possible, have a follow-up discussion with the whole class, sharing strategies and reports.

Optional: Add or take away sticks after each group finishes so that group results change. Follow up by comparing the recorded results: Which group has the most, the least; what are the differences in the totals? You might want to total the results of all groups.

◆ Math Boxes 4.12 (*Math Journal 1,* p. 94)

INDEPENDENT ACTIVITY

Mixed Review This journal page provides opportunities for cumulative review or assessment of concepts and skills.

◆ Home Link 4.12 (*Math Masters,* p. 213)

Home Connection As in their journals, children complete addition facts and color the spaces according to directions to reveal the picture.

3 Options for Individualizing

◆ ENRICHMENT Playing a Variation of *Shaker Addition Top-It*

SMALL-GROUP ACTIVITY ⁙ 15–30 min

A group sits in a circle. One after another, children roll a die. The group figures out the cumulative total until it passes a goal you set before play begins. Children can use their number grids for counting on, or one child can be designated to count on the Class Number Grid Poster.

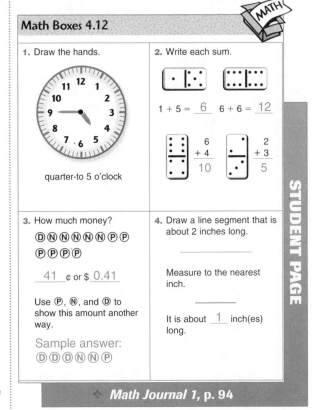

◆ Math Journal 1, p. 94

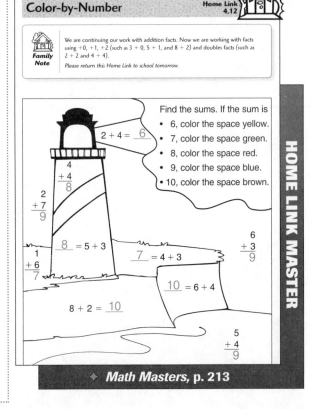

◆ Math Masters, p. 213

NOTE: This is a variation of the basic *High Roller* game introduced in Lesson 4.11.

✦ ENRICHMENT Playing *High Roller* to 20

PARTNER ACTIVITY   **15–30 min**

Each partnership needs one die, a calculator, and a piece of scratch paper to keep score.

Rules

1. Player A rolls the die. If the first roll is not a 6, Player A rolls again and adds the two numbers together. Player B checks the total with a calculator.

2. Player A continues until a 6 is rolled, adding each roll to the previous sum. Player B checks each new total with the calculator. If Player A reaches a total of 10 or more before rolling a 6, he or she scores 1 point.

3. If Player A reaches a total of 20 or more before rolling a 6, he or she scores 1 bonus point.

4. After rolling a 6 or reaching 20, the players switch roles.

Variation: If the player accumulating a total gives the wrong total, his or her turn ends.

✦ EXTRA PRACTICE Minute Math

SMALL-GROUP ACTIVITY   **15–30 min**

To offer children more experience with addition facts, see the following pages in *Minute Math:*

Basic Routines: pp. 8–11 and 16

Operations: p. 39

Number Stories: pp. 79–82

4.13

Unit 4 Review and Assessment

OBJECTIVE To review and assess children's progress on the material covered in Unit 4.

---

1 Assess Progress

learning goals

4a **Beginning/Developing Goal** Use standard units for measuring length. (**Lessons 4.3–4.7**)

4b **Developing Goal** Find simple sums and missing addends. (**Lessons 4.1, 4.2, 4.5–4.9, 4.11, and 4.12**)

4c **Developing Goal** Calculate the values of coin combinations. (**Lessons 4.3 and 4.10**)

4d **Developing Goal** Solve simple number stories. (**Lessons 4.3, 4.6, 4.7, and 4.9**)

4e **Developing/Secure Goal** Order and compare numbers to 22. (**Lessons 4.1, 4.5, 4.8, 4.11, and 4.12**)

4f **Developing/Secure Goal** Tell time to the nearest half-hour. (**Lessons 4.4, 4.5, 4.8, and 4.9**)

activities

❑ Written Assessment, Problems 3–6

❑ Written Assessment, Problems 8–13

❑ Written Assessment, Problem 7
❑ Slate Assessment, Problem 2

❑ Slate Assessment, Problem 9

❑ Slate Assessment, Problems 3 and 4

❑ Written Assessment, Problem 1
❑ Oral Assessment, Problem 5
See **Advance Preparation**

materials

❑ Assessment Masters (*Math Masters,* pp. 307 and 308)

❑ dominoes
❑ tool-kit clock
❑ coins

❑ slate
❑ tool-kit ruler
❑ half-sheet of paper

---

2 Build Background for Unit 5

summaries

Children practice and maintain skills through Math Boxes and Home Link activities.

materials

❑ *Math Journal 1,* p. 95
❑ Home Link Masters (*Math Masters,* pp. 214–217)

Each **learning goal** listed above indicates a level of performance that might be expected at this point in the *Everyday Mathematics* K–6 curriculum. For a variety of reasons, the levels indicated may not accurately portray your class's performance.

Additional Information

Advance Preparation For Part 1, draw a 9|5 domino on the board.

For additional information on assessment for Unit 5, see the *Assessment Handbook,* pages 46–48. For assessment checklists, see *Math Masters,* pages 334 and 335 and 356–358.

Getting Started

Math Message

On a half-sheet of paper, write the three numbers that describe the domino on the board. 9, 5, and 14

1 Assess Progress

◆ Math Message Follow-Up

WHOLE-CLASS ACTIVITY

Collect children's papers. Have a volunteer list the three domino numbers on the board. 9, 5, and 14 Ask someone to explain what each of the numbers represents. The 9 and 5 represent the two sides of the domino. The 14 represents the total number of dots on the domino.

◆ Oral and Slate Assessments

WHOLE-GROUP ACTIVITIES

If the suggested problems below are not appropriate for your class's level of performance, adjust the numbers or the problems themselves to better assess your children's abilities.

Oral Assessment Suggestions

1. Skip count by 2s on the number line, starting with 50; with 100.

2. Count up and back by 5s on the number grid.

3. Count up and back by 10s on the number grid.

4. Stop-and-start count by 10s; then by 5s; then by 1s. For example, count by 10s to 50. Stop. Count by 5s to 75. Stop. Count by 1s to 79.

5. The teacher gives times. Children show them on their tool-kit clocks. Show 8:00; show half-past 5; show half-past 2; show half-past 10; show half-past 9; show quarter-past 7; show quarter-after 11; show quarter-before 6; show quarter-to 3. **Goal 4f**

NOTE: Many of these assessment suggestions relate to learning goals that have been addressed in previous units. Now is a good time to evaluate children's progress toward those goals.

Slate Assessment Suggestions

1. Make a tally for 8; for 12; for 21.

2. Write the amount and then show the amount with coins for 12 cents; 18 cents; 24 cents; 32 cents; 52 cents; 75 cents. **Goal 4c**

3. Write the number that is one more than 14; than 28; than 39; than 50. **Goal 4e**

4. Write the number that is one less than 16; than 20; than 31; than 57. **Goal 4e**

5. Write the numbers 5, 8, and 14. Circle the odd number.

6. Write the numbers 16, 25, and 32. Circle the even numbers.

7. Write the following amounts in dollars-and-cents notation: $1.22; $2.43; $1.80; $3.07; $0.62; $0.07.

8. The teacher shows temperatures on the class thermometer. Children write the temperatures to the nearest 10°F. Show 30°; 70°; 50°; 92°; 58°; 83°. If appropriate, have children try writing a few temperatures to the nearest 2°. Show 62°; 44°; 38°.

9. The teacher tells the following number stories. Children record their answers on their slates. If time permits, children share their strategies for how they figured out the answers. (Encourage children to use manipulatives, drawings, doodles, or other strategies to solve the problems.) **Goal 4d**

   • Martha was bundling craft sticks with her partner Jeremy. Martha made 8 bundles and Jeremy made 6 bundles. How many bundles did Martha and Jeremy make altogether? 14 bundles

   • Nestor picked some flowers from his garden to give to his mom. He picked 12 tulips. He noticed that 2 of them had big brown spots on the petals. He threw those 2 flowers away. How many flowers did Nestor have left for his mom? 10 flowers

   • Lora bought milk and a muffin for lunch. The milk cost 25 cents. The muffin cost 30 cents. How much did Lora spend altogether? 55 cents (*Hint:* The number grid can be used to solve this problem.)

   • When Sidney woke up, it was only 28 degrees Fahrenheit outside. He wore his warmest coat to school. After school, his coat was too warm because the temperature had gone up by 20 degrees. What was the temperature after school? 48° (*Hint:* The number grid can be used to solve this problem.)

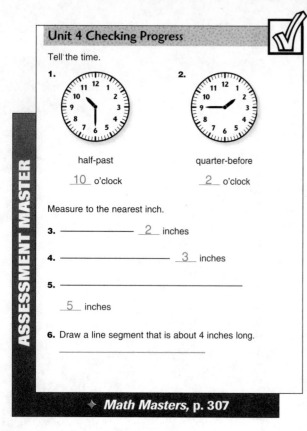

Unit 4 Checking Progress

Tell the time.

1.   2.

half-past   quarter-before

_10_ o'clock   _2_ o'clock

Measure to the nearest inch.

3. ————————— _2_ inches

4. ——————————— _3_ inches

5. ————————————————

   _5_ inches

6. Draw a line segment that is about 4 inches long.

   ———————————————

✦ *Math Masters, p. 307*

Unit 4 Checking Progress (cont.)

7. How much money has Dolores saved?

   Ⓓ Ⓓ Ⓝ Ⓝ Ⓝ Ⓝ Ⓟ Ⓟ Ⓟ Ⓟ Ⓟ   _45_ ¢

   Show the same amount using fewer coins.
   Use Ⓟ, Ⓝ, and Ⓓ.

   Answers vary.

Write each sum.

8.   3 + 5 = _8_

9.   4 + 2 = _6_

10.   _7_ = 4 + 3

11.   5
          + 6
          ————
           11

12.   8
          + 1
          ————
            9

13.   6
          + 9
          ————
           15

✦ *Math Masters, p. 308*

✦ Written Assessment
(*Math Masters,* pp. 307 and 308)

INDEPENDENT ACTIVITY

Read the problems on *Math Masters,* pages 307 and 308 with the class. If appropriate, complete the pages together—that is, wait for children to complete a problem before reading the next one to them. You may want to do an example with the class for each of the problems.

If your class can work independently, have children work alone or with a partner. Circulate and assist as they work.

- Tell the time. (Problems 1 and 2) **Goal 4f**
- Measure to the nearest inch. (Problems 3–5) **Goal 4a**
- Draw a line segment that is about 4 inches long. (Problem 6) **Goal 4a**
- How much money has Dolores saved? Show the same amount using fewer coins. (Problem 7) **Goal 4c**
- Write each sum. (Problems 8–13) **Goal 4b**

✦ ALTERNATIVE ASSESSMENT OPTION
Play *Domino Top-It*

PARTNER ACTIVITY

Use this activity from Lesson 4.1 to assess children's progress on comparing numbers and finding simple sums.

Children record their last round on half-sheets of paper. Children draw their last domino and write the 3 numbers that go with the domino. They circle the total number of dots for their domino and turn in their papers.

✦ ALTERNATIVE ASSESSMENT OPTION
Make a Measurement Page

INDEPENDENT ACTIVITY

Use this activity ("Making a Measurement Book") from Lesson 4.6 to assess children's progress with measuring to the nearest inch.

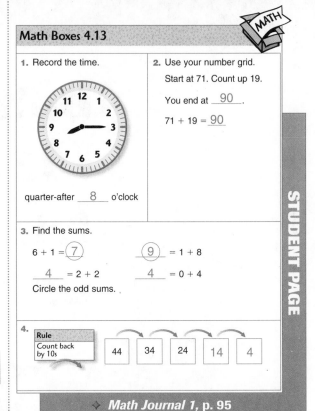
◆ ALTERNATIVE ASSESSMENT OPTION
Order Clocks

SMALL-GROUP ACTIVITY

Use this activity from Lesson 4.8 to assess children's progress with telling time and with ordering clocks according to the times they show.

Work with small groups of children. Assign children a time to show on their tool-kit clocks. The time should be to the nearest hour, half-hour, or quarter-hour. Then have children work together to order their clocks from the earliest time to the latest.

---

2 Build Background for Unit 5

◆ Math Boxes 4.13 (*Math Journal 1*, p. 95)

INDEPENDENT ACTIVITY

Mixed Review This journal page provides opportunities for cumulative review or assessment of concepts and skills.

◆ Home Link 4.13 (*Math Masters*, pp. 214–217)

Home Connection This Home Link is a four-page newsletter that introduces parents and guardians to Unit 5's topics and terms. The letter also offers ideas for home-based mathematics activities that are supportive of classroom work.

Have children write their names and today's date at the top of the first page.

Math Boxes 4.13

1. Record the time.

   quarter-after ___8___ o'clock

2. Use your number grid.
   Start at 71. Count up 19.
   You end at ___90___.
   71 + 19 = ___90___

3. Find the sums.

   6 + 1 = (7)   (9) = 1 + 8

   ___4___ = 2 + 2   ___4___ = 0 + 4

   Circle the odd sums.

4. Rule
   Count back by 10s

   | 44 | 34 | 24 | 14 | 4 |

◆ Math Journal 1, p. 95

Family Letter Home Link 4.13

Unit 5: Place Value, Number Stories, and Basic Facts

As their work in mathematics progresses, children are beginning to use larger numbers. In Unit 5, children will begin to explore the system we use for writing large numbers by focusing on the idea of **place value.** For example, in the number 72, 7 is in the tens place, so there are "7 tens," and 2 is in the ones place, so there are "2 ones." Children will use base-10 blocks to represent numbers and to find the sums of two numbers. They will also use place value to determine "greater than" and "less than" relationships.

tens	ones
7	2

Later in this unit, children will continue to work with addition facts. Shortcuts for learning facts will be introduced. One shortcut is the **turn-around rule,** which states that the order in which numbers are added does not change the sum. For example, 4 + 3 and 3 + 4 both equal 7. Your child will also learn the meaning of adding 0 and 1 to any number. Knowing these shortcuts will make the task of learning addition facts easier.

3 + 4 = 7
4 + 3 = 7
turn-around facts

Children will also practice place value and addition and subtraction facts by acting out number stories. They will act out these stories using concrete objects and begin to represent the stories with **number models.** (See this unit's vocabulary list for more information on number models.)

Children have explored many number patterns in previous lessons. **"What's My Rule?"** is a routine introduced in this unit and found throughout *Everyday Mathematics* that provides practice with number patterns and number relationships. You will receive more detailed information about this routine when we begin to use it in class.

Please keep this Family Letter for reference as your child works through Unit 5.

◆ Math Masters, p. 214–217

Unit 5
Place Value, Number Stories, and Basic Facts

ONE GOAT IS UNDER THE BRIDGE
TWO GOATS ARE ON THE BRIDGE
HOW MANY BILLY GOATS ARE THERE
ALTOGETHER?

overview

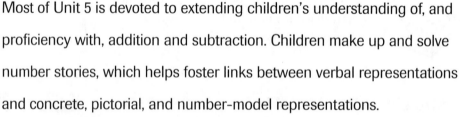

Most of Unit 5 is devoted to extending children's understanding of, and proficiency with, addition and subtraction. Children make up and solve number stories, which helps foster links between verbal representations and concrete, pictorial, and number-model representations.

Children also continue their work with addition facts, with a special focus on +0, +1, doubles, and sums-of-10 facts, and learn that the order in which two numbers are added does not affect the sum.

The exploration of our place-value notational system is begun with the help of base-10 blocks. These manipulatives are then used as an aid to finding sums beyond the basic addition facts.

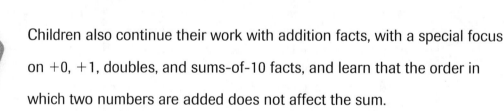

The unit ends with the introduction of the "What's My Rule?" routine. This routine provides additional practice with addition and subtraction facts, number patterns, and place-value relationships.

contents

UNIT
5

learning goals in perspective

learning goals	links to the past	links to the future
5a **Beginning Goal** Find missing numbers and/or the missing rule in "What's My Rule?" problems. **(Lessons 5.10, 5.12, and 5.13)**	Children were introduced to "What's My Rule?" in Kindergarten.	In second grade and third grade, "What's My Rule?" will be extended to include negative numbers, doubles, halves, fact extensions, and multiplication and division. *(Related Grade 1 lesson: 6.8)*
5b **Developing Goal** Understand place value for longs and cubes. **(Lessons 5.1–5.5, 5.8, 5.9, 5.12, and 5.13)**	Children explored place value in Kindergarten using calculators.	Place value is a fundamental concept that will be revisited repeatedly throughout *Everyday Mathematics*. *(Related Grade 1 lessons: 8.2, 8.3, 9.1, 9.2, 9.3)*
5c **Developing Goal** Compare numbers using < and >. **(Lessons 5.3, 5.6–5.9)**	Very young children understand the idea of more and less. In Kindergarten, children compared number size and ordered numbers. *(Related Grade 1 lessons: 1.2, 1.5, 1.6, 2.1, 2.11, 3.5, 3.13, 4.1, 4.9)*	Comparisons are fundamental for understanding many mathematical relationships and number stories, and for analyzing data. Children will make comparisons of many types throughout the grades. *(Related Grade 1 lessons: 6.12, 9.7, 10.1, 10.6)*
5d **Developing Goal** Know +1, +0, doubles, and sums of 10 addition facts. **(Lessons 5.4, 5.5, 5.7, and 5.9–5.11)**	Children have had many experiences with addition in Kindergarten and the beginning of first grade. Fact power was more formally introduced at the end of Unit 4. *(Related Grade 1 lessons: 1.5, 1.13, 2.3, 2.11, 2.13, 3.6, 3.14, 4.11, 4.12)*	Unit 6 focuses on further development of fact power. Addition will also be practiced through games and in a variety of problem-solving situations throughout first grade. *(Related Grade 1 lessons: 6.1–6.5, 6.7, 6.8, 7.2, 8.4, 10.3, 10.4)*
5e **Developing** Solve simple number stories. **(Lessons 5.6–5.10)**	Children began telling and solving number stories in Kindergarten. *(Related Grade 1 lessons: 1.13, 2.12, 2.13)*	Throughout the grades, children will continue to create and solve number stories. *(Related Grade 1 lessons: 6.5, 8.4, 10.3, 10.4)*

assessment
ongoing • product • periodic

☑ Informal Assessment

Math Boxes These *Math Journal* pages provide opportunities for cumulative review or assessment of concepts and skills.

Ongoing Assessment: Kid Watching Use the Ongoing Assessment suggestions in the following lessons to make quick, on-the-spot observationsabout children's understanding of:
- Numeration **(Lessons 5.1, 5.6, and 5.9)**
- Operations and Computation **(Lessons 5.3, 5.5, and 5.7)**
- Measurement and Reference Frames **(Lesson 5.11)**
- Patterns, Functions, and Algebra **(Lessons 5.7, 5.12, and 5.13)**

Portfolio Ideas Samples of children's work may be obtained from the following assignments:
- Making a Number-Story Book **(Lesson 5.8)**
- Solving "What's My Rule?" Problems **(Lesson 5.13)**

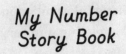

My Number Story Book

☑ Unit 5 Review and Assessment

Math Message Use the question in Lesson 5.14 to assess children's progress toward the following learning goal: Goal 5b

Oral and Slate Assessments Use oral or slate assessments during Lesson 5.14 to assess children's progress toward the following learning goals: Goals 5b, 5d, and 5e

Written Assessment Use a written review during Lesson 5.14 to assess children's progress toward the following learning goals: Goals 5a, 5b, 5c, 5d, and 5e

Performance/Group Assessment Use a small-group activity in Lesson 5.14 to assess children's progress toward the following learning goals: Goals 5b and 5c

assessmenthandbook

For more information on how to use different types of assessment in Unit 5, see the Assessment Overview on pages 55–57 in the *Assessment Handbook*. The following Assessment Masters can be found in the *Math Masters* book:

- Unit 5 Checking Progress, pp. 309 and 310
- Unit 5 Class Checklist, p. 336
- Unit 5 Individual Profile of Progress, p. 337
- Class Checklist: 2nd Quarter, p. 348
- Individual Profile of Progress: 2nd Quarter, p. 349
- Class Progress Indicator, p. 358
- Math Logs, pp. 362–364
- Self-Assessment Forms, pp. 365–366
- Interest Inventory, p. 361
- Midyear Assessment, pp. 318–320

problem solving

A process of modeling everyday situations using tools from mathematics

Encourage children to use a variety of strategies when attacking a given problem—and to explain those strategies. *Strategies children might use in this unit:*

- Working backwards
- Identifying patterns
- Modeling with manipulatives
- Using information in a picture
- Completing number models

- Using a diagram
- Identifying needed information
- Using a number line
- Acting out the problem
- Making a graph

Four Problem-Solving REPRESENTATIONS

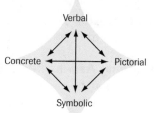

Lessons that teach *through* problem solving, not just *about* problem solving

Lesson	Activity	Lesson	Activity
5.1	Solving Frames-and-Arrows problems	5.7, 5.8	Solving how much more, how much less number stories
5.2	Finding digit patterns in calculator counts by 1s and 10s	5.8	Making up and solving number stories involving addition and subtraction
5.4	Using base-10 blocks to find total weight	5.9	Finding which sum is most likely when two dice are thrown
5.5, 5.6	Solving relation number stories about animal weights	5.12	Solving "What's My Rule?" problems

For more information about problem solving in *Everyday Mathematics*, see the *Teacher's Reference Manual*, pp. 197–208.

cross-curricular links

reading
- Compare the 26 letters that make up all English words with the 10 digits that make up all numbers. **(Lesson 5.2)**

language arts
- List animal names in alphabetical order. **(Lesson 5.6)**

science
- Encourage children to discuss any facts they know about the animals that are being compared in this lesson, such as type of coverings or methods of movement. **(Lesson 5.5)**

literature
- Read stories about "inchlings" from Tom Thumb, a book by Margaret Read MacDonald. **(Lesson 5.11)**

meeting
INDIVIDUAL needs

✦ RETEACHING

The following features provide additional instructional support:

Adjusting the Activity

- **Lesson 5.4, Part 1**
- **Lesson 5.6, Parts 1, 2**
- **Lesson 5.7, Part 1**
- **Lesson 5.9, Part 1**
- **Lesson 5.11, Part 1**
- **Lesson 5.12, Part 1**

✦ ENRICHMENT

The following features suggest enrichment and extension activities:

Adjusting the Activity

- **Lesson 5.1, Part 1**
- **Lesson 5.2, Part 3**
- **Lesson 5.3, Part 1**
- **Lesson 5.4, Part 1**
- **Lesson 5.5, Part 1**
- **Lesson 5.7, Part 1**
- **Lesson 5.8, Part 2**
- **Lesson 5.13, Parts 1, 2**

Options for Individualizing

- **Lesson 5.1** Adding and Taking Away Longs
- **Lesson 5.2** The Role of Digits in Writing Numbers
- **Lesson 5.6** Comparing Animal Weights
- **Lesson 5.7** Comparing the Values of Sets of Coins
- **Lesson 5.8** Making a Number-Story Book
- **Lesson 5.10** Subtraction and the Turn-Around Rules
- **Lesson 5.13** Simulating a Function Machine on the Calculator

✦ MULTIAGE CLASSROOM

The following chart lists related activities from the *Kindergarten Teacher's Guide to Activities* and lessons from Grade 2 that can help you meet your instructional needs:

Grade K Pages	82 131 285	206 285	94 84 170	270 48 212	90 132 290	90 228 132 196	90 202	90 196 228	296 297	132 198 226	132 226 230	99 248– 253	99 248– 253
Grade 1 Lessons	5.1	5.2	5.3	5.4	5.5	5.6	5.7	5.8	5.9	5.10	5.11	5.12	5.13
Grade 2 Lessons	3.1 10.8– 10.10	10.3 10.8– 10.10	1.12	7.6 9.8 10.7	4.8 4.9 11.1	1.12	6.2	2.1 4.1 6.4	7.9 12.7	2.2 2.4	2.2 2.3	2.11 3.6	2.10 2.11

materials

lesson	math masters pages	manipulative kit items	other items
5.1	Home Link Master, p. 218 Teaching Master, p. 52 (optional) **See Advance Preparation, p. 334.**	base-10 blocks slate	tool-kit clock
5.2	Home Link Master, p. 219 Teaching Master, p. 53 (optional) **See Advance Preparation, p. 339.**	base-10 blocks slate overhead base-10 blocks	tool-kit coins calculator
5.3	Home Link Master, p. 220 Teaching Masters, pp. 54 and 55 (optional)	slate 1 die base-10 blocks	tool-kit number cards calculator
5.4	Home Link Master, p. 221 Teaching Masters, p. 56–59 per group Teaching Master, p. 57	slate 64 cubes pan balance base-10 blocks	objects to use as units tool-kit coins extra pennies **See Advance Preparation, p. 350.**
5.5	Home Link Master, p. 222 Teaching Masters, pp. 60–65 and 51 **See Advance Preparation, p. 355.**	base-10 blocks two 6-sided dice	Place-Value Mat 20 pennies/counters for each small group animal cards
5.6	Home Link Master, p. 223 Teaching Masters, pp. 54 and 55 (optional) Teaching Masters, pp. 66 and 67	slate	animal masters and animal cards **See Advance Preparation, p. 360.**
5.7	Home Link Master, p. 224 Teaching Masters, pp. 68 and 69	dominoes slate number cards 1–10	overhead coins (optional) tool-kit coins
5.8	Home Link Master, p. 225		animal cards and masters
5.9	Home Link Master, p. 226 Teaching Master, p. 70	dice base-10 blocks (optional) Class Number Grid Poster	
5.10	Home Link Master, p. 227 Teaching Master, p. 46	2 dice per partnership craft sticks	20 pennies per partnership calculator paper bag
5.11	Home Link Master, p. 228	ruler rulers from Teaching Master, p. 40	calculator objects less than 1 foot long large cup or can pennies
5.12	Home Link Masters, pp. 229–231 Teaching Master, p. 71 **See Advance Preparation, p. 388.**	slate base-10 blocks	calculator
5.13	Home Link Master, p. 232 Teaching Master, p. 72	slate 2 dice per partnership	coins calculator **See Advance Preparation, p. 393.**
5.14	Home Link Masters, pp. 233–236 Assessment Masters, pp. 309–310	slate base-10 blocks 1 die per partnership	tool-kit clocks and coins tool-kit number cards

planningtips

Pacing

Pacing depends on a number of factors, such as children's individual needs and how long your school has been using *Everyday Mathematics*. At the beginning of Unit 5, review your Content by Strand Poster to help you set a monthly pace.

	← MOST CLASSROOMS →	
DECEMBER	JANUARY	FEBRUARY

Using the Projects

As you approach the New Year, use Project 5 to create a calendar for the classroom and personalized calendars for individual children. The Projects can be found at the back of this book.

Home Communication

Share Home Links 5.1–5.13 with families to help them understand the content and procedures in this unit. At the end of the unit, use Home Link 5.14 to introduce Unit 6. Supplemental information can be found in the *Home Connection Handbook*.

NCTM Standards

Standard	1	2	3	4	5	6	7	8	9	10
Unit 5 Lessons	1-13	2, 3, 6, 8, 10-13	1, 4	4, 5	9, 12	1-13	1-13	1-13	1-13	1-13

Content Standards
1 Number and Operation
2 Patterns, Functions, and Algebra
3 Geometry and Spatial Sense
4 Measurement
5 Data Analysis, Statistics, and Probability

Process Standards
6 Problem Solving
7 Reasoning and Proof
8 Communication
9 Connections
10 Representations

PRACTICE *through* Games

Everyday Mathematics uses games to help children develop good fact power and other math skills.

- Practicing comparing numbers in *Top-It* and *Secret Numbers* **(Lesson 5.3)**
- Practice making exchanges with the *Tens-and-Ones Trading Game* **(Lessons 5.3 and 5.12)** and *Penny-Nickel-Dime Exchange* **(Lesson 5.11)**
- Practice basic addition facts in *Shaker Addition Top-It* **(Lesson 5.5)** and *Beat the Calculator* **(Lesson 5.11)** *Two-Fisted Penny Addition* **(Lesson 5.5)**
- Practice adding and comparing with *Domino Top-It* **(Lesson 5.7)**
- Identify facts with *Turn-Around Facts Game* **(Lesson 5.10)**
- Practice sums of 10 in *Penny Cup* **(Lesson 5.11)**

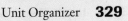

unit 5 content highlights

The notes below highlight the major content ideas presented in Unit 5. These notes may help you establish instructional priorities.

Place Value (Lessons 5.1, 5.2, and 5.5)

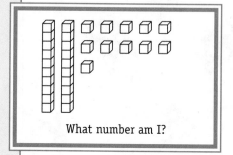

What number am I?

Most of us take our numeration system for granted, yet it is one of the most amazing of human inventions. Our numeration system makes it possible to represent any whole number or decimal, however large or small, by using one or more of the digits 0 through 9 and, sometimes, a decimal point. This is possible because the value of any digit in a numeral is determined by its position in the numeral.

An understanding of place value is essential because it forms the basis for our computational algorithms with whole numbers and decimals. In Lessons 5.1 and 5.2, children begin to explore the idea of place value—using only tens and ones at this stage—with a heavy emphasis on representing numbers with base-10 blocks. Base-10 blocks are then used in Lesson 5.5 to find the sums of 1- and 2-digit numbers. Some of these addition problems require exchanges of cubes (ones blocks) for longs (tens blocks) in order to end up with a numeral that obeys the properties of our numeration system.

Greater Than and Less Than Relationships between Two Numbers (Lesson 5.3 and 5.6)

< is less than
> is greater than
= equals, can replace, means the same as

Write the meanings of the relations symbols on the board whenever they are used in class.

Lesson 5.3 introduces the < and > symbols. These symbols are used in Lesson 5.6 in number models for number stories in which two quantities are compared.

The < and > symbols often cause children more difficulty than the ideas themselves. To help children use these symbols correctly, a reminder of their meanings is printed on most journal pages and other student materials that call for their use. Write these meanings on the board whenever the symbols are used in class. Invent your own ways to help children recall the symbols' meanings until children can remember them without prompts.

Number Stories (Lessons 5.5–5.8)

Math Journal 1, Activity Sheets 7 and 8 feature pictures of animals that can be cut apart and used as a deck of animal cards. The animal cards include information that you and children can use to make up a variety of number stories, both realistic and fanciful. The numbers on the cards vary in size and complexity, so success is possible at many different levels.

These same animal pictures are available on *Math Masters,* pages 60–65, so that they may be displayed for demonstration or arranged in many different ways to make a poster to meet the needs of the current activity.

The cards show "typical" weights and lengths (or heights) for animals, but because animals obviously come in many different sizes, using the language of estimates with children is appropriate, and in fact, essential. This is a good time to remind children that fairly large animals, including human children, come in lots of sizes and shapes and that this is a normal, useful, and inevitable fact of life.

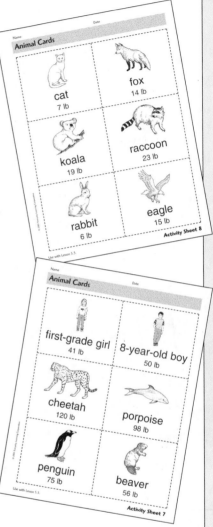

Children were introduced to "change-to-more" and "change-to-less" number stories in Unit 2 and to "parts-and-total" stories in Unit 3. In Lesson 5.7, they begin to solve comparison number stories, which involve finding the difference between two quantities. Then, in Lesson 5.8, they make up and solve all three types of number stories.

Most adults (including many teachers) are quite surprised at the number of solution methods offered and the ingenuity and thoughtfulness of children in devising and sharing their many strategies. In sessions involving mental arithmetic, some children will use subtraction when you expect addition, or addition when you expect subtraction. For example, left to their own devices, some children handle comparison problems by counting up or by asking, "What did I add?" Please don't discourage this—it is important that children see subtraction as being closely linked to addition.

Number Models (Lesson 5.8)

Until now you have been asked to write number models as one of several representations of number stories, but children have not been required to do so themselves. In this lesson children begin to write number models as "shorthand" for illustrating number stories.

As you give examples and talk about children's stories, try to vary the phrases and language used in order to help children forge links among the words, situations, and symbols. (For example, use "About how many does that equal?" "About how many is that altogether?" "About how many does that leave?" "Approximately how much bigger is that?" "Estimate how far from this to that." Please insist that children keep track of the units that go with their solutions and with their number models. For oral discussion, insist that the units be given, for example, "15 what? Years, tons, pounds?" It is often cumbersome to write the unit words next to every number in a number model, so this is a good place to use a unit box as a reminder of what the numbers mean.

Research studies show that children have only a partial understanding of the role of the = symbol in number models. They have no difficulty with number models like $3 + 8 = 11$ and $15 - 7 = 8$. But many children, even those in higher grades, reject number models like $5 = 5$ (they may say there is no problem), $4 = 2 + 2$ (they may say that the answer is on the wrong side), or $4 + 3 = 5 + 2$ (they may say there are two problems but no answers). The origin of these conceptual errors seems very clear: Children in school generally see only number models with a single number on the right of the = symbol. To prevent such misconceptions, get into the habit of writing $12 = 5 + 7$ just as often as $5 + 7 = 12$ and of consistently asking children to say "means the same as" or "looks different, but is really the same," wherever the = symbol appears.

Addition Facts (Lessons 5.9–5.11)

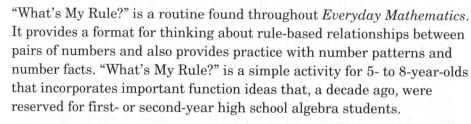

The lessons in this unit continue the work with addition facts—the *Everyday Mathematics* goal is that most children will know many of the addition facts by the end of first grade. The $+0$ and $+1$ facts should be easy to learn. Children also often have an easier time with doubles than with some of the other facts. *Two-Fisted Penny Addition* with 10 pennies, which was introduced in Unit 2, has prepared them for the facts with sums of 10. What is new and most important in these lessons is the discussion of the turn-around rule, which states that we can add numbers in any order without affecting the result. By applying this rule (formally known as the commutative property of addition), children will considerably reduce the number of facts to be learned.

Functions and "What's My Rule?" (Lessons 5.12 and 5.13)

"What's My Rule?" is a routine found throughout *Everyday Mathematics*. It provides a format for thinking about rule-based relationships between pairs of numbers and also provides practice with number patterns and number facts. "What's My Rule?" is a simple activity for 5- to 8-year-olds that incorporates important function ideas that, a decade ago, were reserved for first- or second-year high school algebra students.

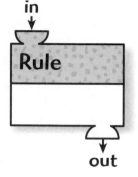

A function machine is simply a diagram or metaphor to indicate how the input and output numbers in "What's My Rule?" tables are produced. The machines are thought of as being "programmed" to take in numbers, change the numbers according to a rule, and then send out new numbers. Thus, there are three parts to a function machine and a "What's My

Rule?" table: *input* (the number that goes in), *output* (the number that comes out), and *rule* (what is done to an input number to change it to the output number). "What's My Rule?" may vary by having partial information about inputs, outputs, or rules.

One option for teaching "What's My Rule?" problems is to set up a class-size function machine so children may act out the problems. The function machine can be as simple or as elaborate as you wish. Some teachers have children sit under a desk or a table to receive the "in" numbers on slips of paper or on a slate, change those numbers according to the rule, and then return the output number on another slip of paper or on a slate. Other teachers have made a large box into a function machine, with slots labeled "in" and "out." A child sits inside the box, receives "in" numbers, changes them according to the rule, and returns the result through the "out" slot.

Moving from *Math Journal 1* to *Math Journal 2*

By the end of Unit 5, most of the *Math Journal 1* pages will have been completed. It may be worthwhile to take the time to look over the journal together with the children, discussing favorite or difficult pages. Children may be able to offer new insights regarding pages not understood earlier. Give them a chance to redo or complete pages.

Children should copy their height measurement, date, and "typical" height for first graders in their class from page 83 of *Math Journal 1* to page 215 of *Math Journal 2*.

Review and Assessment

If you are planning a quarterly assessment for Units 3–5, you may want to refer to the *Assessment Handbook*. The quarterly learning goals Class Checklist and Individual Profile of Progress checklist (*Math Masters*, pages 348–349) are useful tools for keeping track of children's progress.

> **For additional information** on the following topics, see the *Teacher's Reference Manual*:
>
> - addition and subtraction
> - functions
> - number models and number sentences
> - number stories
> - numeration and place value
> - problem solving
> - relations
> - "What's My Rule?"

5.1

Place Value: Tens and Ones

OBJECTIVE To explore place-value concepts for tens and ones.

summaries	materials

1 Teaching the Lesson

Children name numbers less than 100 represented by base-10 blocks. They exchange cubes for longs to represent numbers with the fewest number of base-10 blocks. [Numeration]

- ☐ *Math Journal 1*, pp. 96 and 97
- ☐ Teaching Master (*Math Masters,* p. 52; optional)
- ☐ Teaching Master transparency (*Math Masters,* p. 52; optional)
- ☐ tool-kit clock
- ☐ base-10 blocks (longs and cubes) or pieces that were first used in 4.10

See Advance Preparation

2 Ongoing Learning & Practice

Children solve Frames-and-Arrows problems in which the number in the first frame is missing. [Operations and Computation; Patterns, Functions, and Algebra]

Children practice and maintain skills through Math Boxes and Home Link activities.

- ☐ *Math Journal 1*, pp. 98 and 99
- ☐ Home Link Master (*Math Masters,* p. 218)

3 Options for Individualizing

Enrichment Children explore the changes in the tens digit of a number when longs are added or removed from the base-10 block representation of the number. [Numeration; Operations and Computation]

Extra Practice Children practice counting by 10s on the number grid. [Numeration]

- ☐ *Math Journal 1*, inside back cover
- ☐ base-10 blocks (longs and cubes)
- ☐ slate

Additional Information

Advance Preparation For Part 1, make a transparency of the Tens-and-Ones Mat (*Math Masters,* page 52) to use with base-10 blocks, or draw a mat on the board. Use vertical lines | and dots • to represent longs and cubes on the mat. Make a few extra copies of *Math Masters,* page 52 for children who have a difficult time keeping their journal pages flat enough when working with the base-10 blocks.

Vocabulary • **longs** • **cubes** • **tens place** • **ones place**

Getting Started

Mental Math and Reflexes

Say times on the hour, half-hour, and quarter-hour; children show them on their tool-kit clocks. *Suggestions:* 5 o'clock; quarter-to 3; quarter-past 11; half-past 7; quarter-after 10; quarter-before 6.

Children should be able to show times on the hour and many should be able to show times on the half-hour. Expect that many children may still be struggling with quarter-hour times.

Check to see that when you say a time on the hour, the hour hand is pointing directly to the number. When you say a time between hours, do not worry about the placement of the hour hand; however, check to see that children are pointing the hour hand to the interval between the correct hours.

Math Message

Use the smallest number of longs and cubes to show the number 21.

1 Teaching the Lesson

◆ Math Message Follow-Up

WHOLE-CLASS DISCUSSION

Check that children have displayed 2 longs and 1 cube to represent the number 21.

Note: If children used 1 long and 11 cubes or 0 longs and 21 cubes to show 21, discuss how to get the smallest number of blocks by exchanging 10 cubes for a long.

◆ Naming Numbers with Base-10 Blocks
(*Math Journal 1*, p. 96)

WHOLE-CLASS ACTIVITY

Use the following routine:

1. Place 3 longs and 4 cubes on your Tens-and-Ones Mat transparency or draw them on the board. Children do the same on their mats. *What number do these base-10 blocks show?* 34

2. Write the number on your mat.

Mention that the 3 **longs** stand for 3 tens and that the 4 **cubes** stand for 4 ones. *We say that the 3 in 34 is in the* **tens place** *and the 4 is in the* **ones place.**

Repeat this routine with other numbers, as needed.

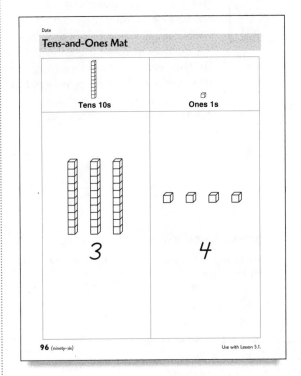

Children place 3 longs and 4 cubes on their Tens-and-Ones Mats (Journal 1, page 96)

Adjusting the Activity Have children line up the 10 cubes next to a long to ascertain that a long is the same as 10 cubes. Then replace the 10 cubes with 1 long.

 ONGOING ASSESSMENT

This is an early exposure to exchanging 10 ones for 1 ten. Encourage children to see that if the number of cubes is greater than 10, they can and should exchange 10 cubes for 1 long. They may not always make accurate exchanges due to counting or other errors.

Tens-and-Ones Riddles

Solve the riddles. Use your base-10 blocks to help you.
Example

3 ☐ and 2 ☐. What am I? __23__

1. 5 ☐ and 6 ☐. What am I? __65__

2. 2 ☐ and 7 ☐. What am I? __27__

3. 4 cubes and 6 longs. What am I? __64__

4. 7 longs and 0 cubes. What am I? __70__

Here are some harder riddles.
You will need to trade to find the answers.

5. 1 long and 11 cubes. What am I? __21__

6. 14 cubes and 2 longs. What am I? __34__

7. Make up your own riddle.
   Ask a friend to solve your riddle.
Answers vary.

STUDENT PAGE

✦ Making Exchanges with Base-10 Blocks
(*Math Journal 1*, p. 96)

WHOLE-CLASS ACTIVITY

Place 2 longs and 15 cubes on your Tens-and-Ones Mat. Children do the same on the mat in their journals. (Or use a copy of *Math Masters*, page 52.) Ask what number is shown. If children do not come up with the answer right away, give them a couple of minutes to discuss the problem among themselves. Someone might suggest trading the 2 longs for 20 cubes and then counting the total number of cubes. If no one brings it up, demonstrate the following exchange:

• Trade 10 of the cubes for 1 long and place the long in the tens column. There are now 3 longs and 5 cubes. What number is shown? 35

Repeat this routine with other combinations of longs and cubes that require an exchange.

 Adjusting the Activity To challenge children, use blocks that represent larger numbers. For example: 24 cubes and 2 longs.

Have children figure each number without making the exchanges. Share strategies for solving these problems. Expect strategies like the following:

▷ I know that 10 cubes equal 1 long, so I can trade 20 cubes for 2 longs. Then I will have 4 longs and 4 cubes left over. Since each long is 1 ten, my answer is 44.

▷ I start at 24 on the number grid and then I count up 10 for each long so I end up at 44.

✦ Numbers for Collections of Base-10 Blocks
(*Math Journal 1*, p. 97)

INDEPENDENT ACTIVITY

As children solve the riddles, encourage them to use their base-10 blocks. When most children have finished the page, you may want to have volunteers read aloud their own riddles for the class to solve.

Ongoing Learning & Practice

◆ Solving Frames-and-Arrows Diagrams
(*Math Journal 1*, p. 98)

INDEPENDENT ACTIVITY

Children solve Frames-and-Arrows problems. They use their calculators or a number line to help them count.

In each of these Frames-and-Arrows diagrams, the numbers in the first frame or two are missing. You may want to let children try solving the problems on their own. If you see many children struggling, ask volunteers to explain their strategies for solving some of the problems.

◆ Math Boxes 5.1 (*Math Journal 1*, p. 99)

INDEPENDENT ACTIVITY

Mixed Review This journal page provides opportunities for cumulative review or assessment of concepts and skills.

◆ Home Link 5.1 (*Math Masters*, p. 218)

Home Connection Children record numbers represented by base-10 blocks. To solve the challenge problem, children need to exchange 10 cubes for 1 long before they can write the number.

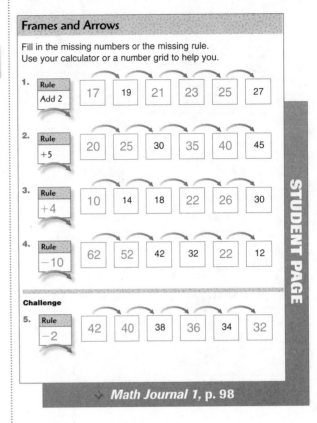

Math Journal 1, p. 98

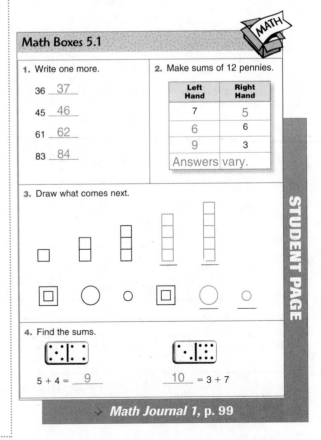

Math Journal 1, p. 99

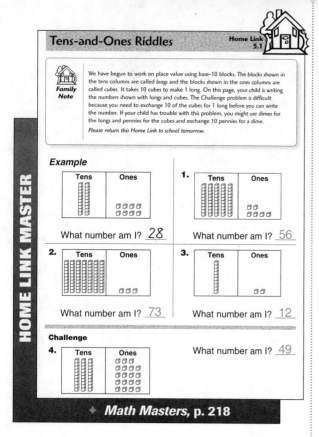

Tens-and-Ones Riddles

Home Link 5.1

Family Note

We have begun to work on place value using base-10 blocks. The blocks shown in the tens columns are called *longs* and the blocks shown in the ones columns are called *cubes*. It takes 10 cubes to make 1 long. On this page, your child is writing the numbers shown with longs and cubes. The Challenge problem is difficult because you need to exchange 10 of the cubes for 1 long before you can write the number. If your child has trouble with this problem, you might use dimes for the longs and pennies for the cubes and exchange 10 pennies for a dime.

Please return this Home Link to school tomorrow.

Example

Tens	Ones

What number am I? __28__

1.

Tens	Ones

What number am I? __56__

2.

Tens	Ones

What number am I? __73__

3.

Tens	Ones

What number am I? __12__

Challenge

4.

Tens	Ones

What number am I? __49__

✦ *Math Masters, p. 218*

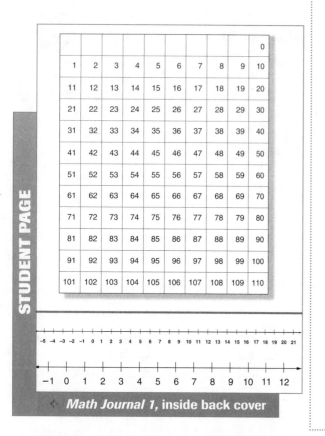

✦ *Math Journal 1, inside back cover*

Options for Individualizing

✦ ENRICHMENT Adding and Taking Away Longs (*Math Journal 1,* inside back cover)

SMALL-GROUP ACTIVITY   15–30 min

Display some longs and cubes on the transparency of the mat. Have children write the number on their slates. Add another long. Have children write the new number and circle the digit that changed. Then have them find the two numbers on their number grids on the inside back covers of their journals.

Repeat as needed. Include problems that involve removing longs instead of adding them. Mention that putting more longs on the mat is like adding tens and removing longs is like taking tens away.

• What's a quick way to count longs from any number on the number grid? Move up or down as many rows as there are longs to be counted.

✦ EXTRA PRACTICE Counting on the Number Grid (*Math Journal 1,* inside back cover)

INDEPENDENT ACTIVITY   5–15 min

Children count up and back by 10s on the number grid, beginning with any number. You may want to choose a number and demonstrate counting up and back to get children started.

5.2 Place Value with Calculators

OBJECTIVE To investigate place-value digit patterns.

summaries	materials

1 Teaching the Lesson

Children use base-10 blocks and their calculators to investigate digit patterns when 1 is added to a number with 9 in the ones place and when 10 is added to a 2-digit number. They discuss the fact that the value of a digit depends on its place in a numeral. [Numeration; Patterns, Functions, and Algebra]

- *Math Journal 1,* pp. 96, 100, and inside back cover
- Home Link 5.1
- Teaching Master (*Math Masters,* p. 53; optional)
- Teaching Master transparency (*Math Masters,* p. 53; optional)
- overhead base-10 blocks (flat, longs, and cubes; optional)
- base-10 blocks (flat, longs, and cubes)
- calculator

***See* Advance Preparation**

2 Ongoing Learning & Practice

Children revisit the *Two-Fisted Penny Addition* activity. [Operations and Computation]

Children practice and maintain skills through Math Boxes and Home Link activities.

- *Math Journal 1,* pp. 71, 72 and 101
- Home Link Master (*Math Masters,* p. 219)
- tool-kit pennies

3 Options for Individualizing

Enrichment Children discuss the similarity between the letters of the alphabet and the 10 digits used in the base-10 numeration system. [Numeration]

Extra Practice Children build structures out of base-10 blocks and write the numbers the blocks represent. [Numeration]

Extra Practice Children name 2-digit numbers with specific numbers in the tens or ones place. [Numeration]

- base-10 blocks
- slate
- half-sheet of paper
- *Minute Math®,* p. 23

Additional Information

Advance Preparation For Part 1, make a transparency of *Math Masters,* page 53 to use with overhead base-10 blocks, or draw a Place-Value Mat on the board. Make a few extra copies of *Math Masters,* page 53 for children who have a difficult time keeping their journal pages flat when working with the base-10 blocks.

Vocabulary • **flat** • **hundreds** • **hundreds place** • **digit**

Getting Started

Mental Math and Reflexes

Place 5 longs and 7 cubes on your Tens-and-Ones Mat.

- *What number do these base-10 blocks show?* 57

Have children record their answers on their slates. Remind children that 5 longs and 7 cubes stand for 5 tens and 7 ones, respectively. The 5 in 57 is in the tens place and the 7 is in the ones place.

Continue with other numbers as time allows.

Children who are having difficulty should model the numbers with base-10 blocks on the Tens-and-Ones Mat on journal page 96.

Math Message

What number comes after 9? After 39? After 99?

Home Link 5.1 Follow-Up

Go over the answers to the Home Link. If appropriate, model the numbers on a Tens-and-Ones Mat. For the Challenge problem, have a volunteer explain why it is necessary to trade 10 cubes for a long. Watch for children who answer 319. You may want to model the problem by counting on the number grid.

---

1 Teaching the Lesson

✦ Math Message Follow-Up
(*Math Journal 1*, p. 100)

WHOLE-CLASS ACTIVITY

As you discuss the numbers that come after 9 and 39, use your Place-Value Mat (see *Math Masters*, page 53), as children follow along on their mats on journal page 100.

1. Place (or draw) 9 cubes (or dots) in the ones column.

2. Add 1 cube to the ones column. Now there are 10 cubes.

3. Exchange the 10 cubes for 1 long and put it in the tens column.

Follow the same procedure when discussing what number comes after 39.

Do the following activity to discuss which number comes after 99.

✦ Adding 1 to 99

WHOLE-CLASS ACTIVITY

Ask children to use longs to cover a **flat** completely. *How many longs are needed to cover a flat?* 10 longs

Have someone choose the base-10 blocks needed to show 99 and put them on your Place-Value Mat. 9 longs and 9 cubes Then add 1 cube to the ones column to show 100.

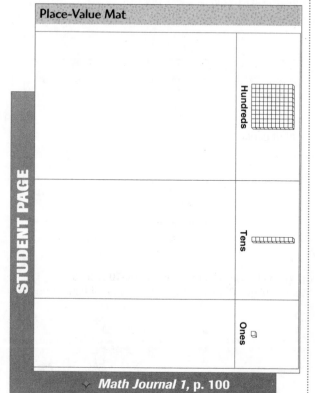

Place-Value Mat

Hundreds

Tens

Ones

Math Journal 1, p. 100

STUDENT PAGE

Ask how we can make 100, using fewer base-10 blocks. Give children plenty of time to share ideas. Exchange 10 cubes for 1 long and put that long in the tens column. Now there are 10 longs. Exchange the 10 longs for 1 flat and put that flat in the hundreds column.

Write 1, 0, 0 in the appropriate columns. Mention that the 1 in 100 stands for 1 hundred and that it is in the **hundreds place.**

NOTE: This is the first exposure to exchanges into **hundreds.** Limit the discussion to this one problem for the time being. Place value to hundreds will be revisited throughout the year.

◆Investigating Digit Patterns in Counts by 1s

WHOLE-CLASS ACTIVITY

Review how to count up by 1s on the calculator, starting at 0. Children use the following steps to program the calculator:

1. Clear the calculator.

2. Enter 0 (the starting number).

3. Press ⊕ (count up).

4. Enter 1 (the number to count by).

After children have programmed their calculators, have them press ⊜ repeatedly, and slowly, while counting together by 1s as the numbers 1 through 9 appear in their displays. Pause at 9.

Ask children what number comes next. Then have them press ⊜ once, observing the change from 9 to 0 in the ones place and the appearance of a 1 in the tens place. *What does the 1 stand for?* 1 ten

Have children continue to press ⊜ and count aloud through 40 or 50, but pause at each number with 9 in the ones place and ask children to predict the next number. Discuss the pattern. The **digit** in the tens place increases by 1, and the digit in the ones place becomes 0.

Ask children to clear their calculators and to program them to count up by 1s, starting at 85. Enter 85 ⊕ 1. Then have them press ⊜ to count past 100.

Have children count aloud, pause at the 9s, and predict transitions. If time permits, try counting past 200 from 196, for example.

◆Investigating Digit Patterns in Counts by 10s

WHOLE-CLASS ACTIVITY

Ask someone to describe how to program the calculator to count up by 10s, starting at 0. Press clear and then 0 ⊕ 10. After children have programmed their calculators, they count aloud as they press ⊜ until they get to 90. Discuss what happens to the digits in the tens place as they count by 10s. *The digit in the tens place increases by 1 with each count. Press ⊜ again. What happens?* 1 appears in the hundreds place and 0 appears in the tens place. Continue the count past 100 and observe the digit patterns.

Next, have someone choose a starting number less than 100. For example, 53. Discuss how to program the calculator to count up by 10s. *Press clear and then* 53 ⊕ 10. As children press ⊜, they observe that the tens digit increases by 1 and the ones digit does not change. Pause just before passing 100 and discuss what will happen next. Similarly, pause and discuss what will happen next just before passing 200.

Optional: By now many counts by 10s have been made on the number grid. Discuss similarities and differences between the use of calculators and the use of a number grid. *Which is faster? Which goes further?*

◆ The Role of Place in the Value of Digits
(*Math Journal 1,* inside back cover)

WHOLE-CLASS ACTIVITY 👥👥👥

Children enter a 2-digit number of their choice ending with 5 in their calculators. Record some of the numbers in a column on the board, all with 5 in the ones place.

Next, children enter a 2-digit number of their choice, beginning with 5. Record some of these numbers in another column, all with 5 in the tens place.

45 52

95 57

25 54

35 56

Have children look up each set of numbers on their number grids on the inside back covers of their journals. Numbers with 5 in the ones place are all in the same column of the number grid; numbers with 5 in the tens place are all in the same row of the number grid.

Repeat this routine for another digit. Discuss the role of the placement of digits within a number, noting how the same digit can represent different values depending on the digit's place in the number.

Ongoing Learning & Practice

◆ **Playing** *Two-Fisted Penny Addition*
(*Math Journal 1*, pp. 71 and 72)

PARTNER ACTIVITY

Partners pool their pennies to find splits of numbers greater than 10. Remind children to record their results on journal pages 71 and 72.

◆ **Math Boxes 5.2** (*Math Journal 1*, p. 101)

INDEPENDENT ACTIVITY

Mixed Review This journal page provides opportunities for cumulative review or assessment of concepts and skills.

◆ **Home Link 5.2** (*Math Masters*, p. 219)

Home Connection Children complete Frames-and-Arrows diagrams for the rules "+10" and "−10." They continue to explore the changes to the digits in a numeral when counting by 10s.

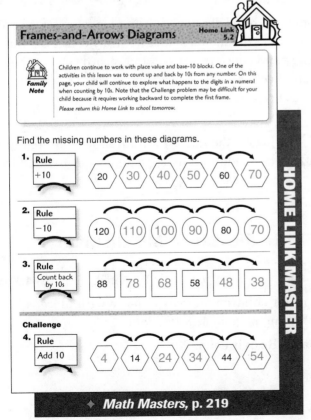

Math Masters, p. 219

Two-Fisted Penny Addition Summary (cont.)

11		12		13		14		15	
Left	Right	Left	Right	Left	Right	Left	Right	Left	Right

Answers vary. Each pair of numbers should total the number at the top of the table.

Math Journal 1, p. 71

▲ Tables continue on journal page 72.

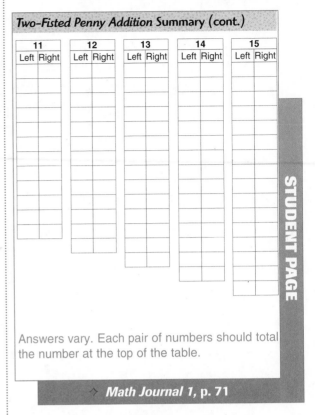

Math Boxes 5.2

1. What time is it?

quarter-before ___3___ o'clock

2. Start at 57. Count up 30.

You end at ___87___.

57
+ 30
87

3. How much money?

Ⓓ Ⓓ Ⓝ Ⓝ Ⓝ Ⓝ Ⓝ Ⓟ

___46___ ¢ or $ _0.46_

4. Circle the winner of *Top-It*.

20   22

Math Journal 1, p. 101

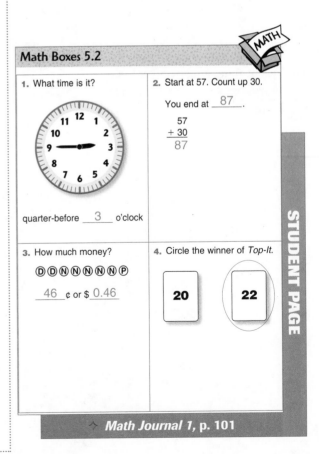

Options for Individualizing

◆ ENRICHMENT Discussing the Role of Digits in Writing Numbers

SMALL-GROUP ACTIVITY 5–15 min

 Reading Link Review the fact that there are 26 letters in our English alphabet. These 26 letters and a few symbols are all that are needed to make all the words, sentences, and stories we say, write, and read. Similarly, the digits 0–9 and a few other symbols are all that are needed to write whole numbers, fractions, decimals, and negative numbers.

Ask children how many digits there are. Write 0, 1, 2, 3, 4, 5, 6, 7, 8, and 9 on the board to verify that there are 10 digits. These 10 digits are enough to write all the counting numbers we use. Ask children to write the largest number they can say on their slates, using any combination of digits. Volunteers come up to the board to write and read their numbers.

◆ EXTRA PRACTICE Building with Base-10 Blocks

INDEPENDENT ACTIVITY 15–30 min

Children build structures using longs and cubes. When they have finished a structure, they count the number of longs and cubes they used and record the number on a half-sheet of paper. Then they record the numbers the blocks represent.

NOTE: Children can use □, l, and • to represent flats, longs, and cubes.

 Adjusting the Activity Children who are ready can use flats in addition to longs and cubes to build their structures.

◆ EXTRA PRACTICE Minute Math

SMALL-GROUP ACTIVITY 5–15 min

To offer children more experience with place value, see the following page in *Minute Math*:

Basic Routines: p. 23

5.3 Relations: Greater Than, Less Than, and Equal To

OBJECTIVE To introduce the relation symbols $<$ and $>$.

summaries	materials

1 Teaching the Lesson

Children discuss methods of distinguishing between the relation symbols $<$ and $>$. They practice using these symbols in number models by playing a variation of *Top-It*. [Numeration; Patterns, Functions, and Algebra]

- ☐ Teaching Masters (*Math Masters*, pp. 54 and 55; optional)
- ☐ Home Link 5.2
- ☐ slate
- ☐ tool-kit number cards

2 Ongoing Learning & Practice

Children play the *Tens-and-Ones Trading Game*. [Numeration]

Children practice and maintain skills through Math Boxes and Home Link activities.

- ☐ *Math Journal 1*, pp. 96, 102, and 103
- ☐ Home Link Master (*Math Masters*, p. 220)
- ☐ die
- ☐ base-10 blocks (cubes and longs)

3 Options for Individualizing

Extra Practice Children play *Secret Number* on the calculator. [Numeration]

Extra Practice Children name numbers that are 10 more or 10 less than given numbers. [Numeration]

- ☐ tool-kit number cards
- ☐ calculator
- ☐ *Minute Math*®, p. 24

Additional Information

Vocabulary • **is more than** • **is less than**

Getting Started

Mental Math and Reflexes

Dictate pairs of numbers. Have children write them on their slates and circle the larger or smaller number. *Suggestions:*

- Write 52 and 58. Circle the smaller number. 52
- Write 31 and 61. Circle the larger number. 61
- Write 27 and 72. Circle the smaller number. 27
- Write 43 and 34. Circle the larger number. 43

Continue as time allows. Adjust the size of the numbers to the ability of your class. Have children share their strategies. Check whether children are focusing on the tens place of each number. Remind them to think of the value of the digits.

Math Message

Henry has 2 nickels and a dime. Ada has 2 dimes and a nickel. Who has more money?

Home Link 5.2 Follow-Up

Briefly review answers. Have volunteers describe the patterns they notice in the completed diagrams.

- How would you use the number grid to help you complete the diagrams? How would you use the calculator?

---

1 Teaching the Lesson

◆ Math Message Follow-Up

WHOLE-CLASS DISCUSSION

Draw coins on the board to represent Ada's and Henry's money. Elicit from the class that Ada has *more* money than Henry because 25 cents (2 dimes and a nickel) *is more than* 20 cents (2 nickels and a dime). Write the following sentence on the board: 25 cents is more than 20 cents.

Tell the class that another way to compare Ada's and Henry's money is to say that Henry has *less* money than Ada because 20 cents *is less than* 25 cents. Write the following sentence on the board, next to the first sentence: 20 cents is less than 25 cents.

◆ Introducing the > and < Relation Symbols
(*Math Masters,* pp. 54 and 55)

WHOLE-CLASS ACTIVITY

Remind children that they have been using the symbol = in number models to stand for the words *is equal to* or *equals*. In the same way, they can use symbols for the words **is more than** and **is less than.** Introduce the symbol > for *is more than* and < for *is less than.* Use the large symbols on *Math Masters,* pages 54 and 55 for display. Children write the symbols on their slates.

▼ Large versions of the symbols < , > and = can be found on *Math Masters,* page 54.

Relation Symbols

< means "is less than."

> means "is more than."

= means "is the same as."

= means "is equal to."

TEACHING MASTER

◆ *Math Masters,* p. 55

Then write 25 cents > 20 cents and 20 cents < 25 cents under the two sentences on the board that express the number relations. (see margin).

Mention that it takes a while to learn which symbol means *is more than* and which symbol means *is less than*. *Can anyone describe an easy way to tell them apart?* Suggest the following strategies:

Strategy 1

Use various animal-related analogies. For example: the animal's open mouth must be larger to swallow the larger number.

Strategy 2

The < symbol for *is less than* looks like the left-hand finger and thumb.

Strategy 3

The meeting point of the two lines always points to the smaller number; the open part of the two lines always points to the larger number.

Strategy 4

Put two heavy dots next to the larger number and one heavy dot next to the smaller number. Then connect the dots to make the symbol.

Dictate pairs of numbers. Have children write them on their slates and write the symbol < or > between them. *Suggestions:* 3 and 12; 9 and 20; 24 and 18; 30 and 27; 14 and 40.

◆ Playing *Top-It* with Relation Symbols

PARTNER ACTIVITY

Players take out their tool-kit number cards and set aside the +, −, ×, ÷, ? cards and the two wild cards, which are not used in the game. They take out the <, >, and = cards, which they will need. Players combine the rest of the cards (the numbers) into a single deck, mix them, and put them in a stack on the table, facedown.

Players sit next to each other. Each partner turns over a card from the top of the stack and places the card faceup next to his or her partner's card with a space between them.

One player then places the correct relation symbol (<, >, or =) between the cards and reads the resulting number model. The player with the larger number then takes both number cards.

When putting the two number cards on the table, players should place them in the same position each time—the first player's card on the left, the second player's card on

25 > 20

20 < 25

20 < 25

25 > 20

Adjusting the Activity Each child takes one card from the top of the deck, places it on the table faceup, then takes another card and places it to the right of the first card; that is, the first card drawn goes in the tens place and the second card goes in the ones place. The game then proceeds as described at left. An alternative is for each player to take two cards at once and choose which card to put in the tens place.

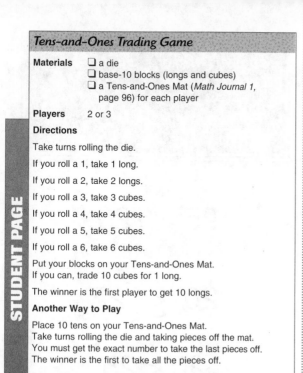

Tens-and-Ones Trading Game

Materials	❑ a die
	❑ base-10 blocks (longs and cubes)
	❑ a Tens-and-Ones Mat (*Math Journal 1*, page 96) for each player
Players	2 or 3

Directions

Take turns rolling the die.

If you roll a 1, take 1 long.

If you roll a 2, take 2 longs.

If you roll a 3, take 3 cubes.

If you roll a 4, take 4 cubes.

If you roll a 5, take 5 cubes.

If you roll a 6, take 6 cubes.

Put your blocks on your Tens-and-Ones Mat. If you can, trade 10 cubes for 1 long.

The winner is the first player to get 10 longs.

Another Way to Play

Place 10 tens on your Tens-and-Ones Mat. Take turns rolling the die and taking pieces off the mat. You must get the exact number to take the last pieces off. The winner is the first to take all the pieces off.

◇ *Math Journal 1, p. 102*

STUDENT PAGE

---

the right. Children should take turns choosing the relation symbol and reading the resulting number model.

Circulate to assess children's ability to determine the correct symbol and to read the number model. Remind children of the strategies for distinguishing between the < symbol and the > symbol.

ONGOING ASSESSMENT
Children record the number models for one or two rounds on their slates, or on a half-sheet of paper.

2 Ongoing Learning & Practice

✦ Playing the *Tens-and-Ones Trading Game* (*Math Journal 1*, p. 102)

PARTNER ACTIVITY

Players take turns putting base-10 blocks on their Tens-and-Ones Mat according to the roll of a die. Whenever possible, they exchange 10 cubes for 1 long. The first player to get 10 longs wins.

✦ Math Boxes 5.3 (*Math Journal 1*, p. 103)

INDEPENDENT ACTIVITY

Mixed Review This journal page provides opportunities for cumulative review or assessment of concepts and skills.

Math Boxes 5.3

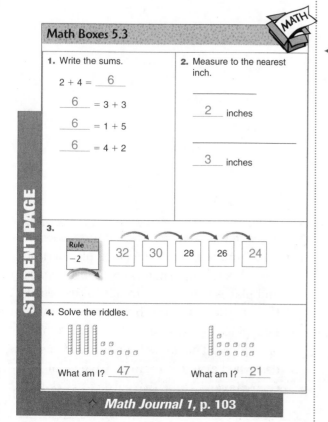

1. Write the sums.

    $2 + 4 =$ __6__

    __6__ $= 3 + 3$

    __6__ $= 1 + 5$

    __6__ $= 4 + 2$

2. Measure to the nearest inch.

    __2__ inches

    __3__ inches

3.

Rule
−2

    | 32 | 30 | 28 | 26 | 24 |

4. Solve the riddles.

    What am I? __47__

    What am I? __21__

◇ *Math Journal 1, p. 103*

STUDENT PAGE

348 **Unit 5** *Place Value, Number Stories, and Basic Facts*

◆ Home Link 5.3 (*Math Masters*, p. 220)

Home Connection Children enter the correct relation symbols between pairs of numbers. Strategies for helping children remember the symbols are provided for parents.

3 Options for Individualizing

◆ EXTRA PRACTICE Playing *Secret Number*

PARTNER ACTIVITY   **15–30 min**

Each partner secretly enters a number less than 100 on his or her calculator. They show each other their numbers and take turns comparing them, using such phrases as *less than, smaller than, larger than, greater than, more than, same as, is equal to,* and *equals.*

 Adjusting the Activity To extend the activity, have children put down their calculators and place the correct symbol card between them.

◆ EXTRA PRACTICE Minute Math

SMALL-GROUP ACTIVITY   **5–15 min**

To offer children more experience with number comparisons, see the following page in *Minute Math:*

Basic Routines: p. 24

PLANNING AHEAD
Starting in Lesson 5.5, each child will need his or her own set of animal cards. These cards are found on Activity Sheets 7 and 8 at the back of the journal. Instead of having children cut them apart, you or an aide may want to do so before the start of the lesson.

NOTE: To assist non-native English speakers with the language of comparisons, pair them with native English speakers.

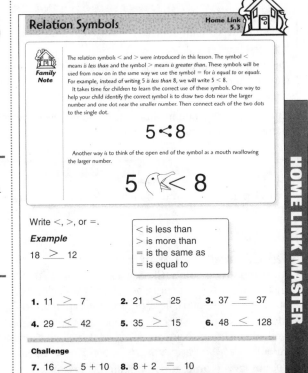

Relation Symbols   Home Link 5.3

Family Note The relation symbols < and > were introduced in this lesson. The symbol < means *is less than* and the symbol > means *is greater than.* These symbols will be used from now on in the same way we use the symbol = for *is equal to* or *equals.* For example, instead of writing 5 *is less than* 8, we will write 5 < 8.

It takes time for children to learn the correct use of these symbols. One way to help your child identify the correct symbol is to draw two dots near the larger number and one dot near the smaller number. Then connect each of the two dots to the single dot.

$$5 < 8$$

Another way is to think of the open end of the symbol as a mouth swallowing the larger number.

$$5 < 8$$

Write <, >, or =.

Example

18 $\underline{>}$ 12

| < is less than |
| > is more than |
| = is the same as |
| = is equal to |

1. 11 $\underline{>}$ 7   **2.** 21 $\underline{<}$ 25   **3.** 37 $\underline{=}$ 37

4. 29 $\underline{<}$ 42   **5.** 35 $\underline{>}$ 15   **6.** 48 $\underline{<}$ 128

Challenge

7. 16 $\underline{>}$ 5 + 10   **8.** 8 + 2 $\underline{=}$ 10

◆ *Math Masters, p. 220*

HOME LINK MASTER

5.4
EXPLORATIONS

Exploring Area, Weight, and Counting

OBJECTIVES To explore area by counting units; to weigh objects with a pan balance; and to practice rational counting.

---

summaries   materials

1 Teaching the Lesson

Exploration A: Following a demonstration of finding area by covering a surface with a unit, children estimate the area of a surface, cover it, and count units to check their estimates. [Measurement and Reference Frames]

Exploration B: Children use a pan balance to find sets of objects that weigh the same. [Measurement and Reference Frames]

Exploration C: Children devise and carry out a plan for counting a large number of pennies. [Numeration]

☐ *Math Journal 1*, p. 96; base-10 blocks; Home Link 5.3

Exploration A: Per small group:
☐ Teaching Master (*Math Masters*, p. 56)
☐ objects to use as units

Exploration B: Per partnership:
☐ Teaching Master (*Math Masters*, p. 57)
☐ pan balance
☐ sets of objects

Exploration C: Per small group:
☐ Teaching Master (*Math Masters*, p. 58; optional)
☐ tool-kit coins and extra pennies
☐ slate; quarter-sheet of paper
***See* Advance Preparation**

2 Ongoing Learning & Practice

Children revisit math games. [Numeration; Measurement and Reference Frames]

Children estimate the number of cubes needed to cover squares and then check their estimates by actually covering the squares. [Measurement and Reference Frames]

Children practice and maintain skills through Math Boxes and Home Link activities.

☐ *Math Journal 1*, p. 104
☐ Teaching Master (*Math Masters*, p. 59)
☐ Home Link Master (*Math Masters*, p. 221)
☐ 64 cubes
☐ materials for math games

3 Options for Individualizing

Extra Practice Children count nickels and dimes forward and back from any amount. [Measurement and Reference Frames]

☐ *Minute Math*®, p. 35

Additional Information

Advance Preparation Choose a surface and a unit for the Math Message. For **Exploration A,** collect objects to use as units, such as blocks, index cards, and floor or wall tiles. For **Exploration B,** you will need a pan balance and sets of objects such as pennies, cubes, longs, flats, or dice. For **Exploration C,** add about 50 pennies to each group's tool-kit pennies.

Math Masters page 58 gives directions for **Exploration C.** You may want to place copies of this master at the appropriate workstations if aides are helping children with this activity. However, this master is not required to do the Exploration. On the other hand, *Math Masters* pages 56 and 57 are required for **Exploration A** and **Exploration B.**

Vocabulary • area • pan balance

Getting Started

Mental Math and Reflexes

Place 4 longs and 9 cubes on your Tens-and-Ones Mat.

• What number do these base-10 blocks show? 49

Children record the answer on their slates.

Remind children that 4 longs and 9 cubes stand for 4 tens and 9 ones. The 4 is in the tens place and the 9 is in the ones place. Continue with other numbers as time allows.

Before recording the number on their slates, children who are having difficulty might model the numbers with base-10 blocks on their Tens-and-Ones Mats on journal page 96.

To extend the activity, try the routine with the following:

▷ base-10 block combinations that require exchanges; for example, 3 longs and 17 cubes.

▷ numbers in the hundreds, using the Place-Value Mat on journal page 100.

Math Message

About how many pieces of (unit) *would you need to cover* (surface)*?* (Post one of the units and indicate the surface to be covered. For example, a playing card and a child's desk top.)

Home Link 5.3 Follow-Up

Briefly review answers. Have children share strategies for solving the Challenge problems.

1 Teaching the Lesson

✦ Math Message Follow-Up

WHOLE-CLASS ACTIVITY

Share answers and strategies. Explain that you can measure and compare the sizes of tabletops, desktops, floors, and other surfaces in a way that is different from using a ruler by finding how many of a unit will cover the surface. Tell children that the unit is usually in the shape of a rectangle or a square.

✦ Covering a Surface

WHOLE-CLASS ACTIVITY

Demonstrate how the rectangular units need to fit closely over a surface without overlaps or gaps between them, as shown in the margin. Explain that there may be open spaces along the edges that can't be filled with whole units. The final count of units can be estimated by adding on *half-units* for larger spaces and ignoring smaller spaces.

Have children act out and solve the Math Message. All children (or groups) should use the same unit. Stress the idea that the surface should be covered completely with no overlaps and no gaps.

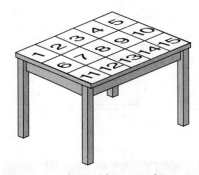

Covering a surface with no overlaps or gaps

Tabletop Area

Materials
- ❑ "units" like same-size blocks, paper, large floor tiles, or same-size books
- ❑ a flat surface
- ❑ slate

Work with the children in your group.   *Answers vary.*

1. Choose a unit and a surface to cover.

   Our unit: _____

   Our surface: _____

2. Estimate how many units you need to cover the surface.

   _____

3. Talk about your estimate with others in your group.

   If you want to change your estimate, write it here.

   _____

4. Cover the surface with units. Count the units.

   Was your estimate close? _____

5. Cover the surface with a different unit.

   Which of the two units is larger? _____

   Did you need more of the larger
   units or more of the smaller units? ___*smaller*___

◆ *Math Masters, p. 56*

TEACHING MASTER

Explore with the Pan Balance

Materials
- ❑ a pan balance
- ❑ sets of objects, such as pennies, base-10 blocks, pattern blocks, paper clips, unused pencils, new crayons

Place objects in the pans to make them balance.

1.

     1 pencil _____ pennies

2.

     2 dice _____ cubes

Choose your own objects.

3.

     _____

4.

     _____

Answers vary.

◆ *Math Masters, p. 57*

TEACHING MASTER

◆ Exploration A: Estimating and Finding the Area of a Surface (*Math Masters*, p. 56)

SMALL-GROUP ACTIVITY

Children work in groups to cover a surface. Before they begin, have them estimate the number of units needed. Encourage conversations about how to estimate. Observe as they cover the surface and count units. Tell them that the result is called the **area** of the surface. *Suggestions:*

▷ Use index cards or playing cards to cover a desktop.

▷ Use pattern-block squares to cover the journal cover.

▷ Use dominoes to cover a slate.

When all the groups have completed this Exploration, bring the class together to discuss estimates and share results.

 Adjusting the Activity If you have a skilled group, encourage them to measure the same surface a second time with a unit of a different size. Discuss why it takes more of some units than others.

◆ Exploration B: Finding Sets of Objects that Weigh the Same (*Math Masters*, p. 57)

PARTNER ACTIVITY

Children use a **pan balance** to find out how many of one kind of object weigh about the same as a number of another kind of object. For example: how many pennies weigh about the same as a pencil). Children record their results on *Math Masters*, page 57.

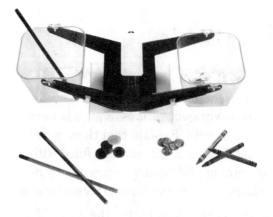

NOTE: Before children begin to use the pan balance, check that the two pans balance when empty. Adjust them if necessary. (A bit of modeling clay on the lighter side usually works well.)

✦ Exploration C: Counting Large Numbers of Pennies (*Math Masters*, p. 58)

SMALL-GROUP ACTIVITY

Children combine their tool-kit pennies with the extra pennies you have provided. (*See* Advance Preparation.) They discuss the best way to share the work of counting the pennies and how to check the total for accuracy.

Encourage children to use their slates. Have them prepare a group report by recording the total number of pennies on a quarter-sheet of paper. The final step is to return the tool-kit pennies to their owners.

After the children in all groups have completed this Exploration, bring the class together to share how they went about completing the task.

Adjusting the Activity Have children exchange pennies for dimes and nickels and show the same amount with the fewest possible coins. They can record their work on a half-sheet of paper. (See below.)

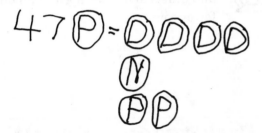

---

2 Ongoing Learning & Practice

✦ Estimating Approximate Area
(*Math Masters*, p. 59)

INDEPENDENT ACTIVITY

Children estimate the number of base-10 cubes needed to cover a 5 cm-by-5 cm square and an 8 cm-by-8 cm square. They check their estimates by covering the squares with ones cubes.

Pile of Money

Materials ☐ all your pennies and about 50 extra pennies

☐ slate

1. Count your pennies. Write the number on your slate.

2. Work with the children in your group. Put your pennies in a pile with everyone else's pennies. Add the extra pennies to the pile.

    Your job is to count the pennies in the pile.

    Before you start counting, make a plan.

    • How will you keep track of your pennies as you count?

    • Make sure everybody gets to count some pennies. How will you do that?

    • How will you check that your count is correct?

3. Record the final total on a quarter-sheet of paper.

4. Take back your pennies and put them in your tool kit.

✦ *Math Masters*, p. 58

TEACHING MASTER

Area

Guess how many cubes are needed to cover each square. Then cover each square with cubes to check your guess.

1. I think it will take

    _____ cubes to cover this square.

    It took _____ cubes to cover this square.

2. I think it will take

    _____ cubes to cover this square.

    It took _____ cubes to cover this square.

    Answers vary.

✦ *Math Masters*, p. 59

TEACHING MASTER

Student Page

Math Boxes 5.4

1. Count up by 10s. You may use a calculator.

77, 87, _97_,

_107_, _117_, _127_,

_137_, _147_, _157_,

_167_, _177_

2.

```
  7      2
+ 3    + 6
 10      8
```

```
  2      8
+ 2    + 1
  4      9
```

3. Record today's temperature.

Answers vary. °F

Odd or even?

Answers vary.

4. Draw the hands.

quarter-to 6 o'clock

✦ *Math Journal 1, p. 104*

Home Link Master

Counting Coins   Home Link 5.4

Family Note

Children are continuing to practice counting coins. The Challenge problem is difficult because the coins are not in any particular order. It might help to sort real coins into groups of like coins (all dimes together, all nickels together) before counting. To find a combination with fewer coins, exchange pennies for nickels and nickels for dimes. Many children are still learning to write amounts of money using dollars-and-cents notation. We will continue to practice this skill during the year.

Please return this Home Link to school tomorrow.

(P) 1 cent	(N) 5 cents	(D) 10 cents
$0.01	$0.05	$0.10
a penny	a nickel	a dime

How much? Write each answer in cents and in dollars-and-cents notation.

1. (D)(N)(N)(N)(N)(P)(P) _32_ ¢ or $ _0.32_

2. (D)(N)(N)(N)(N)(N)(P) _36_ ¢ or $ _0.36_

3. (D)(D)(N)(N)(N)(P)(P)(P) _38_ ¢ or $ _0.38_

Challenge

4. (P)(P)(N)(P)(D)(D)(N)(D)(N)(P)(P) _50_ ¢ or $ _0.50_

On the back of this paper show this amount with fewer coins. Use (P), (N), and (D).

✦ *Math Masters, p. 221*

◆ Playing a Math Game

PARTNER ACTIVITY 👥

Depending on their needs, children can play *Time Match* (see Lesson 4.4), *Two-Fisted Penny Addition* for numbers greater than 10 (see Lesson 2.3), or *Dime, Nickel, Penny Grab* (see Lesson 3.12).

◆ Math Boxes 5.4 (*Math Journal 1,* p. 104)

INDEPENDENT ACTIVITY 👤

Mixed Review This journal page provides opportunities for cumulative review or assessment of concepts and skills.

◆ Home Link 5.4 (*Math Masters,* p. 221)

Home Connection Children calculate the values of combinations of pennies, nickels, and dimes and show a given amount with fewer coins.

---

3 Options for Individualizing

◆ EXTRA PRACTICE Minute Math

SMALL-GROUP ACTIVITY 👥👥 **5–15 min**

To offer children more practice with counting nickels and dimes forward and back, see the following page in *Minute Math:*

Counting: p. 35

5.5

Animal Weights

OBJECTIVE To explore addition of 2-digit numbers.

summaries	**materials**

1 Teaching the Lesson

Children use base-10 blocks to find the total weight of pairs of animals. [Numeration; Operations and Computation]

- ☐ *Math Journal 1,* pp. 105, 106, and Activity Sheets 7 and 8
- ☐ Home Link 5.4
- ☐ Teaching Masters (*Math Masters,* pp. 60–65)
- ☐ Place-Value Mat
- ☐ scissors
- ☐ base-10 blocks (longs and cubes)

***See* Advance Preparation**

2 Ongoing Learning & Practice

Children play *Shaker Addition Top-It.* [Numeration; Operations and Computation]

Children practice and maintain skills through Math Boxes and Home Link activities.

- ☐ *Math Journal 1,* p. 107
- ☐ Teaching Master (*Math Masters,* p. 51)
- ☐ Home Link Master (*Math Masters,* p. 222)
- ☐ two 6-sided dice, or two polyhedral dice marked 0–9
- ☐ 20 pennies/counters for each small group

3 Options for Individualizing

Extra Practice Children play *Animal Weight Top-It.* [Numeration; Operations and Computation]

Extra Practice Children solve problems involving 2-digit addition. [Operations and Computation]

- ☐ animal cards
- ☐ *Minute Math®,* pp. 10, 16, and 39

Additional Information

Advance Preparation In this lesson, you and the children will use data about animals in problem-solving activities. A set of animal masters is provided for posing and discussing a variety of problems. These masters can be arranged into classroom-sized posters; the arrangements of the masters will vary depending on the activity. For example, you might arrange the masters into a poster to match a specific journal page or in other combinations so that children can use them to create mental-arithmetic problems.

In this unit, the 12 animals on *Math Masters,* pages 60 through 65 are used. There are two animals on each master, so cut each master in half. Activity Sheets at the back of their journals provide each child with a set of animal cards to match the animals on the masters. You may want to cut them apart ahead of time, or allow time for children to do so themselves. When not using the cards, children store them in small envelopes in their tool kits.

Getting Started

Mental Math and Reflexes

Show a domino on the overhead projector or draw one on the board. On their slates, children write a number fact using the domino numbers. Show dominoes such as the following:

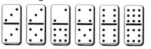

Math Message

A fox weighs 14 pounds.
An eagle weighs 15 pounds.
What is their total weight?

Home Link 5.4 Follow-Up

Briefly go over the answers to the problems and record the answers on the board in both cents and dollars-and-cents notation.

Have children share strategies for finding the total for the Challenge problem and for showing the amount with fewer coins.

Total	
29	
Part	**Part**
14	15

14 lb + 15 lb = 29 lb

▼ Children's animal cards continue on Activity Sheet 8.

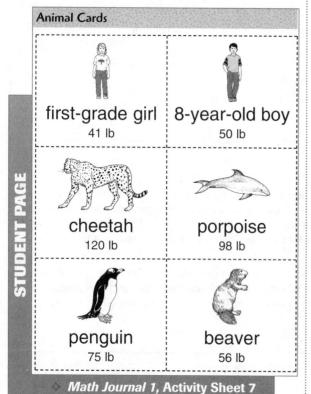

Animal Cards

first-grade girl 41 lb	8-year-old boy 50 lb
cheetah 120 lb	porpoise 98 lb
penguin 75 lb	beaver 56 lb

◆ *Math Journal 1,* **Activity Sheet 7**

STUDENT PAGE

1 Teaching the Lesson

◆ Math Message Follow-Up

WHOLE-CLASS DISCUSSION

Children share their solution strategies. They may have used a variety of strategies, such as modeling with counters or with base-10 blocks, or counting up on the number line or number grid. To summarize, draw a parts-and-total diagram for the number story and write a number model on the board.

◆ Using Base-10 Blocks to Find Total Weight
(*Math Journal 1,* Activity Sheets 7 and 8)

WHOLE-CLASS ACTIVITY

Give children a few minutes to look through their sets of animal cards from Activity Sheets 7 and 8. Point out that the same animal is shown on both sides of a card. A weight for the animal is given on one side and a height or length on the other side. Call their attention to the symbol *lb* for *pound.*

Discuss the fact that the weights and heights shown on the cards are measures one might expect such an animal to have, but that weights and heights vary from animal to animal, just as different children weigh different amounts and are different heights.

Write a unit box for pounds on the board. Display your pictures of the raccoon and the fox from *Math Masters*, pages 62 and 63. Ask children to take out their base-10 blocks.

Demonstrate on the overhead projector or on the board how to use base-10 blocks to find the total weight of the raccoon (23 lb) and the fox (14 lb). On the Place-Value Mat, place 2 longs and 3 cubes to represent the weight of the raccoon, and 1 long and 4 cubes to represent the weight of the fox. Together, there are 3 longs and 7 cubes which represent the number 37 (pounds), the total weight of the two animals.

Display masters of the koala (19 lb) and the cat (7 lb).

On their Place-Value Mats, children use their base-10 blocks to find the total weight of these animals. Ask them to describe what they did to find the answer. As a first step, they probably got a total of 1 long and 16 cubes (1 long and 9 cubes for the koala and 7 cubes for the cat). Review how to exchange the 16 cubes for 1 long and 6 cubes, for a total of 2 longs and 6 cubes, or 26.

Repeat this routine for the following pairs of animals. Each time, children use their base-10 blocks to represent the weight of the animals.

▷ The boy and the girl 5 longs and 4 longs, 1 cube = 9 longs, 1 cube; or 91

▷ The raccoon and the eagle 2 longs, 3 cubes and 1 long, 5 cubes = 3 longs, 8 cubes; or 38

▷ The cat and the eagle 7 cubes and 1 long, 5 cubes = 1 long, 12 cubes = 2 longs, 2 cubes; or 22

▷ The koala and the fox 1 long, 9 cubes and 1 long, 4 cubes = 2 longs, 13 cubes = 3 longs, 3 cubes; or 33

ONGOING ASSESSMENT
· Check that children understand that they are to exchange 10 cubes for 1 long whenever possible.
· Watch for children who are writing 3-digit answers to the problems.

 Adjusting the Activity To challenge children, have them find the total weight of the penguin and the girl. 7 longs, 5 cubes and 4 longs, and 1 cube = 11 longs and 6 cubes = 1 flat, 1 long, and 6 cubes = 116

You might also ask children to find the total weight of three animals, for example, the rabbit, the raccoon, and the cat.

Animal Posters

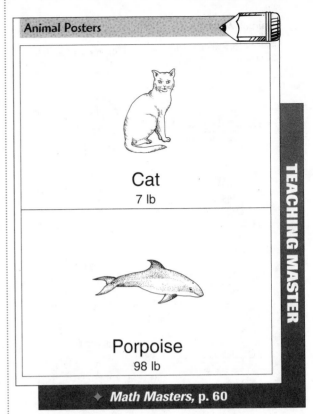

Cat
7 lb

Porpoise
98 lb

◆ *Math Masters,* p. 60

Pictures of other animals may be found on *Math Masters,* pages 61–65.

The *Math Masters* picture the following:

Cheetah: 120 lb	Fox: 14 lb
Koala: 19 lb	Rabbit: 6 lb
Beaver: 56 lb	First-grade girl: 41 lb
Raccoon: 23 lb	8-year-old boy: 50 lb
Penguin: 75 lb	Eagle: 15 lb

Science Link

Invite volunteers to tell any facts they know about the animals shown on the masters. Encourage children to name the type of covering each animal has (fur, feathers, or skin), as well as its method of movement (flying, walking/running, hopping, or swimming).

Animal Weights

Find the total weight of the 2 animals.

"lb" means "pound."

1.

7 lb   6 lb   ? lb

7 lb + 6 lb = __13__ lb

2.

6 lb   14 lb   ? lb

6 lb + 14 lb = __20__ lb

3.

7 lb   23 lb   ? lb

7 lb + 23 lb = __30__ lb

4.

56 lb   6 lb   ? lb

56 lb + 6 lb = __62__ lb

◆ *Math Journal 1, p. 105*

STUDENT PAGE

◆ Finding Total Weight
(*Math Journal 1*, pp. 105 and 106)

INDEPENDENT ACTIVITY

On journal page 105, children find the total weight of pairs of animals.

To complete journal page 106, children mix their animal cards and place them in a stack on the table, weight-side down. They turn over the two top cards, find the total weight of the animals, and fill in the names of the animals and their combined weight in their journals. Children may use any method they wish to find the answers—counters, doodles, a number line, a number grid, or base-10 blocks.

2 Ongoing Learning & Practice

◆ Playing *Shaker Addition Top-It*
(*Math Masters*, p. 51)

PARTNER OR SMALL-GROUP ACTIVITY

Children practice addition facts by playing *Shaker Addition Top-It*. For detailed instructions, see Lesson 4.12.

More Animal Weights

Take 2 animal cards. Write each animal's name and weight. Find their total weight. Answers vary.

1. The _____ weighs _____ pounds.

   The _____ weighs _____ pounds.

   Together, they weigh _____ pounds.

2. The _____ weighs _____ pounds.

   The _____ weighs _____ pounds.

   Together, they weigh _____ pounds.

3. The _____ weighs _____ pounds.

   The _____ weighs _____ pounds.

   Together, they weigh _____ pounds.

4. The _____ weighs _____ pounds.

   The _____ weighs _____ pounds.

   Together, they weigh _____ pounds.

5. Make up an animal story. Ask your partner to solve it.

◆ *Math Journal 1, p. 106*

STUDENT PAGE

Write Addition Facts

TEACHING MASTER

◆ *Math Masters, p. 51*

◆ **Math Boxes 5.5** (*Math Journal 1*, p. 107)

INDEPENDENT ACTIVITY

Mixed Review This journal page provides opportunities for cumulative review or assessment of concepts and skills.

◆ **Home Link 5.5** (*Math Masters*, p. 222)

Home Connection Children find missing addends and sums for dominoes. Children are challenged to draw a domino of their choice and write an addition fact to go with it.

3 Options for Individualizing

◆ **EXTRA PRACTICE** Playing *Animal Weight Top-It*

PARTNER ACTIVITY **15–30 min**

Players combine their decks of animal cards, mix them, and place them in a stack on the table, weight-side down.

Player A turns over the two top cards from the stack. Player B turns over the next card from the top of the stack. Player A finds the total weight of the animals on his or her two cards and tells whether these two animals together weigh more or less than Player B's animal. If they weigh more, Player A takes all three cards. If they weigh less, Player B takes all three cards. Players then trade roles. The game is over when all cards from the stack have been played.

◆ **EXTRA PRACTICE** Minute Math

SMALL-GROUP ACTIVITY **5–15 min**

To offer children more experience with 2-digit addition, see the following pages in *Minute Math*:

Basic Routines: pp. 10 and 16

Operations: p. 39

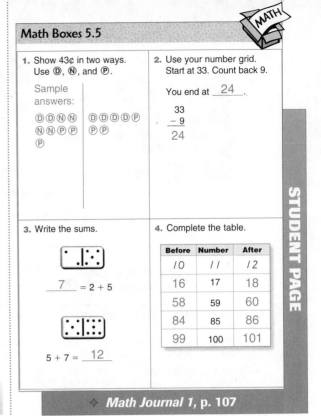

◆ *Math Journal 1*, p. 107

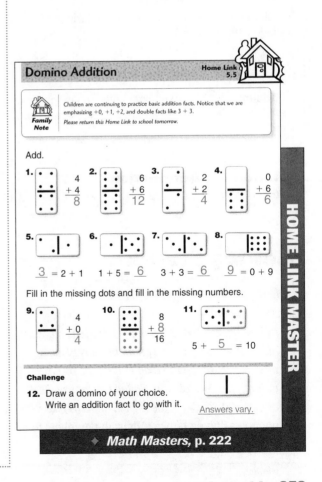

◆ *Math Masters*, p. 222

5.6 More Than and Less Than Number Stories

OBJECTIVES To make up *more than* and *less than* number stories; and to write number models for number stories.

summaries	materials

1 Teaching the Lesson

Children make up stories comparing the weights of animals and write number models for their number stories. [Numeration; Patterns, Functions, and Algebra]

- ☐ *Math Journal 1*, pp. 96 and 108
- ☐ Home Link 5.5
- ☐ Teaching Masters (*Math Masters*, pp. 54 and 55; optional)
- ☐ animal cards and masters
- ☐ slate

***See* Advance Preparation**

2 Ongoing Learning & Practice

Children put their animal cards in order by weight. [Numeration; Measurement and Reference Frames]

Children practice and maintain skills through Math Boxes and Home Link activities.

- ☐ *Math Journal 1*, pp. 109 and 110
- ☐ Home Link Master (*Math Masters*, p. 223)
- ☐ animal cards and masters

3 Options for Individualizing

Enrichment Children compare the total weight of two animals to the weight of a third animal. [Numeration; Operations and Computation]

- ☐ Teaching Masters (*Math Masters*, pp. 66 and 67)
- ☐ animal cards

Additional Information

Advance Preparation Arrange the animal masters into a poster in such a way that they can be easily rearranged.

Getting Started

Mental Math and Reflexes

Write the number:

- *before 30.* 29 *Circle the digit in the tens place.* 2
- *after 19.* 20 *Circle the digit in the tens place.* 2
- *after 39.* 40 *Circle the digit in the tens place.* 4
- *before 60.* 59 *Circle the digit in the tens place.* 5
- *before 100.* 99 *Circle the digit in the tens place.* the first 9

Continue as time permits. Adjust the numbers to suit the abilities of the children in your class.

Math Message

Which is largest? (Remove pictures of four obviously different-size animals from your poster and display them.)

Home Link 5.5 Follow-Up

Briefly review answers. Have volunteers share their own domino facts with the class.

Teaching the Lesson

◆ Math Message Follow-Up

WHOLE-CLASS DISCUSSION

Agree on an answer. Then review the meanings of the relation symbols < and >, using the usual variations in wording.

Display pairs of animal pictures used in the Math Message activity and place a relation symbol between them. As you do, ask: *Is this right?*

◆ Introducing Number Models for Relation Number Stories

WHOLE-CLASS ACTIVITY

Display two of the animal pictures with the correct < or > symbol between them. Tell a number story about the animals, such as the following:

• On Monday morning, the zookeeper weighed some of the animals. She found that the penguin weighed more than the beaver.

Write a number model for your number story, such as 75 pounds > 56 pounds.

Since it is a nuisance to write "pounds" over and over in number models, draw a unit box for pounds on the board; thereafter omit the word *pound* in your number models (75 > 56).

Have children take out their animal cards. Ask several children to tell number stories involving two animals of their choice. Help them illustrate the stories on the board using the appropriate animal pictures and relation symbol. You or children write the number models for the stories; children then read them.

Ask for a few more stories, but this time, do not isolate pairs of animal pictures. Instead, simply point to animals on the animal posters you have created. Children write the number models on their slates.

Penguin
75 lb

Beaver
56 lb

75 pounds > 56 pounds

◯ Language Arts Link

Have children list the animals in alphabetical order.

"Less Than" and "More Than" Number Models

Write < for "is less than" and > for "is more than."

1. 19 lb < 23 lb

2. 41 lb > 14 lb

3. 75 lb > 56 lb

Challenge

4. 7 lb + 6 lb < 15 lb

5. 120 lb > 50 lb + 41 lb

Math Journal 1, p. 108

STUDENT PAGE

Using < and > in Number Models
(*Math Journal 1*, p. 108)

INDEPENDENT ACTIVITY

In Problems 1–3, children compare the weights of two animals. Problems 4 and 5 involve comparing the total weight of two animals to the weight of one animal. Remind children of how they found the total weight of two animals in Lesson 5.5 and of the game *Animal Weight Top-It.*

Adjusting the Activity If children are unsure of which number is larger, have them refer to the Class Number Line or the Class Number Grid Poster.

For the Challenge problems, have children model the problems on the Tens-and-Ones Mat on journal page 96 with base-10 blocks. They should make all necessary exchanges and record the answers.

ONGOING ASSESSMENT

· Watch for children who have trouble getting the < and > symbols pointed in the right direction.

· Remind children of the method of connecting each of two dots near the larger number with one dot near the smaller number.

Ordering Animals by Weight

Order your animal cards from largest to smallest weight. Record the results below.

1st	cheetah	120 lb
2nd	porpoise	98 lb
3rd	penguin	75 lb
4th	beaver	56 lb
5th	8-year-old boy	50 lb
6th	first-grade girl	41 lb
7th	raccoon	23 lb
8th	koala	19 lb
9th	eagle	15 lb
10th	fox	14 lb
11th	cat	7 lb
12th	rabbit	6 lb

Math Journal 1, p. 109

STUDENT PAGE

---

2 Ongoing Learning & Practice

Ordering Animal Cards by Weight
(*Math Journal 1*, p. 109)

INDEPENDENT ACTIVITY

Children put their 12 animal cards in order from heaviest to least heavy animal. They record the order in their journals. When children have completed the page, invite a few children to come to the board to make a parade of the animal masters in order, by weight. As children place animals in line, ask them to name the animal's place in the parade—first, second, third, and so on.

Adjusting the Activity If children are having trouble with ordinal numbers, have them line up and say their ordinal numbers as you point to them. Then have children follow these directions.

1. First person, clap your hands once.

2. Third person, raise your hand.

3. Thirteenth person, stamp your foot once (or clap your hands three times).

4. Tenth person, find the fifteenth person; then return to your place in line.

To close this game and get children seated again, use activities such as the following:

• First person and (*ordinal for last*) person, take your seat.

• All whose numbers end in "-th" and are tenth or less, take your seats.

✦ Math Boxes 5.6 (*Math Journal 1*, p. 110)

INDEPENDENT ACTIVITY

Mixed Review This journal page provides opportunities for cumulative review or assessment of concepts and skills.

✦ Home Link 5.6 (*Math Masters*, p. 223)

Home Connection Children make number models by inserting a relation symbol between pairs of numbers. Children are challenged to insert missing numbers to complete number models.

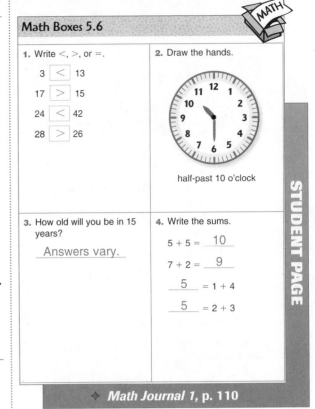

Math Journal 1, p. 110

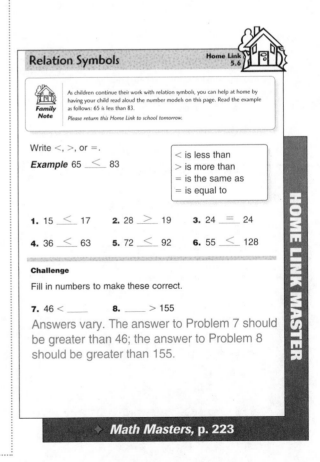

Math Masters, p. 223

Comparing Animal Weights

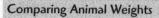

Use your animal cards to complete the page.

Write **more** or **less** and < or >.

< is less than
> is more than

Example

Find the cat, the eagle, and the raccoon cards.

Unit
pounds

Cat
7 lb

Eagle
15 lb

Raccoon
23 lb

Together, the cat and the eagle weigh ___less___ than the raccoon.
(**more** or **less**)

7 + 15 _<_ 23
(< or >)

1. Find the cat, the rabbit, and the eagle cards.

   Together, the cat and the rabbit weigh ___less___ than the eagle.

   7 + 6 _<_ 15

✦ *Math Masters*, p. 66

Comparing Animal Weights (cont.)

2. Find the rabbit, the fox, and the koala cards.

   Together, the rabbit and the fox weigh ___more___ than the koala.

   6 + 14 _>_ 19

3. Find the boy, the beaver, and the cheetah cards.

   Together, the boy and the beaver weigh ___less___ than the cheetah.

   50 + 56 _<_ 120

4. Find the raccoon, the fox, and the beaver cards.

   Together, the raccoon and the fox weigh ___less___ than the beaver.

   23 + 14 _<_ 56

Challenge

5. Find the eagle, the fox, the girl, and the penguin cards.

   Together, the eagle, the fox, and the girl weigh ___less___ than the penguin.

   15 + 14 + 41 _<_ 75

✦ *Math Masters*, p. 67

---

3 Options for Individualizing

✦ **ENRICHMENT** Comparing Animal Weights
(*Math Masters*, pp. 66 and 67)

INDEPENDENT ACTIVITY **5–15 min**

Children compare the total weight of two animals to the weight of a third animal. This is a follow-up to the problems on journal page 106, in which children found the total weight of pairs of animals. To find the total weights, children may use any method they wish—counters, doodles, the Class Number Line, the number grid on the inside back covers of their journals, or base-10 blocks.

Some children may discover that to solve Problems 3 and 4, it is not necessary to find the exact total weight of the animals. For example, in Problem 3, some children may know that 50 + 50 is 100 and so the boy and the beaver must weigh less than the cheetah. Similarly, in Problem 4, it's possible to use estimation to conclude that the total weight of the raccoon and the fox must be less than 50 pounds.

5.7

Comparison Number Stories

OBJECTIVE To introduce number stories that involve finding differences.

summaries	materials

1 Teaching the Lesson

Children compare two sets of pennies and determine how many more pennies there are in one set than in the other. [Numeration; Operations and Computation]

Children play the *Difference Game* to practice finding differences. [Operations and Computation]

- ☐ *Math Journal 1*, p. 111
- ☐ Home Link 5.6
- ☐ Teaching Master (*Math Masters*, p. 68)
- ☐ overhead coins (optional); tool-kit pennies
- ☐ 1–10 number cards (1 set per partnership)

2 Ongoing Learning & Practice

Children play *Domino Top-It*. [Numeration; Operations and Computation]

Children practice and maintain skills through Math Boxes and Home Link activities.

- ☐ *Math Journal 1*, p. 112
- ☐ Home Link Master (*Math Masters*, p. 224)
- ☐ dominoes

3 Options for Individualizing

Extra Practice Children use a number grid to find differences between pairs of numbers. [Operations and Computation]

Enrichment Children compare the values of sets of coins. [Numeration; Measurement and Reference Frames]

Extra Practice Children solve number stories that involve finding differences. [Operations and Computation]

- ☐ *Math Journal 1*, inside back cover
- ☐ Teaching Master (*Math Masters*, p. 69)
- ☐ slate
- ☐ *Minute Math*®, pp. 80, 97, 110, and 127

Additional Information
Vocabulary • difference

Getting Started

Mental Math and Reflexes

1. Draw a set of coins on the board with the Ⓟ, Ⓝ, and Ⓓ symbols. Children record the total value of the coins on their slates. Write the answer under the drawing. (Children having difficulty can use their tool-kit coins to organize the combinations by type of coin.)

2. Draw a second set of coins to the right of the first set. Children record the total value of these coins on their slates.

3. Ask a volunteer to write a < or > symbol between the two amounts. Use problems like these:

ⒹⒹⓃⓅⓅⓅ 28¢ and ⒹⒹⒹⓃⓃⓃⓅ 46¢   ⒹⓃⒹⓃⒹⓃⒹ 55¢ and ⓃⓃⓃⓃⒹⓅⓅ 32¢

ⒹⓃⓃⓃⓃⒹⓅⓅⓅ 38¢ and ⓅⓅⓅⓅⓅⒹⒹⓃ 30¢   ⓃⒹⓃⓅⓅⓃ 27¢ and ⒹⒹⓃⓅⒹ 36¢

Math Message
Lou saved 5 cents. Lisa saved 8 cents.
Who saved more? How much more? Lisa; 3 cents more

Home Link 5.6 Follow-Up
Briefly review the answers. Have volunteers
share their solutions to the Challenge problems.

1 Teaching the Lesson

◆ Math Message Follow-Up

WHOLE-CLASS DISCUSSION

Children share solution strategies. If the following
approach is not mentioned, discuss it with the class. Use
overhead coins or draw pennies on the board.

Lou:

Lisa:

▷ Make rows of pennies, one to represent Lou's coins and
the other Lisa's coins.

▷ Pair as many pennies as possible from one set with a
penny from the other set.

▷ The pennies that are not paired represent how many
more pennies Lisa has than Lou.

Pose the following problem:

Al has 12 cents. June has 7 cents. Who has less? June *How
much less?* 5 cents less

Partners model the solution with their tool-kit pennies
and write their answers on slates. Write the number
model $12 - 7 = 5$ on the board. *The result, 5, is called the*
difference *between 12 and 7.*

Pose two or three more problems, as needed. Children
model the solutions with coins. When summarizing the
solution, write a number model on the board. Make sure
the number model matches children's language. Some
children will count up to find the difference, so the
number model will have a missing addend as in
$7 + \underline{} = 12$.

NOTE: This number story and the Math
Message number story are examples of
comparison situations. "Who has more?" and
"Who has less?" are two ways of expressing
comparison situations. When telling
comparison number stories, be sure to use both
kinds of questions.

✦ Finding How Much More or Less
(*Math Journal 1*, p. 111)

INDEPENDENT ACTIVITY

Children use their tool-kit pennies to find differences.

 Adjusting the Activity To help children who are having difficulty, have them draw large dots in the frames to represent pennies in Problems 3 and 4.

To extend the activity, have children write number models for each of the problems. Note that children may record addition or subtraction number models depending on how they think of the problem.

 ONGOING ASSESSMENT
Children should recognize who has more by looking at the lengths of the frames. Encourage children to make the connection between the length of the frame and the number inside it. Some children may be able to solve the problems using other strategies—like counting up—instead of lining up pennies.

✦ Playing the *Difference Game*
(*Math Masters*, p. 68)

PARTNER ACTIVITY

Explain how the game is played. Partners pool their tool-kit pennies (40 pennies) to create a bank. They mix a deck of 1–10 number cards (four cards of each number) and put the cards facedown in a stack.

In each round, each player takes a card from the top of the stack and takes as many pennies from the bank as the number shown on the card. Both players then figure out how many more pennies one player has than the other. The player who has more pennies keeps that number of pennies (the difference). Both players return the rest of the pennies to the bank.

Play continues in this way until there are not enough pennies left in the bank to play another round. The player who has taken more pennies wins the game.

NOTE: To find the difference between two numbers, it is helpful to ask: *How many more do I need to add to the smaller set to have as many as there are in the larger set?* This "equalize" language encourages children to "add up to subtract."

How Much More? How Much Less?

Find each difference.

1. John ⓟⓟⓟⓟⓟⓟⓟⓟ

   Nick ⓟⓟ

   Who has more? __John__ How much more? _6_ ¢

2. June ⓟⓟⓟⓟⓟⓟⓟⓟ

   Mia ⓟⓟⓟⓟⓟ

   Who has less? __Mia__ How much less? _3_ ¢

3. Carl [12 pennies]

   Mary [20 pennies]

   Who has more? __Mary__ How much more? _8_ ¢

Challenge

4. Dan [56 pennies]

   Bob [72 pennies]

   Who has less? __Dan__ How much less? _16_ ¢

✦ *Math Journal 1*, p. 111

The *Difference Game*

Materials ❑ number cards 1–10 (4 cards of each number)

❑ 40 pennies

Players 2

Directions

1. Mix the number cards. Put them facedown in a stack. Put 40 pennies in the bank.

2. To play a round, you and your partner:
   • each take 1 card from the top of the deck
   • each take the same number of pennies from the bank as you see on your card.

3. Find out how many more pennies one of you has than the other. Pair as many pennies as you can.

   Here is an example.

   Player A ⓟⓟⓟⓟⓟⓟⓟ
   Player B ⓟⓟⓟⓟⓟ

4. The player with more pennies gets to keep the extra pennies.

   The rest of the pennies go back in the bank.

5. The game is over when there are not enough pennies in the bank to play another round.

   The player who took more pennies wins the game.

✦ *Math Masters*, p. 68

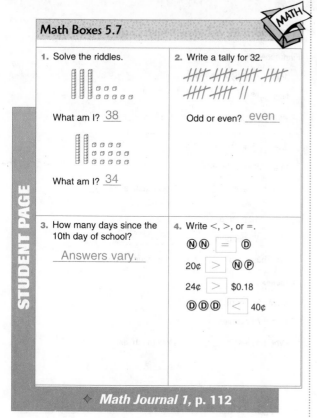

Math Boxes 5.7

STUDENT PAGE

1. Solve the riddles.

What am I? 38

What am I? 34

2. Write a tally for 32.

HHT HHT HHT HHT
HHT HHT II

Odd or even? even

3. How many days since the 10th day of school?

Answers vary.

4. Write <, >, or =.

Ⓝ Ⓝ = Ⓓ

20¢ > Ⓝ Ⓟ

24¢ > $0.18

Ⓓ Ⓓ Ⓓ < 40¢

◆ *Math Journal 1, p. 112*

Adjusting the Activity To extend the activity, encourage children to count up and back by tens on the grid from one row to the next whenever possible. Then they can count by ones the rest of the way.

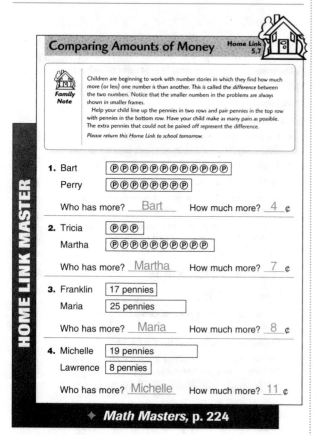

Comparing Amounts of Money Home Link 5.7

Family Note Children are beginning to work with number stories in which they find how much more (or less) one number is than another. This is called the *difference* between the two numbers. Notice that the smaller numbers in the problems are always shown in smaller frames.

Help your child line up the pennies in two rows and pair pennies in the top row with pennies in the bottom row. Have your child make as many pairs as possible. The extra pennies that could not be paired off represent the difference.

Please return this Home Link to school tomorrow.

1. Bart Ⓟ Ⓟ Ⓟ Ⓟ Ⓟ Ⓟ Ⓟ Ⓟ Ⓟ Ⓟ Ⓟ
   Perry Ⓟ Ⓟ Ⓟ Ⓟ Ⓟ Ⓟ Ⓟ

   Who has more? Bart   How much more? 4 ¢

2. Tricia Ⓟ Ⓟ Ⓟ
   Martha Ⓟ Ⓟ Ⓟ Ⓟ Ⓟ Ⓟ Ⓟ Ⓟ Ⓟ Ⓟ

   Who has more? Martha   How much more? 7 ¢

3. Franklin 17 pennies
   Maria 25 pennies

   Who has more? Maria   How much more? 8 ¢

4. Michelle 19 pennies
   Lawrence 8 pennies

   Who has more? Michelle   How much more? 11 ¢

HOME LINK MASTER

◆ *Math Masters, p. 224*

Ongoing Learning & Practice

◆ **Playing *Domino Top-It***

PARTNER ACTIVITY

Children practice addition skills by playing *Domino Top-It*. For detailed instructions, see Lesson 3.14.

◆ **Math Boxes 5.7** (*Math Journal 1*, p. 112)

INDEPENDENT ACTIVITY

Mixed Review This journal page provides opportunities for cumulative review or assessment of concepts and skills.

◆ **Home Link 5.7** (*Math Masters*, p. 224)

Home Connection Children find the difference between sets of pennies. They line up pennies in two rows and pair off as many pennies from the top row with the bottom row as possible to find the difference.

Options for Individualizing

◆ **EXTRA PRACTICE** Finding Differences

SMALL-GROUP ACTIVITY   5–15 min

Children use the number grid on the inside back covers of their journals to find differences between numbers. They write their answers on their slates.

Suggestions

• Find the difference between 10 and 18. 8

• Find the difference between 22 and 35. 13

• Find the difference between 62 and 50. 12

• Find the difference between 75 and 35. 40

• Find the difference between 28 and 59. 31

◆ ENRICHMENT Comparing the Values of Sets of Coins (*Math Masters*, p. 69)

INDEPENDENT ACTIVITY   15–30 min

Children are shown two sets of coins. They decide which set is worth more and how much more it is worth.

After most children have completed the first two problems, bring the class together to discuss solution strategies. One strategy is to count the value of each set of coins and find the difference. Praise children who have used a strategy involving crossing out pairs of matching coins and then comparing the values of the coins that are not crossed out, as shown below.

By using this strategy, it is clear that a nickel remains in Mike's collection and a dime and a penny remain in Anna's collection. Now it is easy to see that Anna has 6 cents more than Mike.

Mike:

Anna:

◆ EXTRA PRACTICE Minute Math

SMALL-GROUP ACTIVITY   5–15 min

To offer children more experience with number stories that involve finding differences, see the following pages in *Minute Math*:

Number Stories: pp. 80, 97, 110, and 127

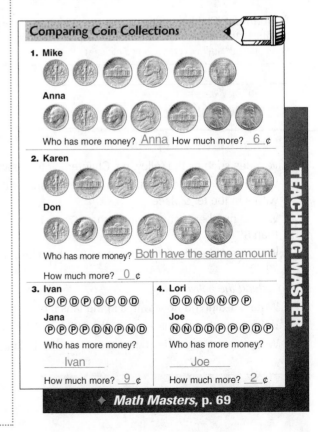

◆ *Math Masters*, p. 69

5.8 Solving Number Stories

OBJECTIVE To make up and solve a variety of number stories involving relations, addition, and subtraction.

summaries	**materials**

1 Teaching the Lesson

Children solve different kinds of number stories. They make up and solve their own number stories and write number models for the stories. [Operations and Computation; Patterns, Functions, and Algebra]

- ☐ *Math Journal 1,* p. 113
- ☐ Home Link 5.7
- ☐ animal cards
- ☐ animal masters

2 Ongoing Learning & Practice

Children use the number line to find differences. [Operations and Computation]

Children practice and maintain skills through Math Boxes and Home Link activities.

- ☐ *Math Journal 1,* pp. 114 and 115
- ☐ Home Link Master (*Math Masters,* p. 225)

3 Options for Individualizing

Enrichment Children make up number stories for a class number-story book or bulletin-board display. [Operations and Computation; Patterns, Functions, and Algebra]

- ☐ half-sheet of paper

Getting Started

Mental Math and Reflexes

Give clues such as the following. Children write answers on slates.

- Write a 2-digit number with 7 in the tens place; with 4 in the tens place; with 9 in the tens place.
- Write a number that is 10 more than 17 27; 10 more than 61 71; 10 more than 88 98.
- Write a number that is 10 less than 22 12; 10 less than 56 46; 10 less than 79 69.

To extend the activity:

- Write a 3-digit number with 5 in the tens place.
- Write a number that is 10 more than 95 105; 10 more than 193 203.
- Write a number that is 10 less than 115 105; 10 less than 208 198.

Math Message

Take out your animal cards. Which animals weigh less than 15 pounds? Which weigh more than 56 pounds?

Home Link 5.7 Follow-Up

Briefly review the answers from the Home Link. Have children share strategies for solving Problem 4.

Teaching the Lesson

✦ Math Message Follow-Up

WHOLE-CLASS ACTIVITY 👥👥👥

Ask volunteers to follow the directions listed below.

Step 1
Find and display the master that shows an animal that weighs 15 pounds. The eagle

Step 2
Find the masters that show animals that weigh less than 15 pounds. The fox, the cat, and the rabbit

Step 3
Line up these masters to the left of the eagle in descending order by weight.

Step 4
Find and display the master that shows an animal that weighs 56 pounds. The beaver

Step 5
Find the masters that show animals that weigh more than 56 pounds. The penguin, the porpoise, and the cheetah

Step 6
Line up these masters to the right of the beaver in ascending order by weight.

✦ Solving Number Stories Involving Addition and Subtraction

WHOLE-CLASS ACTIVITY 👥👥👥

By now, children have had some exposure to the following kinds of number stories:

Relations: My cat weighs 7 pounds and my rabbit weighs 6 pounds. Which weighs more? My cat

Change-to-less: If a 56-pound beaver goes on a diet and loses 6 pounds, how much will it weigh? 50 lb

Change-to-more: Kareem had 3 cats. One of the cats had a litter of 6 kittens. How many cats and kittens does Kareem have in all? 9 cats and kittens

Parts-and-Total: A 50-pound boy holds a 7-pound cat and steps on a scale. How many pounds do they weigh together? 57 lb

Comparison: How much more than my 7-pound cat does a 14-pound fox weigh? 7 lb

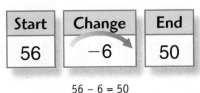

Change-to-less

Start	Change	End
56	−6	50

56 − 6 = 50

Change-to-more

Start	Change	End
3	+6	9

3 + 6 = 9

Parts-and-Total

Total	
57	
Part	Part
50	7

50 + 7 = 57

Comparison

Quantity	
14	
Quantity	Difference
7	7

14 − 7 = 7

Number Stories

Here is a number story Mandy made up.

I have 4 balloons.
Jamal brought 1 more.
We have 5 balloons together.

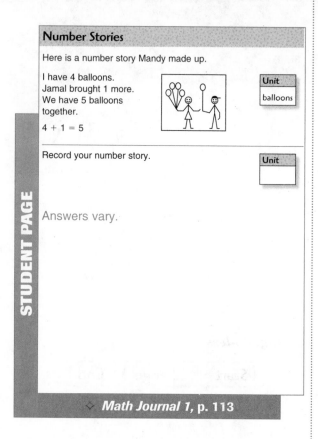

Unit
balloons

4 + 1 = 5

Record your number story.

Unit

Answers vary.

NOTE: Number stories provide good portfolio material. See *Assessment Handbook,* page 25 for a suggested rubric and for number story samples.

Comparisons

Example

Mike ⓅⓅⓅ

Lynn ⓅⓅⓅⓅⓅⓅ

Who has more? __Lynn__ How much more? _4¢_

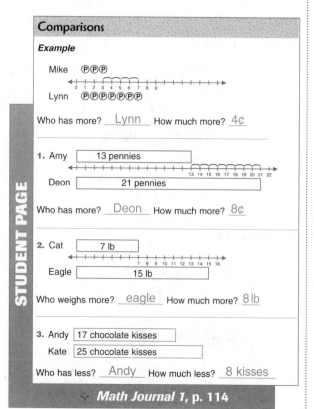

1. Amy [13 pennies]

Deon [21 pennies]

Who has more? __Deon__ How much more? _8¢_

2. Cat [7 lb]

Eagle [15 lb]

Who weighs more? __eagle__ How much more? _8 lb_

3. Andy [17 chocolate kisses]

Kate [25 chocolate kisses]

Who has less? __Andy__ How much less? _8 kisses_

Tell these stories or similar stories and have the class solve them. Ask children to suggest a number model for each. Remember not to force the solution to a number story into a particular mold. The diagrams used for these stories give one way of viewing the problems. The number models may show addition or subtraction. Invite children to make up their own number stories.

If children are having difficulty getting started, you might suggest some of the following situations:

▷ Stories about dominoes: *What is the total number of dots? Which half of the domino has more dots? How many more?*

▷ Stories about money saved, spent, or shared

▷ Stories about candy bought, eaten, or given away

▷ Stories about games: *Sarah played the* Difference Game. *She took 6 pennies in the first round and 3 pennies in the second round. How many more pennies did she take in the first round?*

Continue as long as interest remains high. Plan to hold brief number-story sessions on a regular basis.

◆ Making Up and Solving Number Stories
(*Math Journal 1,* p. 113)

INDEPENDENT ACTIVITY

Discuss Mandy's number story at the top of the journal page. *Can anyone suggest a different story for the picture?* Jean had 4 balloons. Mark gave her one more balloon. How many balloons does Jean have now?

Ask children to make up a number story and to record it on the page, along with a number model. For example, they might make up a story about red and blue crayons (this would be easy to illustrate), or about birds in a tree, some of which are flying away. They may write the story in words, or illustrate it with counters, tallies, or pictures.

2 Ongoing Learning & Practice

◆ Using the Number Line to Find Differences
(*Math Journal 1,* p. 114)

INDEPENDENT ACTIVITY

The problems on this page are familiar difference problems. The diagrams illustrate how to count up on the number line from the smaller to the larger number, which is one way to solve the problems.

Adjusting the Activity Pose similar problems involving larger numbers. Children can solve them by counting up on the number grid. Suggestion: Julie's mom is 35 years old. Her grandfather is 63 years old. How many years older is Julie's grandfather than her mom? 28

To solve the problem, count up to 63 on the number grid, starting at 35.

◆ Math Boxes 5.8 (*Math Journal 1*, p. 115)

 INDEPENDENT ACTIVITY

Mixed Review This journal page provides opportunities for cumulative review or assessment of concepts and skills.

◆ Home Link 5.8 (*Math Masters*, p. 225)

 Home Connection Children find or draw a picture that illustrates a number story. They tell a number story about the picture and write a number model for the number story.

---

3 Options for Individualizing

◆ ENRICHMENT Making a Classroom Number-Story Book

PARTNER ACTIVITY **15–30 min**

Working with a partner, each child tells a number story. Partners then illustrate both stories with pictures and/or write them in words on half-sheets of paper. They write a number model for the story.

Portfolio Ideas

Collect the stories for a classroom book or bulletin-board display. In the course of the next few days, use some of these number stories as *Minute Math* problems.

Math Boxes 5.8

1. Draw the hands.

quarter-after 9 o'clock

2. Circle the tens place.

(7)3

Is the number in the tens place odd or even?

odd

3.
Rule
+10

18   28   38   48   58

4. Draw a line segment about 2 inches long.

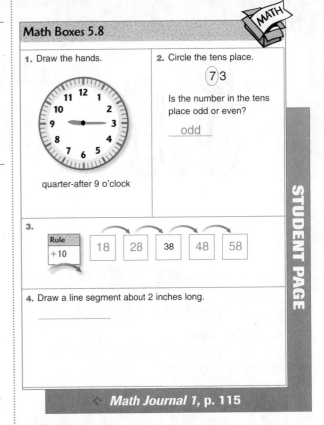

Math Journal 1, p. 115

NOTE: Invite native English speakers to work with non-native English speakers to write number stories.

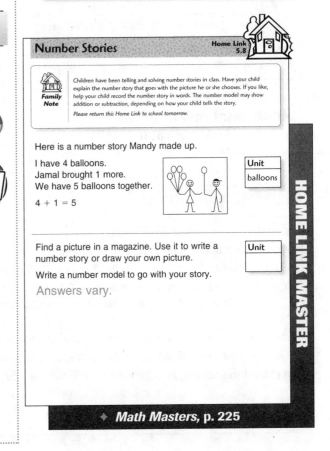

Number Stories   Home Link 5.8

Family Note Children have been telling and solving number stories in class. Have your child explain the number story that goes with the picture he or she chooses. If you like, help your child record the number story in words. The number model may show addition or subtraction, depending on how your child tells the story.

Please return this Home Link to school tomorrow.

Here is a number story Mandy made up.

I have 4 balloons.
Jamal brought 1 more.
We have 5 balloons together.

4 + 1 = 5

Unit: balloons

Find a picture in a magazine. Use it to write a number story or draw your own picture.

Write a number model to go with your story.

Answers vary.

Unit

Math Masters, p. 225

5.9

Dice Sums

OBJECTIVE To investigate sums generated by rolling pairs of dice.

summaries	materials

1 Teaching the Lesson

Children roll pairs of dice and record the sum of the dots. They observe which sums occur most often. [Operations and Computation; Data and Chance]

- ☐ *Math Journal 1*, p. 116
- ☐ Home Link 5.8
- ☐ Class Number Grid Poster
- ☐ dice

2 Ongoing Learning & Practice

Children find differences between pairs of numbers represented by base-10 blocks. [Numeration; Operations and Computation]

Children practice and maintain skills through Math Boxes and Home Link activities.

- ☐ *Math Journal 1*, pp. 117, 118; and 96, optional
- ☐ Home Link Master (*Math Masters*, p. 226)
- ☐ base-10 blocks (optional)

3 Options for Individualizing

Extra Practice Children practice finding sums by completing a color-by-number picture. [Operations and Computation]

- ☐ Teaching Master (*Math Masters*, p. 70)

Additional Information
Vocabulary • **multiple of 10**

Getting Started

Mental Math and Reflexes

Begin to practice place-value and rounding skills. Have children write their answers on their slates.

• Is 18 closer to 10 or 20? 20 • Is 12 closer to 10 or 20? 10 • Is 19 closer to 10 or 20? 20

Explain to the class that the numbers 10, 20, 30, … are called **multiples of 10.** Ask someone to point to the multiples of 10 on the Class Number Grid Poster. Discuss what they have in common. They all end in 0. They are all in the last column on the right.

Ask children to count spaces on their number grids to help them answer the following questions on their slates.

• Is 27 closer to 20 or 30? 30 • Is 54 closer to 50 or 60? 50 • Is 86 closer to 80 or 90? 90

To extend the activity, ask the following: *Is there a way to solve problems like these by just looking at the numbers?* Look at the ones digit. If the ones digit is less than 5, the number is closer to the smaller number. If it is more than 5, the number is closer to the larger number. If it is 5, the number is halfway between the smaller and larger number.

Math Message
Add.

$1 + 6 =$ _7_

_7_ $= 3 + 4$

$5 + 2 =$ _7_

$2 + 5 =$ _7_

_7_ $= 4 + 3$

_7_ $= 6 + 1$

Home Link 5.8 Follow-Up
Briefly go over the answers. Ask several volunteers to tell their number stories and have the class solve them. Share solution strategies for the problems.

1 Teaching the Lesson

◆ Math Message Follow-Up

WHOLE-CLASS DISCUSSION

Briefly go over the answers. *Do these problems remind anyone of the* Two-Fisted Penny Addition *activity with 7 pennies?* Yes, because they are different ways to get 7.

◆ Investigating Frequency of Sums from Dice Rolls (*Math Journal 1*, p. 116)

PARTNER ACTIVITY

Partners investigate which sum is likely to come up most often when two dice are thrown.

They perform the following experiment twice. The first time, they record the results in one partner's journal. The second time, they record the results in the other partner's journal.

Step 1
One partner rolls the two dice.

Step 2
Both partners figure out the sum of the dots on the dice.

Step 3
The other partner marks the first empty box above the sum shown on the journal page with an X.

When the column for any one sum is filled to the top, partners repeat the experiment and record the results in the other partner's journal.

Circulate and chat with children about the facts they know and about how they figure out a sum when they don't know the fact yet.

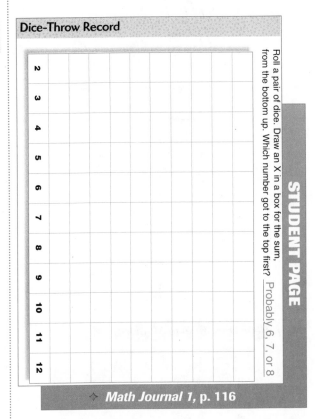

Dice-Throw Record

2 3 4 5 6 7 8 9 10 11 12

Roll a pair of dice. Draw an X in a box for the sum, from the bottom up. Which number got to the top first? Probably 6, 7, or 8.

STUDENT PAGE

✦ *Math Journal 1*, p. 116

ONGOING ASSESSMENT
· Check that children put an 'X' in the correct box on journal page 116. Expect that some children will begin to recognize the more common combinations without counting the dots.

· Some children may still count all of the dots on both dice. Suggest that they use the number line to count up. For example, if the child rolls 5 and 3, put a finger on the number line at 5 and count up 3 to 8.

Filled Columns

2	
3	
4	
5	/
6	////
7	//// ////
8	//// /
9	///
10	//
11	
12	

When children have completed both tables, bring the class together to discuss the results. Make a tally of which columns reached the top for each child.

• **Which sum came up most often?** Probably 6, 7, or 8

If the sum 7 came up most often, ask children why they think this is so. Expect answers like "7 is a lucky number" or "7 is a favorite number." Someone may bring up the fact that there are more different ways for 7 to come up than any of the other numbers, but do not expect it. This idea will be revisited in Lesson 6.1.

Propose the following game: Roll two dice. If a 7 comes up, the teacher wins. If a 2 or a 12 comes up, the class wins. Discuss whether the game is fair; then play it to find out. The game is not fair. The teacher will win most of the time, since 7 comes up more often than 2 and 12 combined.

2 Ongoing Learning & Practice

◆ Comparing Values of Sets of Base-10 Blocks
(*Math Journal 1*, p. 117)

INDEPENDENT ACTIVITY

After most children have completed the first two problems on the journal page, bring the class together to discuss solution strategies. One way to solve the problems is to use a number line or number grid to find differences.

Praise children who have used a method like the following: Cross out pairs of matching base-10 blocks (cross out pairs of longs and pairs of cubes in each set). For example, for Problem 2:

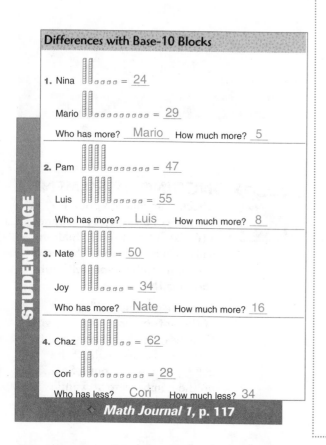

Differences with Base-10 Blocks

1. Nina = 24

   Mario = 29

   Who has more? Mario   How much more? 5

2. Pam = 47

   Luis = 55

   Who has more? Luis   How much more? 8

3. Nate = 50

   Joy = 34

   Who has more? Nate   How much more? 16

4. Chaz = 62

   Cori = 28

   Who has less? Cori   How much less? 34

Math Journal 1, p. 117

This leaves 2 cubes for Pam and 1 long for Luis. The problem has been reduced to finding the difference between 10 and 2. Now it is easy to see that Luis has 8 more than Pam.

Adjusting the Activity Children may use base-10 blocks on their Tens-and-Ones Mat on journal page 96 to help them solve the problems.

◆ Math Boxes 5.9 (*Math Journal 1*, p. 118)

INDEPENDENT ACTIVITY 👤

Mixed Review This journal page provides opportunities for cumulative review or assessment of concepts and skills.

◆ Home Link 5.9 (*Math Masters*, p. 226)

Home Connection Children compare the sum of the dots on pairs of die faces and dominoes. Children are challenged to compare sums of two dominoes that have numbers instead of dots.

3 Options for Individualizing

◆ EXTRA PRACTICE Color-by-Number Picture
(*Math Masters*, p. 70)

INDEPENDENT ACTIVITY 👤   15–30 min ⏱

Children complete a color-by-number picture by finding simple sums.

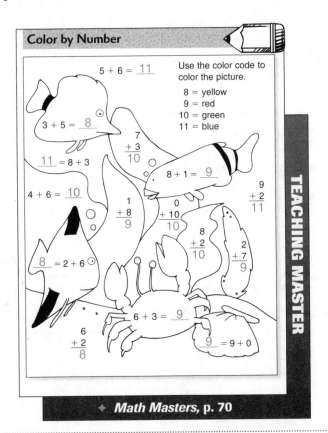

◆ Math Masters, p. 70

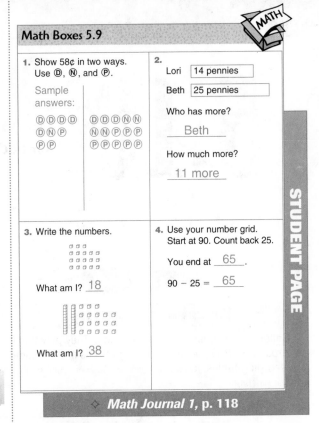

◆ Math Journal 1, p. 118

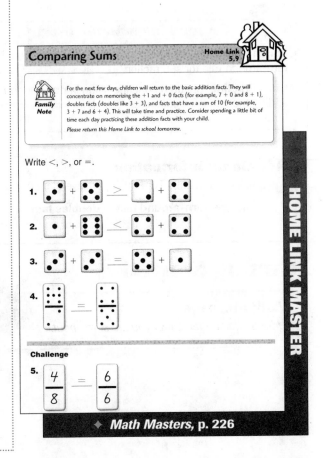

◆ Math Masters, p. 226

5.10 Turn-Around Facts

OBJECTIVE To introduce the turn-around rule for addition.

	summaries		materials

1 Teaching the Lesson

Children investigate turn-around facts. They play the *Turn-Around Facts Game* and look for patterns in their game recording tables. [Operations and Computation; Patterns, Functions, and Algebra]

- ☐ *Math Journal 1,* p. 119
- ☐ Home Link 5.9
- ☐ 20 pennies per partnership
- ☐ 2 dice per partnership

2 Ongoing Learning & Practice

Children play the *Magic Bag Game* in preparation for lessons on the function machine. [Patterns, Functions, and Algebra]

Children practice and maintain skills through Math Boxes and Home Link activities.

- ☐ *Math Journal 1,* p. 120
- ☐ Home Link Master (*Math Masters,* p. 227)
- ☐ paper bag
- ☐ craft sticks
- **See Advance Preparation**

3 Options for Individualizing

Enrichment Children investigate whether or not there is a turn-around rule for subtraction. [Operations and Computation]

Extra Practice Children continue filling in number grids and adding them to their number scrolls. [Numeration; Patterns, Functions, and Algebra]

- ☐ Teaching Master (*Math Masters,* p. 46)
- ☐ calculator

Additional Information

Advance Preparation For Part 2, put several craft sticks in the bottom of a paper bag.

Vocabulary • **turn-around fact** • **doubles fact**

Getting Started

Math Message
Write 5 addition facts that you are sure about.

Home Link 5.9 Follow-Up
Briefly go over the answers.

1 Teaching the Lesson

◆ Math Message Follow-Up

WHOLE-CLASS DISCUSSION

List the children's addition facts on the board. Use a variety of formats.

▷ Write the addends on the left of the = symbol.

▷ Write the addends on the right of the = symbol.

▷ Write the addends in vertical form.

You may want to ask only for facts that have not been listed, or you may wish to make a tally mark by the fact if it has already been listed.

Highlight a pair of **turn-around facts** in the list, such as $3 + 4 = 7$ and $4 + 3 = 7$, or $4 + 2 = 6$ and $2 + 4 = 6$.

• What do these facts have in common? The same numbers are being added. They have the same sum.

• How are they different? The numbers being added are not written in the same order.

Tell the class that facts in which the same two numbers are added but are not added in the same order, are called turn-around facts. Because pairs of turn-around facts have the same answer, you need to learn only one of the facts. If you know one fact, then you also know its turn-around fact.

Ask children to identify other pairs of turn-around facts in the list on the board.

Playing the *Turn-Around Facts Game*
(*Math Journal 1*, p. 119)

PARTNER ACTIVITY 👥

Partners use the table in one of the players' journals. They will need 20 pennies for the bank and 2 dice.

Players take turns. At each turn, a player does the following:

1. Rolls the dice and finds the total number of dots on the two dice.

2. Writes the total in an appropriate box in the table in the journal and then writes the sum in the box for the turn-around fact, if there is one.

3. Takes one penny from the bank for each box in the table he or she has filled in.

If the box has already been filled in, the player takes no pennies from the bank and loses the turn. The game is over when all of the pennies have been taken. The player who took more pennies wins. Children play a second game, using the other player's unused journal page to record the game.

Discussing Patterns in the Turn-Around Facts Record (*Math Journal 1,* p. 119)

WHOLE-CLASS DISCUSSION 👥👥👥

When children have played two *Turn-Around Facts* games, ask them to complete the facts in their tables that have not been solved. Then bring the class together to discuss patterns in the table.

Review the meanings of *row, column,* and *diagonal*. Rows go across; columns go up and down; diagonals slant up or down from right to left or from left to right.

• Which facts do not have a turn-around fact? $1 + 1 = 2$, $2 + 2 = 4$, $3 + 3 = 6$, $4 + 4 = 8$, $5 + 5 = 10$, and $6 + 6 = 12$

Tell the class that these facts are called **doubles facts.** In a doubles fact, both numbers that are being added are the same. Elicit from the class that doubles facts are found on the diagonal that goes from the upper left-hand corner of the table to the lower right-hand corner.

• Are the sums of doubles facts even or odd numbers? Even numbers

Turn-Around Facts Record

$1 + 6 = 7$	$2 + 6 = 8$	$3 + 6 = 9$	$4 + 6 = 10$	$5 + 6 = 11$	$6 + 6 = 12$
$1 + 5 = 6$	$2 + 5 = 7$	$3 + 5 = 8$	$4 + 5 = 9$	$5 + 5 = 10$	$6 + 5 = 11$
$1 + 4 = 5$	$2 + 4 = 6$	$3 + 4 = 7$	$4 + 4 = 8$	$5 + 4 = 9$	$6 + 4 = 10$
$1 + 3 = 4$	$2 + 3 = 5$	$3 + 3 = 6$	$4 + 3 = 7$	$5 + 3 = 8$	$6 + 3 = 9$
$1 + 2 = 3$	$2 + 2 = 4$	$3 + 2 = 5$	$4 + 2 = 6$	$5 + 2 = 7$	$6 + 2 = 8$
$1 + 1 = 2$	$2 + 1 = 3$	$3 + 1 = 4$	$4 + 1 = 5$	$5 + 1 = 6$	$6 + 1 = 7$

Math Journal 1, p. 119

Help children notice one other doubles-facts pattern: When the sums are listed in order, they are counts by 2s. Discuss other patterns.

• What is the pattern in the sums in each row? Each sum is 1 more than the sum before it. Each column? Each sum is 10 more than the sum above it.

• How would you describe the pattern of all sums of 7? They are found on the diagonal that goes from the upper right-hand corner to the lower left-hand corner. This pattern also occurs in sums that are the same. They are all found on diagonals from right to left as you go down from row to row.

2 Ongoing Learning & Practice

✦ Playing the *Magic Bag Game*

WHOLE-CLASS ACTIVITY

This activity provides good preparation for the lessons on the function machine (Lessons 5.12 and 5.13). Try to use this activity before the start of Lesson 5.12.

Use a paper bag and craft sticks to play a guessing game. Begin the game by explaining that the bag is magic. Put 1 stick in the bag, say a "magic word" or two, and take 2 sticks out of the bag. Then put 2 sticks in and pull 3 out. Repeat several times until the children can predict how many sticks will come out. Discuss rules that fit the bag's action such as: "add 1," "1 more," and "the next number."

Next, tell children that you are going to change the magic rule. (The magical incantations are left to your imagination!) Play the game again with "add 2." Repeat with one or two more rules like "subtract 1" or "double."

✦ Math Boxes 5.10 (*Math Journal 1,* p. 120)

INDEPENDENT ACTIVITY

Mixed Review This journal page provides opportunities for cumulative review or assessment of concepts and skills.

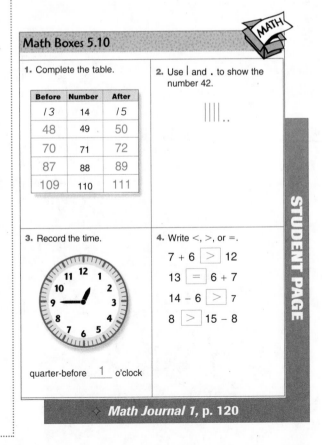

Math Boxes 5.10

1. Complete the table.

Before	Number	After
13	14	15
48	49	50
70	71	72
87	88	89
109	110	111

2. Use | and . to show the number 42.

|||| ..

3. Record the time.

quarter-before __1__ o'clock

4. Write <, >, or =.

$7 + 6$ > 12

13 = $6 + 7$

$14 - 6$ > 7

8 > $15 - 8$

✦ *Math Journal 1,* p. 120

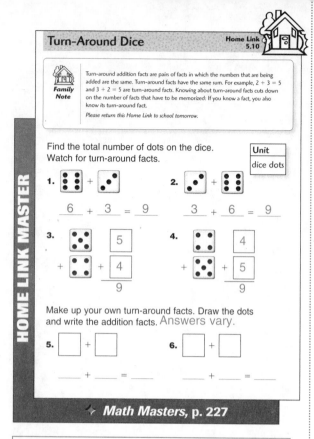

Family Note Turn-around addition facts are pairs of facts in which the numbers that are being added are the same. Turn-around facts have the same sum. For example, 2 + 3 = 5 and 3 + 2 = 5 are turn-around facts. Knowing about turn-around facts cuts down on the number of facts that have to be memorized: If you know a fact, you also know its turn-around fact.

Please return this Home Link to school tomorrow.

Find the total number of dots on the dice.
Watch for turn-around facts.

Unit
dice dots

1. $\underline{6} + \underline{3} = \underline{9}$

2. $\underline{3} + \underline{6} = \underline{9}$

3. 5 + 4 = 9

4. 4 + 5 = 9

Make up your own turn-around facts. Draw the dots and write the addition facts. Answers vary.

5. ☐ + ☐
___ + ___ = ___

6. ☐ + ☐
___ + ___ = ___

HOME LINK MASTER

✦ *Math Masters, p. 227*

NOTE: For negative numbers, some basic calculators show the negative symbol after the number (3–) instead of before the number (–3), as it is usually written or printed. Other calculators show the negative symbol at the far left of the display, so children may not notice it.

TEACHING MASTER

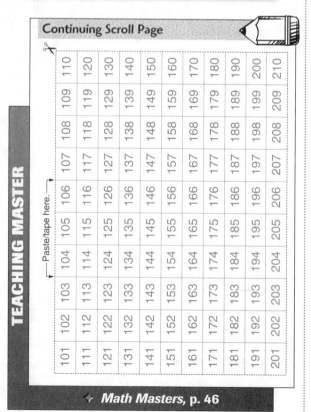

Continuing Scroll Page

Paste/tape here.

✦ *Math Masters, p. 46*

✦ **Home Link 5.10** (*Math Masters*, p. 227)

Home Connection Children find the total number of dots on pairs of "turn-around" die faces and make up a set of turn-around facts.

3 Options for Individualizing

✦ **ENRICHMENT** **Investigating Subtraction and the Turn-Around Rule**

SMALL-GROUP ACTIVITY  **15–30 min**

Ask someone to make up a subtraction fact. *What would its turn-around fact look like?* Write both facts on the board. For example: write 12 – 8 = ___ and 8 – 12 = ___. Ask children to solve both problems on their calculators.

• Are these turn-around facts? no Why or why not? The numbers are the same, but the answers are not.

Ask children to experiment with other turn-around subtraction problems.

• When you enter an addition problem into your calculator, does it matter which number you enter first? No; you will get the same answer. What about subtraction problems? It does matter; you will not get the same answer.

Assist children in coming to the conclusion that there is no turn-around rule for subtraction, since the answers for turn-around facts are not the same.

✦ **EXTRA PRACTICE** **Continuing Work on Number Scrolls** (*Math Masters*, p. 46)

INDEPENDENT ACTIVITY   **15–30 min**

Have children continue filling in number grids and adding the grids to their number scrolls. You might suggest that they use a pattern to fill in the grid. Sample patterns are described in Lesson 4.10.

5.11

"Easy" Facts

OBJECTIVE To explore some easily mastered addition facts: the +0, +1, and doubles facts and facts whose sums are 10.

summaries	materials

1 Teaching the Lesson

Children review the meaning of turn-around facts. They explore patterns in the +0 and +1 facts and identify and complete the doubles facts and the facts whose sums are 10. Children play *Beat the Calculator*. [Operations and Computation; Patterns, Functions, and Algebra]

☐ *Math Journal 1*, pp. 121 and 122
☐ Home Link 5.10
☐ coloring pencils
☐ calculator

2 Ongoing Learning & Practice

Children measure objects and line segments to the nearest inch. They also draw a line segment with a ruler. [Measurement and Reference Frames]

Children practice and maintain skills through Math Boxes and Home Link activities.

☐ *Math Journal 1*, pp. 123 and 124
☐ rulers from *Math Masters*, p. 40
☐ Home Link Master (*Math Masters*, p. 228)
☐ 3 objects less than 1 foot long per partnership; 6-inch ruler
☐ *Tom Thumb* by Margaret Read MacDonald (optional)

3 Options for Individualizing

Extra Practice Children play *Penny Cup*. [Operations and Computation]

☐ large cup or can per partnership
☐ pennies

Getting Started

Mental Math and Reflexes

To review ordinal numbers, perform several actions in sequence.

1. Jump.
2. Clap.
3. Snap your fingers.

Ask the following questions:
- What did I do first? jump
- What did I do second? clap
- What did I do third? Snap fingers

Repeat with other sequences of actions: sitting, standing, raising a hand, waving, and so on. Then have children perform sequences of actions. Repeat as time allows. Ask children to use ordinal numbers to identify each step in the sequences.

Math Message

Write the turn-around fact for each of these facts:

$0 + 4 = 4$
$8 = 3 + 5$
$6 + 5 = 11$
$10 = 2 + 8$

Home Link 5.10 Follow-Up

Invite children to share some of the facts they made up for the class to solve.

Facts Table

0 +0 = 0	0 +1 = 1	0 +2 = 2	0 +3 = 3	0 +4 = 4	0 +5 = 5	0 +6 = 6	0 +7 = 7	0 +8 = 8	0 +9 = 9
1 +0 = 1	1 +1 = 2	1 +2 = 3	1 +3 = 4	1 +4 = 5	1 +5 = 6	1 +6 = 7	1 +7 = 8	1 +8 = 9	1 +9 = 10
2 +0 = 2	2 +1 = 3	2 +2 = 4	2 +3 = 5	2 +4 = 6	2 +5 = 7	2 +6 = 8	2 +7 = 9	2 +8 = 10	2 +9 = 11
3 +0 = 3	3 +1 = 4	3 +2 = 5	3 +3 = 6	3 +4 = 7	3 +5 = 8	3 +6 = 9	3 +7 = 10	3 +8 = 11	3 +9 = 12
4 +0 = 4	4 +1 = 5	4 +2 = 6	4 +3 = 7	4 +4 = 8	4 +5 = 9	4 +6 = 10	4 +7 = 11	4 +8 = 12	4 +9 = 13
5 +0 = 5	5 +1 = 6	5 +2 = 7	5 +3 = 8	5 +4 = 9	5 +5 = 10	5 +6 = 11	5 +7 = 12	5 +8 = 13	5 +9 = 14
6 +0 = 6	6 +1 = 7	6 +2 = 8	6 +3 = 9	6 +4 = 10	6 +5 = 11	6 +6 = 12	6 +7 = 13	6 +8 = 14	6 +9 = 15
7 +0 = 7	7 +1 = 8	7 +2 = 9	7 +3 = 10	7 +4 = 11	7 +5 = 12	7 +6 = 13	7 +7 = 14	7 +8 = 15	7 +9 = 16
8 +0 = 8	8 +1 = 9	8 +2 = 10	8 +3 = 11	8 +4 = 12	8 +5 = 13	8 +6 = 14	8 +7 = 15	8 +8 = 16	8 +9 = 17
9 +0 = 9	9 +1 = 10	9 +2 = 11	9 +3 = 12	9 +4 = 13	9 +5 = 14	9 +6 = 15	9 +7 = 16	9 +8 = 17	9 +9 = 18

◆ *Math Journal 1,* p. 121

Easy Addition Facts

Complete.

Doubles Facts

0 +0 = 0	6 +6 = 12
1 +1 = 2	7 +7 = 14
2 +2 = 4	8 +8 = 16
3 +3 = 6	9 +9 = 18
4 +4 = 8	10 +10 = 20
5 +5 = 10	

10 Sums

0 +10 = 10	6 +4 = 10
1 +9 = 10	7 +3 = 10
2 +8 = 10	8 +2 = 10
3 +7 = 10	9 +1 = 10
4 +6 = 10	10 +0 = 10
5 +5 = 10	

◆ *Math Journal 1,* p. 122

1 Teaching the Lesson

◆ Math Message Follow-Up

WHOLE-CLASS DISCUSSION

Go over the answers. *What if we had a new student who didn't know about the turn-around facts? How would you explain how it works? Why does it make learning the facts easier?* You can add two numbers in different order and get the same answer. When you learn one fact, you are really learning two facts.

Tell the children that today they will be learning about other ways to make learning the facts easier.

◆ +0 and +1 Fact Patterns (*Math Journal 1,* p. 121)

WHOLE-CLASS ACTIVITY

Ask children to turn to the Facts Table in their journals. Read and recite together the facts in the 0-column (the first column). Discuss the results. Children should notice that the sum is always the same as the number you start with. *Can anyone tell why this is so?* You may want to have children illustrate this concept with a zero number story.

Ask children to shade all the +0 facts lightly with a pencil and then to shade the turn-around facts for the +0 facts (the first row).

Next turn to the +1 facts. Again, read and recite together the facts in the 1-column (the second column). Children should notice that the sum is always the number that comes after the number you start with. Have them shade all the +1 facts and their turn-around facts.

Pose several problems with numbers that are not in the table, such as 17 + 0, 98 + 0, 53 + 1, and 69 + 1.

◆ Doubles Facts and Facts Whose Sums Are 10 (*Math Journal 1,* pp. 121 and 122)

WHOLE-CLASS ACTIVITY

Help children find and shade the doubles facts in the Facts Table on journal page 121. Ask children to recite them in unison. Then ask them to find and shade all of the facts in the table whose sums are 10. They should notice that these facts and the doubles facts are found on diagonals that go in opposite directions.

Remind children that they have already been working with the facts whose sums are 10 when doing *Two-Fisted Pennies Addition*.

Next, have children complete the problems on journal page 122. Tell them to do as many problems as they can without using the Facts Table. However, if they are unsure of an answer, they should look it up in the table. When they have completed the page, have partners check each other's work.

Explain that for the next few weeks, the children will concentrate on memorizing the facts they have shaded in the Facts Table, and that they will also start working on some of the other facts.

NOTE: Doubles facts are usually easy for children. A brief survey can determine if this is true for your class.

◆ Introducing *Beat the Calculator*

WHOLE-CLASS ACTIVITY

Divide the class into two groups. Children in one group (the "Calculators") use their calculators to find the sum for a fact given by the "Caller." They hold up the calculator with the answer showing as they call out the correct answer. Children in the other group (the "Brains") do the problem in their heads, without using a calculator, and say the answer as soon as they have it.

Adjusting the Activity If necessary, children who are playing the role of the "Brain" may use counters and fingers to help them at this point in the year. As your work with fact power continues, you should encourage children to rely on memory.

To extend the activity, have one child play as "Brain" against the class.

For today, you be the "Caller." Emphasize +0, +1, +2, and doubles facts and facts with sums of 10, but also include a few "hard" facts so that children with calculators also win.

Play this game every day for the next few days, then every once in awhile over the next few months. This game will be played again in second grade. The eventual goal is to beat the calculator on all the addition facts.

Discuss the fact that some problems can be solved more easily and quickly in one's head than on a calculator.

One of the goals of *Everyday Mathematics* is to develop the ability to choose the most efficient method of solving a computation problem.

Measurement Practice

1. Name or draw an object. Estimate its length to the nearest inch. Measure it with a ruler to the nearest inch.

Object (Name it or draw it)	My estimate	My measurement
	about _____ inches	about _____ inches
	about _____ inches	about _____ inches
	about _____ inches	about _____ inches

Measure these line segments to the nearest inch.

2. _____ about 2 in.

3. _____ about 5 in.

4. _____ about 3 in.

5. Draw a line segment 4 inches long.

   _____

Challenge

6. Measure to the nearest half-inch.

   _____ about $3\frac{1}{2}$ in.

7. Draw a line segment 5 and a half inches long.

   _____

◆ **Math Journal 1, p. 123**

Literature Link

Children will enjoy hearing the stories about "inchlings" found in *Tom Thumb* by Margaret Read MacDonald, which is part of the Oryx Multicultural Folktale Series (Oryx Press, 1993).

---

2 Ongoing Learning & Practice

◆ Measuring to the Nearest Inch
(*Math Journal 1*, p. 123; *Math Masters*, p. 40)

PARTNER ACTIVITY

Remind children that when they measure with a ruler, they should align the left end of the object with the 0-mark on the ruler. If the object is longer than the ruler, you may have to guide them. The following directions are for a 6-inch ruler cut from *Math Masters*, p. 40.

1. Align the left end of the object to be measured with the 0-mark on the ruler.

2. Make a mark on the object at the 6-inch mark on the ruler.

3. Align the 0-mark on the ruler with the mark you just made on the object and measure on.

4. Then count on from 6 inches to the second measurement or add the second measurement to 6 inches. For example, if the distance from the mark on the object to the end of the object is 4 inches, count on 4 inches from 6 inches: 7, 8, 9, 10; or add 6 inches + 4 inches = 10 inches.

Partners select objects to measure. They draw or name the objects in the table on the journal page, estimate the total length of each object, and then measure and record the actual lengths. Partners can compare their estimates and measurements. To complete the journal page, partners measure and draw line segments. You may need to remind them how to draw a line segment.

ONGOING ASSESSMENT

Most children should be able to measure objects shorter than 6 inches to the nearest inch. Children should be developing the ability to measure objects that are longer than the ruler they are using; however, expect that many children may still be struggling with the idea that they add the length of the ruler and the number of inches for the second measurement.

 Adjusting the Activity Children who are able should measure objects to the nearest half-inch and quarter-inch.

◆ Math Boxes 5.11 (*Math Journal 1*, p. 124)

INDEPENDENT ACTIVITY

 Mixed Review This journal page provides opportunities for cumulative review or assessment of concepts and skills.

◆ Home Link 5.11 (*Math Masters*, p. 228)

 Home Connection Children ask someone at home to give them a 1-digit number and then some 2- and 3-digit numbers. They add 0 and then 1 to the numbers and tell the results. They record at least four of the results.

3 Options for Individualizing

◆ EXTRA PRACTICE Playing *Penny Cup*

PARTNER ACTIVITY  **15–30 min**

Children practice with sums of 10 by playing *Penny Cup*. For detailed instructions, see Lesson 2.8.

Math Boxes 5.11

1. Roger Ⓓ Ⓟ Ⓟ Ⓓ Ⓓ

Lauren Ⓓ Ⓟ Ⓟ Ⓝ Ⓟ Ⓝ Ⓝ

Who has more?

___Roger___

How much more?

___4¢, or $0.04 more___

2. Write the numbers.

What am I? _70_

What am I? _42_

3. Fill in the dots and numbers.

9 = 7 + _2_   _4_ + 4 = 8

3 + _7_ = 10   7 = 1 + _6_

4. **Judy's Dice Rolls**

1 2 3 4 5 6

How many times did Judy roll? _17 times_

What number came up the most? _5_

♦ *Math Journal 1*, p. 124

STUDENT PAGE

Adding 0 and 1   Home Link 5.11

 Family Note Give your child several 1-digit, 2-digit, and 3-digit numbers. Ask him or her to add 0 and 1 to each.
Use some numbers with 9 in the ones place like 9, 49, 79, 129, 359, and 789. Also use 0 in the tens and ones places, like in 208 and 320.
Please return this Home Link to school tomorrow.

1. Ask someone at home to say a 1-digit number; for example, 7. Add 0 to the number and give the answer. Then add 1 to the number and give the answer.

2. Have someone say a 2-digit or 3-digit number. Add 0 and 1 to this number.

3. Find the answers to more +0 and +1 problems with 2-digit or 3-digit numbers. Write them in the table below.

Example   25   25 + 0 = 25
            + 1
            26

Number Models

	Number	+0	+1
Example	25	25 + 0 = 25	25 + 1 = 26
1-digit number			
2-digit number			
3-digit number			
Your choice			

◆ *Math Masters*, p. 228

HOME LINK MASTER

5.12

"What's My Rule?"

OBJECTIVE To introduce the "What's My Rule?" routine.

summaries	materials

1 Teaching the Lesson

Children look for common attributes first in a set of dominoes and then in characteristics of some classmates. They solve "What's My Rule?" problems—find and apply rules—using a function machine. [Patterns, Functions, and Algebra; Operations and Computation]

☐ *Math Journal 1*, p. 125
☐ Home Link 5.11
☐ calculator
☐ slate
See **Advance Preparation**

2 Ongoing Learning & Practice

Children play the *Tens-and-Ones Trading Game.* [Numeration]

Children practice and maintain skills through Math Boxes and Home Link activities.

☐ *Math Journal 1*, p. 126
☐ Home Link Masters (*Math Masters*, pp. 229–231)
☐ base-10 blocks

3 Options for Individualizing

Extra Practice Children practice solving "What's My Rule?" problems. [Operations and Computation; Patterns, Functions, and Algebra]

☐ Teaching Master (*Math Masters*, p. 71)
See **Advance Preparation**

Additional Information

Advance Preparation For Part 1, draw a function machine on the board in semipermanent chalk.

For the optional Extra Practice activity in Part 3, make a copy of *Math Masters,* page 71. On the copy, write a set of "What's My Rule?" problems. See the activity on page 392 for suggestions.

Vocabulary • **function machine**

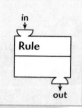

Getting Started

Mental Math and Reflexes

Play *Beat the Calculator.* Emphasize +0, +1, and doubles facts. Add a few difficult facts so that Calculators can win some of the time.

Math Message

Draw a row of 3 horizontal dominoes on the board with the dots for these number combinations: 4|2, 4|4, and 4|blank.

How are these dominoes alike?

Home Link 5.11 Follow-Up

Children share some of the +1 problems they recorded in their Number Models tables.

Teaching the Lesson

◆ Math Message Follow-Up

WHOLE-CLASS DISCUSSION

Children share their answers. If no one mentions them, discuss the following common attributes:

▷ They all have 4 dots on at least one of the sides of the domino (the left side).

▷ The number of dots on any one side is an even number.

▷ The sum of the dots is an even number.

▷ The sum of the dots is less than 9.

▷ No half has more than 4 dots.

Ask four children who have a common attribute to come to the front of the class. For example, all four children might be wearing brown shoes; their names might start with the same letter; they might all be girls; or they might all have the same color hair. Tell the class that all four children have something in common. Can they guess what it is?

Repeat this with other children and with different common attributes.

◆ Introducing the "What's My Rule?" Routine

WHOLE-CLASS ACTIVITY

Point to the **function machine** on the board and tell the class that it works like the *Magic Bag*. (See Lesson 5.10.) But instead of using craft sticks, it uses numbers. If you put a number into the machine, it will do something to the number and a different number will come out. It will do the same thing to any number you put in. For example, if you put in a 5, a 6 will come out. If you put in a 12, a 13 will come out. If you put in a 19, a 20 will come out.

• Can you guess what number will come out if you put in a 26? 27

Ask someone to give you a number to put into the machine.

• What number will come out? The number that is 1 more than the number that was put in.

• Can you figure out what the function machine does to the numbers you put in? It adds 1 to them.

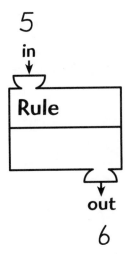

A function machine

You say:	Record
	in → out
I put in a 4; a 14 comes out	4 → 14
I put in a 12; a 22 comes out	12 → 22
I put in a 20; a 30 comes out	20 → 30
I put in a 15; what number comes out?	15 → ? 25
I put in a 56; what number comes out?	56 → ? 66
What's my rule? Add 10	

in → out	in → out
3 → 5	15 → 5
7 → 9	26 → 16
18 → 20	49 → 39
6 → ? 8	32 → ? 22
21 → ? 23	50 → ? 40
Add 2 to the "in" number	Subtract 10 from the "in" number

Suggested "What's My Rule?" Problems

All function machines don't work the same way. For example, one machine might subtract 2 from any number you put in, another machine might add 10, and so on. Tell the children that they are going to play a guessing game called "What's My Rule?" The object of the game is to figure out what rule a function machine uses to do something to the numbers that are put in.

When posing a "What's My Rule?" problem, record each number you put into the machine (the input), followed by an arrow and the number that comes out (the output). For example, you might pose the problem shown in the margin.

Encourage children to describe the rule in different ways. Expect responses such as the following:

▷ The "out" number is always 10 more than the "in" number.

▷ The function machine is adding 10 to the "in" number.

▷ The "in" number gets bigger by 10.

▷ The machine adds 1 to the tens digit.

Do a few more "What's My Rule?" problems (see margin). Have children write the missing "out" numbers on their slates. For each problem, ask what the function machine does to the "in" numbers.

Function machines are not restricted to adding or subtracting the same number to the input number, as illustrated by the following problems. Try them with your class, but don't expect most children to solve them at this time.

in → out	in → out
2 → 4	5 → 50
6 → 12	2 → 20
3 → 6	4 → 40
5 → ? 10	3 → ? 30
9 → ? 18	10 → ? 100
Double the "in" number	Put the "in" number in the tens place of the "out" number and a 0 in the ones place

◆ Solving "What's My Rule?" Problems
(*Math Journal 1*, p. 125)

INDEPENDENT ACTIVITY

Explain that the numbers under the headings "in" and "out" on the journal page show what numbers go into the function machine and what numbers come out. Tell children to figure out the rule that determines what numbers come out of the machine and use that rule to find the missing output numbers. You might want to do the first problem with the whole class to make sure children understand what they are to do.

 Adjusting the Activity Children can use counters to explore the relationship between input and output numbers. For problems involving addition and subtraction, have children line up counters for a pair of input and output numbers in two rows, and then match pairs of counters in the two rows, one to one. The unmatched counters will give a clue to the relationship between pairs of "in" and "out" numbers.

 Ongoing Learning & Practice

◆ Playing the *Tens-and-Ones Trading Game*

PARTNER ACTIVITY

Children practice counting and exchange skills by playing the *Tens-and-Ones Trading Game*. For detailed instructions, see Lesson 5.3.

◆ Math Boxes 5.12 (*Math Journal 1*, p. 126)

INDEPENDENT ACTIVITY

 Mixed Review This journal page provides opportunities for cumulative review or assessment of concepts and skills.

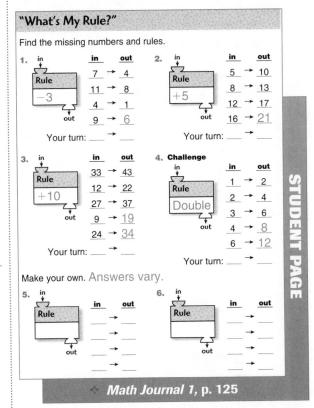

Math Journal 1, p. 125

 ONGOING ASSESSMENT
Check that children understand that the same rule is applied to all the number pairs in a problem.

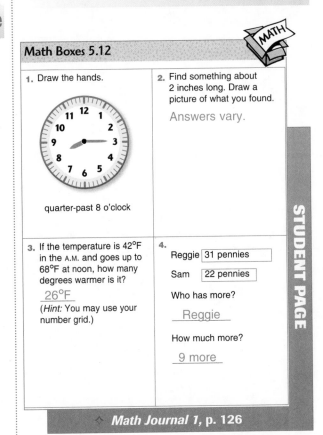

Math Journal 1, p. 126

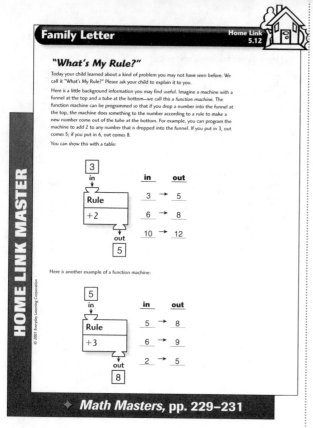

"What's My Rule?"

Today your child learned about a kind of problem you may not have seen before. We call it "What's My Rule?" Please ask your child to explain it to you.

Here is a little background information you may find useful. Imagine a machine with a funnel at the top and a tube at the bottom—we call this a *function machine*. The function machine can be programmed so that if you drop a number into the funnel at the top, the machine does something to the number according to a rule to make a new number come out of the tube at the bottom. For example, you can program the machine to add 2 to any number that is dropped into the funnel. If you put in 3, out comes 5; if you put in 6, out comes 8.

You can show this with a table:

Here is another example of a function machine:

◆ *Math Masters,* pp. 229–231

"What's My Rule?" 1

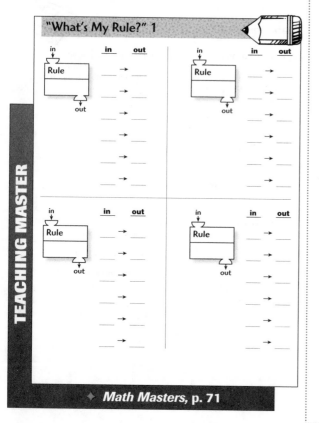

◆ *Math Masters,* p. 71

◆ **Home Link 5.12** (*Math Masters,* p. 229–231)

Home Connection Children solve "What's My Rule?" problems. Home Link 5.12 includes a two-page Family Letter explaining "What's My Rule?" problems.

3 Options for Individualizing

◆ **EXTRA PRACTICE** Solving "What's My Rule?" Problems (*Math Masters,* p. 71)

INDEPENDENT ACTIVITY   15–30 min

Prepare a set of "What's My Rule?" problems. Leave one or two sets blank for children to make up their own problems. *Suggestions:*

in → out	in → out	in → out
2 → 8	10 → 1	14 → 18
10 → 16	20 → 11	8 → 12
16 → 22	60 → 51	15 → 19
6 → 12	40 → 31	6 → 10
9 → 15	50 → 41	10 → 14
12 → 18	80 → 71	24 → 28
Rule: +6	Rule: −9	Rule: +4

Challenge problems:

in → out	in → out
15 → 5	14 → 5
27 → 7	43 → 7
32 → 2	25 → 7
56 → 6	18 → 9
14 → ? 4	33 → ? 6
41 → ? 1	82 → ? 10
Rule: − the tens digit	Rule: Add the digits.

5.13

Applying Rules

OBJECTIVE To find the output for given rules and input numbers.

summaries	materials

1   Teaching the Lesson

Children use a rule and an input number to find an output number. They record the input and output in a table.
[Operations and Computation; Patterns, Functions, and Algebra]

☐ *Math Journal 1*, p. 127
☐ Home Link 5.12
☐ calculator
☐ slate
***See* Advance Preparation**

2   Ongoing Learning & Practice

Children play *Penny–Nickel–Dime Exchange*. [Numeration; Measurement and Reference Frames]

Children practice and maintain skills through Math Boxes and Home Link activities.

☐ *Math Journal 1*, p. 128
☐ Home Link Master (*Math Masters*, p. 232)
☐ 20 pennies, 10 nickels, 10 dimes per partnership
☐ 2 dice per partnership

3   Options for Individualizing

Extra Practice Children practice solving a variety of "What's My Rule?" problems. [Operations and Computation; Patterns, Functions, and Algebra]

Enrichment Children program their calculators to simulate a function machine. [Operations and Computation; Patterns, Functions, and Algebra]

☐ Teaching Master (*Math Masters*, p. 72)
☐ calculator
***See* Advance Preparation**

Additional Information

Advance Preparation For Part 1, draw a function machine on the board in semipermanent chalk.

For the first activity in Part 3, make a copy of *Math Masters*, page 72. On the copy, write a set of "What's My Rule?" problems. You may want to look at journal page 127 for a typical set of problems. To extend the activity, fill in two or three number pairs and either an "in" or "out" number for the other pairs in each problem and have the children figure out the rule and fill in the missing numbers.

Vocabulary • **rule**

Getting Started

Mental Math and Reflexes

Play *Beat the Calculator*. See *Lesson 5.11* for detailed instructions.

Math Message

If you put a 7 in the function machine, what number will come out?

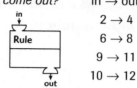

in → out

2 → 4
6 → 8
9 → 11
10 → 12

Home Link 5.12 Follow-Up

Go over the answers. Ask children to state a rule for each problem.
1. Add 1. **2.** Subtract 2. **3.** Add 10.
4. Find half of the "in" number.

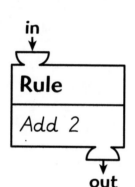

1 Teaching the Lesson

◆ Math Message Follow-Up

WHOLE-CLASS DISCUSSION

Ask what the function machine does to each of the numbers that is put in. It adds 2 to it. Write "Add 2." or "+ 2" on the machine on the board and tell the class that this is the **rule** that describes what the function machine does to the numbers that are put in.

◆ Applying Rules

WHOLE-CLASS ACTIVITY

Do several more function-machine problems with the class, using the format of the Math Message problem. Write several pairs of input and output numbers and have children find the rule and supply the missing outputs. Record the rule on the function machine. Use rules like "Add 3," "+ 5," "− 3," "Subtract 10," and "Double."

Once children are comfortable with finding, stating, and applying a rule, give them a problem with just a rule and an input number. Children use the rule to find the output. For example: *If the rule is "Subtract 3." and the input is 9, what is the output?* 6 Ask children to suggest other inputs.

Point out that it takes time to draw an arrow for each pair of numbers and that the numbers may not always line up exactly. An easier way to keep track of the input and output numbers is to record them in a table.

Draw a table on the board (see margin). Write a simple rule on the function machine. Write a number in the "in" column of the table. Have children report the number that goes in the "out" column. Repeat the procedure with several other input numbers.

Repeat this activity with other rules you feel are appropriate for your class. Use the table format to record inputs and outputs.

in	out
5	7
9	11
17	19
48	50

Rule: Add 2

ONGOING ASSESSMENT

Have children record output numbers on their slates to check that they understand how to apply the rules. Record each output in your table after the children show it on their slates.

Adjusting the Activity Instead of having children find the output for a given input, ask them to find the input for a given output. For example: *The rule is "Add 1." If I put a number in the machine and a 9 comes out, what number did I put in?* 8

If the rule is "Subtract 1" and I put a zero in the machine, what number will come out? −1 Keep the rules simple for this variation.

◆ Finding and Applying Rules
(*Math Journal 1*, p. 127)

PARTNER ACTIVITY

Children complete the problems and make up problems for their partners to solve.

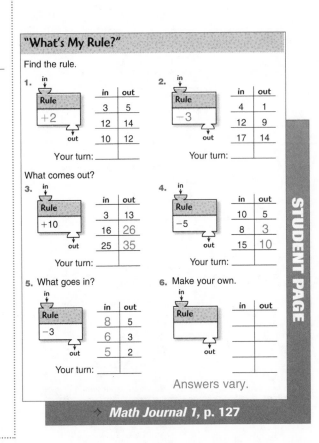

"What's My Rule?"

Find the rule.

1. Rule +2

in	out
3	5
12	14
10	12

Your turn: _____

2. Rule −3

in	out
4	1
12	9
17	14

Your turn: _____

What comes out?

3. Rule +10

in	out
3	13
16	26
25	35

Your turn: _____

4. Rule −5

in	out
10	5
8	3
15	10

Your turn: _____

5. What goes in? Rule −3

in	out
8	5
6	3
5	2

Your turn: _____

6. Make your own. Rule

in	out

Answers vary.

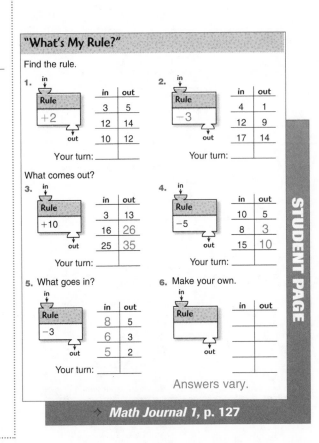

Math Journal 1, p. 127

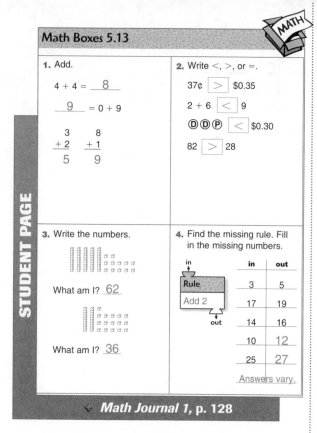

Math Boxes 5.13

1. Add.

$4 + 4 = \underline{8}$

$\underline{9} = 0 + 9$

$\begin{array}{r} 3 \\ +2 \\ \hline 5 \end{array}$ $\begin{array}{r} 8 \\ +1 \\ \hline 9 \end{array}$

2. Write <, >, or =.

37¢ $\boxed{>}$ $0.35

$2 + 6$ $\boxed{<}$ 9

Ⓓ Ⓓ Ⓟ $\boxed{<}$ $0.30

82 $\boxed{>}$ 28

3. Write the numbers.

What am I? 62

What am I? 36

4. Find the missing rule. Fill in the missing numbers.

Rule
Add 2

in	out
3	5
17	19
14	16
10	12
25	27

Answers vary.

Math Journal 1, p. 128

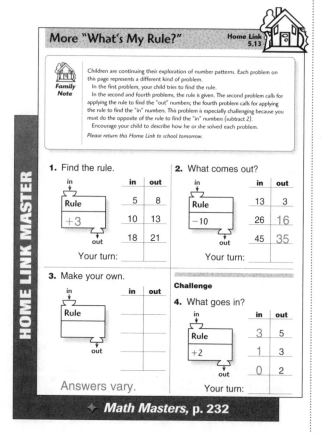

More "What's My Rule?"

Home Link 5.13

Family Note

Children are continuing their exploration of number patterns. Each problem on this page represents a different kind of problem.

In the first problem, your child tries to find the rule.

In the second and fourth problems, the rule is given. The second problem calls for applying the rule to find the "out" numbers; the fourth problem calls for applying the rule to find the "in" numbers. This problem is especially challenging because you must do the opposite of the rule to find the "in" number (subtract 2).

Encourage your child to describe how he or she solved each problem.

Please return this Home Link to school tomorrow.

1. Find the rule.

Rule
+3

in	out
5	8
10	13
18	21

Your turn:

2. What comes out?

Rule
−10

in	out
13	3
26	16
45	35

Your turn:

3. Make your own.

Rule

in	out

Challenge

4. What goes in?

Rule
+2

in	out
3	5
1	3
0	2

Your turn:

Answers vary.

Math Masters, p. 232

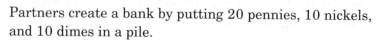

Ongoing Learning & Practice

◆ Playing *Penny–Nickel–Dime Exchange*

PARTNER ACTIVITY

Partners create a bank by putting 20 pennies, 10 nickels, and 10 dimes in a pile.

Players take turns. At each turn, a player rolls two dice and collects the amount shown on the dice from the bank. Whenever players have at least 5 pennies, they say "Exchange" and trade 5 of their pennies for a nickel in the bank. Whenever players have at least 2 nickels or 5 pennies and 1 nickel, they say "Exchange" and trade them for a dime.

The game ends when there are no more dimes in the bank. The player who has more dimes wins. If players have the same number of dimes, the player who has the greater amount of money wins.

 Adjusting the Activity To extend the activity, children play with a larger bank and two polyhedral dice.

◆ Math Boxes 5.13 (*Math Journal 1*, p. 128)

INDEPENDENT ACTIVITY

Mixed Review This journal page provides opportunities for cumulative review or assessment of concepts and skills.

◆ Home Link 5.13 (*Math Masters*, p. 232)

Home Connection Children complete a page of "What's My Rule?" problems including one in which they make up their own rule.

3 Options for Individualizing

◆ **EXTRA PRACTICE** Solving "What's My Rule?" Problems (*Math Masters*, p. 72)

INDEPENDENT ACTIVITY   **15–30 min**

Prepare a set of mixed "What's My Rule?" problems. (You might want to pattern the problems after those on journal page 127.)

Portfolio Ideas

To extend the activity, fill in two or three number pairs and either an "in" or an "out" number for the other pairs in each problem. Children must figure out the rule and fill in the missing numbers.

◆ **ENRICHMENT** Simulating a Function Machine on the Calculator

PARTNER ACTIVITY   **15–30 min**

The same calculator function that was used to count up and back can be used to simulate a function machine with an addition or subtraction rule. For example, to program the calculator to simulate a function machine for the rule "Add 5," do the following:

▷ Clear the calculator.

▷ Press ⊕ 5 ⊜ 0.

The display will show the number 0. The calculator is now ready to act as a function machine.

If you enter any input number and press ⊜, the display will show the output number. For example, if you enter the input number 9 and press ⊜, the display will show the output number 14. **Do not clear the calculator before entering the next input number.**

Use an overhead calculator, if one is available, to guide children through several examples. Enter a secret rule; then ask a volunteer to enter a number and press ⊜. Repeat this procedure several times. Record each input and output number in a table. Then have the class figure out the rule.

After you have done a few examples with the class, have partners take turns programming their calculators and figuring out the rule.

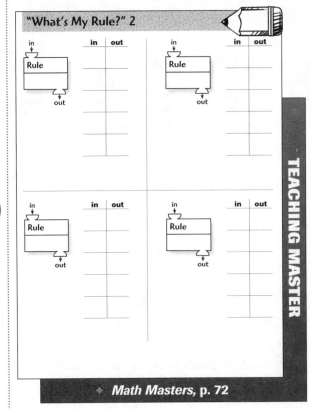

◆ *Math Masters*, p. 72

TEACHING MASTER

5.14 Unit 5 Review and Assessment

OBJECTIVE To review and assess children's progress on the material covered in Unit 5.

1 Assess Progress

learning goals

5a **Beginning Goal** Find missing numbers and/or the missing rule in "What's My Rule?" problems. (**Lessons 5.10, 5.12, and 5.13**)

5b **Developing Goal** Understand place value for longs and cubes. (**Lessons 5.1–5.5, 5.8, 5.9, 5.12, and 5.13**)

5c **Developing Goal** Compare numbers using < and >. (**Lessons 5.3, 5.6–5.9, 5.12 and 5.13**)

5d **Developing Goal** Know +1, +0, doubles, and sums of 10 addition facts. (**Lessons 5.4, 5.5, 5.7, and 5.9–5.11**)

5e **Developing Goal** Solve simple number stories. (**Lessons 5.6–5.11**)

activities

- ☐ Written Assessment, Problems 16 and 17

- ☐ Oral Assessment, Problem 3
- ☐ Slate Assessment, Problem 5
- ☐ Written Assessment, Problems 9 and 10

- ☐ Written Assessment, Problems 11–14

- ☐ Slate Assessment, Problem 4
- ☐ Written Assessment, Problems 1–8

- ☐ Slate Assessment, Problem 6
- ☐ Written Assessment, Problem 15

materials

- ☐ *Math Journal 1*, Activity Sheet 2
- ☐ Assessment Masters (*Math Masters*, pp. 309 and 310)
- ☐ Home Link 5.13
- ☐ quarter-sheet of paper
- ☐ tool-kit clocks

- ☐ tool-kit coins
- ☐ slate
- ☐ tool-kit number cards
- ☐ base-10 blocks (longs and cubes)
- ☐ die (1 per partnership)

2 Build Background for Unit 6

summaries

Children practice and maintain skills through Math Boxes and Home Link activities.

materials

- ☐ *Math Journal 1*, p. 129
- ☐ Home Link Masters (*Math Masters*, pp. 233–236)

Each **learning goal** listed above indicates a level of performance that might be expected at this point in the *Everyday Mathematics* K–6 curriculum. For a variety of reasons, the levels indicated may not accurately portray your class's performance.

Additional Information

Background Information For additional information on assessment for Unit 5, see the Assessment Handbook, pages 49–51. For assessment checklists, see *Math Masters*, pages 336, 337, and 356–358.

Getting Started

Math Message

Rita said that the blocks show 214.
On a quarter-sheet of paper, write
the number you think the blocks show.

Home Link 5.13 Follow-Up

Briefly go over the missing numbers and missing rules. Have volunteers share problems they created.

1 Assess Progress

✦ Math Message Follow-Up

WHOLE-CLASS DISCUSSION

Briefly discuss Rita's mistake. She did not exchange 10 of the cubes for a ten.

✦ Oral and Slate Assessments

WHOLE-GROUP ACTIVITY

If the suggested problems below are not appropriate for your class's level of performance, adjust the numbers or the problems themselves to better assess your children's abilities.

Oral Assessment Suggestions

1. Count up by 10s on the number grid. Begin with 0; with 35; with 52; with 89; with 130.

2. Count back by 10s on the number grid. Begin with 100; with 75; with 98; with 120; with 142.

3. Stop-and-start count by 10s, then 5s, and finally by 1s. For example: count by 10s to 70, by 5s to 95, and then by 1s to 99. **Goal 5b**

4. Show 3 o'clock on your tool-kit clock. Show half-past 5; two-thirty; quarter-past 10; eight fifteen; quarter-to 5.

5. Show 17 cents with coins. Show 32 cents; 55 cents; 94 cents.

Slate Assessment Suggestions

1. Write 2 dollars and 15 cents in dollars-and-cents notation. Write 3 dollars and 9 cents; 4 dollars and 75 cents; 81 cents; 3 cents.

2. Write the number that is 1 more than 37; 1 more than 59; 1 more than 100.

NOTE: Many of these assessment suggestions relate to learning goals that have been addressed in previous units. Now is a good time to evaluate children's progress toward those goals.

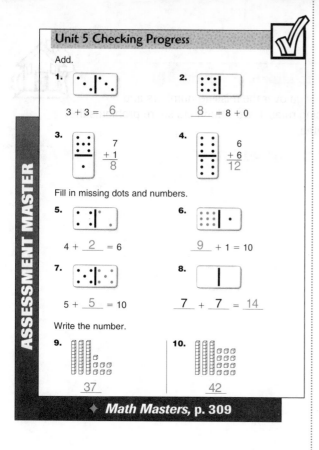

Unit 5 Checking Progress

Add.

1. $3 + 3 = \underline{6}$

2. $\underline{8} = 8 + 0$

3. $\begin{array}{r} 7 \\ +\ 1 \\ \hline 8 \end{array}$

4. $\begin{array}{r} 6 \\ +\ 6 \\ \hline 12 \end{array}$

Fill in missing dots and numbers.

5. $4 + \underline{2} = 6$

6. $\underline{9} + 1 = 10$

7. $5 + \underline{5} = 10$

8. $\underline{7} + \underline{7} = \underline{14}$

Write the number.

9. $\underline{37}$

10. $\underline{42}$

✦ Math Masters, p. 309

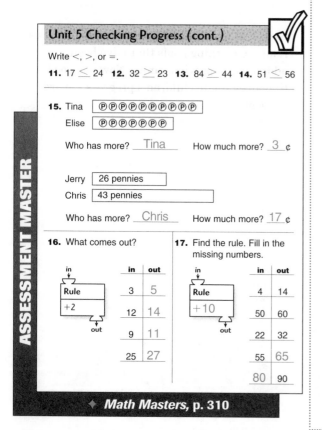

Unit 5 Checking Progress (cont.)

Write <, >, or =.

11. $17 \underline{<} 24$ 12. $32 \underline{>} 23$ 13. $84 \underline{>} 44$ 14. $51 \underline{<} 56$

15. Tina ⓅⓅⓅⓅⓅⓅⓅⓅⓅ

Elise ⓅⓅⓅⓅⓅⓅ

Who has more? <u>Tina</u> How much more? <u>3</u> ¢

Jerry | 26 pennies

Chris | 43 pennies

Who has more? <u>Chris</u> How much more? <u>17</u> ¢

16. What comes out?

in	out
3	5
12	14
9	11
25	27

Rule +2

17. Find the rule. Fill in the missing numbers.

in	out
4	14
50	60
22	32
55	65
80	90

Rule +10

✦ Math Masters, p. 310

ASSESSMENT MASTER

---

3. Write the number that is 1 less than 42; 1 less than 80; 1 less than 100.

4. Write the number that is 10 more than 20; 10 more than 45; 10 more than 77; 10 more than 98. Write the number that is 10 less than 18; 10 less than 39; 10 less than 82; 10 less than 105. **Goal 5d**

5. Write 28. Circle the tens digit. Repeat with 57; 94; 106; 152. **Goal 5b**

6. Write the answers to these number stories. **Goal 5e**

   • Judith had 18 pennies. Marvin had 15 pennies. How many more pennies did Judith have?
   3 more pennies

   • Rachel sent out 12 birthday invitations to her party. Nine friends came to the party. How many children who were invited did not come to the party?
   3 children

   • Brett has a collection of sports balls. He has 4 baseballs, 3 basketballs, and 3 soccer balls. How many sports balls does he have altogether? 10 balls

   • Carlos was working on a crossword puzzle. The puzzle had 15 word clues to solve. He had already figured out 4 of the words. How many words did he still have to find? 11 words

✦ Written Assessment
(*Math Masters,* pp. 309 and 310)

INDEPENDENT ACTIVITY

Read the problems on *Math Masters,* pages 309 and 310 with the class. If appropriate, complete the pages together—that is, wait for children to complete a problem before reading the next one. You may want to do an example with the class for each of the problems.

If your class can work independently, have them work alone or with a partner. Circulate and assist as children work.

• Add. (Problems 1–4) **Goal 5d**

• Fill in missing dots and numbers. (Problems 5–8) **Goal 5d**

• Write the number. (Problems 9 and 10) **Goal 5b**

• Write <, >, or =. (Problems 11–14) **Goal 5c**

• Who has more? How much more? (Problem 15) **Goal 5e**

• What comes out? (Problem 16) **Goal 5a**

• Find the rule. Fill in the missing numbers. (Problem 17) **Goal 5a**

◆ ALTERNATIVE ASSESSMENT OPTION
Play *Top-It* with Relation Symbols

PARTNER ACTIVITY

Use this activity from Lesson 5.3 to assess children's progress in comparing numbers and finding simple sums. Children record the last round on quarter-sheets of paper.

◆ ALTERNATIVE ASSESSMENT OPTION
Play the *Tens-and-Ones Trading Game*

PARTNER OR SMALL-GROUP ACTIVITY

Use this activity from Lesson 5.3 to assess children's progress on understanding place value for tens and ones. Stop the game after a predetermined length of time. Children record their final totals on a quarter-sheet of paper by drawing the longs and cubes and writing the total the blocks represent.

◆ Midyear Assessment (*Math Masters,* pp. 318–320)

The Midyear and End-of-Year Assessment Masters (*Math Masters,* pages 318–327) provide additional assessment opportunities that you may want to use as part of your balanced assessment plan. These tests cover only some of the important concepts and skills in *First Grade Everyday Mathematics.* They should be used along with ongoing, product, and periodic assessment opportunities within the lessons and at the ends of the units. Please see pages 73 and 74 of the *Assessment Handbook* for answers to the Midyear Assessment.

2 Build Background for Unit 6

◆ Math Boxes 5.14 (*Math Journal 1,* p. 129)

INDEPENDENT ACTIVITY

 Mixed Review This journal page provides opportunities for cumulative review or assessment of concepts and skills.

◆ Home Link 5.14: Unit 6 Family Letter
(*Math Masters,* pp. 233–236)

 Home Connection This Home Link is a four-page newsletter that introduces parents and guardians to Unit 6's topics and terms. The letter offers ideas for home-based activities that are supportive of classroom work.

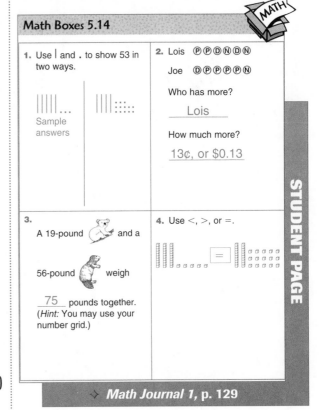

✦ Math Journal 1, p. 129

✦ Math Masters, pp. 233–236

STUDENT PAGE

HOME LINK MASTERS

Appendices

PROJECT 1

Apple Math

OBJECTIVE To classify, count, measure, weigh, and compare apples.

background information

Recommended Use: During or after Unit 2

See the discussion of Projects in the Management Guide section of the *Teacher's Reference Manual*.

materials

Comparing Numbers

☐ apples

☐ Class Data Pad (optional)

☐ construction paper: green, brown, apple-colored (red, yellow, …)

☐ scissors

☐ paste or tape

Measuring Length and Weight

☐ 1 apple per partnership

☐ tape measure

☐ spring scale

☐ quarter-sheet of paper or stick-on note

☐ knife; bath scale; pan balance

☐ *Ten Apples Up on Top, Apple Pigs* (optional)

***See* Advance Preparation**

Project Information

This project is divided into two parts. The first part involves classifying, counting, and comparing numbers of apples; the second involves measuring the girth and weight of apples. It would be practical to do the parts on different days.

Advance Preparation Comparing Numbers: You will need at least one apple for every two children. Try to obtain as many different colors, shapes, sizes, and varieties of apples as possible.

Measuring Length and Weight: You will need a spring scale, which children also will use. Be sure you are familiar with the adjustment mechanism before demonstrating the scale.

The unit lines on a spring scale are tricky. The ounce scale is best for weighing apples, even if it is marked only with even unit numbers. (You might want to write in the odd unit numbers.) If necessary, mark the pointer with a red marker to help children see it clearly.

You will need something to attach to the spring scale to hold at least one apple, such as a plastic bag, a mesh bag (the kind in which onions are sold), or the foot from a pair of panty hose.

spring scale

For the Literature Link in Part 2, obtain one of the following books: *Ten Apples Up on Top* by Theo LeSieg (Dr. Seuss), (Random House, 1987); *Apple Pigs* by Ruth Orbach (out of print, but possibly in libraries).

Vocabulary • girth

1 Doing the Project

COMPARING NUMBERS

◆ Classifying, Counting, and Comparing Apples

Have children help you sort the apples. On the board or Class Data Pad, list the different colors (red, yellow, green, …), shapes (round, oval, …), and sizes (small, medium, large). Also list the varieties (Red Delicious, Macintosh, and so on) if known. Count the total number of each color, shape, size, and variety. Record the numbers in the list with tally marks.

Compare results; for example, ask, *Are there more red apples or green apples? Are there fewer yellow apples or red apples? Which variety do we have the most/fewest of?*

Encourage children to make their own comparisons.

Optional: Make a graph of the data.

◆ Making Apple Trees

Have children make apple trees out of green and brown construction paper. They cut out any number of apples they choose from construction paper and fasten them onto their trees. Then they number their apples 1, 2, ….

The partners compare the numbers of apples on their trees. They decide how to describe the comparison, and write it on a sheet of paper.

MEASURING LENGTH AND WEIGHT

◆ Using a Tape Measure

If tape measures were not distributed previously, pass them out and allow a few minutes for exploration. Remind children of the "2-inch no-zap rule" if they are using retractable tape measures: *Do not zap the tape measure shut unless no more than 2 inches show.*

If the tape measures have two units—inches and centimeters—identify the inch scale. That is what children should use. Say that the symbol for *inch* is *in.*

Ask children to measure items around them: the widths of their desks, readers, crayon boxes, and so on.

Check children's techniques. Be sure they line up the zero point with an edge of what is being measured. Then help them read the inch number nearest the other edge.

Children make apple trees and number the apples.

NOTE: Even if they have not yet completed the lessons on the comparison symbols <, >, and =, some children may be familiar with the symbols. Mention that they will be doing more work with the symbols later in the year.

Even adults get confused by the symbols < and >. One memory aid is that the arrow points to the smaller number. The equal sign, with no "pointers," means the two parts are the same.

Suggest that they measure around their partner's wrist to practice measuring a curved object.

Ask children to tell the measurements of similar objects, such as the width of their desks. The measurements will not all be the same. Help them understand that the numbers they get with a tape measure or ruler depend on the units they use and on how accurately they measure.

◆ Measuring the Girth (Circumference) of Apples

Give each partnership an apple. Have the partners measure the **girth** or widest part of their apple to the nearest inch. This is like measuring an apple around its "waist."

The partners will record their measurement on a quarter-sheet of paper. Remind them to write the symbol for *inch* (*in.*) after the number.

Collect the slips. Have the class help you arrange the apples in order of "waist" size.

◆ Weighing Apples

If you haven't done so previously, introduce the spring scale. Say that it is for weighing light objects, and that the units you will use are called *ounces*. Also show a bath scale, which is used to weigh heavier objects in pounds.

Discuss weight with the children. Ask what it means to weigh something.

Hang an empty bag on the spring scale and adjust the spring scale to show 0 ounces. Put an apple into the bag and point out how the apple pulls the spring down so that the indicator points to the weight in ounces. Say that the symbol for *ounce* is *oz*.

Again demonstrate weighing an apple. Then have several pairs of children weigh their apples. Ask all partners to weigh their apples—today or during their free time over the next few days—and to write the weight on a slip of paper. Remind them to write the symbol for *ounce* (*oz*) after the number. Collect and discuss the weights when everyone has finished.

Weigh one apple again. Record its weight. Then:

• Cut it into fractional pieces and ask which fractions the pieces represent: one-half, one-quarter, and so on.

• Ask whether cutting the apple into pieces affects the apple's total weight (all its pieces together).

• Check by weighing the separate pieces. Add the weights.

Invite children to explore the bath scale and the pan balance.

✦ Measuring Parts of the Body

Have children use tape measures to measure around at least five parts of their bodies. Partners may help where necessary. On a sheet of paper, have them draw a stick figure or other picture and label all the parts they measured with both the number and the unit, *in*.

2 Extending the Project

✦ Extension Suggestions

- Measure in metric as well as in U.S. customary units.
- Cook applesauce or bake an apple pie.
- Take a field trip to an apple orchard and explore the kinds of apples that grow there and how much they cost.
- Have children tell about a visit to a pick-your-own apple orchard. Which kind of apples were there? How much did they cost?

Literature Link Read or have children read *Ten Apples Up on Top* by Theo LeSieg (Dr. Seuss), (Random House, 1987) or *Apple Pigs* by Ruth Orbach (out of print, but possibly in libraries).

Social Studies Link Have children find out where and how apples are grown.

Health Link Have children find nutrition information for apples and apple products.

✦ Home Link Suggestions

Suggest that children check refrigerators and pantries at home for apple products—apple juice, apple tarts, applesauce, and so on. They can count the number of different products and draw some of them.

Have children ask their families which weighing tools might be found in a home, store, or business—bath scale, diet scale, postal scale, scientific balance, and so on. Together they look for such tools. They draw pictures of what they find.

PROJECT

2

Autumn Leaves

OBJECTIVE To collect, observe, compare, and sort fall leaves.

background information

Recommended Use: During or after Unit 2

See the discussion of Projects in the Management Guide section of the *Teacher's Reference Manual*.

materials

- ☐ Project Master (*Math Masters*, p. 136)
- ☐ fall leaves
- ☐ chart paper for class graphs
- ☐ tape or stapler; magnifying glass (optional)
- ☐ paint; hard, smooth objects
- ☐ newspaper and cardboard for pressing
- ☐ clear material for sealing; ruler or tape measure
- ☐ crayons or brushes and paint; iron (optional)
- ☐ *My Favorite Trees: Terrific Trees of North America* (optional)
- ☐ *Familiar Trees of North America: Eastern Region* (optional)
- ☐ *Familiar Trees of North America: Western Region* (optional)

***See* Advance Preparation**

Project Information

Advance Preparation For the Science Link in Part 2, you may want to obtain the following books: *My Favorite Trees: Terrific Trees of North America* by Diane Iverson (A Sharing Nature with Children Book. Dawn, 1999); *Familiar Trees of North America: Eastern Region* and *Familiar Trees of North America: Western Region* edited by Jane Friedman (National Audubon Society Pocket Guides. Knopf, 1987).

1 Doing the Project

◆ Collecting Fall Leaves

Each child needs a collection of as many different kinds of fall leaves as possible. These can be obtained in several ways:

1. After establishing some ground rules, take the class outside for a short walk to pick up leaves.

2. Have children pick up leaves in their own yards or neighborhoods and bring them to school.

3. Collect and bring to school a bag of leaves for children to share, or ask a parent or volunteer to collect leaves for the class.

Encourage children to take only one of each kind of leaf.

Make a graph of the different kinds of leaves on chart paper. Attach a sample of each kind of leaf at the bottom of the graph. Find out how many of each kind of leaf have been collected, and color squares above each leaf to represent the number.

Ask questions such as, *How many different kinds of leaves did the class find? Which kind did we find the most of? The least of? Did we find the same number of any kinds? How does the graph show how many more we found of one kind of leaf than another? How does the graph show how many less?*

Make a graph of the number of leaves collected by each class member. Ask questions such as, *Who collected the most? The fewest? From the graph, is it possible to know which kind each person collected? Why not?*

◆ Describing and Comparing Leaves

The children examine their leaves, using magnifying glasses if available. Discuss features that they find. *For example:*

- colors
- shapes
- edge patterns
- veins (Ask, *Why do leaves have veins?* To carry food and water for the tree *Do we have veins?*)
- size (Ask, *Do the biggest leaves come from the biggest trees?* Not necessarily.)
- symmetry (Ask, *Can we fold a leaf so that the two halves match?*)

◆ Measuring Leaves (*Math Masters,* p. 136)

Children do the following:

1. Arrange their leaves in order of apparent size, using visual clues, not measures.

2. Use a ruler or tape measure to measure widths or lengths (or both) of a selection of flattened leaves. Ask for some observations. For example: *Do the widest leaves have the largest area? Do bigger leaves have similar shapes? Do smaller leaves have similar shapes?*

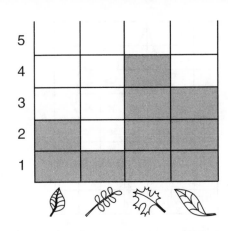

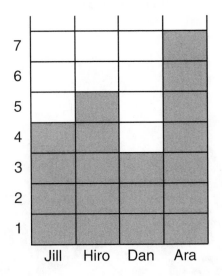

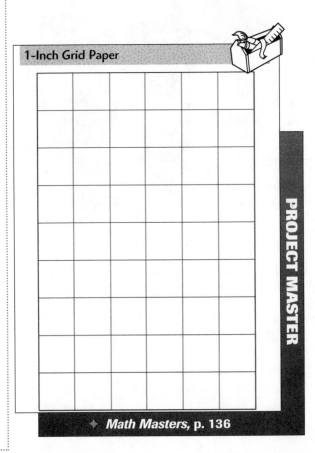

1-Inch Grid Paper

◆ *Math Masters,* p. 136

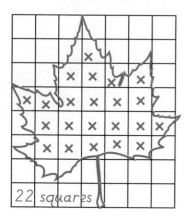

22 squares

Area estimates can be made by taping leaves to 1-inch grid paper.

Kyle

A leaf collage

3. Estimate the areas of leaves. Good area estimates can be made by taping or stapling leaves to 1-inch grid paper (*Math Masters,* page 136). Children carefully rub a crayon around the edges of the leaves, or paint with a brush or sponge, overlapping the paper. Spatter painting also works. Once the paint has dried, they carefully remove the leaves from the grid paper. Then they count the squares inside the leaf pattern. If half or more than half a square is inside the pattern, tell children to count the square. If less than half a square is inside the pattern, tell them not to count the square.

4. Compare estimates of areas from grid counts.

✦ Sorting Leaves by Attributes

After a brief discussion, let children decide on rules for sorting leaves. Some obvious rules might be according to size, shape, or color. Less obvious rules might include sorting according to vein structure or edge patterns. Ask several children to explain their rules for sorting.

✦ Making Leaf Art

▷ Make leaf stencils or prints.

Use fresh leaves.

Using the techniques described for making area estimates, have children make artistic leaf stencils.

Have them make leaf prints by "inking" the leaf with paint or ink and pressing a piece of paper over it. Explain that carefully rubbing with a hard, smooth object (such as the back of a spoon) helps make a good print.

▷ Make leaf collages.

Have children select a variety of leaves to arrange between double sheets of newspaper labeled with their names. They stack all the "sandwiches" between two pieces of cardboard and tie them together into a bundle. Then they stack books or heavy objects on the bundle. It takes several days of pressing to get leaves that are easy to work with.

Help children preserve pressed leaves by laminating them, ironing them between two sheets of waxed paper, or covering them with clear contact paper. Helpers are essential for this activity. Children can use sealed leaves to make mobiles, window displays, bookmarks, collages, and place mats.

Extending the Project

✦ Extension Suggestions

Have children observe leaves through the seasons. They might adopt a tree near the school, and sketch or photograph it as it looks now. They could watch it throughout the school year, sketching or photographing it again in the middle of winter, in early spring, and just before the end of the school year. Display the pictures. Ask them to observe and report on the tree; for example, on what day did the last leaves fall off? On what day did the first leaves appear? Are there any nests in the tree?

Science Link Help children find books about trees and leaves; for example, *My Favorite Trees: Terrific Trees of North America* by Diane Iverson (A Sharing Nature with Children Book. Dawn, 1999); *Familiar Trees of North America: Eastern Region* and *Familiar Trees of North America: Western Region* edited by Jane Friedman (National Audubon Society Pocket Guides. Knopf, 1987). They can use the books to help classify and label leaf samples. They also might find out about different types of trees (deciduous and evergreen), the importance of trees for the environment, what leaves do, why leaves are usually green, and so on.

✦ Home Link Suggestion

Have children investigate their own yards or neighborhood for leaves and trees discussed in class. They might bring in kinds not already displayed.

Pumpkin Math

OBJECTIVE To estimate the weight and girth of pumpkins, compare pumpkins in several ways, and count pumpkin seeds.

background information

Recommended Use: During or after Unit 2

See the discussion of Projects in the Management Guide section of the *Teacher's Reference Manual*.

materials

□ Project Master (*Math Masters*, p. 137)

□ pumpkin(s)

□ bath or postal scale

□ string or yarn

□ scissors; knife; colander

□ paper towels

□ glue and paper for seed collage; tape measure

□ quarter-sheet of paper per child

□ oil, salt, and an oven or other means for roasting or frying seeds (optional)

□ calculators (optional)

□ *The Biggest Pumpkin Ever* (optional)

□ *Clifford's First Halloween* (optional)

□ *Pumpkins: A Story for a Field* (optional)

***See* Advance Preparation**

Project Information

Advance Preparation You will need at least one pumpkin, and preferably several pumpkins of various sizes. You will need a bath scale, or a postal scale with enough capacity to weigh pumpkins.

Next to the Math Message, place a pumpkin, a supply of quarter-sheets of paper, and a box to collect the sheets.

Parts of this project can be messy.

For the Literature Link in Part 2, you may want to obtain the following books: *The Biggest Pumpkin Ever* by Steven Kroll (Holiday House, 1984); *Clifford's First Halloween* by Norman Bridwell (Harcourt Brace, 1996); and *Pumpkins: A Story for a Field* by May Lyn Ray (Harcourt Brace, 1996).

Vocabulary • girth

Math Message

Guess the pumpkin's weight in pounds. Write your guess on a quarter-sheet of paper. Put the sheet in the box.

Doing the Project

✦ Weighing Pumpkins

Write a variety of responses to the Math Message on the board. Label each weight with "lb" or "pounds." Discuss which estimates seem reasonable.

Weigh the pumpkin and record its weight to the nearest pound. Compare the actual weight with the estimates.

If you have more than one pumpkin, weigh each one. Label each with its weight.

Weigh a child. Ask, *About how many pumpkins would weigh the same as [name]?* Use pumpkins to show other comparisons or equivalents.

Optional: Have the children use calculators to find the total weight of all of the pumpkins.

✦ Estimating and Measuring the Girth of Pumpkins

Ask several children to cut lengths of string or yarn to represent their estimates of the pumpkin's **girth,** or distance around its widest part. Tape the estimates on the board.

Wrap a string around the pumpkin and cut it to show the actual girth. Tape this string on the board along with the estimates, and label it "actual."

Repeat for other pumpkins.

Optional: Have a volunteer measure each piece of string with a tape measure. The class compares the estimates with the actual girth.

✦ Relating Weight and Girth

If you have more than one pumpkin, ask:

• Which pumpkin has the largest girth? Does the largest pumpkin weigh the most?

• Which pumpkin has the smallest girth? Does the smallest pumpkin weigh the least?

Pumpkin Seeds
by Esther Weiss

The pumpkin is a clever squash,
With seeds all hidden in—
I always start a wondering
How many are within.
We'll cut a hole to count the seeds
(First wash and let them dry!)
Then we'll count and count and count
(This will be fun to try.)
First find 100 seeds
And not one single more
Fill the grids by row
To have a perfect score.
Then count by groups of ten—
And then one at a time
I'll show how many seeds there were.
Does yours have more than mine?

Number Grid

0	1	2	3	4	5	6	7	8	9
10	11	12	13	14	15	16	17	18	19
20	21	22	23	24	25	26	27	28	29
30	31	32	33	34	35	36	37	38	39
40	41	42	43	44	45	46	47	48	49
50	51	52	53	54	55	56	57	58	59
60	61	62	63	64	65	66	67	68	69
70	71	72	73	74	75	76	77	78	79
80	81	82	83	84	85	86	87	88	89
90	91	92	93	94	95	96	97	98	99
100	101	102	103	104	105	106	107	108	109
110									

Use with Project 3.   137

Math Masters, p. 137

◆ Making Other Comparisons Using Pumpkins

- If you have more than one pumpkin, count the ridges on the pumpkin shells. Ask, *Do bigger pumpkins have more ridges?* No. The ridges and the pumpkins just get larger as they grow.

- Draw several geometric shapes on the board—triangle, square, circle, and so on. Ask children to name them. Using these shapes, cut a top out of the pumpkin, and carve a face. Scrape out the pulp and seeds onto a paper towel. Save all the parts.

- Weigh all the parts of the pumpkin—shell, top, cutout pieces, pulp, and seeds. Ask, *Does the total weight of the parts equal the original weight?*

Optional: Have children draw pumpkin faces with geometric shapes.

◆ Counting Pumpkin Seeds
(*Math Masters*, p. 137)

Remove the pulp. Wash the seeds in a colander and spread them out to dry overnight. If you have other pumpkins, extract the seeds from them as well. Ask children to estimate the total number of seeds in each pumpkin.

When the seeds are dry, divide the class into groups of 3 or 4. Give each group some of the seeds from one pumpkin, or all of the seeds from an individual pumpkin. Ask children to count their group's seeds. Make number grids (*Math Masters*, page 137) available. Observe the different ways the groups count, and encourage efficient methods. Groups can switch seeds and recount.

Record each group's total. Compare findings and methods, and use a calculator to determine the total of all the seeds.

If more than one pumpkin is used, ask, *Does the largest pumpkin have the most seeds?*

Extending the Project

✦ Extension Suggestions

- Use seeds that have not been handled by children. Bake or fry them in a small amount of oil and salt. Share the seeds with children.

- If your class is having pumpkin pies for a Halloween treat, talk about and name fraction parts as you divide and serve the pies.

- Do the old favorite finger-play "Five Little Pumpkins" (see margin).

  Optional: Copy the finger rhyme and let children illustrate it. Collect their drawings in a "Five Little Pumpkins" book.

- Have children measure in metric as well as customary units.

- Take a field trip to a pumpkin farm.

 Literature Link Children might explore books about pumpkins and Halloween, such as *The Biggest Pumpkin Ever* by Steven Kroll (Holiday House, 1984), *Clifford's First Halloween* by Norman Bridwell (Harcourt Brace, 1996), *Pumpkins: A Story for a Field* by May Lyn Ray (Harcourt Brace, 1996).

 Social Studies Link Children can find out where and how pumpkins are grown.

Health Link Have children search for nutrition information for pumpkin products.

✦ Home Link Suggestions

Send home additional Number Grids. Children can use the grids to help count the seeds from any Halloween pumpkins they might have at home.

Start a classroom seed collection, beginning with pumpkin seeds. Have children bring seeds from home, such as apple seeds, corn kernels, sunflower seeds, acorns, and so on. The seeds can be compared, labeled, and made into seed mosaics.

Five Little Pumpkins

Five little pumpkins were sitting on a gate.
(Hold up one hand with fingers spread out; hold the other hand under the first hand with fingers held vertically to look like fence rails.)

The first pumpkin said, "Oh my, it's getting late."
(Wiggle finger as each pumpkin speaks.)

The second one said, "There are witches in the air."

The third one said, "I don't care."

The fourth one said, "Let's run, Let's run."

The fifth one said, "It's only Halloween fun."

Whoo went the wind.
(Make an appropriate sound.)

And out went the light.
(Clap hands on the word "out.")

And five little pumpkins rolled out of sight.
(Roll hands over one another in spinning motion.)

PROJECT 4

Geometric Gift Wrap and Greeting Cards

OBJECTIVE Use geometric shapes to create designs for gift wrap or greeting cards.

background information

Recommended Use: During or after Unit 3

See the discussion of Projects in the Management Guide section of the *Teacher's Reference Manual*.

materials

- ☐ tempura or finger paints
- ☐ paper towels or pieces of sponge
- ☐ plastic trays (for example, the kind meat and vegetables are packaged on in supermarkets)
- ☐ Pattern-Block Template
- ☐ pattern blocks
- ☐ plain paper for gift wrap (newsprint is fine)
- ☐ paper for greeting cards

1 Doing the Project

✦ Using Pattern-Block Shapes to Create Designs

Working in small groups, have children use pattern-block shapes to create designs for wrapping paper or greeting cards.

Two techniques are suggested.

STENCILING WITH THE PATTERN-BLOCK TEMPLATE

Show children how to use small pieces of sponge or crumpled paper towels as daubers. As they use the template as a stencil, they should hold it against the paper, and fill in an open area with paint. The secret is to keep the daubers fairly dry.

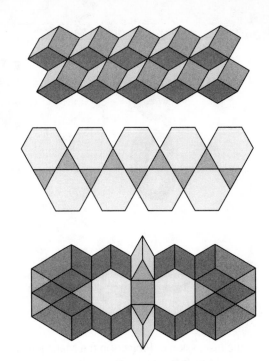

Children can make small "stamp pads" from folded paper towels saturated with tempera paint. They need to keep these in plastic trays. Ask them to put paint on one side of a pattern block by pressing it against the "stamp pad," and then press the block on the paper.

Alternatively, they might spread finger paint on flat trays or other waterproof surfaces, and use them as stamp pads to put paint on the blocks.

Encourage children to include patterns in their designs. *For example:*

- patterns in which two or three different shapes and colors repeat

- patterns in which the sizes of the shapes vary

- patterns that are symmetric

Point out that new shapes can be made by combining pattern-block shapes; for example, three rhombuses form a regular hexagon (sides equal and angles equal). A regular hexagon will *tessellate*—that is, the whole paper can be covered by hexagons without gaps or overlaps.

After children have made a variety of gift wrap and greeting cards, bring them together to describe their designs. Help them name the shapes they used. If appropriate, count various shapes.

Extending the Project

✦ Extension Suggestions

Provide additional shapes to include in designs, such as circular discs and letters of the alphabet.

Language Arts Link Suggest that children use the alphabet shapes to form names or words in repeating patterns.

✦ Home Link Suggestions

If children have created greeting cards, help them write messages inside the cards to family members.

PROJECT

Calendar for the New Year

OBJECTIVE To create a calendar for the classroom.

background information

Recommended Use: Near the beginning of the new calendar year

See the discussion of Projects in the Management Guide section of the *Teacher's Reference Manual.*

materials

Classroom calendar

☐ Project Masters (*Math Masters,* pp. 138 and 139)

☐ at least 12 sheets of $8\frac{1}{2}"\times11"$ drawing paper

☐ 24 sheets of $9"\times12"$ construction paper; crayons or markers

☐ glue; hole punch; 2 or 3 metal rings or string loops

Personal calendar

per child:

☐ Project Master (*Math Masters,* p. 140; at least 12 copies)

☐ stapler; crayons or markers

☐ *Chicken Soup with Rice: A Book of Months; Frog and Toad All Year; The Snowy Day* (optional)

***See* Advance Preparation**

Project Information

Advance Preparation Plan to divide the class into 6 or 12 groups. Make 1 copy of *Math Masters,* page 138, per group, and make at least 12 copies of *Math Masters,* page 139. Refer to a calendar or almanac for the coming year, and fill in the variable dates. You may want to add dates for other holidays, school vacations, or school events. Then make copies for the groups.

Before class begins, or with the help of the class, write on the board the names of the months and the days of the week. After the name of each month, write the number of days in that month (28 or 29 for February), and the day of the week on which the month begins in the coming year.

For the Literature Link in Part 2, you may want to obtain the following books: *Chicken Soup with Rice: A Book of Months* by Maurice Sendak (HarperTrophy, 1991); *Frog and Toad All Year* by Arnold Lobel (HarperCollins, 1985); and *The Snowy Day* by Ezra Jack Keats (Viking, 1981).

1 Doing the Project

◆ Making a Classroom Calendar
(*Math Masters,* pp. 138 and 139)

Assign one month (or two months) to each group. Have groups complete a calendar page for each assigned month.

Ask them to first print the name of the month on the line above the calendar grid.

Next, each group uses the information on the board to locate the space for the first day of that group's month. As children point to that space, circulate and check. They then write "1" in the space for the first day of the month.

Discuss which months have 28, 29, 30, or 31 days, so that each group will know the length of its month. Then the groups fill in the dates on their calendars.

Each group decides on an illustration for its assigned month and draws it on a sheet of paper. The drawings might be seasonal, thematic, or geometric, or they might reflect work in math.

Children also can add illustrations for special days listed on *Math Masters,* page 138.

Glue the 24 sheets onto construction paper and bind them with rings or string into a single classroom calendar.

◆ Making Personal Calendars
(*Math Masters,* p. 140)

Children can use the classroom calendar as a reference for creating personal monthly calendars, using copies of *Math Masters,* page 140. This master provides a grid for dates and space for an illustration. They can personalize the calendar by noting their own birthdays, family birthdays and events, and so on.

Extending the Project

◆ Extension Suggestions

- Children may want to make additional calendars for people in the school, such as the school nurse, principal, and so on.

Literature Link You might want to read aloud these classic books about the months and the seasons: *Chicken Soup with Rice: A Book of Months* by Maurice Sendak (HarperTrophy, 1991), *Frog and Toad All Year* by Arnold Lobel (HarperCollins 1985), and *The Snowy Day* by Ezra Jack Keats (Viking, 1981).

◆ Home Link Suggestion

Children can bring their personal calendars home and ask family members to help them add additional family birthdays and upcoming family events to their calendars.

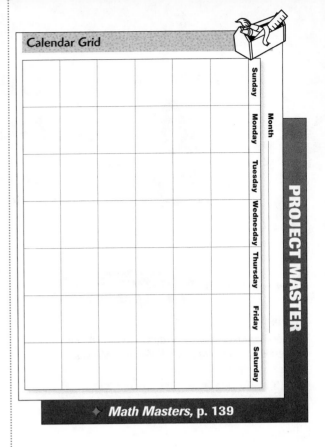

Calendar Grid

	Month					
Sunday	Monday	Tuesday	Wednesday	Thursday	Friday	Saturday

◆ *Math Masters,* p. 139

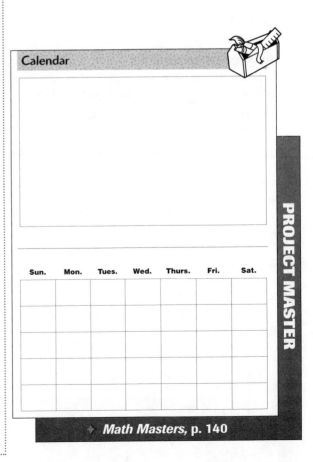

Calendar

Sun.	Mon.	Tues.	Wed.	Thurs.	Fri.	Sat.

◆ *Math Masters,* p. 140

PROJECT

6

Celebrate the Hundredth Day

OBJECTIVE To celebrate the hundredth day of first grade.

background information

Recommended Use: Around the hundredth day of school

See the discussion of Projects in the Management Guide section of the *Teacher's Reference Manual.*

materials

Depending on your choice of activity:

☐ 100 jelly beans; container

☐ 100 one-inch squares of construction paper

☐ 12-inch ruler

☐ classroom books

☐ collections of 100 small items

☐ 100-piece jigsaw puzzle

☐ transparent container with 100 small objects

☐ 100 toothpicks; large piece of paper

☐ calculator

☐ blank number grids

☐ 100 6-inch strips of paper; glue or paste

Project Information

Advance Preparation Ask each child to collect and bring to school 100 small items, such as 100 paper clips, 100 packaging "peanuts," 100 pennies, and so on. These will be put into a Hundreds Museum.

Look through the suggested activities on pages 421–423 and obtain materials for those you choose to use.

1 Doing the Project

◆ Sharing the Hundreds Collections

Have children show and describe their collections of 100 items.

Make a class Hundreds Museum with the collections. Use some of the collections for the Suggested Celebration Activities on the next page.

◆ Suggested Celebration Activities

Following are suggestions for ways of celebrating the 100th day of first grade. Some teachers may choose to devote the whole day to doing 100th day activities; others may spend only part of the day. Choose those activities you wish to use, and add your own.

1. Put 100 jelly beans of various colors into a container. Have children estimate how many jelly beans each child would get if the collection of 100 were shared equally. Once you have a consensus, ask each child to take that number of beans. Have each child report the number of each color while you tally the numbers on the board. (You report on the colors of any leftover jelly beans.) Make a bar graph: the x-axis is the color of jelly beans; the y-axis is the number of jelly beans.

2. For each partnership or small group, have available 100 one-inch squares (or other shapes) of different colors of construction paper. Let children make patterns, mosaics, or designs by gluing the squares onto paper.

3. With children's help, use a 12-inch ruler to measure off 100 feet in the hallway.

   During a recreation time, have a 100-foot race.

   Ask children to estimate where they would end up if they took 100 heel-to-toe steps from a given place. Then have them actually take the steps.

4. Invite children to locate page 100 in several books.

5. Ask children to help you weigh collections of 100 small items from the Hundreds Museum.

6. Provide 100-piece jigsaw puzzles for children to work on during free time.

7. Fill a transparent container with more than 100 small items, such as pretzels, circular-shaped breakfast cereal, or erasers. Have children estimate the number of items, and tally the estimates on the board. Reveal the exact number (count to double-check), then share the items with children.

8. Give 100 toothpicks to each group. Ask children to estimate how many toothpicks they would get if the toothpicks were shared equally. Check their estimates, and then have each child glue that number of toothpicks on a large sheet of paper to make a group 100-toothpick design.

9. Have children say when they think 100 seconds has passed while you time them. Then ask them to estimate how many times they can say the alphabet in 100 seconds, and then try it. Ask, *How many hours are in 100 minutes?* about $1\frac{1}{2}$ hours

10. Have children use their calculators. Tell them to press **ON/C** 10 ⊕ 10, and then ⊜ 100 times, and report the result.

11. Ask children to fill in the numbers from 1 to 100 on a blank number grid.

12. Cut out 100 6-inch strips of paper. Have children construct a 100-link paper chain. Hang the chain in the classroom, and ask them how long it is.

Extending the Project

✦ Extension Suggestions

1. Graph the results of weighing 100 small items.

2. Line up 100 centimeter cubes along a meterstick. Remind children of the meaning of the prefix *centi-*. Ask, *How many centimeters are there in 1 meter?* 100 centimeters

✦ Home Link Suggestions

Ask children to count 100 days from today on a calendar at home. (If children made a personal calendar as part of Project 5, they might want to use that one.) Have them discuss with a family member what they might be doing 100 days from now. *What month will it be? What season of the year? Will they be celebrating a family birthday or other occasion at that time?*

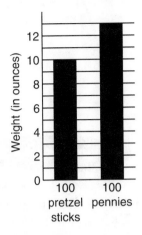

Results of weighing groups of 100 items

PROJECT

7

Amaryllis Plant

OBJECTIVE To grow an amaryllis plant from a bulb and to graph the plant's growth.

background information

Recommended Use: During or after Unit 7

See the discussion of Projects in the Management Guide section of the *Teacher's Reference Manual.*

materials

☐ amaryllis bulb (These are usually for sale at nurseries until April. *Warning:* The bulb is poisonous if eaten.)

☐ plant pot (This should be slightly larger than the diameter of the bulb and should have a small draining hole.)

☐ potting soil; saucer; container of lukewarm water

☐ measuring tape or yardstick; magnifying lens

Project Information

An amaryllis grows quickly. As much as 24 inches of stem growth can be observed over a period of 6 to 8 weeks. This provides marvelous opportunities for measurement and graphing.

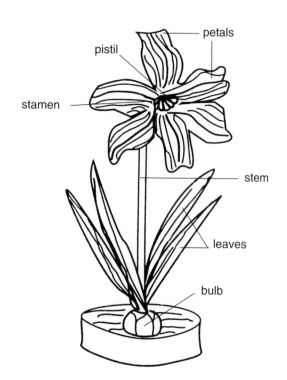

petals
pistil
stamen
stem
leaves
bulb

1 Doing the Project

◆ Planting the Amaryllis Bulb

Soak the bulb and roots in a container of lukewarm water for several hours before planting.

Plant the bulb so that $\frac{1}{3}$ of it rises above the potting soil. Be careful not to damage the roots.

Put the pot on a saucer for drainage. Place the plant in as much light as possible; direct sunlight and warm room temperatures stimulate growth.

Water sparingly until green shoots begin to appear. Then add more water as needed.

The plant probably will grow quickly to about two feet in height. It should flower about six to eight weeks after the bulb is planted.

✦ Graphing the Growth of the Amaryllis Plant

Have children measure the plant stem at regular intervals—daily, if you wish.

When the plant is measured, be sure the measurements are taken from the same spot at the bottom of the plant.

The following graphing methods work well:

▷ Have children cut strips of construction paper equal in length to the height of the plant. Date these strips and mount them on a baseline on the board or bulletin board.

▷ Draw a grid like the one in the margin on chart paper. Allow for 24 inches of growth over 6 to 8 weeks. Have children mark heights above the corresponding dates on the graph. It doesn't matter if measurements are skipped for some dates, but it does matter if measurements are recorded on incorrect dates.

Have children make estimates of future growth. For example, ask them what they think the height will be on a particular date. Follow up by comparing their estimates with the actual measurement for that day.

Mark on the graph when buds and blossoms appear.

Allow time for children to closely examine the large flowers by using a magnifying lens. Discuss the different parts of the plant and the flower.

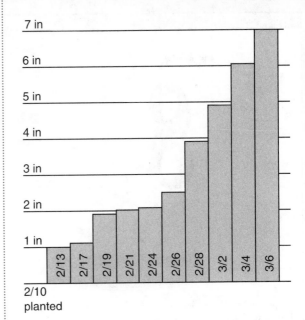

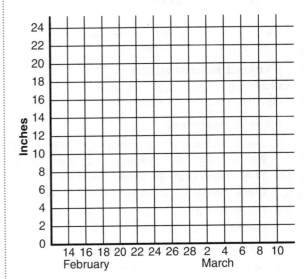

Extending the Project

✦ Extension Suggestions

▷ Photograph the plant from time to time; date and display the photos with the graph.

▷ Measure and graph the growth of other plants.

▷ Help children find out more about the amaryllis by consulting an encyclopedia or reference book.

▷ Have children find out more about the parts of plants.

✦ Home Link Suggestion

Children grow plants at home, measure and graph their growth, and report back to the class. Green beans and sunflowers are good plants to use because of their rapid growth.

PROJECT

8

A Flea Market

OBJECTIVE To handle money in a buying-and-selling situation.

background information

Recommended Use: During or after Unit 8

See the discussion of Projects in the Management Guide section of the *Teacher's Reference Manual*.

materials

☐ unwanted toys, books, puzzles, and other items from home

☐ money; stick-on notes, price tags, or other means for labeling items with prices; calculator

***See* Advance Preparation**

Project Information

Children bring unwanted toys, books, puzzles, stuffed animals, and other items from home. These are offered for sale in a classroom flea market. Children practice using coins, adding prices, and making change.

Advance Preparation

1. Decide on the kind and amount of money you will use.
   Real money Children should bring coins from home. Specify an amount such as 50 cents.
   Play money (tool-kit coins) Decide on an amount for each child to use.
   Class money Class members create and name their own money. They draw it, copy it, cut it out, and distribute it equally.

2. Decide how items will be sold. (Each child sells his or her own items; or cashiers sell all the items. Children take turns being cashier.)

3. Set a date for the flea market. Decide whether the market will be open for one day, several days, or from time to time.

4. Send a letter home that explains the project.

1 Doing the Project

◆ Discussing the Flea Market

Explain that a flea market provides an opportunity for people to sell items they no longer want, or to exchange them for items they might be able to use. Tell children to talk with an adult at home about items they might bring to school for the flea market. These could include unwanted toys, books, puzzles, stuffed animals, and so on.

Set a date for the flea market. Children should bring in items several days before.

◆ Pricing the Items

Set a range in which all items will be priced; 5 to 25 cents works well. Be sure children understand the idea of the price range. Children can price items as they are brought to class. Display the items for a few days before the market opens. Leftover items can be reduced in price during the last few minutes of the sale.

Talk about money and change. Ask questions like these:

- If I have nickel and a dime, how much money do I have?
- Suppose I bought your toy car for 5 cents and gave you a dime. How much should you give me back?
- I have 35 cents. Can I buy a book for 10 cents and a pen for 30 cents?

◆ Holding the Flea Market and Reviewing the Results

If children sell their own items, have each child report the amount of money received. Use a calculator to find the grand total. If cashiers sold the items, have children work in groups to count the money received.

Compare the total received with the total available (for example, 12 dollars if 24 children each have 50 cents). Ask whether everything was spent.

Have children talk about their experiences. For example, did cheaper items sell faster? Were some items overpriced?

Flea market items

2 Extending the Project

◆ Extension Suggestions

▷ If real money was collected, discuss how it might be spent, or decide if it should be given to charity. Have children vote for their preferences and then tally and record their votes on a bar graph.

▷ If children decide to buy something for the classroom, bring in school supply catalogs so that children can determine if they have enough money to buy the items they want.

◆ Home Link Suggestion

Suggest that parents take their children on a shopping trip, give their children an amount of money, and have children decide how to spend it.

First Grade Key Vocabulary

For a more extensive glossary that includes additional illustrations and references, please refer to the *Teacher's Reference Manual*.

addend One of two or more numbers that are added.

addition A mathematical operation based on putting together two or more quantities.

Addition and Subtraction Facts Table A tool used for finding and learning addition and subtraction facts.

addition fact Two 1-digit numbers and their sum, such as 9 + 7 = 16.

A.M. The abbreviation for *ante meridiem,* which means "before the middle of the day"; from midnight to noon.

analog clock A clock that shows the time by the positions of the hour and minute hands.

analog clock

angle A figure that is formed by two rays or line segments having a common endpoint.

arithmetic fact Any of the basic addition facts with addends 9 or less; the subtraction facts that are the inverses of these; the multiplication facts with factors 9 or less; and the division facts that are inverses of these (exception: no division by 0).

arm span The distance from fingertip to fingertip of a person's outstretched arms.

arrow path In *Everyday Mathematics,* a route to follow on a number grid.

arrow rule In *Everyday Mathematics,* the operation that determines the number that goes in the next frame in a Frames-and-Arrows diagram. See *Frames and Arrows.*

arrows In *Everyday Mathematics,* the links representing the rule that determines which numbers go in the frames of a Frames-and-Arrows diagram. See *arrow rule.*

attribute A feature of an object or a common feature of a set of objects. Examples of attributes include size, shape, color, and number of sides. See *property.*

bar graph A graph that shows the relationships among variables by the use of bars to represent quantities.

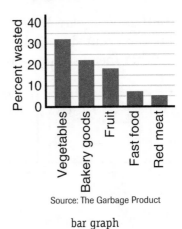

Source: The Garbage Product

bar graph

base 1. The flat face or faces that define shape when classifying a polyhedron.
2. Any side of a polygon, usually used along with the altitude perpendicular to it, for computing area.

base-10 shorthand In *Everyday Mathematics,* a system to represent base-10 blocks.

Name	Base-10 block	Base-10 shorthand
cube	▫	▪
long	▯	|
flat	▦	▢

calendar A reference frame used to help keep track of the passage of time and on which appointments, special days, and other markings can be recorded.

capacity A measure of how much a container can hold, usually in units such as quarts, gallons, cups, or liters.

Celsius The temperature scale on which 0° is the temperature at which pure water at sea level freezes and 100° is the temperature at which it boils. The Celsius scale is used in the metric system.

centimeter (cm) In the metric system, a unit of length equivalent to 10 millimeters, $\frac{1}{10}$ of a decimeter, and $\frac{1}{100}$ of a meter.

centimeter cube In *Everyday Mathematics,* the term for the smallest of the base-10 blocks, measuring 1 cm on each edge.

change diagram In *Everyday Mathematics,* a diagram used to represent situations in which quantities are either increased or decreased.

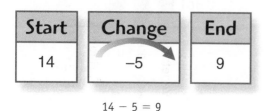

14 − 5 = 9

circle The set of all points in a plane that are equally distant from a given point in the plane called the *center* of the circle.

center

Class Data Pad In *Everyday Mathematics,* a large pad of newsprint where data collected by the class can be stored for use (and reuse) throughout the year.

column A vertical arrangement of objects or numbers in an array or table.

commutative property A property of addition and multiplication (but not of subtraction or division) that says that changing the order of the elements being added or multiplied will not change the sum or product.

cone A 3-dimensional shape having a circular base, a curved surface, and one vertex, called the apex.

congruent figures Two figures that are the same size and shape. If you put one on top of the other, they would match exactly. Congruent figures are said to be *congruent to* each other.

consecutive Following one another in an uninterrupted order, such as A, B, C, D or 6, 7, 8, 9.

corner See *vertex.*

counting numbers The numbers used to count things. The set of counting numbers is {1, 2, 3, 4, …}. Sometimes 0 is included with the counting numbers.

cube A polyhedron with six square faces. One of the five regular polyhedra. See *regular polyhedron.*

cubit An ancient unit of length, measured from the point of the elbow to the end of the middle finger. It has been standardized at various times to be between 18 and 22 inches.

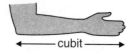

cubit

cup In the U.S. customary system, a unit of capacity equal to 8 fluid ounces; $\frac{1}{2}$ pint.

customary system The measuring system used most often in the United States, in contrast to the metric system used nearly everywhere else. See *U.S. customary system.*

cylinder A 3-dimensional shape having a curved surface and parallel circular or elliptical bases that are the same size. A can is an object shaped like a cylinder.

data Information gathered by observing, counting, or measuring. *Data* is the plural of *datum.*

decimal point The mark that separates the whole number from the fraction in decimal notation; in expressing money, it separates the dollars from the cents.

degree (°) A unit for measuring temperature. Also a unit of measure for angles based on dividing one complete circle (rotation) into 360 equal parts. The small raised symbol ° is called the *degree symbol.*

denominator The number written below the line in a fraction. In a part-whole fraction, the number of equal parts into which the whole (ONE) is divided. Compare to *numerator.*

diagonal (of a table) A line of objects or numbers from upper left to lower right, or from lower left to upper right in an array or a table.

difference The amount by which one number is greater or less than another number.

digit In the base-10 numeration system, one of the symbols 0, 1, 2, 3, 4, 5, 6, 7, 8, and 9, which can be used to write any number.

digital clock A clock that uses numbers to show the time in hours and minutes, with a colon used to separate them.

digital clock

doubles fact The addition and multiplication facts without turn-around partners. A doubles fact names the sum or product of a 1-digit number and itself, such as $4 + 4 = 8$ or $3 \times 3 = 9$.

edge A line segment where two faces of a polyhedron meet.

equivalent names Different ways of naming the same number. For example: $2 + 6$, $4 + 4$, $12 - 4$, $18 - 10$, $100 - 92$, $5 + 1 + 2$, eight, VIII, and ~~HHT~~ /// are equivalent names for 8. See *name-collection box.*

estimate 1. *n.* A close, rather than exact, answer. A number close to another number. 2. *v.* To make an estimate.

even number A whole number that can be evenly divided by 2. It has 0, 2, 4, 6, or 8 in the ones place. Compare to *odd number.*

Exploration In *Everyday Mathematics,* an independent or small-group activity that may involve concept development, manipulatives, data collection, problem solving, games, and skill reviews.

face A surface that bounds a 3-dimensional shape. It may be curved (on a cylinder or a cone) or flat (on a prism).

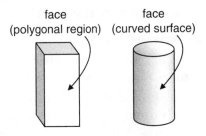

face
(polygonal region)　　　face
(curved surface)

fact family A collection of related addition and subtraction facts, or multiplication and division facts, made from the same numbers. For 5, 6, and 11, the addition/subtraction family consists of $5 + 6 = 11$, $6 + 5 = 11$, $11 - 5 = 6$, and $11 - 6 = 5$. For 5, 7, and 35, the multiplication/division family consists of $5 \times 7 = 35$, $7 \times 5 = 35$, $35 \div 7 = 5$, and $35 \div 5 = 7$.

fact power   In *Everyday Mathematics,* a term that refers to the ability to recall basic number facts automatically without having to figure them out.

Fact Triangle   Triangular flash card labeled with the numbers of a fact family for practice with addition/subtraction or multiplication/division facts. The two one-digit numbers and their sum or product (marked with a dot) appear in the corners of each triangle. See *fact family.*

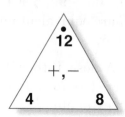

Fact Triangle

Fahrenheit   The temperature scale on which pure water at sea level freezes at 32° and boils at 212°. The Fahrenheit scale is widely used in the U.S. but in few other places.

flat   In *Everyday Mathematics,* the term for the base-10 block consisting of 100 cm cubes.

foot (ft)   In the U.S. customary system, a unit of length equivalent to 12 inches or $\frac{1}{3}$ of a yard.

fraction   A number in the form of $\frac{a}{b}$ or a/b that names part of an object or collection of objects, compares two quantities, or represents division. A fraction names equal parts of a whole.

Frames and Arrows   In *Everyday Mathematics,* diagrams used to represent number sequences—a list of numbers often generated according to one or more rules. The diagrams consist of *frames* in which numbers are written and *arrows* that represent rule(s) for moving from one frame to another.

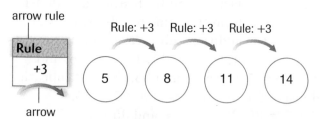

Frames and Arrows diagram

function machine   In *Everyday Mathematics,* a diagram of an imaginary machine programmed to process numbers according to a certain rule. A number (input) is put into the machine and is transformed into a second number (output) through the application of a rule.

in	out
1	2
2	4
3	6
5	10
10	20
20	40

function machine with input/output table

geometric solid   A 3-dimensional shape bounded by surfaces. Common geometric solids include the rectangular prism, square-based pyramid, cylinder, cone, and sphere.

geometry   The study of spatial objects and their properties and relationships. The word geometry is derived from the Greek words for "earth" and "measure."

hand span   The distance from the tip of the thumb to the tip of the little finger of an outstretched hand. The hand span is standardized at 9 inches for adults.

height   A measure of how tall something is.

heptagon   A 7-sided polygon.

hexagon   A 6-sided polygon.

Home Link   In *Everyday Mathematics,* a suggested follow-up or enrichment activity to be done at home.

inch (in.)   In the U.S. customary system, a unit of length equal to $\frac{1}{12}$ of a foot and to about 2.54 centimeters.

input A number inserted into an imaginary function machine, which processes numbers according to a designated rule. See *function machine.*

kite A quadrilateral with exactly two pairs of adjacent sides that are the same length. (A rhombus is not a kite.)

length of a rectangle Usually, but not necessarily, the longer dimension of a rectangle or a rectangular object.

line A straight path that extends infinitely in opposite directions.

line segment A straight path joining two points.

long In *Everyday Mathematics,* the term for the base-10 block consisting of 10 cm cubes.

Math Boxes In *Everyday Mathematics,* a format to provide review problems and to practice skills. A set of Math Boxes for each lesson are in the student *Math Journals.*

mathematics A study of relationships among numbers, shapes, systems, and patterns. It is used to count and measure things, to discover similarities and differences among them, to solve problems, and to learn about and organize the world.

Math Journal In *Everyday Mathematics,* a student record of mathematical discoveries and experiences. It provides visual models for conceptual understanding and problems, and includes activities for individuals and small groups.

Math Masters In *Everyday Mathematics,* pages ready for duplicating. Most of these are used by children in carrying out suggested activities. Some will be used more than once during the school year.

Math Messages In *Everyday Mathematics,* activities for children to complete at the start of each lesson. Math Messages may be problems that introduce the day's lesson, directions to follow, sentences to complete or correct, or reading assignments.

mental arithmetic Computations done by people "in their heads," either in whole, or in part.

Mental Math and Reflexes In *Everyday Mathematics,* exercises (usually oral) suggested at the start of most lessons. They are designed to strengthen children's number sense and to review and advance essential basic skills.

meter (m) In the metric system, the fundamental unit of length, equal to 10 decimeters, 100 centimeters, or 1,000 millimeters.

metric system A measurement system based on the base-ten numeration system and used in most countries in the world. Units for linear measure (length, distance) include millimeter, centimeter, meter, and kilometer; units for mass (weight) include gram and kilogram; units for capacity include milliliter and liter; the unit for temperature change is degrees Celsius.

middle value The number in the middle when a set of data is organized in sequential order; also called the median. If there is an even number of data, the median is the number halfway between the two middle values.

name-collection box In *Everyday Mathematics,* a boxlike diagram tagged with a given number and used for collecting equivalent names for that number. See *equivalent names.*

25	37 − 12	20 + 5
~~HHT~~ ~~HHT~~ ~~HHT~~ ~~HHT~~ ~~HHT~~		
twenty-five	X X X X X	
	X X X X X	
veinticinco	X X X X X	
	X X X X X	
	X X X X X	

name-collection box

number grid   A table in which consecutive numbers are arranged in rows of ten. A move from one number to the next within a row is a change of one; a move from one number to the next within a column is a change of ten.

number-grid puzzle   In *Everyday Mathematics,* a piece of a number grid in which some, but not all, of the numbers are missing. Number-grid puzzles are used for practice with place-value concepts.

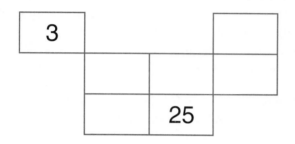

number-grid puzzle

number line   A line on which points correspond to numbers. Used as a frame of reference for counting and numeration activities. Every number has a point on the line, and every point has a number.

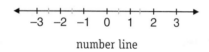

number line

number model   A number sentence that models or fits a situation. For example: the situation, *Sally had $5 and then she earned $8,* can be modeled as $5 + 8 = 13$.

number scroll   In *Everyday Mathematics,* number-grid pages taped together. See *number grid.*

number sequence   A list of numbers, often generated by some rule, which generate number sequences. See *Frames and Arrows.*

number story   A story that contains a problem that can be solved using one or more of the four basic arithmetic operations or by sorting out relations such as equals, is less than, or is greater than.

numerator   The number written above the line in a fraction. In a part-whole fraction, where the whole is divided into an equal number of parts, the numerator is the number of equal parts being considered. Compare to *denominator.*

octagon   An 8-sided polygon.

odd number   A number that cannot be evenly divided by two. It has 1, 3, 5, 7, or 9 in the ones place. Compare to *even number.*

ONE   In *Everyday Mathematics,* a way of denoting the unit whole in part-whole fractions and other similar situations.

ones   The place-value position equal to the unit value.

ordinal number   A number used to express position or order in a series, such as first, third, and tenth. Generally, ordinal numbers are used to name dates; for example, "May fifth," rather than "May five."

outcome   A possible result of a random process. Heads and tails are the two outcomes of tossing a coin.

output   The number resulting from the application of a function rule to a given input number. See *function machine.*

pan balance   A device used to weigh objects or compare their weights.

parallel   Lines, rays, line segments, or planes that are equidistant at all points, no matter how far extended; never meeting.

parallelogram   A quadrilateral that has two pairs of parallel sides and opposite sides that are congruent.

parts-and-total diagram In *Everyday Mathematics,* a diagram used to represent problems in which two or more quantities are combined to form a total quantity. It is often used when the parts are known and the total is unknown. It can also be used when the total and one or more parts are known, but one part is unknown.

Total	
13	
Part	**Part**
8	?

parts-and-total diagram

pattern A model or plan by which objects or numbers can be arranged so that what comes next can be predicted.

Pattern-Block Template In *Everyday Mathematics,* a sheet of plastic with geometric shapes cut out, used to draw patterns and designs.

pentagon A 5-sided polygon.

pictograph A graph constructed with pictures or symbols. A pictograph makes it possible to compare at a glance the relative amounts of two or more counts or measures.

Trees Planted in Park

pictograph

place value The relative worth of each digit in a number, which is determined by its position. Each place has a value ten times that of the place to its right and one-tenth of the value of the place to its left.

P.M. An abbreviation for *post meridiem,* which means "after the middle of the day"; from noon to midnight.

point An exact location in space. Points are usually labeled with capital letters.

polygon A closed 2-dimensional figure formed by three or more line segments that meet only at their endpoints. The word comes from Greek: *poly* means many and *gon* (from *gonia*) means angle.

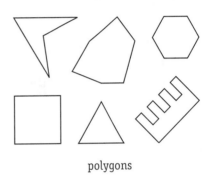

polygons

polyhedron A closed 3-dimensional shape, all of whose surfaces (faces) are flat. Each face consists of a polygon and the interior of the polygon.

poster In *Everyday Mathematics,* a page displaying a collection of numerical data. The poster may be referred to as a source of data for developing number stories in lessons following the lesson in which it is introduced.

pound (lb) In the U.S. customary system, a unit of weight equal to 16 ounces and defined as 0.45359237 kilogram.

prism A polyhedron with two parallel flat faces (bases) with the same size and shape. The other faces are bounded by parallelograms. Prisms are classified according to the shape of the two parallel bases.

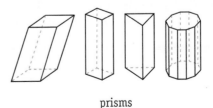

prisms

probability   A number from 0 to 1 that indicates the likelihood that an event will happen. The closer a probability is to 1, the more likely it is that the event will happen. The closer a probability is to 0, the less likely it is that the event will happen. For example, the probability that a fair coin will show heads is 1/2.

Project   In *Everyday Mathematics,* a thematic activity to be completed in one or more days by small groups or by the whole class. Projects often involve collecting and analyzing data and are usually cross-curricular in nature.

property   A feature of an object. For example, size, shape, color, and number of sides are all properties. Same as *attribute.*

pyramid   A polyhedron (3-dimensional shape) in which one face (the base) is a polygon and the other faces are triangles with a common vertex called the apex. A pyramid is classified according to the shape of its base.

quadrangle   A 4-sided polygon. Same as a *quadrilateral.*

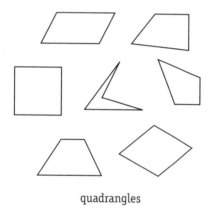

quadrangles

quadrilateral   A 4-sided polygon. Same as a *quadrangle.*

range   The difference between the greatest and least numbers in a set of data.

rectangle   A parallelogram whose angles are all right angles. See *parallelogram.*

rectangular prism   A prism whose bases are all rectangles.

rectangular pyramid   A pyramid whose base is a rectangle.

regular polygon   A polygon whose sides are all the same length and whose angles are all equal.

regular polygons

regular polyhedron   A polyhedron whose faces are all congruent regular polygons and with the same number of faces meeting at every vertex, all at the same angle.

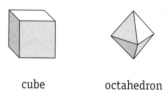

cube   octahedron

relation symbol   A symbol used to express a relationship between two quantities. Some relation symbols used in number sentences are = (is equal to), < (is less than), and > (is greater than).

rhombus   A parallelogram whose sides are all the same length. The angles may be right angles, in which case the rhombus is a square.

right angle   A square corner; a 90° angle. See *angle.*

round   1. To express a number in a simplified way. Examples of rounding include expressing a measure of weight to the nearest pound and expressing an amount of money to the nearest dollar. 2. Circular in shape.

rule table   In *Everyday Mathematics,* a table for displaying the input, output, and rule of a function in the "What's My Rule?" routine.

scale (on the thermometer)   A vertical number line used for measuring temperature.

second   1. A unit of time. There are 60 seconds in a minute. 2. An ordinal number in the sequence first, second, third…

set   A collection or group of objects, numbers, or other items.

side Any one of the line segments that make up a polygon. Sometimes a face of a 3-dimensional figure is called a side.

slate Lap-size (about 8" × 11") chalkboard or whiteboard that children use in *Everyday Mathematics* for a variety of purposes, including recording responses during group exercises and informal group assessments.

sphere A 3-dimensional shape whose curved surface is, at all points, a given distance from its center point. A ball is shaped like a sphere. A sphere is hollow; it does not include the points in its interior.

square A rectangle whose sides are all the same length.

standard unit A unit of measure that has been defined by a recognized authority, such as a government.

straightedge A tool, such as a ruler, used to draw line segments. It does not need to have measure marks on it.

subtraction A mathematical operation based on taking away one quantity from another or decreasing a quantity.

sum The result of adding two or more numbers. For example, in 5 + 3 = 8, 8 is the sum. See *addition.*

survey A study that collects data. In *Everyday Mathematics,* surveys are used to generate data for graphing and analysis.

symmetry The property of having exact balance in a figure; having the same size and shape across a dividing line or around a point.

line symmetry

tally Marks (卌 ////) used to keep track of a count.

tens The place-value position equal to ten times the unit value.

3-dimensional (3-D) Objects that are not completely within a single flat surface; objects with thickness as well as length and width.

timeline A device for showing in sequence when events took place. A timeline is a number line with the numbers naming years, days, and so on.

tool kit In *Everyday Mathematics,* a bag or a box containing a calculator, measuring tools, and manipulatives often used in the program.

trapezoid A quadrilateral that has exactly one pair of parallel sides. No two sides need be the same length.

triangle A 3-sided polygon.

triangular prism A prism whose bases are triangles.

triangular pyramid A pyramid in which all faces are triangles, any one of which can be called the base.

turn-around facts A pair of addition or multiplication (but not subtraction or division) facts in which the order of the addends or the factors is reversed. For example, 3 + 5 = 8 and 5 + 3 = 8 or 3 × 9 = 27 and 9 × 3 = 27. If a fact is known, its turnaround is also known.

2-dimensional (2-D) Objects completely within a flat surface; objects with length and width, but not thickness.

unit A label, descriptive word, or unit of measure used to put a number in context. Using a unit with a number reinforces the idea that numbers refer to something. Fingers, snowballs, miles, and cents are examples of units.

unit box In *Everyday Mathematics*, a rectangular box displayed alongside a set of numbers or problems. It contains the unit for the numbers in use.

unit box

U.S. customary system The measuring system most frequently used in the United States. Units of measure for length include inch, foot, yard, mile; units for weight include ounce and pound; units for capacity include cup, pint, quart, gallon; the unit for temperature change is degrees Fahrenheit.

vertex (vertices) The point at which the rays of an angle, sides of a polygon, or the edges of a polyhedron meet. Same as *corner*.

weight A measure of how heavy something is.

"What's My Rule?" In *Everyday Mathematics,* a routine that involves a set of number pairs in which the numbers in each pair are related to each other according to the same rule. The problems are usually displayed in table form in which two of the three parts (input, output, rule) are known and the goal is to find the unknown part.

in	out
1	2
2	4
3	6
5	10
10	20
20	40

a "What's My Rule?" problem

width of a rectangle Length of one side of a rectangle or rectangular object; often the shorter side.

yard (yd) Historically, the distance from the tip of the nose to the tip of the longest finger. In the U.S. customary system, a unit of length equivalent to 3 feet or 36 inches.

Scope and Sequence Chart

Throughout *Everyday Mathematics,* children repeatedly experience concepts and skills in each of the mathematical strands. Each exposure builds on and extends children's understanding. They study important concepts over consecutive years through a variety of formats. The Scope and Sequence Chart shows the units in which exposures occur and the developmental level of the skill or concept. The three levels of skill and concept development used in the chart are Beginning, Developing, and Secure. These levels refer here to unit content within the *K–6 Everyday Mathematics* curriculum rather than performance expectations for children.

The skills and concepts are divided according to the mathematical strands below.

Mathematical Strands	Pages
Numeration	440–443
Operations and Computation	444–445
Patterns, Functions, and Algebra	446–447
Geometry	448–449
Measurement and Reference Frames: Measurement	450–453
Measurement and Reference Frames: Reference Frames	454–455
Data and Chance	456–457

How to Read the Scope and Sequence Chart

Each section of the chart includes a mathematical strand title, three grade level columns (divided by months for Kindergarten and units for Grades 1 and 2), and a list of specific skills and concepts grouped by major concepts.

Numeration

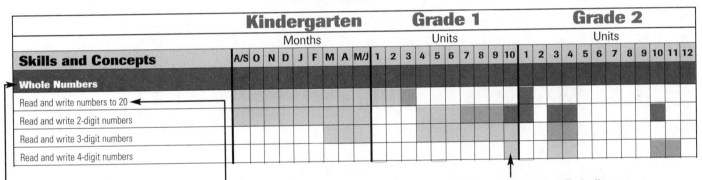

—Major mathematical concepts within each strand. A list of related skills and concepts appear below this head.

Find specific skills and concepts in this list and then follow across the row for units in which they appear at each grade level.

The shading in the cells indicates the skill and concept development level for a particular exposure. The lightest shading shows beginning exposures, the medium shading designates developing exposures, and the darkest shading indicates secure exposures.

Numeration

Skills and Concepts	Kindergarten (Months)									Grade 1 (Units)										Grade 2 (Units)											
	A/S	O	N	D	J	F	M	A	M/J	1	2	3	4	5	6	7	8	9	10	1	2	3	4	5	6	7	8	9	10	11	12
Whole Numbers																															
Read and write numbers to 20																															
Read and write 2-digit numbers																															
Read and write 3-digit numbers																															
Read and write 4-digit numbers																															
Read and write ordinal numbers																															
Order numbers to 20																															
Order 2-digit numbers																															
Order 3-digit numbers																															
Order 4-digit numbers																															
Order larger numbers																															
Compare numbers to 20																															
Compare 2-digit numbers																															
Compare 3-digit numbers																															
Compare 4-digit numbers																															
Compare larger numbers																															
Compare numbers using <, >, and = symbols																															
Perform rote counting																															
Perform rational counting																															
Skip count by 2s, 5s, and 10s																															
Count by 25s																															
Count by 100s, 1,000s and 10,000s																															
Count using a calculator																															

Whole Numbers (cont.)

Use Roman numerals

Identify even and odd numbers

Find equivalent names for numbers

Make and solve number-grid puzzles

Explore place value using a number grid

Identify place value in 2-digit numbers

Identify place value in 3-digit numbers

Identify place value in 4-digit numbers

Make exchanges among place values

Find complements of 10

Find complements for multiples of 10

Display and read numbers on a calculator

Money and Decimals

Use cents notation

Use dollars-and-cents notation

Display money amounts on a calculator

Identify equivalencies and make coin exchanges

Identify equivalencies and make coin/bill exchanges

Show money amounts with coins

Show money amounts with coins/bills

Beginning   **Developing**   **Secure**

Numeration (cont.)

Scope and Sequence Chart

	Kindergarten — Months										Grade 1 — Units										Grade 2 — Units											
Skills and Concepts	A/S	O	N	D	J	F	M	A	M/J	1	2	3	4	5	6	7	8	9	10	1	2	3	4	5	6	7	8	9	10	11	12
Money and Decimals (cont.)																														
Compare money amounts using <, >, and = symbols																														
Identify pennies and dimes as fractional parts of a dollar.																														
Calculate the value of coin combinations																														
Calculate the value of coin/bill combinations																														
Explore uses for decimals																														
Fractions																														
Understand the meaning of fractions																														
Identify numerator and denominator																														
Identify fractional parts of a region																														
Identify fractional parts of a set																														
Find equivalent fractions																														
Compare and order fractions																														
Explore uses of fractions																														
Use fractions in number stories																														

Legend: ■ Beginning   ■ Developing   ■ Secure

Operations and Computation

Skills and Concepts	Kindergarten (Months)										Grade 1 (Units)											Grade 2 (Units)												
	A/S	O	N	D	J	F	M	A	M/J		1	2	3	4	5	6	7	8	9	10		1	2	3	4	5	6	7	8	9	10	11	12
Addition and Subtraction																																	
Understand meaning of addition/subtraction																																	
Solve addition/subtraction number stories																																	
Make up addition/subtraction number stories																																	
Find/use complements of 10																																	
Find/use complements of 100																																	
Solve change-to-more and change-to-less number stories/diagrams																																	
Solve parts-and-total number stories/diagrams																																	
Solve comparison number stories																																	
Find patterns in addition/subtraction facts																																	
Add/subtract using a number line																																	
Add/subtract using a number grid																																	
Add/subtract using a calculator																																	
Find sums of even and odd numbers																																	
Practice basic facts																																	
Use mental arithmetic to add/subtract																																	
Investigate relationships between addition and subtraction																																	
Add/subtract multiples of 10																																	
Add/subtract multiples of 100																																	
Add/subtract money amounts/decimals																																	
Add 3 or more 1-digit numbers																																	
Add/subtract 2-digit numbers																																	

Addition and Subtraction (cont.)

- Add 3 or more 2-digit numbers
- Add/subtract 3- and 4-digit numbers
- Investigate properties of addition/subtraction
- Use an Addition/Subtraction Facts Table
- Make change
- Use estimation to add/subtract
- Use addition/subtraction algorithms

Multiplication and Division

- Understand meaning of multiplication/division
- Solve multiplication/division number stories
- Make up multiplication/division number stories
- Solve problems involving ratios
- Investigate properties of multiplication/division
- Practice multiplication/division facts
- Explore square numbers
- Investigate relationships between multiplication and division
- Multiply/divide using a number line
- Find patterns in multiplication/division facts
- Find patterns in multiples of 10, 100, and 1,000
- Use a Multiplication/Division Facts Table
- Use mental arithmetic to multiply/divide

Legend: ☐ Beginning ☐ Developing ■ Secure

Patterns, Functions, and Algebra

Skills and Concepts	Kindergarten — Months										Grade 1 — Units										Grade 2 — Units											
	A/S	O	N	D	J	F	M	A	M/J		1	2	3	4	5	6	7	8	9	10	1	2	3	4	5	6	7	8	9	10	11	12
Visual Patterns																																
Create patterns with 2-dimensional shapes																																
Sort and identify shapes/objects by attributes																																
Explore and extend visual patterns																																
Find patterns in the real world																																
Find common attributes in objects and people																																
Number Patterns																																
Count up and back on a number grid																																
Investigate even and odd number patterns																																
Identify and use patterns on a number grid																																
Add and subtract using a number grid																																
Find patterns in addition and subtraction facts																																
Find patterns in multiplication and division facts																																
Find equivalent names for numbers																																
Investigate square numbers																																
Explore patterns in doubling numbers																																
Sequences																																
Count up and back on a number line																																
Make/complete a number line																																
Count by 2s, 5s, and 10s																																
Count by numbers greater than 10																																

Sequences (cont.)

- Complete number sequences
- Solve Frames-and-Arrows problems with one rule
- Solve Frames-and-Arrows problems with two rules
- Explore counting patterns using a calculator

Functions

- Solve "What's My Rule?" (function machine) problems

Number Sentences

- Use symbols $+$, $-$, $=$
- Write/solve addition and subtraction number sentences
- Write/solve number sentences with missing addends
- Explore number properties (commutative, zero, and identity)
- Use symbols $\times$, $\div$, $=$
- Write and solve multiplication number sentences
- Write and solve number sentences with missing factors
- Write and solve division number sentences
- Make up/solve number sentences involving parentheses

Inequalities

- Compare numbers using $<$, $>$ symbols

■ **Beginning**　■ **Developing**　■ **Secure**

Notes on Scope and Sequence

Geometry

Skills and Concepts	Kindergarten Months									Grade 1 Units										Grade 2 Units											
	A/S	O	N	D	J	F	M	A	M/J	1	2	3	4	5	6	7	8	9	10	1	2	3	4	5	6	7	8	9	10	11	12
2-Dimensional Shapes (Polygons)																															
Identify 2-dimensional shapes	▒									▒			▒				▒	▒		▒	▒						▒		▒		
Create/extend designs with 2-dimensional shapes				▒													▒		▒		▒			▒			▒				
Make 2-dimensional shapes on a geoboard																						▒					▒	▒			
Record geoboard shapes on dot paper																								▒							
Draw triangles and quadrilaterals	▒						▒																	▒							
Explore shape relationships				▒		▒	▒									▒						▒									
Identify characteristics of 2-dimensional shapes																				▒						▒					
Compare 2-dimensional shapes																							▒	▒							
Construct 2-dimensional shapes			▒	▒																							▒				
Solve 2-dimensional-shapes problems																															
Record designs with 2-dimensional shapes						▒													▒					▒		▒					
Compare polygons and non-polygons																															
Complete shape patterns																▒					▒										
Sort shapes by attributes			▒																				▒	▒							
Explore similarities and differences among quadrilaterals						▒	▒							▒		▒		▒		▒											
Form shapes by combining polygons				▒							▒													▒				▒	▒	▒	
Model polygons with rope				▒																											
Classify and name polygons																▒							▒								
Construct models of polygons with straws				▒																											

3-Dimensional Shapes

- Identify 3-dimensional shapes
- Identify characteristics of 3-dimensional shapes
- Construct 3-dimensional shapes
- Explore similarities and differences among 3-dimensional shapes
- Explore the relationship among the number of faces, edges, and vertices of pyramids

Symmetry

- Fold and cut symmetrical shapes
- Create/complete a symmetrical design
- Identify symmetrical figures
- Identify lines of symmetry
- Make symmetrical shapes on a geoboard

Points, Lines, and Angles

- Draw line segments with a straightedge
- Identify parallel and nonparallel line segments
- Identify and name points
- Identify and name line segments
- Model parallel lines on a geoboard
- Draw parallel lines with a straightedge

Beginning **Developing** **Secure**

Measurement and Reference Frames: Measurement

Skills and Concepts	Kindergarten Months										Grade 1 Units										Grade 2 Units											
	A/S	O	N	D	J	F	M	A	M/J		1	2	3	4	5	6	7	8	9	10	1	2	3	4	5	6	7	8	9	10	11	12
Length																																
Estimate and compare distances																																
Estimate and compare lengths/heights of objects																																
Measure lengths with nonstandard units																																
Measure to the nearest foot																																
Measure to the nearest inch																																
Investigate the yard																																
Measure to the nearest centimeter																																
Investigate the meter																																
Solve length/height number stories																																
Name tools used to measure length																																
Measure to the nearest $\frac{1}{2}$ inch																																
Measure to the nearest $\frac{1}{2}$ centimeter																																
Measure to the nearest yard																																
Identify equivalent customary units of length																																
Identify equivalent metric units of length																																
Choose the appropriate unit of measure																																
Measure to the nearest decimeter																																
Investigate the mile																																
Investigate the kilometer																																
Solve distance number stories																																
Measure to the nearest meter																																
Use a mileage map																																

Capacity and Volume

- Compare capacities of containers
- Name tools used to measure capacity
- Identify customary units of capacity
- Identify equivalent customary units of capacity
- Identify metric units of capacity
- Identify equivalent metric units of capacity
- Measure capacities of irregular containers
- Name tools used to measure volume
- Find volume
- Estimate volume
- Choose the appropriate unit of measure

Weight

- Use a pan balance
- Solve weight number stories
- Identify customary units of weight
- Identify metric units of weight
- Use a spring scale
- Name tools used to measure weight
- Choose the appropriate unit of measure
- Estimate and compare weights
- Use a bath scale
- Identify equivalent customary units of weight
- Identify equivalent metric units of weight

Beginning   **Developing**   **Secure**

Measurement and Reference Frames: Measurement (cont.)

	Kindergarten — Months	Grade 1 — Units	Grade 2 — Units
	A/S O N D J F M A M/J	1 2 3 4 5 6 7 8 9 10	1 2 3 4 5 6 7 8 9 10 11 12

Skills and Concepts

Perimeter and Area
- Investigate area
- Estimate area
- Name tools used to measure area
- Find the perimeter of irregular shapes
- Find the perimeter of regular shapes
- Find the area of regular shapes
- Estimate perimeter
- Compare perimeter and area
- Find the area of irregular shapes

Money
- Recognize pennies and nickels
- Use cents notation
- Calculate the value of coin combinations
- Recognize dimes
- Use dollars-and-cents notation
- Compare values of sets of coins
- Recognize quarters
- Show money amounts with coins
- Show money amounts with coins/bills
- Recognize dollars
- Solve money number stories
- Make change

Money (cont.)

- Calculate the value of coin/bill combinations
- Calculate the value of bill combinations
- Identify equivalencies and make coin exchanges
- Identify equivalencies and make bill exchanges
- Add money amounts
- Subtract money amounts
- Estimate costs
- Identify pennies and dimes as fractional parts of a dollar

■ Beginning ■ Developing ■ Secure

Notes on Scope and Sequence

Measurement and Reference Frames: Reference Frames

Skills and Concepts	Kindergarten — Months								Grade 1 — Units										Grade 2 — Units											
	A/S	O	N	D	J	F	M	A	M/J	1	2	3	4	5	6	7	8	9	10	1	2	3	4	5	6	7	8	9	10	11	12
Time																															
Use the calendar		■								■										■	■										■
Compare the hour and minute hands							■			■	■		■							■	■										
Tell time on the hour					■					■	■	■		■	■	■				■	■										
Investigate A.M. and P.M.																															■
Estimate the duration of a minute					■							■																			
Investigate the duration of an hour												■																			
Tell time on the half-hour										■	■		■	■	■	■				■	■	■	■								
Tell time on the quarter-hour											■				■	■	■	■		■	■	■	■								
Use digital notation							■									■	■	■		■	■	■									
Tell time to the nearest 5 minutes							■									■					■	■								■	■
Investigate the second hand						■										■															
Solve time number stories																	■			■	■	■		■							
Investigate 1-minute intervals							■													■											
Calculate elapsed time												■																			■
Show days/events on a timeline					■						■																				■
Number and name the months in a year		■								■																					■
Write today's date		■																													
Tell time to the nearest minute																				■	■		■								
Name tools used to measure time																					■			■							
Identify time equivalencies																															■
Read time in different ways																															■

Temperature
Use the Fahrenheit temperature scale
Use a thermometer
Solve temperature number stories
Use a weather map
Use the Celsius temperature scale

■ Beginning ■ Developing ■ Secure

Notes on Scope and Sequence

Data and Chance

	Kindergarten — Months									Grade 1 — Units										Grade 2 — Units											
Skills and Concepts	A/S	O	N	D	J	F	M	A	M/J	1	2	3	4	5	6	7	8	9	10	1	2	3	4	5	6	7	8	9	10	11	12
Collecting Data																															
Collect data by counting																															
Collect data by interviewing																															
Collect data from print sources																															
Collect data from posters																															
Collect data from a map																															
Make predictions about data																															
Conduct a survey																															
Recording/Displaying Data																															
Make a tally chart																															
Make a bar graph																															
Record data in a table/chart																															
Make a frequency table																															
Make a line plot																															
Evaluating Data																															
Find the range																															
Find the mode																															
Find the median																															
Compare two sets of data																															

Evaluating Data (cont.)

- Find the minimum/maximum
- Read tables, graphs, and maps
- Use data in problem solving
- Summarize and interpret data

Probability and Chance

- Explore equal-chance events
- Predict outcomes
- Conduct experiments
- Explore *fair* and *unfair* games

▇ **Beginning**   ▇ **Developing**   ▇ **Secure**

Notes on Scope and Sequence

Notes on Scope and Sequence

Notes on Scope and Sequence

Index

Doubles facts, 380
Drawing
    line segments, 278

E

Edge, 747–748
Elapsed time, 198–199, 731
Equal-chance events, 43–46, 375–376
Equal parts, 640–642, 643
    cutting crackers into, 641–642
Equal shares, 639–643
Equal to (=), 345–349
Equivalent fractions, 706–710
Equivalent names, 483, 492–497, 501
Estimates, 108, 277
    area, 352, 353
    lengths, 118, 276–280
Even numbers, 162–163, 174–176, 389
    Exploration, 184–185
    exploring, 183–186
    modeling, 177
    patterns, 173–177
    sums of, 235
Even/odd number patterns, 181
Everything Math Deck, 34, 51
Exchanges, money, 125–129, 610
Explorations
    addition facts in, 520
    area in, 352
    attribute-block designs, 572
    attribute blocks in, 59
    Attribute Train Game, 571–572
    base-10 blocks in, 58, 288
    capacity, 693
    counting in, 353
    data in, 287
    dominoes in, 118, 184
    even numbers in, 184
    Fact Platter, 572
    fact triangles, 655
    fractional parts, 655
    geoboards in, 58, 287, 520
    heights in, 287, 694
    introducing, 57
    manipulative materials in, 56–59
    odd numbers in, 184
    pattern blocks in, 58, 185, 519, 654
    patterns in, 185
    rulers in, 118
    rules for, 57
    shapes in, 185, 287, 520
    symmetry, 694
    weight in, 352
Explorer, 57

F

Faces of prisms, 585
Fact families, 482–483, 498–502, 505
    from fact triangles, 511
Fact platters, 570–573
    Exploration, 572

Fact power, 253, 307–311, 474–553
Fact Power Game, 481, 506–507
Facts
    addition, 307–311, 312–316, 332, 383–387, 482
    basic, 242–321
    doubles, 384–385
    +1 facts, 384
    +0 facts, 384
    whose sums are 10, 384–385
Fact Triangles, 482, 503–508, 521
    Exploration, 655
    fact families from, 511
Fahrenheit, 62, 256, 753
Fahrenheit thermometer, 62–63
    coloring the zones on a, 64
Family letter, 75, 153
Flat, 340
Flea market, buying and selling at a, 426–427, 784–785
Folding symmetrical shapes, 594–595
Foot
    personal, 251, 265–269
    standard, 251, 265–269
    tracings, 267, 275
4-digit numbers, 755–756
Fourths, 641
    folding squares to make, 697–698
Fractional parts, 646, 653–656
    Exploration, 655
    of geometric figures, 646
    names for, 706–710
    of shapes, coloring, 698
    of the whole, 696–700
Fraction
    book, 648
    creatures, 652
Fractions, 602–661, 644–648, 662–715
    combinations equivalent to $\frac{1}{2}$, 719
    comparing, 701–705
    concepts, 612–613, 672–673
    equivalent, 706–710, 715
    notation, 612–613, 645
    readiness for, 518–522
Frames, 202
Frames-and-Arrows
    calculator, checking problems with a, 215
    completing diagrams, 220, 240
    diagram, 165, 202, 259, 337
    problems, 203, 205, 206–209, 685
    routine, 201–205
Frequency table, 375–376
Function machines, 332–333, 389, 393–397
    simulating on a calculator, 397

G

Games
    Addition Top-It, 481, 489, 495, 511, 547, 609, 651
    Animal Weight Top-It, 359, 362

Attribute Train Game, 561, 571–572
Base-10 Exchange, 609, 633, 660
Beat the Calculator, 385, 481, 506, 542, 552, 723, 732, 733
Before and After, 161, 168, 170, 186
Buyer and Vendor, 723, 737, 742
Coin-Dice, 161, 226, 240, 249, 268
Coin Exchange, 481, 537, 609, 615
Coin Top-It, 83, 134, 161, 221, 481, 532
Dice-Roll and Tally Game, 44
Difference Game, 367, 481, 502
Dime-Nickel-Penny Grab, 161, 226, 354, 481, 526
Domino Top-It, 161, 233, 234, 238, 249, 258, 279, 294, 320, 329, 368
Fact Power Game, 481, 506–507
Guess the Rule, 571
High Roller, 142, 249, 311, 316
Magic Bag Game, 381
Nickel/Penny Grab, 83, 138, 152
Number-Grid Game, 669, 681, 682
Number-Line Squeeze, 9, 11, 18, 19, 34, 37, 58, 74, 75
One-Dollar Exchange, 609, 621, 647, 660, 669, 709
$1, $10, $100 Exchange Game, 723, 738–739
Penny-Cup, 83, 124, 139, 329, 387
Penny-Dice Game, 9, 12, 24, 28
Penny-Drop Addition, 83, 136–137
Penny Grab, 83, 123
Penny Guessing, 83, 129
Penny/Nickel/Dime Exchange, 396
Penny/Nickel Exchange, 83, 133, 161, 176, 186, 214
Rolling for 50, 83, 88, 89, 119
Scissors, Paper, Stone, 9, 46
Secret Number, 349
Shaker Addition Top-It, 249, 313–314, 315, 329, 358, 481, 508
Stand Up If..., 561, 596
Tens-and-Ones Trading Game, 329, 348, 391, 401, 516, 561, 586
3, 2, 1 Game, 609, 637
Time Match, 249, 274, 305, 354, 481, 538, 723, 734
Top-It, 9, 12, 13, 36–37, 41, 53, 58, 74–75, 83, 88, 91, 329, 347–348, 401
Turn-Around Facts Game, 329, 380
Two-Fisted Penny Addition, 83, 85, 97, 98–99, 100, 105, 119, 152, 186, 249, 263, 282, 294, 343, 354, 385
Who Am I Thinking Of?, 143, 569
Geoboards, 58, 287
    Exploration, 58, 287, 520
    investigating polygons, 591
Geometric
    designs, 25
    gift wrap and greeting cards, 774–775
    shapes, identifying, 616

notes

notes

notes

notes

notes